Webster's Reference Library

CONCISE EDITION
ENCYCLOPEDIA

GEDDES &
GROSSET

This revised edition published 2008 by Geddes & Grosset,
David Dale House, New Lanark, ML11 9DJ, Scotland

First published 2002

© 2002, 2008 Geddes & Grosset

This book is not published by the original publishers of
Webster's Dictionary or by their successors

ISBN 978 1 84205 180 1

Printed and bound in the UK

Contents

Entries are given in A–Z order. Cross references to entries within sections are indicated by SMALL CAPITALS, cross references to other sections are indicated by sanserif type.

Space and Astronomy

Aldebaran *see* RED GIANT.

Andromeda *see* GALAXY.

antimatter MATTER that is made up of antiparticles, that is, particles that have the same mass as ordinary matter but have opposite values for other properties (e.g. charge). So if matter is made up of electrons, neutrons and protons, antimatter is composed of *positrons*, anti-neutrons and anti-protons. The coming together of matter and antimatter results in the destruction of both particles and the production of energy. *See also* S&T atom.

aphelion the point in its orbit at which the Earth is furthest from the Sun, the opposite to PERIHELION.

Ariel *see* URANUS.

asteroid or meteorite or planetoid a rocky or metallic body that is one of many orbiting the SUN between the ORBITS of MARS and JUPITER. Most of these tiny PLANETS are small, some reaching a few hundred miles across, but the largest, the dwarf planet *Ceres*, has a diameter of about 667 miles (1,000 kilometres). Collisions between asteroids sometimes produce smaller pieces that occasionally fall to EARTH. These are also called meteorites. The many craters seen on the surfaces of some planets are probably the result of asteroid impact.

Meteors, or *shooting stars*, are the remnants of COMET debris that, should they fall into the Earth's atmosphere, burn up as they are destroyed by friction.

astronaut a person who has undergone very special and rigorous training to prepare for space travel.

The first astronaut was Yuri Gagarin, who orbited the EARTH in 1961 in his SPACECRAFT, *Vostok I*. Valentina Tereshkova was the first woman in space. Both were from the former Soviet Union (now Russia). July 1969 saw an American team landing on the MOON, followed by numerous Russian missions (and later joint missions with the USA) to an orbiting SPACE STATION. The exploration of space is no longer the preserve of the USA and Russia. Europe has launched several missions, as has Japan.

When a rocket is launched from Earth there are tremendous forces pushing down on the astronaut because of the enormously high acceleration required to reach orbit. An astronaut must therefore be very fit and highly skilled in science and technology so that he or she can operate the equipment in the spacecraft and carry out numerous experiments in space. Over 400 people have now flown in space.

When in space, the astronaut must wear a space suit designed to cater for his or her safety. The suit is made up of layers of special material with tubular networks. It provides protection from radiation and the cold of space and supplies air from a portable pack (or life-support system). The helmet has a visor to cut out harmful rays from the SUN and a microphone with headphones to allow communication.

With the increasing frequency of flights, space tourism is becoming a reality and already several wealthy individuals have paid to be blasted into space through a commercial company working with the Russian Soyuz programme. More companies are becoming involved including Sir Richard Branson through his Virgin Galactic venture.

astronomy the scientific study of the various bodies in the 'heavens'. From earliest times, people plotted the positions of the STARS and PLANETS, devising a yearly CALENDAR governed by the movements of the EARTH and MOON relative to the SUN. When making journeys, people in early times used the positions of the various heavenly bodies to determine the direction that they should take. Some knowledge of astronomy was therefore important to early travellers and explorers.

Early astronomers gained a great deal of knowledge from their studies and were able to predict the appearance of COMETS and ECLIPSES. It became possible to make many more discoveries in astronomy following the invention of the lens TELESCOPE in 1608. This was devised by a Dutchman, Hans Lippershey, who was a maker of spectacles. Until the Middle Ages, it was thought that the Earth was at the centre of the universe and that other heavenly bodies revolved around it. Nicolaus Copernicus, during the 1540s, put forward the idea (that had first been taught in 170 BC by Aristarchus) that the Earth travelled around the Sun. The idea of the Sun being the centre of the SOLAR SYSTEM gradually gained acceptance.

Since the latter half of the 20th century, SATELLITES and SPACE PROBES have given us new and exciting information about the farthest regions of space, and modern astronomers now study the wealth of data sent back to Earth by such space probes.

Atlas *see* SATURN.

aurora luminous and often highly coloured streaks or sheets of light in the sky formed by high-speed electrically charged solar particles entering the upper atmosphere of the EARTH where they give up electrons, and molecules are created associated with the release of light. These effects are related to SUNSPOT activity and are called the Northern Lights (*aurora borealis*) in the northern hemisphere and the Southern Lights (*aurora australis*) in the southern hemisphere.

big-bang theory a theory put forward by some scientists to explain the origins of the universe. It proposes that about 15,000 million years ago there was a vast explosion that sent all the material spinning rapidly outwards as a mass of atoms. Physicists think that in a matter of minutes a huge cloud of hydrogen atoms formed and continued to spread outwards, dispersing into separate clouds as it did so. These hydrogen atoms make up about 90 per cent of the universe, and the clouds formed GALAXIES of stars including the MILKY WAY. The outward expansion is still continuing but it is thought that this may one day cease. All the material may eventually collapse and collide together (the BIG-CRUNCH THEORY), but it is thought that before this occurs the SUN will burn hotter and the EARTH will be consumed in about 5000 million years' time.

There is speculation about the origin of the dust and gases that were scattered at the time of the big bang and also about the possible cause of the huge explosion.

big-crunch theory gravity attracts the GALAXIES in the universe together and the force it exerts depends on their mass, but it is over-ridden by the expansion and moving apart that is still continuing, possibly as a result of the BIG BANG. The big-crunch theory proposes that there may be hidden material (consisting of single atomic particles) between the galaxies, which, if present in sufficient quantities, could add to the gravitational pull. This extra gravity might be enough to slow down and halt the expansion and indeed put it into reverse. If this occurs the galaxies would be pulled together, would collide and be destroyed in the big crunch.

binary star a pair of STARS that ORBIT around each other, held together by the force of gravity. These double stars may be so close to one another that each goes round the other in a few hours. In this instance they are so close as to be almost touching and travel very fast. Others are vast distances apart and travel around each other in thousands or even millions of years. Many stars in the MILKY WAY are binary stars, and each member of the pair may differ in shape, size, and brightness.

black dwarf *see* STAR.

black hole it is thought that there are black holes in space that are collapsed STARS, a proposal first put forward by Karl Schwarzschild, a German astronomer, in 1916. It is believed that when a star (which may be many times larger than our SUN) comes to the end of its 'life', it collapses so quickly that no material, not even light, can be emitted. This type of event is known as an *implosion* and because of the enormous gravitational force of the collapsed material, it is seen as a hole from which no light escapes. The space around the black hole is curved into a complete circle. It is thought that many apparent single stars are in fact BINARY STARS with a black hole as a partner. Much work on black holes has been carried out by Stephen Hawking, the British physicist (*see also* NEUTRON STAR).

blue shift the opposite of RED SHIFT, blue shift is the decrease in wavelength of

light emitted from an object that is moving towards the observer. The decrease in wavelength, due to the Doppler effect (*see* S&T Doppler effect), makes the object appear bluer than it actually is because of a shift to the blue end of the electromagnetic spectrum. Thus when a star is travelling towards Earth its light appears bluer (the light waves are shortened, shortening the wavelength).

brightness ratio a comparison of the brightness of two celestial objects such as PLANETS and STARS. It is defined as 2.512 raised to the difference of the MAGNITUDES of the objects. Thus, a 1st magnitude star is 2.512 times brighter than a 2nd magnitude star and if two objects have a difference of 5 in their magnitudes of 2 and 7, their brightness ratio is 2.512 to the 5th power, which is about 100.

calendar a system devised by human beings to mark the passage of time. Early astronomers based their calendars on the phases of the MOON or on the orbit of the EARTH around the SUN. The 365-day year was based on the *Julian* calendar, which was introduced by the Roman statesman Julius Caesar in 46 BC. However, the Earth takes $365\frac{1}{4}$ days to go once around the Sun (a solar year), so with this system, every fourth or *leap* year, an extra day has to be added.

Callisto *see* JUPITER.

Calypso *see* SATURN.

Charon *see* PLUTO.

comet a celestial body composed of rock, ice, dust, and frozen gases that usually cannot be seen. A comet becomes visible when it approaches closer to the SUN because it appears to flare up and look bright. It has a *head*, consisting of a solid core or nucleus of rock surrounded by a layer of gas, the *corona*. The nucleus is irregular in shape and just a few miles in diameter (in fact Halley's comet is elongated and is roughly 10 x 2.75 miles or 15 x 4 kilometres). A comet moves in a long, eccentric ORBIT around the Sun, and one complete cycle is called a *period*. The orbit may take the comet a long distance from the Sun when it cannot be seen. Near to the Sun, particles of dust and gas are knocked away from the head of the comet and trail

out to form a brightly glowing *tail*. Comets are believed to be leftover remnants of the BIG BANG explosion, and each time they approach the Sun, some of the ice melts. Eventually, it is thought that a comet loses its ice, dust and gas and becomes a piece of orbiting rock. The shortest period belongs to Ericke's comet and is only $3\frac{1}{2}$ years. Others have much longer periods lasting hundreds or even thousands of years. The most familiar comet is Halley's comet, which appears every 76 years and is next due in 2062. In 1986 the SPACECRAFT *Giotto*, belonging to the European Space Agency, flew to within 359 miles (539 kilometres) of the comet, gaining some valuable information and photographs.

constellation a group of STARS that are placed together and given a name although there is no scientific basis for the grouping. Many were named by astronomers of the Babylonian empire, some 2,000 years before the birth of Christ, and the most ancient form the twelve signs of the zodiac. There are 39 constellations visible in the northern hemisphere and 46 in the southern. Familiar examples in the northern hemisphere include the Great Bear (*Ursa Major*) and the Hunter (*Orion*).

corona the coloured rings (seen through thin cloud) around the SUN or MOON, caused by diffraction (*see* S&T diffraction) of light by water droplets.

cosmic rays 'rays' composed of ionizing radiation from space and consisting mainly of protons (*see* S&T atom) and alpha particles (helium nuclei) (*see* S&T radioactivity), and a small proportion of heavier atomic nuclei. When these particles interact with the EARTH's atmosphere, secondary radiation is created, including mesons, neutrons (*see* S&T elementary particles), positrons (*see* S&T antimatter) and electrons (*see* S&T atom). Cosmic rays seem to come from three sources: galactic rays, possibly formed from SUPERNOVA explosions, solar cosmic rays, and the SOLAR WIND.

cosmology the study of the entire universe, which can be traced back to the ancient Greeks.

dark matter scientists have postulated the existence of so-called 'dark matter' to explain the difference between the visible material of galaxies and hot gas and the material calculated to be present in the whole universe. In effect, gravity, the force of attraction for and between all matter, holds the universe together, but the clouds of hot gas between galaxies and the galaxies themselves were seen to be affected by gravitational forces larger than could be generated by the visible matter, leading to the suggestion that much matter must be invisible. The matter is called dark because it does not emit any light, but its presence can be inferred by its gravitational effects on visible objects. It is suggested that dark matter may amount to around 85 per cent of the universe. Recent research has established more data about dark matter including its speed—9 km/s—which is much faster than anticipated.

daylength the length of daylight changes throughout the year except at the Equator where there are approximately 12 hours of light and 12 hours of darkness. The changes occur because the EARTH is tilted on its axis, and it alters on a daily basis as the Earth proceeds on its ORBIT around the SUN. At any point in the year, while countries in the northern hemisphere are tilted more towards the Sun, those in the south are farther away, and vice versa. This governs the onset of the four different seasons of the year. Latitude also affects daylength, and those countries at latitudes greater than 67° north or south experience the midnight sun during midsummer when it does not become dark at all. The lengths of day and night are the same throughout the world on the two equinoxes (21 March and 23 September).

Deimos *see* MARS.

Dog Star *see* SIRIUS.

dwarf planet a new category in a three-fold classification system for bodies that orbit the Sun. It was set up in 2006 and there are three such planets: *Eris*, PLUTO and *Ceres*.

Earth the Earth is one of a group of eight PLANETS (and three DWARF PLANETS) that ORBIT a STAR that we call the SUN. It occurs in one small part of the GALAXY (also called the MILKY WAY) that is referred to as the SOLAR SYSTEM. The Earth is the fifth largest of the planets and the third nearest to the Sun. Most of the Earth's surface is covered by oceans—about two thirds compared to one third that is land. A layer of air, the atmosphere (*see* S&T atmosphere), surrounds Earth, which is subdivided into a number of different regions according to height above the surface. Earth, as viewed from space, is like a blue ball or sphere that is flattened at both the poles. At the Equator, the radius of the Earth is 3,963 miles or 6,378 kilometres.

The Earth itself is composed of four main layers; an outer *crust* overlying a *mantle*, followed by an *outer core* and *inner core*. The rocky crust varies in thickness, being about 27 miles (40 kilometres) thick under the continents and 5 miles (8 kilometres) under the oceans. It 'floats' on the mantle, which is made up of extremely hot rock and is about 1,933 miles (2,900 kilometres) thick (*see* G&G plate tectonics). The core is so hot that it is part liquid, with a temperature in the region of 6,500 K (11,240°F, 6227°C). The outer core is believed to be about 1,500 miles (2,250 kilometres) thick, and is thought to be more liquid than the inner core, which is solid and composed mainly of iron and nickel. The Earth is the only one of the planets able to support life, which exists entirely in a narrow band on or near the crust. The Earth's weight increases every day by about 25 tons because fine space dust finds its way down to the surface.

eclipse the name given to a total or partial disappearance of a PLANET or moon by passing into the shadow of another. A *solar eclipse* occurs when a new Moon passes between the EARTH and the SUN. A *lunar eclipse* happens when the Sun, Earth and Moon are in a line and the Earth is situated between the Moon and the Sun and its shadow falls on the Moon. Different types of eclipse happen each year but a solar eclipse usually appears as partial when viewed from Earth. Even during a complete solar eclipse, the Moon is only just large enough to cover the Sun, and the shadow that it throws on to one part of the Earth is only a few miles wide so few people are able to see it.

Ericke's comet *see* COMET.

escape velocity is the velocity that is necessary for a rocket or SPACE PROBE to escape from the pull exerted by the gravity of a PLANET. The velocity varies according to the mass and diameter of the planet. For the EARTH it is 25,000 mph (37,500 km/h) and for the MOON 5,350 mph (8,025 km/h). No light escapes from a BLACK HOLE because the escape velocity is greater than the speed of light.

Europa *see* JUPITER.

Evening Star *see* VENUS.

expansion theory the theory that the GALAXIES of space are still rapidly moving apart, which may have been caused by the BIG BANG explosion. The speed at which the galaxies are travelling is calculated by studying a property of light known as the *red shift*. For every extra million LIGHT YEARS of distance (one light year is around 5.9 million million miles (9.5 million million kilometres), the speed the galaxies are travelling increases by about 10 miles (15 kilometres) per second. The relationship between speed and distance is called *Hubble's law*.

galaxy the name given to a huge group or band of STARS. Our galaxy, which includes the SUN, is also called the MILKY WAY, and it contains about 100,000 million stars. It is thought that there are millions more galaxies, and the nearest large one to us is called *Andromeda*. Galaxies have different shapes, the Milky Way and Andromeda being spiral-shaped, others appearing as saucers. The Milky Way is approximately 10^5 LIGHT YEARS across.

Ganymede *see* JUPITER.

gas giant any of the four PLANETS that are composed mainly of gases, JUPITER, NEPTUNE, SATURN and URANUS.

Great Red Spot *see* JUPITER.

Halley's comet *see* COMET.

heat shield a SPACECRAFT encounters extreme and intense heat, especially when it re-enters the EARTH's atmosphere from space. The heat is caused by friction because the space ship is travelling so fast. A heat shield is a special heat-resistant layer that prevents the spacecraft from burning up. A SPACE SHUTTLE has special heat-resistant tiles, composed of silicon and carbon, which can be used again.

Hertzsprung-Russell diagram *see* STAR.

Hubble's law *see* EXPANSION THEORY.

Hubble telescope launched from a SPACE SHUTTLE in 1990, the Hubble telescope was the first major optical telescope to be placed in space, above the distortion of the atmosphere. As a result astronomers gained an unobstructed view of the universe and can now observe the most distant stars and galaxies as well as the planets in our solar system. A successful repair mission was carried out in 1993 and the final service will be undertaken in 2008. Hubble weighs 11,110 kg (24,500 lbs) and is 13.3 m (43.5 ft) long. Its primary mirror is 2.4 m (7 ft 10.5 in) across and in over 15 years of activity it has taken roughly 750, 000 images and probed about 24,000 celestial objects. (*See* SPACE TELESCOPE).

implosion the opposite of an explosion. It is a rapid inrushing or collapse of materials inwards instead of outwards. STARS may *implode*, the gravitational force pulling all materials inwards. These collapsed stars are very dense in the centre and form a BLACK HOLE or NEUTRON STAR.

inferior planet *see* PLANET.

infrared astronomy the study of infrared radiation (*see* S&T electromagnetic waves) given off from heavenly bodies such as the STARS and PLANETS. Infrared radiation has a wavelength of 0.8 to 1,000μm, which is shorter than that of radio waves and longer than that of visible light. Infrared radiation passes through parts of the GALAXY obscured by dust, highlighting otherwise invisible structures. More infrared radiation is emitted by hotter structures than by colder ones, and it penetrates the EARTH's atmosphere more readily than visible light. The radiation tends to be obscured by water vapour in the Earth's atmosphere, but this problem can be partially overcome by siting observatories at high altitudes. Infrared astronomers are then able to gain valuable information about distant space bodies and have discovered 'young' stars that have not begun to glow brightly.

interstellar medium the matter found throughout space and comprising gas and dust—mainly hydrogen, helium, and interstellar molecules. In all it amounts to about 10 per cent of the mass of the GALAXY.

Io *see* JUPITER.

Jupiter the giant planet of our SOLAR SYSTEM, more than 1,000 times larger than EARTH. It is one of the GAS GIANTS, being composed mainly of hydrogen. Its atmosphere is made up of hydrogen with approximately 15 per cent helium and traces of water, ammonia, and methane. This forms a liquid 'shell' surrounding a zone of metallic hydrogen (that is, the hydrogen is compressed so much that it behaves like metal), which itself surrounds a core made partly of rock and ice. This core has a mass 10 times greater than that of the Earth. Violent storms and winds rage around Jupiter, whipping up bands of frozen chemicals such as ammonia. One such storm is the *Great Red Spot,* visible on the surface as an enormous cyclone that has probably lasted for hundreds of years.

Jupiter spins very rapidly so that one of its days lasts for only 9 hours and 50 minutes. This rapid spin drags the whirling gases into bands that appear dark and light. A year on Jupiter lasts for nearly 12 Earth years because the planet is farther from the SUN and has a greater ORBIT. Jupiter is the fifth planet from the Sun and because of its rapid rate of spin, it bulges outwards at its equator. As a result the diameter at its equator is 95,200 miles (142,800 kilometres) compared to 89,333 miles (134,000 kilometres) at the poles. The outermost layers of Jupiter are very cold, in the region of −334°F (−150°C), but the very centre of the planet is extremely hot, probably exceeding the temperature of the Sun.

Jupiter's great mass means that it exerts a strong gravitational pull and is able to hold down the molecules of gas that swirl around its bulk. A person on Jupiter would be twice as heavy compared to his or her weight on Earth. Jupiter has its own SATELLITES, or moons, orbiting around it, and some of these are as large as Earth's Moon. The *Voyager* SPACECRAFT passed close to Jupiter in 1979 and sent fascinating information about the planet and its moons back to Earth. Two of the moons, *Ganymede* and *Callisto,* have craters pitting their surface like Earth's Moon. Another moon, *Europa,* was shown to be a ball of yellow ice. The closest moon to

Jupiter, *Io,* has several erupting volcanoes and a surface of yellow sulphur. Enormous electrical energy exists between Io and Jupiter, estimated to be equivalent, in any one second, to all the electrical power generated in the USA.

light year a measure of the distance travelled by light in one year, which is in the region of 5.8784 x 10^{12} miles (9.467 x 10^{12} kilometres). Light travels at 186,171 miles per second (299,792 kilometres per second) and it takes 8 minutes for it to reach EARTH from the SUN. The great distances between the various GALAXIES and heavenly bodies can be measured in light years. The nearest star to Earth (after the Sun) is more than four light years distant and is called PROXIMA CENTAURI. *See also* PARSEC.

lunar eclipse *see* ECLIPSE.

Magellanic clouds two separate GALAXIES, detached from the MILKY WAY, which appear, when viewed from the southern hemisphere, as diffuse patches of light. The largest is approximately 180,000 LIGHT YEARS away and the smallest is 230,000 light years distant. Both contain several thousand million STARS. They were first discovered by the Portuguese navigator Magellan in 1520 and can be viewed only from near the Equator or in the southern hemisphere.

magnitude a measure of the brightness of a star. When this property was measured accurately, it was discovered that each magnitude is rougly 2.5 times the next, so from magnitude 1 to 6 is a brightness increase of roughly 100. *Apparent magnitudes* are those measured from Earth and the *absolute magnitude* is the brightness of a star if it were 10 parsecs or 33 light years from Earth.

Mars the fourth PLANET in the SOLAR SYSTEM and the one nearest to EARTH. Its orbit lies between that of Earth and JUPITER, and it is about half the size of Earth. It has a thin atmosphere, exerting a pressure less than one hundredth of that of Earth. It also has a small mass, about one tenth of that of Earth, so that a person on Mars would weigh about 60 per cent less than Earth weight. Mars is often called the *Red Planet* as it has a dusty, reddish surface strewn with rocks. It is much colder than Earth with an atmosphere mainly of carbon dioxide, which is frozen at the two poles. The polar ice caps melt and re-form as the seasons change. Minimum surface temperatures are in the region of –148°F (–100°C), with the maximum only about –22°F (–30°C). A year on Mars lasts for 687 Earth days and the length of one day is almost the same, 24 hours and 37 minutes. The diameter of Mars is 4,529 miles (6,794 kilometres), and the crust in the northern part of the planet is composed of basalt (volcanic rock, *see* G&G igneous rocks). There are many extinct volcanoes, canyons, and impact craters, and there is evidence of water erosion at some stage in the planet's history. The mountains are much higher and the valleys deeper than those that exist on Earth, so there must have been violent movements of the crust in the past. The deepest valley, called *Valles Marineris*, is 2,667 miles (4,000 kilometres) long, 50 miles (75 kilometres) wide and up to 4.67 miles (7 kilometres) deep. The highest mountain, *Olympus Mons*, rises 15.3 miles (23 kilometres) from the surface of Mars and is three times taller than Mount Everest.

There are two small, irregularly shaped SATELLITES, or moons, orbiting Mars, called *Phobos* and *Deimos*. Phobos, the larger, is only 18 miles (27 kilometres) from one end to the other and just 4,000 miles (6,000 kilometres) above the planet's surface. Its ORBIT is a gradually descending spiral, and it is estimated that in 40 million years' time it will collide with Mars. Mars is currently being studied by means of three orbiting SPACECRAFT as well as two Mars Exploration Rovers.

matter any substance that occupies space and has mass, the material of which the UNIVERSE is made.

megaparsec a unit for defining the distance of objects outside the GALAXY, equal to 10^6 PARSECS (or 3.26×10^6 LIGHT YEARS).

Mercury the first PLANET of the SOLAR SYSTEM and nearest to the SUN. It has no atmosphere, so during the day the surface temperature reaches 797°F (425°C) (enough to melt lead), but at night the heat all escapes and it becomes intensely

cold, –274°F (–170°C). A day on Mercury lasts for 59 EARTH days, but the planet travels its ORBIT so fast that a year is only 88 days. Mercury is a very dense planet, for, although it is only slightly bigger than the MOON, it has an enormous mass that is almost the same as that of Earth. It is thought that this is accounted for by Mercury having a huge metallic core. Very little was known about the surface of the planet until it was visited by the *Mariner 10* SPACECRAFT, which passed to within 533 miles (800 kilometres) of it in 1974. It revealed that Mercury has a wrinkled surface with thousands of craters that have been caused by the impact of meteors and other larger space bodies. The largest crater, 867 miles (1,300 kilometres) across and known as the *Caloris Basin*, must have been caused by the collision of an enormous space body. Mercury has very little gravity and an elliptical orbit that takes it to within 31 million miles (46 million kilometres) of the Sun at its nearest point and 47 million miles (70 million kilometres) when farthest away.

meteor, meteorite *see* ASTEROID.

Milky Way the GALAXY that includes the SOLAR SYSTEM and consists of millions of STARS and NEBULAE. It stretches for about 100,000 LIGHT YEARS, and our solar system is in the region of 30,000 light years from the centre. It has a spiral shape with trailing *arms* that slowly revolve around the centre. The solar system is one tiny part occurring a long way out on one of the trailing spiral arms. There are probably millions of galaxies, including others with the same spiral shape. The Milky Way appears as a glowing cloud of light thrown out by the many millions of stars it contains.

Miranda *see* URANUS.

Moon the EARTH's one SATELLITE, which ORBITs the Earth at an average distance of 256,267 miles (384,400 kilometres). It has no atmosphere, water, or magnetic field, and surface temperatures reach extremes of 261°F (127°C) and –279°F (–173°C). It takes nearly 28 days to complete its orbit around Earth and always presents the same face towards Earth. As it orbits around Earth every 28 days, the Moon passes through *phases*, from new to first quarter to full to last quarter, and back to new again. One half of the Moon is always in sunlight and the phases depend upon the amount of the lit half that can be seen from Earth. A *new moon* occurs when the Earth, Moon and Sun are approximately in line with one another and none of the lit half can be seen at all; it appears that there is no Moon. About a week later a small *sliver* of the lit half can be seen from Earth, and this grows throughout the month until the whole of the lit half is visible at *full moon*. In the second half of the cycle, the amount of the lit half of the Moon that can be seen from Earth gradually declines once more. When the Moon is apparently growing in size it is called *waxing* and when it is declining it is called *waning*.

The diameter of the Moon is 2,317 miles (3,476 kilometres) and its mass is 0.0123 of that of Earth. Its density is 0.61 of that of Earth, and it has a thick crust up to 83 miles (125 kilometres) made up of volcanic rocks. There is probably a small core of iron, with a radius of approximately 200 miles (300 kilometres).

The surface of the Moon is heavily cratered, probably from meteorite impact, and the largest (viewed from Earth) is 200 miles (300 kilometres) across and surrounded by gigantic cliffs up to 14,000 feet (4,250 metres) high. The dark side of the Moon was a mystery until 1959 when *Luna 3*, a Russian space rocket, took photographs of it as it flew around. The surface is dry and rocky, and in 1969 the American astronauts, Neil Armstrong and Edwin Aldrin, made the first human footprints on its dusty surface. Other SPACECRAFT have since landed and brought back samples of lunar rock and soil, and analysis of these has revealed that the Moon must be at least 4,000 million years old. Interest has recently been rekindled in the Moon with the discovery of ice in March 1998. This makes it feasible to customise the Moon and use it as a base for further exploration into space. A distinctive feature of the Moon is its *maria* (singular *mare*), which are huge dry plains that were once thought to be seas. The name was coined before modern study found them to be dry, but their origin is not yet established although it is thought that they date from 3,300

million years ago. The tendency now is to dispense with the Latin name, e.g. *Sea of Showers* instead of *Mare Imbrium*.

Morning Star *see* VENUS.

nebula (*plural* **nebulae**) a cloud of interstellar MATTER, consisting of gases and dust, in which STARS originate and also die. When stars die, their gases and dust are poured back out into space, forming *planetary nebulae*. Dark patches in the MILKY WAY GALAXY are nebulae that obliterate the light from the stars behind them. Sometimes surrounding stars throw their light on to a nebula, making it glow brightly. The *Orion Nebula* has a cluster of stars being formed within its cloud. It is 1300 LIGHT YEARS away and about 15 light years from one side to the other.

Neptune normally the eighth PLANET of the SOLAR SYSTEM with its ORBIT between that of URANUS and PLUTO. For about 20 years in every 248 years, however, Pluto's orbit approaches closer to the SUN than Neptune's. Neptune is a vast planet, one of the GAS GIANTS, and is around 2,998 million miles (4,497 million kilometres) from the Sun. It is extremely cold, with surface temperatures of about −328°F (−200°C), and the atmosphere consists mainly of methane, hydrogen and helium. The diameter at the poles is 32,467 miles (48,700 kilometres) and at the equator it is 32,267 miles (48,400 kilometres), which is about four times that of the EARTH. The mass of the planet is 17 times greater than that of Earth, and it takes 165 years to circle once around the Sun. Neptune is such a long way from the Earth that it can be viewed only by using the most powerful TELESCOPES, and even then it appears to be minute. Two astronomers, John Couch Adams in 1845 in Britain and Urbain Leverrier in France in 1846, worked out the existence and position of Neptune before it could actually be seen. They noticed that the path of the ORBIT of nearby URANUS was not as expected and worked out that it was being affected by the gravitational pull of another planet. A year later Neptune was viewed for the first time. Neptune spins once on its axis every 18 to 20 hours and probably has a core of frozen rock and ice.

Most information about Neptune was obtained from the *Voyager 2* SPACE PROBE in August 1989. It took 9,000 photographs that show that Neptune is surrounded by a faint series of rings. There is a large dark cloud the size of the Earth, called the *Dark Spot*, that has a spinning oval shape. Winds whip through the atmosphere at velocities of 1,333 miles (2,000 kilometres) per hour and there are white methane clouds that constantly change shape. Neptune has eight SATELLITES, or moons, two of which are large and known as *Triton* and *Nereid*. Triton is the largest moon and is about the same size as MERCURY; its orbit is in the opposite direction from that of the other moons. It has a frozen surface with icy volcanic mountains and appears to have lakes of frozen gas and methane. The thin atmosphere of Neptune itself is composed mainly of nitrogen gas.

Nereid *see* NEPTUNE.

neutron star a small body with a seemingly impossibly high density. A STAR that has exhausted its fuel supply collapses under gravitational forces so intense that its electrons and protons are crushed together and form neutrons. This produces a star ten million times more dense than a WHITE DWARF – equivalent to a cupful of matter weighing many million tons on EARTH. Although no neutron stars have definitely been identified, it is thought that PULSARS may belong to this group.

Northern Lights *see* AURORA.

nova (*plural* **novae**) in the literal sense this is a new STAR (*nova* being Latin for 'new'), but it may also be a star that suddenly burns brighter by a factor of 5,000 to 10,000. It seems that a nova is one partner in a BINARY STAR. The smaller star burns much hotter than the SUN while the other partner is a vast expanse of hot red mist called a RED GIANT. An explosion results if cooler gas from the red cloud reaches the hot star, causing it to burn up more brightly—a nova. A red giant may eventually become a WHITE DWARF.

orbit the path of one heavenly body moving around another which results from the gravitational force attracting them together. The lighter body moves around the heavier one, which is itself also in motion.

The speed at which a heavenly body travels depends upon the size of its orbit. This is itself determined by the distance between the two heavenly bodies.

parallax the apparent movement in the position of a heavenly body resulting from a change in the position of the observer. It is therefore caused, in reality, by EARTH moving through space on its ORBIT. The distance of a heavenly body from Earth can be calculated by astronomers using parallax. The direction of the body from Earth is measured at two six-month intervals when the Earth is at either side of its orbit. From the apparent change in position, the distance of the body from Earth can be deduced.

parsec an astronomical unit of distance used for measurements beyond the SOLAR SYSTEM and corresponding to a PARALLAX of one second of arc (there are 3,600 arc seconds in one degree). A parsec is 20,571,000,000,000 miles (30,857,000,000,000 kilometres) or 3.2616 LIGHT YEARS. The nearest star to EARTH has been calculated as being 1.3 parsecs distant.

perihelion the point in its orbit at which the Earth is nearest to the Sun, the opposite to APHELION.

Phobos *see* MARS.

planet the name given originally to seven heavenly bodies that were thought to move among the STARS, which were themselves thought to be stationary. It is derived from the Greek word for 'wanderer'. The term is now used to describe those heavenly bodies moving in definite ORBITS around the SUN which, in order of distance, are: MERCURY, VENUS, EARTH, MARS, JUPITER, SATURN, URANUS and NEPTUNE. IN 2006, PLUTO was reclassified as a DWARF PLANET with *Ceres* and *Eris* (the ninth largest body that orbits the Sun). Mercury and Venus are termed the *inferior planets* and Mars to Neptune the *superior planets*, the latter because they revolve outside the Earth's orbit. Each planet travels its own particular orbit but they are all moving in the same direction.

planetoid *see* ASTEROID.

Pluto once considered to be the ninth and smallest PLANET in the SOLAR SYSTEM and the one that lies farthest away from the SUN, but since reclassified as a DWARF PLANET. It is thought to be the largest member of a region called the Kuiper belt. The existence of Pluto was predicted by an American astronomer called Percival Lowell from the behaviour of the ORBITS of its closest neighbours, NEPTUNE and URANUS. Pluto was finally spotted in 1930, 14 years after Lowell died. Pluto appears as a tiny speck when viewed from EARTH and little is known about it, but it probably has an iron core and a rocky surface with a covering of methane ice. Since it is so far from the sun (a maximum of 4,892 million miles, 7,338 million kilometres), it must be extremely cold, in the region of –382°F (–230°C). A day on Pluto lasts for almost seven Earth days and a year is 248.4 Earth years. At its equator, the planet has a diameter in the region of 2,333 miles (3,500 kilometres). Pluto has a wide elliptical orbit that sometimes brings it closer to the Sun. In 1989 it was at its closest point to the Sun (called its PERIHELION), but this occurs only every 248 years. During this phase of its orbit, Pluto apparently has a thin atmosphere composed of methane gas. When it moves away from the Sun again, however, it is possible that this becomes frozen once more. In 1979 it was discovered that Pluto has one small SATELLITE (which was named *Charon*) that is about a quarter of the size of Pluto. The two bodies effectively form a binary system but as yet there is no official definition for binary dwarf planets.

Prometheus *see* SATURN.

Proxima Centauri a small, faint, red, STAR that is the closest one to the SOLAR SYSTEM (some 4.3 LIGHT YEARS away) yet to be discovered. It occurs in the constellation of *Centaurus* and is the third and smallest member of a series of three stars called *Alpha Centauri*. It takes about a million years for it to ORBIT the other two stars, which are larger and brighter. Proxima Centauri occasionally burns more brightly for short periods of time but is usually quite dim.

pulsar what is thought to be a collapsed, rotating NEUTRON STAR, all that is left after a SUPERNOVA explosion. A pulsar is a source of radio frequency radiation that is given out in regular short bursts. The radiation is in the form of a beam that sweeps through space as the pulsar rotates and is detected on EARTH if Earth happens to lie in its path. The first pulsar was found to emanate from the *Crab Nebula*, which is a supernova.

quasar any of the quasi-stellar objects (that is, like STARS) that are extremely compact, give out light and yet are enormously distant bodies—up to 10^{10} LIGHT YEARS away.

radio astronomy the detection of a large range of radio waves (especially radiation given off by hydrogen atoms in space) that are emitted by numerous sources. These include the SUN, PULSARS, remnants of SUPERNOVAe and QUASARS.

radiotelescope the instrument used to detect and analyse extraterrestrial electromagnetic radiation (light and radio waves). There are two types—the *parabolic reflector*, which focuses the radiation on to an antenna, and the *interferometer*, where an interference pattern (*see* S&T diffraction) of 'fringes' is formed and precise wavelength measurements can be made. The latter is more accurate while the former is easier to move. The parabolic reflector is in the form of a large metal dish that can be pointed in different directions, used in conjunction with others and mounted on a rail so that it can be moved. The largest individual radiotelescope is the Ratan-600 in the Caucasus Mountains in Russia which has a circular antenna with a diameter of 576 metres (1,890 feet). Other notable systems include the Arecibo, which is built across a valley at Arecibo in Puerto Rico and is 305 metres (1,000 feet) across, and the Effelsberg (Germany) and the Green Bank (USA) which are 100 metres (328 feet) across.

red giant an ageing STAR that is extremely hot and has used up about 10 per cent of its hydrogen. The outer layers are cooler than the intensely hot centre. As the name implies, these are very large stars. The red giant *Aldebaran*, with a diameter of 33,400,000 miles (50,100,000 kilometres), is 35 times larger than the SUN. Some red giants go on to become WHITE DWARFS, using up their hydrogen at an increased rate. The Sun will eventually become a red giant, in about 5,000 million years time.

red shift *see* EXPANSION THEORY.

satellite any body, whether natural or manmade, that ORBITS a much larger body under the force of gravitation. The MOON is therefore a *natural satellite* of the EARTH. All the PLANETS except MERCURY and VENUS have at least one natural satellite. *Artificial satellites* are manmade SPACE-CRAFT launched into orbit from Earth. The first satellite to be launched was the Russian *Sputnik I* in 1957, but many hundreds have followed since then. Some satellites, especially those used for communications, are placed in a special *geostationary* orbit. This orbit is about 24,000 miles (36,000 kilometres) above the Earth's surface. The satellite orbits Earth in the same period of time as Earth rotates on its axis (24 hours). The satellite therefore maintains the same position relative to the Earth and appears to be stationary and equipment on Earth does not need to be adjusted to follow the satellite. Satellites are used for other purposes such as meteorological recordings and weather forecasting. Each satellite has a dish antenna facing towards Earth and *thruster* motors to help maintain its position. When the fuel supply for the thrusters is exhausted, the satellite drifts out of its orbit and can no longer be used. The equipment on board a satellite or spaceship requires electricity, which is usually derived from solar-powered cells (*see* S&T photoelectric cell). Spacecraft travelling long distances away from the SUN, however, have electricity generated by small nuclear reactors.

Saturn one of the four GAS GIANTS, the second largest PLANET and sixth in the SOLAR SYSTEM, with an ORBIT between that of JUPITER and URANUS. Saturn has a diameter at its equator of about 80,533 miles (120,800 kilometres) and is a maximum distance of 1,004,666,667 miles (1,507,000,000) kilometres from the SUN. Saturn rotates very fast, and this causes it to flatten at its poles and bulge at its equator. A day on Saturn lasts for $10^{1}/4$ hours, and a year (or one complete orbit of the Sun) for 29.45 EARTH years. Saturn is a cold planet of frozen gases and ice and has a surface temperature in the region of -274°F (-170°C). It is mainly gaseous with an outer zone of hydrogen and helium over a metallic hydrogen layer and a core of ice silicate. The atmosphere is rich in methane and ethane. Saturn is well known for its *rings*, which are in fact ice particles and other debris thought to be the remains of a SATELLITE that broke up close to the planet. The rings are wide, in the region of 178,584 miles (267,876 kilometres) across, but they are extremely thin (only a few miles). *Voyager* SPACECRAFTS approached close to Saturn in 1980 and 1981 and photographs taken then revealed that there were many more rings than had previously been detected. They are brighter than those of any other planet.

Saturn has 24 satellites, or moons, some of which were discovered by the *Voyager* spacecraft, including *Atlas, Prometheus* and *Calypso*. *Titan* is the largest moon and, with a diameter of 3,467 miles (5,200 kilometres), is larger than Mercury. It is the only moon known to have a detectable atmosphere, a layer of gases above its surface.

Sirius also known as the *Dog Star* because it occurs in the CONSTELLATION called the *Greater Dog, Canis Majoris*, the brightest STAR in the night sky. It is a BINARY STAR with a WHITE DWARF as its partner and shines brightly because it lies quite close to EARTH, only 0.5 LIGHT YEARS distant.

shooting star *see* ASTEROID.

solar energy energy that reaches EARTH from the SUN in the form of heat and light; 85 per cent of solar energy is reflected back into space and only 15 per cent reaches the Earth's surface, but it is this energy that sustains all life.

solar flare *see* SUNSPOTS.

solar system the system comprising the SUN (a STAR of spectral type G) around which revolve the eight PLANETS in elliptical ORBITS. Nearest the Sun is MERCURY, then VENUS, EARTH, MARS, JUPITER, SATURN, URANUS and NEPTUNE. (PLUTO was recently reclassified as a dwarf planet). In addition, there are numerous SATELLITES, a few thousand ASTEROIDS (so far discovered) and millions of COMETS. The age of the solar system is put at 4.5 to 4.6 billion years, a figure determined by the *radiometric dating* (uranium-lead content) of iron meteorites (*see* G&G dating methods). They are thought to be fragments or cores from early planets and thus representative of the early stages of the solar system.

solar wind the term for the stream of charged high-energy particles (mainly electrons, protons, and alpha particles) given out by the SUN. The particles travel at hundreds of miles per second, and the wind is greatest during flare and SUNSPOT activity. Around the EARTH, the particles have velocities of 200–333 miles (300–500 kilometres) per second, and some become trapped in the magnetic field to form the VAN ALLEN RADIATION BELT. Some reach the upper atmosphere, however, and move to the poles, producing AURORA.

Southern Lights *see* AURORA.

spacecraft a manned or unmanned vehicle that ORBITS the EARTH or travels to other heavenly bodies for the purposes of research, etc.

space probe an unmanned SPACECRAFT, such as *Voyager 1* and *2*, launched to travel through the SOLAR SYSTEM and beyond and programmed to send back data and photographs. Space probes eventually move so far away that contact with them is lost forever, but they continue to travel for thousands of years. Vehicles from space probes have landed on VENUS and MARS, obtaining valuable information, while over recent years probes have been sent to observe more planets including SATURN (*Cassini*) and MERCURY (*Messenger* arriving in orbit in 2011). Other probes have specific non-planetary missions such as sampling asteroids and gathering interstellar dust. *Voyager 1* and *2* have now left the solar system, becoming interstellar probes.

space shuttle a SPACECRAFT that is reusable as it does not burn up on re-entry to the EARTH's atmosphere and can be landed on a runway. The first space shuttle was used in 1982.

space station a manned space research centre, including living accommodation, in which astronauts live and work for several months at a time. The first manned space station, *Mir*, of the former Soviet Union, was launched in 1986. The International Space Station (ISS) combines the planned US *Freedom Space Station* and the Russian *Mir 2* project. Construction began in 1998 and the first crew arrived on the station in 2000 since when it has been occupied. The ISS is the joint effort of five space agencies—NASA, and agencies from Russia, Canada, Japan and Europe. Five space tourists have visited the station, each for a fee of $25 million.

space telescope a telescope that is launched into ORBIT in order to obtain images of STARS and other heavenly bodies that are much clearer than if obtained from EARTH. Images viewed through Earth-based TELESCOPES are subject to distortion because of atmospheric factors, but such problems do not affect telescopes that are sited in space. Space telescopes have a special mirror, and the images are radioed back to Earth where they can be studied on a screen and photographs obtained. (*See* HUBBLE TELESCOPE.)

space time *see* S&T relativity.

star a body of fiery gas, similar to the SUN, which is contained by its own gravitational field. Stars are glowing masses that produce energy by thermonuclear reactions (S&T nuclear fusion). The core acts as a natural nuclear reactor, where hydrogen is consumed and forms helium with the production of electromagnetic radiation. A classification system for stars, based upon the spectrum of light they emit, groups stars as various *spectral types*. The sequence, in order of descending temperature, is: O—hottest blue stars; B—hot blue stars; A—blue-white stars; F—white stars; G—yellow stars; K—orange stars; M—coolest red stars. Stellar evolution encompasses the various stages in the life of a star, beginning with its creation from the condensation of gas, primarily hydrogen. The growth of the gas cloud pulls in more gas, and the increase in gravity compresses the molecules together, attracting more material and creating a denser mass. The heat normally produced by molecules because of their vibratory motion is increased greatly and the temperature is raised to millions of degrees, which enables nuclear fusion to take place. The supply of hydrogen continues to be consumed (and the star occupies the main sequence of the Hertzsprung-Russell diagram) until about 10 per cent has gone. (The Hertzsprung-Russell diagram is a graph of star types from hot to cooler, depending upon the stage each has reached in its evolution.) When 10 per cent of the hydrogen has been consumed, the rate of combustion increases. This is accompanied by collapses in the core and an expansion of the hydrogen-burning surface layers, forming a RED GIANT. Progressive gravitational collapses and burning of the helium (which is generated by the consumption of the hydrogen) results in a WHITE DWARF, which is a sphere of enormously dense gas. The white dwarf cools over many millions of years and forms a *black dwarf*—an invisible ball of gases in space. Other sequences of events may occur, depending upon the size of the star formed. BLACK HOLES and NEUTRON STARS may form RED GIANTS via a SUPERNOVA stage.

Sun the STAR nearest to EARTH around which Earth and the other PLANETS move in elliptical ORBITS. It is one of millions of stars in the MILKY WAY but is the centre of the SOLAR SYSTEM. It was formed around 5,000 million years ago and is about halfway through its life cycle. It has a diameter of 928,000 miles (1,392,000 kilometres) and the interior reaches a temperature of 23,400,032 degrees Fahrenheit (13 million degrees centigrade) while the visible surface is about 10,832°F (6,000°C). The internal temperature is such that thermonuclear reactions occur, converting hydrogen to helium with the release of vast quantities of energy. The Sun is approximately 90 per cent hydrogen and 8 per cent helium and will one day become a RED GIANT.

sunspots the appearance of dark areas on the surface of the SUN. The occurrence reaches a maximum approximately every eleven years in a phase known as the *sunspot cycle*. They are usually short-lived (less than one month) and are caused by magnetism drawing away heat to leave a cooler area, which is the sunspot. The black appearance is because of a lowering of the temperature to about 4,000 K (6,740.3°F, 3,726.8°C). Sunspots have

intense magnetic fields and are associated with magnetic storms and effects such as the *aurora borealis* (*see* AURORA). They may send out *solar flares*, which are explosions occurring in the vicinity of the sunspots.

superior planet *see* PLANET.

supernova (*plural* **supernovae**) a large STAR that explodes, it is thought, because of the exhaustion of its hydrogen (*see* SUN), whereupon it collapses, generating high temperatures and triggering thermonuclear reactions. A large part of its matter is thrown out into space, leaving a residue that is termed a WHITE DWARF star. Such events are very rare, but at the time of the explosion the stars become one hundred million times brighter than the Sun. A supernova was sighted in 1987 in the large MAGELLANIC CLOUD, 170,000 LIGHT YEARS away.

telescope an instrument for magnifying an image of a distant object, the main types of astronomical telescopes being *refractors* and *reflectors*. The refracting type has lenses to produce an enlarged, upside-down image. In the reflecting type there are large mirrors with a curved profile that collect the light and direct it onto a second mirror and into the eyepiece (*see also* RADIOTELESCOPE).

Titan *see* SATURN.

Titania *see* URANUS.

Triton *see* NEPTUNE.

universe all matter, energy, and space that exists which is continuing to expand since its formation (*see* BIG-BANG THEORY).

Uranus the seventh PLANET in the SOLAR SYSTEM and one of the four GAS GIANTS, with an ORBIT between those of SATURN and NEPTUNE. Uranus has a diameter at its equator of 33,387 miles (50,080 kilometres) and lies at an average distance of 1,913,066,667 miles (2,869,600,000 kilometres) from the SUN. The surface temperatures are in the region of –400°F (–240°C). It is composed mainly of gases, with a thick atmosphere of methane, helium and hydrogen. Uranus was the first planet to be observed with a TELESCOPE and was discovered by William Herschel, a German astronomer, in 1781. Uranus remained a mystery until quite recently, but in 1986 *Voyager 2* approached close to the planet and obtained valuable information and photographs. The planet appeared to be blue because of its thick atmosphere of gases and there was a faint ring system consisting of 13 main rings. Uranus was known to have five moons but a further 10, some less than 50 kilometres in diameter, were discovered by *Voyager 2*. A day on Uranus lasts for about 17¹/2 hours and a year is equivalent to 84 EARTH years. Its largest moon is *Titania*, with a diameter of 1,067 miles (1,600 kilometres). All five of the known moons are very cold and icy, with a surface covered in craters and cracks. *Ariel* has deep wide valleys, and *Miranda*, the smallest moon, is a mass of canyons and cracks with cliffs reaching up to 13 miles (20 kilometres). Uranus has a greatly tilted axis so that some parts of the planet's surface are exposed to the Sun for half of the planet's orbit (about 40 years) and are then in continuous darkness for the rest of the time. Because of the tilt of the axis, the Sun is sometimes shining almost directly on to each of Uranus's poles during parts of its orbit.

Van Allen radiation belts two belts of radiation consisting of charged particles (electrons and protons) trapped in EARTH's magnetic field. The result is the formation of two belts around the Earth. They were discovered in 1958 by an American physicist called James Van Allen. The lower belt occurs between 1,333 and 3,333 miles (2,000 and 5,000 kilometres) above the Equator and its particles are derived from the Earth's atmosphere. The particles in the upper belt, at around 13,333 miles (20,000 kilometres), are derived from the SOLAR WIND. The Van Allen belts are part of the Earth's magnetosphere, an area of space in which charged particles are affected by Earth's magnetic field rather than that of the Sun.

Venus the second PLANET in the SOLAR SYSTEM, with its ORBIT between those of MERCURY and EARTH. It is also the brightest planet and is known as the *Morning* or *Evening Star*. Venus is about 67,000,000 miles (100,500,000 kilometres) from the SUN and is extremely hot, with a surface temperature in the region of –878°F

(470°C). It has a thick atmosphere of mainly carbon dioxide, sulphuric acid, and other poisonous substances that obscures its surface. The size of Venus is similar to that of Earth, with a diameter at its equator of 8,200 miles (12,300 kilometres). The atmosphere of carbon dioxide traps heat from the Sun (the greenhouse effect), allowing none to escape. The surface rocks are, therefore, boiling hot and winds whip through the atmosphere at speeds in excess of 213 miles per hour (320 kilometres per hour). Venus is unusual in being the only planet to spin on its axis in the opposite direction from the path of its orbit. It also spins very slowly so that a day on Venus is very long, equivalent to 243 Earth days. A year is 225 days. Venus has no SATELLITES, and because its surface is hidden much of the known information about the planet has been obtained from SPACE PROBES. The *Magellan* space probe, launched by the USA in 1989, visited Venus, sending back valuable photographs. *Venera 13*, a Russian probe, landed on Venus in 1982 and obtained a rock sample and other information. The surface of the planet has been shown to be mountainous, with peaks 8 miles (12 kilometres) high. It is covered with craters and also has a rift valley. It is possible that there are active volcanoes.

white dwarf a type of STAR that is very dense with a low luminosity. White dwarfs result from the explosion of stars that have used up their available hydrogen. Because of their small size, their surface temperatures are high, and they appear white (*see also* SUPERNOVA).

X-ray astronomy STARS emit a variety of electromagnetic radiation including X-rays (*see* S&T electromagnetic waves), but this is unable to penetrate the EARTH's atmosphere to be detected. Very hot stars send out large amounts of X-rays that can be detected by equipment contained on space SATELLITES. The satellite ROSAT, launched in 1990, has equipment to undertake X-ray astronomy and obtain information about distant bodies in space (e.g. WHITE DWARFS and SUPERNOVAE) that are emitting X-rays.

Geography and Geology

alluvium deposits produced as a result of the action of streams or RIVERS. Moving water carries sediment, particles of sand, mud and silt and the faster it moves the greater the load it can carry. When the velocity of the water is checked because it meets a stationary or slower moving body of water, then much or all of the sediment is dropped, forming alluvium. In mountainous regions where streams descend to lowlands, a fan, or cone, of sediment may build up. Rivers in areas of less extreme geography deposit alluvium on the flood plain, where the water changes velocity along the curving course of the river, or when rivers overflow their banks during floods.

anticyclone *see* CYLONE.

aquifer a layer of rock, sand, or gravel that is porous and therefore allows the passage and collection of water. If the layer has sufficient porosity and permeability, it may provide enough GROUNDWATER to produce springs or wells. If the layers above and below the aquifer are impermeable, the water is under pressure (*hydrostatic pressure*) and can be extracted in an *artesian well* while the level of the well is lower than that of the WATER TABLE. Where the supply of water is diminishing because the water table and pressure has fallen as a result of prolonged water extraction, pumps may be required to raise the water to the surface.

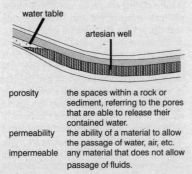

porosity	the spaces within a rock or sediment, referring to the pores that are able to release their contained water.
permeability	the ability of a material to allow the passage of water, air, etc.
impermeable	any material that does not allow passage of fluids.

artesian well a well in which water rises to the surface by internal pressure. *See also* AQUIFER.

atmosphere the layer of gases and dust surrounding the Earth that can be divided into shells, the lowermost being the TROPOSPHERE, which is overlain by the STRATOSPHERE. The density falls with height, and because the atmosphere is thinner at high altitudes breathing is more difficult. Almost 75 per cent of the total mass is contained within the troposphere. The main gases found in the atmosphere are nitrogen (78 per cent), oxygen (21 per cent), the inert gas argon (0.9 per cent), carbon dioxide (0.03 per cent), and then very small amounts of other inert gases, with methane, hydrogen, water vapour and ozone. The ozone exists mainly in a layer (*see* OZONE LAYER) at a height of about 15 to 20 miles (24 to 32 kilometres) although it is found elsewhere within the stratosphere.

Atmospheric pressure is the downward force of the atmosphere on the surface of the Earth and is roughly equivalent to a force of 1 kilogram per centimetre (2.2 pounds per square inch). It was originally defined as the pressure that will support a column of mercury 760 millimetres (30 inches) high at 0°C (32°F), sea level and a latitude of 45 degrees (*see* S&T barometer).

Beaufort scale a system for indicating wind strength, developed in 1805 by the British Admiral Sir Francis Beaufort. Measurements are taken 10 metres (33 feet) above the ground. It has 12 levels, each of which is characterised by particular features of the landscape or certain effects upon people or objects. Wind speed is measured in metres per second.

boulder clay a deposit that is glacial in origin and made up of boulders of varying sizes in finer grained material, mainly clay. It is laid down beneath a glacier or ice sheet and shows little or no structure. Large blocks plucked from the terrain over which the ice has moved may be found in a matrix of finer material that has been ground down by the glacier. An alternative and more frequently used term is *till*, of which several types have been defined depending upon their specific mode of formation and position within the ice body. *Moraine* is an associated term referring to ridges of rock debris carried and deposited by ice sheets or glaciers of the various types; *lateral moraine* accumulates at the edge of a glacier and *terminal moraine* at the leading edge. *Ground moraine* is the same as boulder clay.

chalk a soft, fine-grained SEDIMENTARY ROCK made of calcium carbonate formed mainly from the skeletons and shells of very small marine organisms. It is formed primarily as deposits of calcareous mud in shallow seas, but it can also be formed by chemical precipitation. Chalk deposited in the Upper Cretaceous, approximately 100 million years ago, now covers much of northwest Europe and can be seen in the White Cliffs of Dover in southern England and in cliffs near Calais in northern France. Chalk produces a particular scenery, with low rolling hills, dry valleys and steep *scarps* (an escarpment or steep slope that ends a flat or gently sloping area). Chalk is an important AQUIFER and is used in the manufacture of cement and fertilisers.

climate characteristic weather conditions produced by a combination of factors, such as rainfall and temperature. Whether taken singly or jointly, these factors, together with influencing features such as altitude and latitude, produce a distinctive arrangement of zones around the Earth, each with a generally consistent climate when studied over a period of time. The major climatic zones are, from the Equator:

humid tropical: hot and wet

subtropical, arid and semi-arid: desert conditions, extremes of daily temperature

humid temperate: warm and moist with mild winters

boreal (Northern Hemisphere): long, cold winters; short summers

sub-arctic (or sub-Antarctic): generally cold with low rainfall

polar: always cold

Climatic patterns are very dependent upon heat received from the Sun, and at the Poles the rays have had to travel further and in so doing have lost much of their heat, producing the coldest regions on Earth. Conversely, air near the Equator is very warm and can therefore hold a great deal of water vapour, resulting in hot and wet conditions—humid tropical. There are more complex systems of climate classification, e.g. Köppen and Thornthwaite, which are based upon precipitation and evaporation, characteristic vegetation and temperature. In each system, the Earth can be split into numerous provinces and smaller areas, producing quite a detailed overall picture.

climate change and global warming there have been many periods of dramatic climate change throughout the course of the Earth's history. Evidence for this can be found in rocks that are exposed on the surface. They reveal phases of immense variation, ranging from the extreme cold of an ice age to the intense heat of a desert climate. These periods of change were driven by entirely natural cycles and events including alterations in the amount of solar energy reaching the Earth, changes in the composition and proportions of atmospheric gases, volcanic eruptions, 'wobbles' of the planet on its axis and the impact of METEORITES. However, the majority of scientists believe that the current period of climate change, which is a phase of *global warming*, is being driven by the activities of human beings and in particular, industrial processes and the burning of FOSSIL FUELS.These processes are artificially adding GREEENHOUSE GASES to the planet's atmosphere and overbalancing and disrupting the natural cycle known as the 'GREENHOUSE EFFECT' leading to a global rise in average temperatures. It is believed that the effects of the change will be more marked at the POLES and greater in winter than in summer. It is happening very rapidly, giving little time for life to adapt. It is thought that the effects will include a rise in sea levels and widespread flooding caused by the melting of polar ice, changes to, or possibly the 'switching off' of, some ocean currents, desertification and increasing frequency and severity of storms and hurricanes.

cloud a mass of droplets of water or ice formed by the condensation of moisture in a mass of rising air. Water vapour formed by evaporation from seas, lakes and rivers is ordinarily contained in air and becomes visible only when it condenses to form water droplets. Warm air can hold more water vapour than cold air, so when air rises, becoming cooler, it becomes saturated ('full') of water, and eventually droplets form, as cloud, each droplet forming around a central nucleus such as dust, pollen, or a smoke particle.

Clouds are classified firstly by their shape and also by their height. There are three major groups: *cumulus* ('heap' clouds), *stratus* (sheet-like) and *cirrus* (resembling fibres), which are divided further as cloud forms show a mix of shape, e.g. *cirrocumulus*.

coal a mineral deposit that contains a very high carbon content and occurs in banded layers (*seams*) resembling rock. It is formed from ancient forest vegetation that has accumulated and been transformed into PEAT. With time, increasing pressure from sediments above and some heating, the peat becomes coal of various types, each type (or *rank*) being marked by the carbon content, which increases with pressure and temperature, and the volatiles content, which decreases at the same time. Volatiles are substances that readily become gas, specifically, in this case, a mixture of hydrogen, methane and carbon dioxide that is released when coal is heated.

The coal of highest rank is anthracite, which is 95 per cent carbon with a little moisture and volatile matter. Bituminous coals contain from about 45 to 75 per cent carbon while lignite has 70 per cent moisture and volatiles.

Coal beds occur in sequences of sandstone and shale called, collectively, *coal measures*. Most of the world's anthracite and bituminous coals accumulated in the Carboniferous period (*see* GEOLOGICAL TIMETABLE), and the coal measures reach thousands of feet in thickness in many countries. The countries with the greatest reserves of coal include the United States, Russia, China, Australia and Germany. Although coal is used less than it was as a primary energy source, its by-products are still used in the chemicals industry, for the manufacture of dyes, drugs, pesticides and other compounds.

continent any one of the several large landmasses that cover 29 per cent of the Earth's surface. Some 65 per cent of the continents are in the Northern Hemisphere. Where a continent's edge meets the sea there is a *continental shelf* and *slope*, which is often cut by submarine canyons. Farther oceanward lie the deepest parts of the ocean, the *abyssal plain*. There are seven continents making up the Earth:

	Highest point		Area	
	m	(ft)	sq km	(sq mi)
Asia	8,848	(29,028)	43,608,000	(16,832,688)
Africa	5,895	(19,340)	30,335,000	(11,709,310)
North and Central America	6,194	(20,321)	25,349,000	(9,784,714)
South America	6,960	(22,834)	17,611,000	(6,797,846)
Antarctica	5,140	(16,863)	14,000,000	(5,404,000)
Europe	5,642	(18,510)	10,498,000	(4,052,228)
Oceania	4,205	(13,796)	8,900,000	(3,435,400)

crystal a solid that has a particular ordered structure and shape with usually flat faces and a chemical composition that varies little. The arrangement of the atoms in the crystal in a specific framework gives it a characteristic shape. If conditions permit when the crystal is growing, the crystal faces are arranged in a constant geometric relationship. Many solids have a crystalline structure, from household items such as sugar and salt to chemicals, metals and the minerals within rocks. If a solution of a chemical or a MAGMA is allowed to cool slowly, crystals will develop. Similarly, if a crystal is placed in a saturated solution of the same compound, *crystallisation* will occur. If, however, the solution or magma is cooled suddenly, either the crystals formed are microscopic or the resulting solid exhibits no crystalline form (it is *amorphous*).

The regular formation of crystal faces

is part of a crystal's *symmetry*, which is described for each crystal system by three properties: planes, axes and a centre of symmetry. These properties together create six crystal systems. These are:

cubic	common salt
tetragonal	zircon
hexagonal	calcite; quartz
orthorhombic	topaz; barytes; sulphur
monoclinic	gypsum
triclinic	feldspars

Crystallography is the scientific study of crystals, their form and structure.

cyclone an area of low atmospheric pressure with closely packed isobars producing a steep pressure gradient and therefore very strong winds. Because of the Earth's rotation, the winds circulate clockwise in the Southern Hemisphere and anticlockwise in the Northern Hemisphere. In tropical regions, cyclones (tropical hurricanes) combine very high rainfall with destructive winds, which result in widespread damage and possible loss of life.

Outside the tropics, in more temperate climates, the word *depression* (or *low*) is replacing the term cyclone. In a depression the pressure may fall to 940 or 950 millibars. Compare this with the average pressure at sea level, which is 1013 millibars. An *anticyclone* is a high-pressure area (1030–1050 millibars) that usually results in stable weather.

dating method a way of identifying the age of an object or sample used in a number of scientific disciplines, e.g. geography, geology and archaeology. There are several ways in which this can be done. In many instances, a relative age can be determined quite readily. For example, in geology one rock cutting across another can provide clues as to the order of formation of rock sequences or the order in which rocks were folded or deformed (*see* FOLDS AND FAULTS). To obtain an *absolute* or true age (bearing in mind any experimental errors), however, the radioactive decay of isotopes can be employed—*radiometric dating*.

Radiocarbon dating is one such method. This relies upon the uptake by plants and animals of small quantities of naturally occurring radioactive ^{14}C (carbon –14) in the atmosphere. When the organism dies, the uptake stops and the ^{14}C decays with a half-life (*see* S&T radioactivity) of 5730 years, and the age of a sample can be calculated from the remaining radioactivity. This method is useful for dating organic material within the last 70,000 years, but the accuracy of the methods falls between 40,000 and 70,000 years.

Rocks can be dated by one of several methods, each of which relies upon the radioactive decay of one element to another. In these cases the half-life is very long, enabling the dating of very old rocks. Uranium lead was an early method in which uranium –238 (^{238}U) decays to lead –206 with a half-life of 4.5 billion years. Other systems are:

Rb/Sr	rubidium –87 decays to strontium –87; half-life of 50 billion years.
K/Ar	potassium –40 decays to argon –40; half-life of 1.5 billion years.
Th/Pb	thorium –232 decays to lead –208; half-life of 14 billion years.
Sm/Nd	samarium –147 decays to neodymium –143; half-life of 2.5 billion years.

The long half-lives make these systems useful in dating Lower Palaeozoic and Precambrian rocks (*see* GEOLOGICAL TIMESCALE). Sm/Nd is resistant to metamorphism and can be used on extraterrestrial materials. Th/Pb is often used with other methods because it is not an accurate method on its own. Rb/Sr is useful for dating metamorphic rocks. In general the best results for dating are obtained from igneous or metamorphic rocks.

depression *see* CYCLONE.

desert an arid or semi-arid (that is, dry and parched with under 10 inches/25 centimetres of rainfall annually) region in which there is little or no vegetation. The term was always applied to hot tropical and subtropical deserts but is equally applicable to areas within continents where there is low rainfall and perennial ice-cold deserts.

The vegetation is controlled by the rainfall and varies from sparse, drought-resistant shrubs and cacti to sudden blooms of annual plants following a short period of torrential rain. If the groundwater conditions permit, e.g. if the water table is near to the surface, creating a spring, or the geology is such that an artesian well (*see* AQUIFER) is created, then an oasis may develop within a hot desert, providing an island of green.

Hot deserts are found in Africa, Australia, the United States, Chile and cold deserts in the Arctic, eastern Argentina and mountainous regions. Some hot desert extremes are:

extreme of shade temperature: Death Valley, California maximum 28°C (82°F); maximum daily range 41°C (106°F)

max. ground surface temperature: Sahara 78°C (172°F)

extreme of rainfall: Chicama, Peru, 4mm (0.15in) per year

The process whereby desert conditions and processes extend to new areas adjacent to existing deserts is called *desertification*.

drainage the movement of water derived from rain, snowfall and the melting of ice and snow on land (and through it in subterranean waterways) that results eventually in its discharge into the sea. Underlying rocks, how they are arranged and whether there are any structural features that the water may follow influence the flow of streams and rivers. Further factors affecting drainage include soil type, climate and the influence of people.

There are a number of recognisable patterns that can be related to the geology:

dendritic	a random branching unaffected
trellis	by surface rocks; streams aligned with the trend of underlying rocks.
parallel	streams running parallel to each other because of folded rocks or steep slopes with little vegetation.
rectangular	controlled by faults and joints, the latter often in igneous rocks.
annular	formation of streams in circular patterns around a structure of the same shape (e.g. an igneous intrusion).
barbed	a drainage pattern where the tributaries imply a direction of flow contrary to what actually happens.
radial	streams flowing outwards from a higher area.

centripetal	the flow of streams into a central depression where there may be a lake or river.

When a drainage pattern is a direct result of the underlying geology, it is said to be *accordant* (the opposite case being *discordant*).

earthquake movement of the earth, which is often violent, caused by the sudden release of stress that may have accumulated over a long period. Waves of disturbance—*seismic* waves—spread out from the origin, or *focus*, of the earthquake, which is most likely to be movement along a FAULT, although some are associated with volcanic activity.

Earthquakes are classified by their depth of focus: shallow (less than 70 kilometres/44 miles); intermediate (70–300 kilometres/44–187 miles); deep (more than 300 kilometres/187 miles).

Over three-quarters of earthquake energy is concentrated in a belt around the Pacific. This is because most seismic activity occurs at the margins of tectonic plates (*see* PLATE TECTONICS). This means that certain regions of the world are more likely to suffer earthquakes, e.g. the West Coast of North and South America, Japan, the Philippines, Southeast Asia and New Zealand.

Areas of earthquake activity

The effects of earthquakes are naturally very alarming and can be quite catastrophic. Near the focus, ground waves actually throw the land surface about. Surface effects may include the opening of fissures (large cracks), the breaking of roads and pipes, buckling and twisting of railroad lines, and the collapse of bridges and buildings. Secondary effects can be equally destructive if the ground vibrations initiate landslides, avalanches and TSUNAMI or cause fires. There are several systems of measuring the intensity of earthquakes. The one in common use was devised by Charles Richter, an American seismologist. The Richter Scale is:

Rating	Identifying features
1 instrumental	detected only by seismographs.
2 feeble	noticed by sensitive people.
3 slight	similar to a passing truck.
4 moderate	loose objects are rocked.
5 rather strong	felt generally.
6 strong	trees sway; loose objects fall.
7 very strong	walls crack.
8 destructive	chimneys fall; masonry cracks.
9 ruinous	houses collapse where ground starts to crack.
10 disastrous	ground badly cracked; buildings destroyed.
11 very disastrous	bridges and most buildings destroyed; landslides.
12 catastrophic	ground moves in waves; total destruction.

Because this is a logarithmic scale, the magnitude of one level is very much more than the previous level. During the last ninety years of the 20th century not many earthquakes registered over 8 on the Richter scale. They include San Francisco (1906), Kansu in China (1920), Japanese Trench (1933), Chile (1960) and offshore Japan (1968). However, in the early years of the 21st century several exceeded 8 on the scale including: Hokkaido, Japan (8.3); Peru (8.4); Northern Sumatra (8.6) and the largest at 9.1 off the west coast of northern Sumatra. This last earthquake caused the Asian tsunami of December 2004. *See also* SEISMOGRAPH.

erosion the destructive breakdown of rock and soil by a variety of *agents* that, together with weathering, form *denudation*, or a wearing away of the land surface. Erosion occurs because of the mechanical action of material carried by agents: water (rivers, currents and waves), ice (glaciers) and wind. Wind laden with sand can scour rock; rocks embedded in glaciers grind down the rocks over which they pass;

and gravel and pebbles in streams and rivers excavate their own course, creating potholes, undercut banks, etc. Water can also carry material in solution. There are six different kinds of erosion process:

Process	Effect
abrasion	wearing away through grinding, rubbing and polishing.
attrition	the reduction in size of particles by friction and impact.
cavitation	characteristic of high-energy river waters (e.g. waterfalls, cataracts) where air bubbles collapse, sending out shock waves that impact on the walls of the river bed (a very localised occurrence).
corrasion	the use of boulders, pebbles, sand, etc, carried by a river to wear away the floor and sides of a river bed.
corrosion	all erosion achieved through solution and chemical reaction with materials encountered in the water.
deflation	the removal of loose sand and silt by the wind.

The effect of these processes can be very marked with time and can combine to deepen gorges, create and enlarge waterfalls and result in the movement of a waterfall upstream. The latter occurs through undercutting of lower, softer rocks that then cause the collapse of overhanging ledges.

evaporite a sedimentary rock formed by the evaporation of water containing various salts, resulting in their deposition. The particular sediment created depends upon the concentration of ions (*see* S&T ion) in solution and the solubility (*see* S&T solution) of each salt formed. The least soluble—calcium carbonate and magnesium carbonate—precipitate first, followed by sodium sulphate, then sodium chloride, potassium chloride and magnesium sulphate. A typical sequence of evaporite deposits could show calcite, possibly dolomite, gypsum (or anhydrite), rock salt and finally potassium and magnesium salts (e.g. carnallite, $KCl.MgCl.6H_2O$).There are several major deposits of evaporites in the world, e.g. in Texas and New Mexico, the Stassfurt deposits in Germany, the Wieliczka salt mines in Poland, in Chile and in Cheshire in England. Some of these deposits are over 11,500 feet (3500 metres) thick and since about 16 feet (5 metres) of evaporites would require the evaporation of nearly 1000 feet (300 metres) of seawater, it is clear that very special conditions existed in the past. To accumulate such vast thicknesses, there must be a shallow area of water from which evaporation and precipitation proceed and which is periodically refilled with salt water and there must be a gradual subsidence of the land to permit continued build-up of the salts. Modern evaporites are being formed in places such as the Caspian Sea and the Arabian Gulf and deposits have been formed recently in Eritrea.

faults *see* FOLDS.

flood where land not normally covered by water is temporarily underwater. A flood can occur for several reasons, and the scale of a flood may vary enormously. An increase in rainfall, particularly if prolonged, may lead to flooding, as may a sudden thaw of lying snow. Flooding of coastal areas by the sea may be caused by the combination of a very high tide and stormy conditions generating high waves. Perhaps most devastating of all are the TSUNAMIS, which are caused by earthquakes. Large areas of, e.g. Southeast Asia, continually face the threat of floods.

When a river is in flood it carries a far greater load of rocks, boulders, sand and silt, and its destructive power is therefore increased. In some cases flood waters have been powerful enough to carve new channels for the river and in so doing to demolish houses, roads, bridges, wash away trees and soil, and transport vast piles of boulders and masonry seemingly impossible distances.

floodplain the area in a river valley that may be covered by water when a river is in flood and that is built up of ALLUVIUM. The floodplain develops with a river's movement with time and the deposition and transport of sediment. Whether it is the result of existing features along a river's course or is simply caused by turbulence of flow and subsequent deposition of material where a river slows, the course of a river will include numerous bends. Subsequent ero-

sion and deposition of sediment result in a meandering (*see* RIVERS) of the river, with deposition of alluvium and a progressive movement along the river bends, forming a floodplain.

folds and faults geological features that develop through tectonic activity. Folds are produced when rock layers undergo compression, resulting in a buckling and folding of the rocks: a *ductile* or flowing deformation. There is an almost infinite variety in the shape, size and orientation of folds, and an earlier generation of folds may be refolded by subsequent periods of deformation. Their size may range from microscopic to folds occupying hillsides or even whole mountains.

The way folds are formed depends upon the amount of compression, the rock types involved, and the thickness of the layers because different rocks respond in different ways, but each fold possesses certain common features. The zone of greatest curvature is the *hinge*, and the *limbs* lie between hinges or on either side of the hinge. The *axial plane* is an imaginary feature bisecting the angle between limbs, and the *fold axis* is where the axial plane meets the hinge zone.

Faults are generally planar features and are caused by *brittle* deformation. Rocks are moved, or *displaced*, across faults by as little as a few fractions of an inch or as much as several miles (although possibly not all in the same event). There are several types of faults, depending upon the movement across the fault and the orientation of the fault plane. The measurement of movement uses horizontal and vertical components, the *heave* and *throw* respectively. If the movement is up or down the fault plane, it is a *dip-slip fault*; if it is sideways, the term is *strike-slip*.

Many faults produce associated features such as zones of crushed rock or striations (grooves), known as *slickensides*, on adjacent rock surfaces where minerals such as quartz or calcite may grow.

Major faults today account for many surface features and are an important part of the PLATE TECTONIC structure and development of the Earth.

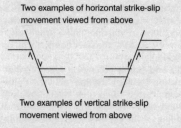

Two examples of horizontal strike-slip
movement viewed from above

Two examples of vertical strike-slip
movement viewed from above

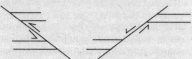

fossils the remains of once living plants and
animals, or evidence of their existence,
that have been preserved (usually) in the
rock layers of the Earth. The term may
include the preservation in ice of woolly
mammoths, which lived 20,000 years,
although anything younger than about
10,000 years is not generally considered
a fossil.

Fossils may be bones, shells, borings,
trails, casts and the fossilised remains of
something associated with or caused by
an organism; for example, animal tracks
or worm burrows are called *trace fossils*.
Although many rock sequences contain
a large number of fossils, conditions prevailing at the time have to be just right to
ensure preservation. A vital part of the
process is that the organism be covered
quickly with sediment, something that
will happen more readily in marine rather
than terrestrial conditions. Even then,
significant changes may occur— soft parts
usually decay and shells may be replaced
chemically or dissolved away, leaving a
mould to be filled by a different material. Occasionally, a whole insect may be
preserved in amber. The study of fossils is
called *palaeontology.*

fossil fuels fuels that are created by the
fossilisation of plant and animal remains,
including PETROLEUM (oil), COAL and
NATURAL GAS. Oil and gas are often found
together, with the gas lying over the oil
and beneath the impermeable layer that
seals the reservoir.

geochemistry a part of GEOLOGY that deals
with the chemical make-up of the Earth,
including the distribution of elements (and
ISOTOPES) and their movement within the
various natural systems (ATMOSPHERE, etc).
Recently, it has also been taken to include
other planets and moons within the solar
system. The geochemical cycle, in broad
terms, illustrates the way in which elements from MAGMA (the 'starting point')
move through different processes and
geochemical environments.

geochronology the study of time on a
geological scale using *absolute* or *relative*
DATING METHODS. Absolute methods provide an age for a rock and involve the use
of radioactive elements with known rates
of decay. Relative ages are determined by
putting rock sequences in order through
study of their sequence of deposition or
folding. Fossils can also be used in relative
age dating.

geography the study of the Earth's surface, including all the landforms (*see*
GEOMORPHOLOGY), their formation and
associated processes, which comprises
physical geography. Such aspects as climate, topography and oceanography are
covered. *Human geography* deals with the
social and political perspectives of the
subject, including populations and their
distribution. In addition, geography may
cover the distribution and exploitation
of natural resources, map-making and
REMOTE SENSING.

geological timescale a division of time
since the formation of the Earth (4600
million years ago) into units, during which
rock sequences were deposited, deformed
and eroded, and life of diverse types
emerged, flourished, and, often, ceased.

The following table shows the various
subdivisions, many of the names owing
their derivation to particular locations,
rock sequences and so on:

Era	Epoch	Life form
Cenozoic	Recent	modern man.
	Pleistocene	Stone Age man.
	Pliocene	many mammals, elephants.
	Oligocene	pig and ape ancestors.
	Eocene	
	Palaeocene	horse and cattle ancestors.

Mesozoic	Cretaceous	end of the dinosaurs and the ammonites.
	Jurassic	appearance of birds and mammals.
	Triassic	dinosaurs appear; corals of modern type.
Palaeozoic	Permian	amphibians and reptiles more common; conifer trees appear.
	Carboniferous	coal forests; reptiles appear, winged insects.
	Devonian	amphibians appear; fishes more common; ammonites appear; early trees; spiders.
	Silurian	first coral reefs; spore-bearing land plants appear.
	Ordovician	first fish-like vertebrates: trilobites and graptolites common.
	Cambrian	first fossils period; trilobites, graptolites, mollusks, crinoids, radiolaria, etc.
	Precambrian	sponges, worms, algae, bacteria; all primitive forms.

'Palaeozoic' means 'ancient life'. The Roman name for Wales (*Cambria*) led to 'Cambrian', while the names of two Celtic tribes, *Silures* and *Ordovices*, provided two of the Palaeozoic names. 'Carboniferous' is related to the spread of coal (i.e. carbon), and 'Cretaceous' comes from *creta*, meaning 'chalk'. The Triassic is a threefold division in Germany, while the *Jura* Mountains in France lent their name to the 'Jurassic'.

geology the scientific study of the Earth, including its origins, structure, processes and composition. It includes a number of topics that have developed into subjects in their own right: GEOCHEMISTRY, MINERALOGY, petrology (study of rocks), structural geology, GEOPHYSICS, PALAEONTOLOGY, STRATIGRAPHY, economic and physical GEOLOGY.

geomagnetism the study of the Earth's magnetic (*geomagnetic*) field, which has varied with time. At mid-oceanic ridges (*see* PLATE TECTONICS) where new crust is created, measurement of the geomagnetic field shows stripes relating to reversals of the Earth's magnetic field, which is taken up in the newly formed rocks. This provides a tool in determining the age of much of the oceanic crust and is a vital piece of evidence in supporting the theory of plate tectonics.

geomorphology a subject that grew out of geology around the middle of the 19th century and is the study of *landforms*, their origin and change, that is, the study of the

Geomagnetic fields of the mid-Atlantic ridge

Earth's surface. Landforms are composed of various rock types and are formed from the surface materials of the Earth by geomorphologic processes that originate from tectonic movements and the climate. Landforms can be arranged into certain categories based upon factors such as the underlying structural geology, the nature of the topography, that is, the surface features and the terrain (soil, vegetation, etc), and the type of geomorphologic processes dominant.

geophysics the study of all processes *within* the Earth (that is, the crust and the interior) and concerned with the physical properties of the Earth. Included are seismology (*see* SEISMOGRAPH), GEOMAGNETISM, gravity, HYDROLOGY, oceanography (the study of the oceans, currents, tides, sea floor and so on), heat flow within the Earth and related topics. As with many other subject areas, the component topics often develop to the point of becoming subjects in their own right and boundaries between subjects merge.

geothermal energy the temperature within the Earth increases with depth (this is called the *geothermal gradient*), although not uniformly, and the average gradient is in the range 20–40°C per kilometre (68–104°F per 3280 feet). At the edges of some tectonic plates (*see* PLATE TECTONICS) the gradient increases dramatically, and it is sometimes possible to harness this heat as geothermal energy.

The high heat flow may be caused by magmatic activity (*see* MAGMA) or by the radioactive decay of certain elements. When water or brine (water that contains dissolved salts) circulates through these rocks, it becomes heated and may appear at the surface as a warm spring. If it is temporarily contained and heated further, it may force out a body of steam and water as a *geyser* (derived from *geysir*, the Icelandic for 'gusher' or 'roarer').

Geothermal energy is 'tapped' all over the world, including in Iceland, New Zealand, California and Italy. Iceland, New Zealand and Kenya have geothermal power plants.

glacier an enormous mass of ice, on land, that moves very slowly. About 10 per cent of the Earth's land is covered by glaciers although during the last glaciation this was nearer 30 per cent. Glaciers that cover vast areas of land, e.g. Greenland, Antarctica, are called ice sheets (or ice caps if smaller), and these hide the underlying land features. The more typical glaciers are either those that flow in valleys or those filling hollows in mountains. Glaciers can be classified further into polar (e.g. Greenland), sub-polar (e.g. Spitzbergen), and temperate (e.g. the Alps), depending upon the temperature of the ice.

Although glaciers move slowly, they act as powerful agents of erosion on the underlying rocks. Large blocks may be dragged off the underlying rock, become embedded in the ice, and then scratch and scour the surface as the glacier moves. This produces smaller particles of rock debris, and the blocks themselves may be broken. Debris is also gathered from valley sides and carried along. Ridges or piles of this rock debris are called *moraine* and, depending upon position

relative to the glacier, may mark present or former edges of the ice. In addition to the formation of moraine and associated characteristic formations, glaciers produce some typical large-scale features such as *U-shaped valleys* and *truncated spurs*.

Glaciation is the term meaning an ice age or a part of an ice age when glaciers and ice sheets are enlarged significantly.

grassland one of the four major types of vegetation, the others being forest, savanna and DESERT. Grasslands are characterised by seasonal drought, limited precipitation and occasional fires. These all, together with grazing by animals, restrict the growth of trees and shrubs. Typical grasslands include the pampas of Argentina, the veldts of South Africa, the steppes in Russia and other western Asian countries, and the prairies of central North America.

The coverage of grasslands expanded after the last glaciation when climates became generally hotter and drier and there was an increase in the number of large grazing mammals.

Savanna is similar to grassland but with scattered trees and is found extensively in South America, southern Africa and parts of Australia. There are usually well-defined seasons: cool and dry, hot and dry, followed by warm and wet, and during the latter there is a rich growth of grasses and small plants. Although savanna soils may be fertile they are highly porous and water therefore drains away rapidly.

groundwater water that is contained in the voids within rocks, i.e. in pores, cracks and other cavities and spaces. It often excludes *vadose* water, which occurs between the water table and the surface. Most groundwater originates from the surface, percolating through the soil (*meteoric water*). Other sources are *juvenile water*, generated during and coming from deep magmatic processes, and *connate water*, which is water trapped in a sedimentary rock since its formation.

Groundwater is a necessary component of most weathering processes, and of course its relationship to the geology, water table and surface may lead to the occurrence of AQUIFERS and artesian wells.

hardness of minerals the physical hardness of minerals differ, and a test introduced in 1822 by a German mineralogist, Friedrich Mohs, is still in use today to aid mineral classification. Mohs scale lists 10 minerals ranked by hardness, each mineral scratching those lower on the scale, where talc is the softest and diamond the hardest. In addition, it is common to use a fingernail (equivalent to 2.5 on the scale) or a penknife (5.5) to assist in the determination.

Mohs scale of hardness

1 talc	6 orthoclase (feldspar)
2 gypsum	7 quartz
3 calcite	8 topaz
4 fluorite	9 corundum
5 apatite	10 diamond

humidity the amount of moisture in the Earth's atmosphere. *Absolute humidity* is the actual mass of water vapour in each cubic metre of air while *relative humidity* is:

$$\frac{\text{water vapour content of air at a given temperature x 100\%}}{\text{water vapour content required for saturation at that temperature}}$$

The relative humidity of air therefore varies with temperature, cold air holding little moisture, warm air much more. A *hygrometer* is the instrument used to measure relative humidity.

hurricane a wind that on the BEAUFORT SCALE exceeds 75 miles per hour (120 kilometres per hour). It is also used to describe an intense, tropical cyclonic storm that has a central calm area—the *eye*—around which move winds of very high velocity (over 100 miles/160 kilometres per hour). There is usually very heavy rain with thunderstorms, and the whole system may be several hundred miles across.

Such storms occur mainly in the Caribbean and the Gulf of Mexico and often affect the southern states, creating considerable destruction. In August 2005 HurricaneKatrina caused a huge storm surge that inundated New Orleans when major levees were breached. More than 1,400 people died; over three-quarters of New Orleans was flooded (in places under 15 feet of water) and all but 10 per cent of the residents of southeast Louisiana were evacuated.

hydrology the study of water and its cycle, which covers bodies of water and how they change. All physical forms of water – rain, snow, surface water – are included, as are such aspects as distribution and use. The way in which water circulates between bodies of water, such as seas, the atmosphere and the Earth forms the *hydrological cycle.*

The cycle consists of various stages: water falls as rain or snow, of which some runs off into streams and then into lakes or rivers while some percolates into the ground. Plants and trees take up water and lose it by transpiration to the atmosphere, while evaporation occurs from bodies of water. The water vapour in the air then condenses to cloud, which eventually repeats the cycle.

The hydrological cycle

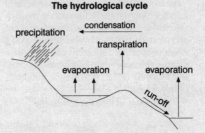

Of the 53,000 billion cubic feet (1500 billion cubic metres) of water on the Earth, the oceans hold 93.9 per cent, groundwater 4.4 per cent, polar ice 1.0 per cent, with rivers, lakes, the atmosphere and soil holding the remainder.

ice age a period in the history of the Earth when ice sheets expanded over areas that were normally ice-free. The term is usually applied to the most recent episode in the Pleistocene (*see* GEOLOGICAL TIMESCALE), but the rock record indicates that there have been ice ages as far back as the Precambrian. Within ice ages there are fluctuations in temperature, producing interglacial stages when the temperatures increase.

igneous rocks one of the three main rock types. Igneous rocks crystallise from MAGMA and are formed at the surface as LAVA flows (*extrusive*) or beneath the surface as *intrusions*, pushing their way into existing rocks. There are numerous ways of classifying igneous rocks, from mineral content to crystal size and mode of origin and emplacement. Typical rocks are basalt, granite and dolerite.

Rocks erupted at the surface as lava are called *volcanic*, while *plutonic rocks* are those large bodies solidifying at some depth; *hypabyssal rocks* are smaller and form at shallow depths. When a body of magma has time to crystallise slowly, large mineral crystals can develop while extrusion at the surface leads to a rapid cooling and formation of very small crystals (or none, if molten rock contacts water, as in a glass). A further division—into acid, intermediate, basic and ultrabasic rocks—is based upon silica (SiO_2) content, this being greatest in acid rocks.

Igneous intrusions may occur in several forms, either parallel to or cutting through the existing rocks, and the commonest are *sills* (concordant) and *dykes* (discordant). *Plugs* commonly represent the neck of a former volcano, while *batholiths* are massive elongate bodies that may be hundreds of miles long.

Examples of igneous intrusions

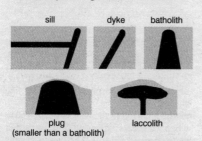

sill   dyke   batholith

plug
(smaller than a batholith)

laccolith

irrigation the process by which water is taken to dry land to encourage or facilitate plant growth. The water may be applied by means of canals, ditches, sprinklers, or the flooding of the whole area. Flood irrigation is not always a good idea because the water evaporates from the flooded field, leaving behind any salts that were dissolved in the water. If this is done repeatedly, the build-up of salts may harm the soil and make it infertile. Water may be conserved and used more effectively by means of a pipe with small holes being laid

around a plant, allowing the water to drip from the holes on to the soil. Irrigation can transform arid regions, but rivers from which water is diverted will inevitably be much reduced.

isobar a line on a weather map that joins points of equal pressure connected for the varying heights of recording. Over a large area, isobars produce a map of pressure lines, similar to contours on a topographic map, which identify the high and low centres, that is, the anticyclones and depressions (*see* CYCLONE).

jet stream westerly winds at high altitudes (above 8 miles/12 kilometres), found mainly between the poles and the TROPICS that form narrow jet-like streams. The air streams move north and south of their general trend in surges, which are probably the cause of depressions and anticyclones. There are a number of separate jet streams, but the most constant is that of the subtropics. Jet stream speed and location are of importance to high-flying aircraft.

latitude and longitude the system of angular distances used to measure points on the Earth's surface. *Latitude* is the angular distance north or south of the Equator. The Equator is 0 degrees, and points can therefore be measured in degrees south or north of this line. The imaginary lines drawn on a map or globe are the lines of latitude.

Longitude is the angular distance of a point measured on the Earth's surface to the east or west of a 'central' reference point. The referent point in this case is the plane created by a *meridian* (an imaginary circle that cuts the Poles and goes over the Earth's surface and the point in question) going through Greenwich in England. A point may be 0 degrees longitude if it sits on this line or a number of degrees east or west. The Greenwich Meridian, based upon the Greenwich Observatory, was established by an international agreement in 1884. There is a time difference of one hour when travelling 15 degrees of longitude at the Equator (*see also* TROPICS).

lava molten rock at about 1100 or 1200°C (2012 or 2192°F) erupted from a VOLCANO or a similar fissure. It may flow onto the ground (*subaerial*) or onto the sea floor (*submarine*). Because of rapid cooling in air or water, most lavas show a fine-grained or glassy structure. The way lava is erupted, how it flows, and its shape as a flow is determined by its viscosity. *Pahoehoe lava* is a fluid basaltic type that forms rope-like flows because of molten lava in the centre of the flow dragging the solidifying crust into folds. A more viscous lava, *AA* (both terms are Hawaiian words), flows more slowly and forms jagged, pointed blocks. Often a stream of lava is contained by craggy sides of partly solidified lava. *Pillow lavas* are formed on the sea floor and, as their name suggests, consist of pillow-like shapes built up and out from the source, with one pillow rupturing at some point to allow more lava out to form another pillow. *Pumice* is lava filled with small air bubbles, creating a light, rough stone.

There are roughly 10,000 active volcanoes, occurring in belts coinciding with the margins between TECTONIC PLATES. Lavas may cover vast areas, e.g. 96,500 square miles (250,000 square kilometres) of the Deccan Plain of India, and 80,780 square miles (130,000 square kilometres) in the Columbia River plateau region of the United States. Such eruptions have occurred throughout geological time.

lightning and thunder *lightning* is the discharge of high voltage electricity between a CLOUD and its base and between the base of the cloud and the Earth. (It has been shown that in a cumulonimbus cloud, positive charge collects at the top and negative at the base.) Lightning occurs when the increasing charge (of electricity) in the cloud overcomes the resistance of the air, leading to a *discharge*, seen as a flash. The discharge to ground is actually followed by a return discharge up to the cloud, and this is the visible sign of lightning. There are various forms of lightning, including *sheet*, *fork* and *ball*, and it may carry a charge of around 10,000 amps.

Thunder is the rumbling noise that accompanies lightning. It is caused by the sudden heating and expansion of the air by the discharge, causing sound waves. The sound often continues for some time because sound is generated at various points along the discharge—the latter can be several miles long. The thunder comes after the lightning because sound travels more slowly than light. This allows an approximate measure of distance from the flash to be made: for every 5 seconds between the flash and the thunder, the lightning will be roughly 1 mile away.

limestone a sedimentary rock that is made up mainly of calcite (calcium carbonate, $CaCO_3$) with dolomite $(CaMg(CO_3)_2)$. There are essentially three groups of limestone: *chemical*, *organic* and *detrital*. These groups reflect the enormous variety of limestones, which may contain the broken remains of marine organisms—shells, coral, etc (detrital). Minute organic remains of, e.g. algae, foraminifera, as in chalk, make an *organic* limestone, and grains formed as concentrically layered pellets (ooliths and pisoliths) in shallow marine waters, with EVAPORITES are examples of chemical limestones.

Limestones are important economically and have many uses. They form AQUIFERS and reservoirs for oil and gas, and they are used in the manufacture of cement, in agriculture and as roadstone. When cut and finished, slabs of it are used to face buildings. Where limestone outcrops appear at the surface, the process of water flow and dissolution of the rock may lead to karst topography. This is a topography that has a virtual absence of surface drainage so groundwater moves along joints into holes, enlarging them over time to form potholes and caves. In well-developed and extensive cases, this may result in collapses of rock over caves and voids to produce towering rock pinnacles (as in China). *See also* STALACTITES.

longitude *see* LATITUDE.

low *see* CYCLONE.

magma the fluid, molten rock beneath the surface of the Earth. Magma may undergo many stages of change and movement before being extruded at the surface as *lava*, or intruded at some depth as an intrusion (*see* IGNEOUS ROCKS). The composition varies, because in moving upwards through the crust, volatiles (gases and liquids) may be lost and some minerals may crystallise out, thus changing the nature of the remaining melt. Magma reaches the surface through pipes into volcanoes or through fissures, but at depth it may form bodies many miles across.

Magmas are formed by the partial melting of *mantle* (the layer between the Earth's crust and core) in areas of *subduction*, where tectonic plates are destroyed (*see* PLATE TECTONICS) as one plate descends beneath another. Magmas can undergo many changes in composition as they move towards the surface.

mantle *see* MAGMA; PLATE TECTONICS

map a flat, two-dimensional representation of a three-dimensional subject, e.g. an area of land, that contains a variety of data that will differ depending upon the type of map. Differing scales, that is, the ratio of a distance on the map to the actual distance on the ground, enable smaller or larger areas of land to be represented.

A standard topographical map indicates the shape of the land by means of *contours* (lines joining points of equal height), and on it the roads, rivers, railroad lines, towns, forests, and parkland may be marked. Maps can be drawn up to illustrate land usage, relief (that is, the shape of the land surface), superficial deposits (river and glacial deposits on top of the underlying rocks), or solid geology (the rocks shown with all things above stripped away).

A *map projection* is the representation of the complete surface of the Earth on a plane. There are many such projections, each presenting the globe in a different way and thus finding different uses:

Projection	Types	Used for
Mercator	cylindrical	navigation.
conical	conic	maps of a small continent.
gnomonic	azimuthal	seismic survey; navigational.
Peter's	modified cylindrical	depicts the Earth's densely populated areas in proportion.
stereographic	azimuthal	used widely in structural geology, crystallography.

One of the commonest is the Mercator projection, named after the Flemish

geographer who used it for his world map of 1569.

Projections are often used in the analysis of directional data. A grid, without the world map, can be used in the study of geological data, e.g. the orientation of folds.

meridian *see* LATITUDE.

metamorphic rocks rocks that are formed by the alteration or recrystallisation of existing rocks by the application of heat, pressure, volatiles (gases and liquids), or a combination of these. There are several categories of *metamorphism* based upon the conditions of origin:

regional—high pressure and temperature as found in orogenic (mountain-building) areas;

contact—where the rocks are adjacent to an igneous body and have been altered by the heat (with little or no pressure);

dynamic—very high, confined pressure with some heat, as generated in an area of faulting or thrusting, that is, where rock masses slide against each other;

burial—which involves high pressure and low temperature, e.g. as found at great depth in sequences of sedimentary rocks.

The key feature of all metamorphic rocks is that the existing *assemblage* (group) of minerals is changed by the pressure and/or heat and the presence of volatiles. New minerals grow that are characteristic of the new conditions. Typical metamorphic rocks are schist, slate, gneiss, marble, quartzite and hornfels. Depending on the type of metamorphism, there are systems of classification into *zones* or *grades* where specific minerals appear in response to increasing pressure and/or temperature.

meteorology the scientific study of the conditions and processes within the Earth's atmosphere.including the pressure, temperature, wind speed, cloud formations, etc, that, over a period of time, enable meteorologists to predict likely future WEATHER patterns. Information is generated by weather stations and by satellites in orbit around the Earth.

mineralogy the scientific study of MINERALS, i.e. any chemical element or compound extracted from the Earth. It involves the following properties: colour, CRYSTAL form and cleavage, HARDNESS, specific gravity, lustre (how the mineral reflects light) and streak (the colour created by scratching the mineral on a special porcelain plate). Together, these properties help to identify and classify minerals.

One of the most important features is the *cleavage*, which is the tendency for minerals to split along particular, characteristic planes that reflect and are controlled by the internal structure of the crystal. The plane of splitting is that which is weakest, because of the atomic structure of the crystal.

mineral a naturally occurring inorganic substance that has a definite and characteristic chemical composition and CRYSTAL structure. Minerals have particular features and properties (*see also* HARDNESS OF MINERALS *and* MINERALOGY). Some elements occur as minerals, such as gold, diamond and copper, but most minerals are made up of several elements (*see* S&T element). Rocks are composed of minerals.

There are about 2000 minerals, although the commonest rocks contain combinations from about 30 minerals, which in addition to quartz and calcite come from five or six main groups, all silicates. Silicate minerals are the most abundant rock-forming minerals and comprise about 95 per cent of the Earth's crust, reflecting the fact that oxygen and silicon are the two commonest elements in rocks. The average make-up of rocks in the crust is as follows:

Mineral	Formula	Percentage
silicia	SiO_2	59.3%
alumina	Al_2O_3	15.3%
iron	FeO	3.7%
oxides	Fe_2O_3	3.1%
lime	CaO	5.1%
soda	Na_2O	3.8%
potash	K_2O	3.1%
magnesia	MgO	3.5%
titania	TiO_2	0.7%
water	H_2O	1.3%
phosphorus pentoxide	P_2O_5	0.3%

Silicate minerals are based upon a tetrahedral arrangement of four oxygen ions with one silicon ion, and these tetrahedral units are joined in various ways to each other and differing metal ions.

typical tetrahedral arrangement of a silicate mineral with the silicon ion shown at the centre

Some mineral groups are listed below.

Group	Example	Structure
feldspars	orthoclase	framework (tectosilicate)
pyroxenes	augite	single-chain (inosilicate)
amphiboles	hornblende	double-chain (inosilicate)
micas	biotite	flat sheets (phyllosilicate)
clays	kaolinite	flat sheets (phyllosilicate)
garnet	pyrope	linked tetrahedra (neosilicate)

Minerals are mined and extracted for diverse purposes, e.g. ornamental stone (in the form of rocks), to generate metals for further use (gold, copper, iron, etc) or as valuable items in their own right, e.g. diamonds.

Mohs scale *see* HARDNESS OF MINERALS.

monsoon in general, winds that blow in opposite directions during different seasons. Monsoons are related to temperature changes in the subtropics and pressure alterations associated with changing JET STREAMS. The word is derived from the Arabic *mausim*, which means 'season', and its meaning has been extended to include the rains that accompany the wind. The Indian subcontinent has a rainy season in its southwesterly monsoon, and other areas where monsoons are seen to strongest effect are Southeast Asia, China and Pakistan. However, monsoons also occur in northern Australia and East and West Africa.

moraine *see* BOULDER CLAY; GLACIER.

mountains the formation of mountain chains clearly involves phenomenal movements of the Earth's crust and unimaginable forces even although the process takes place over many millions of years. The process of mountain building (*orogeny* or *orogenesis*) involves the accumulation of enormous thicknesses of sediments that are subsequently folded, faulted and thrusted, with igneous intrusions at depth (plutons of granite), producing rock complexes involving sedimentary, igneous and metamorphic rocks. A massive linear area that has been compressed in this way is called an *orogenic belt*, and the formation of such belts is interpreted by means of PLATE TECTONICS. Different mechanisms are postulated for the formation of mountain chains: e.g. by subduction of the oceanic lithosphere for the Andes; the collision of continents for the Himalayas; and the addition of vast basins of sedimentary rocks and *island arcs* on to an existing plate in the case of the North American Cordillera (*see* PLATE TECTONICS *for definition of terms*).

The result of these global crustal movements are the mountain ranges as we see them today, where the higher peaks belong to the younger ranges. The highest points on each of the seven continents are as follows:

Peak	Height		Country
	metres	feet	
Everest	8848	29,028	Nepal/China
Aconcagua	6960	22,832	Argentina
McKinley	6194	20,321	USA (Alaska)
Kilimanjaro	5895	19,340	Tanzania
Elbrus	5642	18,510	Russia/Georgia
Vinson Massif	5140	16,863	Antarctica
Mauna Kea	4205	13,796	USA (Hawaii)

Mountains have a considerable effect on local weather conditions: south-facing slopes in the Northern Hemisphere are warmer and drier than north-facing slopes because they receive more sun. When warm, moist air reaches a mountain, it cools as it rises, releasing moisture so that on the leeward side the air descends and absorbs moisture. In many instances, deserts occur on the leeward side of a mountain range, e.g. the Gobi Desert (Asia) and the Mojave Desert of western North America.

It is well known that the temperature falls with height on a mountain—approximately 6°C (43°F) for each 100 metres (328 feet). Mountains thus show a variety of plants that vary with altitude.

natural gas hydrocarbons in a gaseous state which when found are often associated with liquid petroleum. The gas is a mixture of methane and ethane, with propane and small quantities of butane, nitrogen, carbon dioxide and sulphur compounds.

As with PETROLEUM, gas owes its origin to the deposition of sediments that contain a lot of organic matter. After deposition and burial, and through the action of heat, with time, oil and gas are produced. These migrate to a suitable reservoir rock where they reside until extracted by drilling. The massive gas reserves of western Canada were first discovered towards the end of the 19th century when drilling for water was being carried out during construction of the Canadian Pacific Railway. By the end of 2006 the significant reserves were found to be in USA (6 trillion cubic metres), Venezuela (4.3), Saudi Arabia (7), UAE (6), Nigeria (5), Algeria (4.5), but these are all dwarfed by the projected reserves of Russia (48 trillion cubic metres), Iran (28) and Qatar (25).

ocean technically, a body of water that occupies an ocean basin, the latter beginning at the edge of the continental shelf. Marginal seas such as the Mediterranean, Caribbean and Baltic are not classed as oceans. A more general definition is all the water on the Earth's surface, excluding lakes and inland seas. The oceans are the North and South Atlantic Oceans, the North and South Pacific Oceans, the Indian Ocean and the Arctic Ocean. Together with all the seas, the salt water covers almost 71 per cent of the Earth's surface.

From the shore the land dips away gently in most cases—the *continental shelf*—after which the gradient increases on the *continental slope*, leading to the deep-sea platform (at about 2.5 miles'/4 kilometres' depth). There are many areas of shallow seas on the continental shelf (*epicontinental seas*), e.g. the North Sea, Baltic Sea and Hudson Bay. In the ice age, much of the shelf would have been land, and, conversely, should much ice melt the continents would be submerged further. The floors of the oceans display both mountains, in the form of the mid-oceanic ridges and deep trenches. The ridges rise 1–2 miles (2–3 kilometres) from the floor and extend for thousands of miles, while the trenches reach over 7 miles (11 kilometres) below sea level at their deepest (Mariana Trench, southeast of Japan).

The six ocean zones are:

littoral zone	between low and high water spring tides.
pelagic zone (0–180m/0–590ft)	floating plankton and swimming nekton.
neritic zone (low tide–180m/590ft)	benthic organisms.
bathyal zone (180–1800m/590–)	beyond light penetration, but much benthic life (crawling, burrowing or fixed plants and animals)
abyssal zone (>1,800m/5,900ft)	
abyssal plain (~4,000m/13,120ft)	ooze of calcareous and siliceous skeletal remains; red clay only below 5,000m (16,400ft)

The oceans contain *currents*, i.e. faster-moving large-scale flows (the slower movements are called *drifts*). Several factors contribute to the formation of currents: the rotation of the Earth, prevailing winds, and differences in temperature and seawater densities. Major currents move clockwise in the Northern Hemisphere and anticlockwise in the Southern Hemisphere. Well-known currents include the Gulf Stream and the Humboldt Current.

The major currents

Oceanography is the study of all aspects of the oceans, from their structure and composition to the life within and the movements of the water.

ore a naturally occurring substance that contains metals or other compounds that are commercially useful and which it is economically feasible to mine for profit.

Native ores, such as gold and copper, occur as the metallic element itself and not in a compound, but most metals have to be extracted from compounds, commonly the oxide or sulphide. Minerals containing metallic elements are called ore minerals, and ore deposits are aggregates of these minerals.

Extraction of an ore commonly involves removal from a pit (opencast mine) or shaft (in a deep mine). The ore rock is then crushed, and possibly washed and sorted before being treated with heat or mixed with chemicals. A furnace may then be used to smelt the ore to produce the metal, which separates off from the waste or slag.

Ores are produced geologically in several ways. Some mineral concentrations are associated with magmas, e.g. nickel, cobalt, chromium, platinum, or tungsten compounds. Ore minerals are usually found in veins with no obvious connection to igneous activity, and in this case may be formed by percolation of hot water laden with metals. Weathering and erosion can also lead to the concentration of certain ore minerals (bauxite or gold and zircon respectively).

orogeny *see* MOUNTAINS.

ozone layer a part of the Earth's atmosphere, at a height of approximately 10–20 miles (16–32 kilometres), that contains ozone. Ozone is present in very small amounts (1 to 10 parts per million), but it fulfils a very important role by absorbing much of the Sun's ultraviolet radiation, which in excess has harmful effects, causing skin cancer and cataracts, and unpredictable consequences to crops and plankton. Recent scientific studies have shown a thinning of the ozone layer over the last 25 years, with the appearance of a hole over Antarctica in 1985. This depletion has been caused mainly by the build-up of CFCs (chlorofluorocarbons) from aerosol can propellants, refrigerants and chemicals used in some manufacturing processes. The chlorine in CFCs reacts with ozone to form ordinary oxygen, lessening the effectiveness of the layer. CFCs are now being phased out, but the effects of their past use will affect the ozone layer for some time to come.

In 2006 the average area of the ozone hole was the largest measured (at over 10 million square miles) although it was enlarged due to colder temperatures in the stratosphere. Substances that caused depletion of the ozone layer reached their peak in the lower atmosphere in 1995 and in the Antarctic stratosphere in 2001. The hole has been slowly decreasing in size since and despite it being affected by weather variations, it is calculated that the hole will be gone by about 2065.

peat an organic deposit formed from plant debris that is laid down with little or no alteration or decomposition (breakdown) in a waterlogged environment. Peat is produced in bogs, fens, swamps, moors and wetlands, with some variation in peat structure depending upon the acidity of the conditions.

The conditions are vital so that oxygen is not available for the decay of plant material. As peat accumulates over the years, water is squeezed out and the lower peat layers shrink. However, air-drying is essential when peat is cut for fuel. Acid conditions are commonest, and *sphagnum moss* is the dominant peat vegetation. Peat may form in shallow lakes through the gradual takeover by marsh vegetation, or it may develop in shallow lagoons, floodplains, or deltas. Conditions for peat formation are currently found all over the world. It is found on the coastal plains of Virginia and North Carolina, in the Everglades of Florida, in Ireland and Scotland, Indonesia, India and Malaysia. After the last ice age there were lengthy periods of peat formation. The preserving properties of peat bogs have been seen to great effect over recent years when the bodies of whole baby woolly mammoths and human beings have been found.

permafrost ground that is permanently frozen except for surface melting in the summer. It is technically defined as being when the temperature is below freezing point for two consecutive years, and it can extend to depths of several hundred feet. The top layer, which thaws in the summer, is called the *active layer*, and there may be unfrozen ground between this and the permafrost, a zone that is called *talik*. Depths of 5000 feet (1500 metres) in Siberia and 2000 feet (650 metres) in North America have been recorded, and today permafrost underlies 20–25 per cent of the Earth's land area—a figure that was much greater during parts of the Pleistocene.

The ground in areas of permafrost shows distinctive features, including patterns of circles, polygonal cracks, mounds and pingos. Polygonal cracks are the result of contraction caused by cooling in winter, and in Spitzbergen the polygons may reach 650 feet (200 metres) across. Mounds are caused simply by the increase in volume that accompanies the freezing of water, which pushes up surface layers of soil. Large mounds, up to 130–165 feet (40–50 metres) high, are called *pingos*.

petroleum or crude oil a mixture of naturally occurring hydrocarbons (*see* S&T hydrocarbons), formed by the decay of organic matter, that, under pressure and increased temperatures, forms oil. The often mentioned '*reservoir*' is the rock in which oil (and gas) are found, and common types of reservoir rock are sandstone, LIMESTONE, or dolomite. The oil migrates after formation from the source rocks to the reservoir (because such vast quantities could not have been formed in place) where it must be contained by a *trap*. A trap is a particular geological configuration where the oil is confined by impermeable rocks.

Most of the world's petroleum reserves are in the Middle East, although the United States, Russia and other former Soviet republics currently produce a significant proportion of the world's oil.

The modern oil industry began over a century ago when a well was bored for water in Pennsylvania, and oil appeared. Petroleum also occurs in the form of *asphalt* or *bitumen*, syrupy liquids or near solid in form, and there are significant deposits today. The Pitch Lake of Trinidad, over 1,640 feet (500 metres) across and about 130 feet

(40 metres) deep, is fed from beneath as the asphalt is removed. There are similar occurrences in Venezuela and California, and in Alberta, Canada, are the famous Athabasca Oil Sands, where the sandstone is full of tar, an oil of asphalt.

Petroleum consists of many hydrocarbons of differing composition with small amounts of sulphur, oxygen and nitrogen. The components are separated and treated chemically to provide the basic building blocks and products for the vast petrochemicals industry (*see* S&T petrochemicals).

plate tectonics a concept that brings together the variety of features and processes of the Earth's crust and accounts for continental drift, sea-floor spreading, volcanic and earthquake activity and crustal structure.

It has long been noticed how coastlines on opposite sides of oceans, e.g. the Atlantic, seemed to fit together. Other geological features led to the theory that continents were joined together millions of years ago. This theory was supported by a reconstruction of fossil magnetic poles and, in 1962, by the idea of sea-floor spreading where ocean ridges were the sites of new crust formation, with slabs of crust moving away from these central sites. All this was brought together with the idea that the *lithosphere* (the crust and uppermost part of the mantle) is made up of seven large and twelve smaller plates composed of oceanic or continental crust. The plates move relative to each other with linear regions of creation and destruction of the lithosphere.

There are three types of plate boundary: *ocean ridges*, where plates are moving apart (constructive); *ocean trenches*, where plates are moving together (also for young mountain ranges) (destructive); *transform faults*, where plates move sideways past each other (conservative).

At destructive plate boundaries, one tectonic plate dips beneath the other at an oceanic trench in a process called *subduction* and in so doing old lithosphere is returned to the mantle. *Island arcs* are an example of volcanic activity associated with subduction at an ocean trench, where

there are very often also earthquakes. Where two continental plates converge, the continents collide to produce mountains, as seen in the Alps and Himalayas today. The transform faults of conservative plate boundaries are generated by the relative motion of two plates alongside each other, and the best-known example is the San Andreas Fault in California, a region that suffers earthquakes along this major fracture.

projection *see* MAP.

radiometric dating *see* DATING METHOD.

rain one form of precipitation in which drops of water condense from the water vapour in the atmosphere to form rain drops. Other types of precipitation, all water in some liquid or solid form, include snow, hail, sleet, drizzle and also dew. Snow forms below freezing (0°C or 32°F) and, depending upon the temperature, occurs in different shapes. When the temperature is well below freezing, it forms ice *spicules*, which are small and needle-like. Nearer to freezing, the characteristic snowflakes grow, but at extremely low temperatures snow becomes powdery. Because snow can vary in its form and accumulation, accurate measurement of falls is difficult, but 1 inch (2.54 centimetres) of water will be produced by about 12 inches (30 centimetres) of newly fallen snow.

Hail is a small pellet of frozen water that forms by raindrops being taken higher into colder parts of the atmosphere. As the hailstone falls, it grows as layers of ice are added as the result of condensation of moisture upon the cold nucleus. *Dew* is the condensation of water vapour in the air caused by a cooling of the air.

remote sensing the collection of a variety of information without contact with the object of study. This includes aerial photography from both aircraft and satellites and the use of infrared, ultraviolet and microwave radiation emitted from the object, e.g. an individual site, a part of a town, or crop and forest patterns. Another type of remote sensing involves the production of an impulse of light, or radar, which is reflected by the object, the image then being captured on film or tape.

Large areas of ground can be studied

by using these various techniques, and surprisingly sharp pictures can be obtained that can be used in many ways. Remote sensing is used in agriculture and forestry, civil engineering, geology, geography and archaeology, amongst other areas. In addition, it is possible to create pictures with a remarkable amount of detail that would otherwise take a very long time to collect.

Richter scale *see* EARTHQUAKE.

river a stream of water that flows into the sea or in some cases into lakes or swamps. Rivers form part of the cyclical nature of water, comprising water falling from the atmosphere as some form of precipitation (*see* RAIN) and being partly fed by groundwaters or run-off from the melting of glaciers (both of which in any case are derived from atmospheric water).

Rivers develop their own immediate scenery, and a river valley will owe its form to the original slope of the land, the underlying rocks and the climate. A river with its tributaries is called a *river system*, and the area from which its water is derived is the *drainage basin* (*see also* DRAINAGE). As rivers grow in size and velocity, rock and soil debris washed into them is carried downstream, eroding the riverbed and sides as it goes. As a river continues to flow and carry debris, depositing much material in times of FLOOD, it widens its valley floor, forming a FLOODPLAIN. As it does so, the river swings from side to side, forming wide loops called *meanders*. Eventually, as meanders develop into ever more contorted loops, a narrow neck of land may be left that is eventually breached. Thus the river alters and shortens its course, leaving a horseshoe-shaped remnant, or *ox-bow* lake.

rocks aggregates of MINERALS or organic matter. They can be divided into three types, based upon the way they are formed: IGNEOUS ROCKS, SEDIMENTARY ROCKS, and METAMORPHIC ROCKS.

savanna *see* GRASSLANDS.

scarps *see* CHALK.

sedimentary rocks rocks that are formed from existing rock sources by the processes of erosion and weathering. They include rocks of organic or chemical origin and can

be divided into *clastic* rocks, that is, made of fragments, *organic*, or *chemical*.

The clastic rocks are further divided on grain size into coarse (or *rudaceous*, grains of 1–2 millimetres), medium (or *arenaceous*, e.g. sandstone), and fine (or *argillaceous*, up to 0.06 millimetre). When the grains comprising clastic rocks are deposited (usually in water), compaction of the soft sediment and subsequent *lithification* (that is, turning into rock) produce the layered effect, or *bedding*, that is often visible in cliffs and outcrops in rivers. It is also common for original features to be preserved, e.g. ripples, small or large dune structures that appear in an exposed rock face as inclined beds called *current bedding*. *Graded bedding* shows a gradual change in grain size from the base, where it is coarse, to the top of a bed, where it is fine, and this results from the settling of material on to the sea floor from a current caused by some earth movement.

Many sedimentary rocks, particularly shale, limestone and finer sandstone, contain FOSSILS of animals and plants from millions of years ago, and, with the original features mentioned above, these are useful in working out the sequence of events in an area where the rocks have been strongly folded.

seismograph an instrument that is used in the study of earthquakes (*seismology*) to record the shock waves (*seismic waves*) as they spread out from the source. The seismograph has some means of conducting the ground vibrations through a device that turns movement into a signal that can be recorded). There are numerous seismic stations around the world that record ground movements, each containing several seismographs with numerous *seismometers* (the actual detector linked to a seismograph).

soil the thin layer of uncompacted material comprising organic matter and minute mineral grains that overlies rock and provides the means by which plants can grow. Soil is formed by the breakdown of rock in a number of ways. Rock is initially fractured and broken up by weathering, the action of water, ice and wind, and the effects of any acids dissolved in water moving over or percolating through the rock. This allows into the rock various organisms that speed up the breakdown process. Mosses, lichens and fungi can then take hold, and after a while there forms a mixture of organisms (including bacteria, decayed organic material, weathered rock, and *humus*) that is called *topsoil*. Humus is decomposing (breaking down) organic material that is produced from dead organisms, leaves, and other organic material by the action of bacteria and fungi.

The texture of the soil affects its ability to support plants, and the most fertile soils are *loams*, which contain mixtures of sand, silt and clay with organic material. This ensures that there are sufficient water and minerals (which 'stick' to the finer particles), while the coarser sand grains provide air spaces that are vital to roots. In addition to plant roots, soil contains an enormous number of organisms, including fungi, algae, insects, earthworms, nematodes (roundworms) and several billion bacteria. Earthworms are useful in that they aerate the soil and the bacteria alter the mineral composition of the soil.

The parent rock is the primary factor in determining the nature of a soil. While sand, silt and clay produce a loam, sand alone is too porous and clay too compacted and impervious (doesn't allow water through). A clay soil can be improved by adding lime, hence a *marl* (a lime-rich clay) forms a good soil. Limestone itself does not produce a soil. The rate of breakdown of the rock is also important. Granites decompose slowly, but basaltic rocks are the opposite and therefore yield their soil components quickly. This is seen particularly in volcanic areas where lava flows and volcanic ash quickly lead to very productive soils. It can take hundreds of years for soils to become fertile, but to be productive agriculturally, the soil has to be cared for, with irrigation, fertilisation and prevention of erosion all being important factors. This is apparent when you consider that the soil provides approximately 40 pounds (18 kilograms) of nitrogen, 9 pounds (4 kilograms) of potassium and 6 pounds (3 kilograms) of phosphorus to grow one ton of wheat grain.

stalactites and stalagmites in areas of LIMESTONE where caves form and streams trickle through the rocks and caves, calcium-rich waters tend to drop from cave roofs. As there is a little evaporation from these drops of water, some of the dissolved calcium is deposited as calcite (calcium carbonate, $CaCO_3$). This deposit builds up very slowly into a stalactite, which projects down from the roof. If water continues to drop on to the ground, a complementary upward growth develops into a stalagmite—and often the two meet to form a column, or pillar.

Many limestone caves exhibit spectacular developments, e.g. the Carlsbad Caverns in New Mexico, which contains the world's largest single cave, Mammoth Cave in Kentucky, the world's most extensive complex of caves, La Cave in the Dordogne in France, Wookey Hole in southwest England and many other places.

stratigraphy the branch of geology concerned with the study of stratified rocks, that is, rocks that were originally laid down in layers. It deals with the position of rocks in geological time and space, their classification and correlation between different areas. Rock units can be identified and differentiated by several means.

Stratigraphy began about two hundred years ago when it was first realised that in a normal sequence of rocks relatively unaffected by any tectonic movements, younger rocks would lie above older rocks. This was known as the 'law' of superposition, but it soon became apparent that all sorts of geological events could upset this simplistic theory.

stratosphere one of the layers of the ATMOSPHERE, lying above the TROPOSPHERE. It lies at a height of between 6 and 30 miles (10 and 50 kilometres) and shows an increase in temperature from bottom to top where it is at freezing point (0°C or 32°F). A very large part of the ozone (*see* OZONE LAYER) in the atmosphere is found in the stratosphere and the absorption of ultraviolet radiation contributes to the higher temperature in the upper reaches. This inversion of temperature creates a stability that limits the vertical extent of cloud and produces the sideways extension of a cumulonimbus cloud into its characteristic shape.

thunder *see* LIGHTNING.

tide the regular rise and fall of the water levels in the Earth's oceans and seas, which is caused by the gravitational effect of the Moon and Sun. The Moon exerts a stronger pull than the Sun (roughly twice the effect). The relative positions of the three bodies and the distribution of water on the Earth cause variation in tides. When the Sun, Moon and Earth are aligned, the effects are combined and result in a maximum, the high *spring tide* (when the Moon is new or full). Conversely, when the Sun is at right angles to the Moon, the effect is minimised, resulting in a low *neap tide*.

The effect of tides in the open oceans is negligible, perhaps three feet and enclosed areas of water, such as the Black Sea, exhibit differences in the order of inches. However, in shallow seas where the tide may be channelled by the shores, tides of 20 to 30 feet may be created.

A major factor that influences tides is the *Coriolis force*. This is when air or water is pushed to the side because of the Earth's rotation. In the Northern Hemisphere, water moving across the water's surface is pushed to the right (and conversely to the left in the Southern Hemisphere). The Coriolis force is particularly noticeable in the Irish Sea where a tidal wave passes northwards creating higher tides on the Welsh and English coasts of Britain than on the Irish coast.

The potential for generating energy from tides has long been realised. The first tidal power plant was built on the River Rance in Brittany in France and made operational in 1967, and studies have been carried out on the feasibility of a tidal power plant across the Bay of Fundy in Nova Scotia.

time zones zones that run north-south, with some variations, across the Earth and represent different times. Each zone is one hour earlier or later than the adjacent zone and is 15 degrees of *longitude*. The zones were devised for convenience, but to compensate for the accumulated time change, the *International Date Line*

was introduced. The line runs roughly on the 180-degree meridian although it does detour around land areas in the Pacific Ocean. To cross it going east means repeating a day, while crossing it going west means losing a day.

tornado a narrow column of air that rotates rapidly and leaves total devastation in its path. It develops around a centre of very low pressure with high velocity winds (well over 185 miles/300 kilometres per hour) blowing anticlockwise and with a violent down draught. The typical appearance is of a funnel or snake-like column filled with cloud and usually no more than 500 feet (150 metres) across. A tornado is often informally called a *twister*.

The precise way in which tornadoes form is not known although it involves the interface of warm moist air with dry cooler air and an inversion of temperatures, with some event acting as a trigger, possibly an intense cold front. These conditions are found in many countries at mid-to-low latitudes but particularly so in the Midwest of the United States. The destruction created by tornadoes results partly from the violent winds and partly from the very low pressure. This has the effect of causing buildings to explode outwards because the pressure outside exceeds that inside, and although a tornado may affect an area only 300–500 feet (90–150 metres) across, the destruction is total. Tornadoes are often unpredictable in their behaviour and can lose contact with the ground or retrace their routes. When a tornado moves out over the sea, and once the funnel has joined with the waves, a *waterspout* is formed.

tropics two lines of LATITUDE that lie 23.5 degrees north and south of the Equator. The northern line is the *Tropic of Cancer* and the southern the *Tropic of Capricorn*, and the region between them is called the tropics.

The term 'tropical' is often used to describe climate, vegetation, etc, but it is not an accurate usage of the word. In general, a tropical climate does not have a cool season, and the mean temperature never falls below 20°C (68°F). Rainfall can be very high indeed, and in many countries these conditions produce a dense, lush vegetation, e.g. tropical rain forests.

troposphere the part of the Earth's atmosphere between the surface and the *tropopause* (the boundary with the stratosphere). The tropopause is the point at which the change in temperature with height (the lapse rate) stops and the temperature remains constant for several miles. Within the troposphere itself, the temperature decreases approximately 6.5°C (43.7°F) for each kilometre (3,280 feet) of height. The troposphere is also the layer that contains most of the water vapour and about 75 per cent of the weight of gas in the atmosphere, and it is the zone where turbulence is greatest and where most weather features occur.

The level of the tropopause, and therefore the top of the troposphere, varies from about 10 miles (17 kilometres) at the Equator, falling to 6 miles (9 kilometres) or lower at the Poles. The height variation relates to temperature and pressure at sea level.

tsunami (*plural* **tsunami**) an enormous sea wave caused by the sudden large-scale movement of the sea floor, resulting in the displacement of large volumes of water. The cause may be an earthquake, volcanic eruption, a submarine slide or a slump of sediment, which may itself have been started by an earthquake or tremor. The slipping of thousands of tons of rock from the sides of fjords may also cause tsunami.

The effect of this sea-floor movement in the open ocean may not be seen at all, as the resulting wave may be only one metre or less in height. Because the whole depth of water is affected, however, there is a vast amount of energy involved, so when the waves reach shallow water or small bays, the effects can be catastrophic. The waves may travel at several hundred miles per hour and reach heights of 50–100 feet (15–30 metres). The devastation caused is clearly going to be terrible, and there are many such instances on record.

The word originates from the Japanese (*tsu*, 'harbour', and *nami*, 'waves'), and in Japan there have been many instances of destructive tsunami. In 1933, an earth-quake triggered tsunami with waves up to 90 feet (27 metres) high, and as a result thousands of people were drowned along the Japanese coast. The waves were actually recorded about ten hours later in San Francisco, having crossed the Pacific Ocean. It seems that tsunami are generated by submarine earthquakes registering 8 or over on the Richter scale (*see* earthquake). The largest in recent times was the December 2004 tsunami caused by an earthquake registering 9.1 on the Richter scale (the second largest ever recorded) centred 250 km off the west coast of northern Sumatra. There were almost 230,000 dead and missing.

tundra the treeless region between the snow and ice of the Arctic and the northern extent of tree growth. Large treeless plains can be found in northern Canada, Alaska, northern Siberia and northern Scandinavia. The ground is subject to permafrost, but the surface layer melts in the summer, so soil conditions are very poor, being waterlogged and marshy. The surface therefore can support little plant life.

Cold temperatures and high winds also limit the diversity of plants, restricting the flora to grasses, mosses, lichens, sedges and dwarf shrubs. Some areas of tundra receive the same low level of precipitation as deserts yet the soil remains saturated because of the partial thaw of the permafrost. Most growth occurs in rapid bursts during the almost continuous daylight of the very short summers.

Because of the inhospitable conditions, animal life is also limited, although more numerous in summer. In addition to insects (midges, mosquitoes, etc) and migratory birds, there are wolves, arctic foxes, lemmings, hares, snowy owls and the herbivorous reindeer in Europe and caribou in North America. Polar bears occur at the coast.

In addition to this arctic tundra, there is also *alpine tundra*, which is found on the highest mountain tops and is therefore widely spread. However, conditions differ because of daylight throughout the year and plant growth in the tropical alpine tundra also occurs all year round.

unconformity a break in the deposition of SEDIMENTARY ROCKS, representing a gap in the geological record. The unconformity is the junction between younger rocks, which lie above and older rocks and is formed by a succession of rocks being pushed and possibly folded, eroded and then submerged again so that new sediment is deposited on the older rocks. Usually the rocks above and beneath the unconformity lie at different angles. It is possible, however, for an unconformity to be represented by differing beds with the same orientation (*disconformity*), or simply by a surface that indicates non-deposition but shows no other apparent breaks, or by sediments being deposited on an igneous intrusion that has been eroded.

volcano a natural vent or opening in the Earth's crust that is connected by a pipe, or *conduit*, to a chamber at a depth that contains MAGMA. Through this pipe (usually called a *vent*) LAVA, volcanic gases, steam and ash may be ejected, and it is the amount of gas held in the lava and the way in which it is released on reaching the surface that determines the type of *eruption*.

Volcanoes may be *active*, that is, actually erupting, whether just clouds of ash and steam or lava; *extinct*, that is, the activity ceased a long time ago; or *dormant*. Dormant volcanoes have often in the past been thought to be extinct, only to erupt again with startling ferocity.

Volcanoes can be described by the type of eruption, which is named after a particular volcano that exhibits a specific eruption pattern. These are:

Hawaiian	violent eruptions with viscous lava and nuées ardentes*.
Peléean	moderate eruptions, small explosions and lava of average viscosity.
Strombolian	very explosive after a dormant period with ash/gas clouds and gas-filled lava.

* nuées ardentes: an old term meaning an incandescent ash flow that moves rapidly.

| Vesuvian | very explosive, with pyroclastics* ejected in a column up to 160 feet (50 metres) high, producing thick air-fall deposits. |
| Plinian | outpouring of fluid lava and little explosive activity. |

* pyroclastic: volcanic rocks formed from broken fragments, e.g. bombs, pumice, ash and cinders.

Volcanoes of the Hawaiian type are also called *shield* volcanoes. The sides of the volcanoes are almost flat because of the rapid flow of the lava. *Composite* volcanoes show greater angles of slope because of a build-up of lava and pyroclastic material. Both shield and composite types are also called *central type* because the supply comes from a central vent, as opposed to *fissure* volcanoes, which erupt through splits where the crust is under tension.

Active volcanoes occur in belts associated with the tectonic plates (*see* PLATE TECTONICS), with about 80 per cent of the active subaerial volcanoes at destructive plate margins, 15 per cent at constructive plate margins, and the remainder within plates. Most submarine volcanism is at constructive plate margins.

The environmental effect of volcanoes can be very significant, whether it be the enormous amounts of ash ejected into the atmosphere or the consequences of lava flows consuming the countryside. At the time of eruption, volcanic materials are often over 1000°C (1832°F), so flows either burn, push over or cover whatever they meet. Over 500 volcanoes have been active in historic times, but only about 50 erupt each year, often on a very small scale.

waterspout *see* TORNADO.

water table the level below which water saturates the spaces in the ground; the top of the zone where groundwater saturates permeable rocks. It is where atmospheric pressure is equalled by the pressure in the groundwater. The position (*elevation*) of the water table varies with the amount of rainfall, etc, loss through evaporation and transpiration from vegetation, and percolation through the soil. A spring, or seepage, occurs when, because of geological conditions, the water table rises above ground level (*see also* AQUI-FER).

weather the combined effect of atmospheric pressure, temperature, sunshine, cloud, humidity, wind and the amount of precipitation that together make up the weather for a certain place over a particular (usually short) time period. The weather varies enormously around the Earth, but some countries have a stable weather pattern. Some parts of the world, particularly at the edges of continents, have changeable weather because they are at locations where many different air masses meet. The surface at which two air masses with different meteorological properties meet is called a *front*.

A *warm front* occurs in a depression, between warm air moving over cold air, and it heralds drizzle followed by heavy rain that then gives way to rising temperatures. A *cold front* is the leading edge of a cold air mass, which moves under warm air, forcing the latter to rise. The result is a fall in temperature, with rainfall passing behind the front.

weathering a combination of chemical and physical processes on the surface of the Earth, or very near to it, that breaks down rocks and minerals. Weathering takes various forms and can be divided into mechanical, chemical and organic:

mechanical	freeze-thaw action – alternate freezing and thawing of water in cracks, producing widening or break-up. exfoliation – peeling off in thin rock layers (like onion skin). disintegration – into grains.
chemical	carbonation – the reaction of weak carbonic acid (H_2CO_3) with the rock. hydrolysis – combination of water with minerals to form insoluble residues (e.g. clay, minerals). oxidation and reduction.
organic	breakdown by flora and fauna, e.g. burrowing animals, tree roots and the release of organic acids from decomposed plants that react with minerals.

These weathering processes together produce a layer of material that may then be moved by processes of EROSION.

wind a generally horizontal or near horizontal movement of air caused by changes in atmospheric pressure in which air normally moves from areas of high to low pressure. Wind speed is greater when the ISOBARS (lines joining points at the same pressure) are closely packed on weather maps, and the BEAUFORT SCALE provides a systematic guide to wind speed. Because of the Earth's rotation and the effect of the Coriolis force (*see* TIDES), air in the Northern Hemisphere flows clockwise around a high-pressure area and anticlockwise around a low.

The *trade winds* play an important part in the atmospheric circulation of the Earth, and they are mainly easterly winds that blow from the subtropics to the Equator. The *westerlies* flow from the high pressure of the subtropics to the low pressure of the Temperate Zone. The westerlies form one of the strongest wind flows, their strength increasing with height (*see* JET STREAM). Depressions are most common in this wind system. The *doldrums* is a zone of calm, or light, winds around the Equator, applied particularly to the oceans, with obvious links to the time when sailing ships were becalmed. Also linked to sailing are the *Roaring Forties*, which are westerlies in the Southern Hemisphere where they tend to be stronger. The supposed link of trade winds with early travel on the sea is incorrect, however, as their origin is from the Latin word meaning 'constant'.

Wind provides an additional hazard when combined with cold. Wind chill is the effect that the wind has in lowering apparent temperatures by increasing heat loss from the body. For example, in calm conditions at –12°C (10°F) there is little danger for someone properly clothed, but if the wind speed is 25 miles (40 kilometres) per hour, then the wind chill creates an equivalent temperature of –34°C (–29°F), which is potentially harmful.

Natural History

acid rain rain that contains a high concentration of dissolved chemical pollutants such as sulphur and nitrogen oxides. The pollutants arise as gases, given off mainly by the burning of fossil fuels (coal and oil) by industries, vehicles and power stations. The wind may carry the acid gases a long way from their source, but eventually they dissolve in water and fall elsewhere as acid rain. Both the gases and the acid rain cause damage to plant and animal life and lead to an increase in the acidity of water sources such as lakes and rivers. This may cause long-term deterioration in the natural environment, affecting numerous plants, animals and micro-organisms.

Actinozoa or Anthozoa a CLASS of small marine animals belonging to the PHYLUM Coelenterata (CNIDARIA), which includes sea pens, sea pansies, sea feathers, sea fans, sea anemones and corals and also includes jellyfish and hydras. They are very simple animals with a circular body plan (known as *radial symmetry*) in the form of a structure called a *polyp*. A polyp is a small cylinder attached to an underlying surface such as a rock, the free end usually having a ring of tentacles for feeding. The polyps may exist alone or in colonies, as with many of the corals. Corals have hard external skeletons (*exoskeletons*) made of calcium carbonate, which are often delicately shaped and coloured. Other animals in this group have structures forming a simple internal skeleton.

adaptation a feature or characteristic of an organism that has evolved under the processes of natural selection. It enables the organism to exploit a particular aspect of its environment more efficiently. All organisms have adaptations enabling them to survive in their habitat.

Familiar adaptations include the shape and size of birds' beaks and animals' teeth (according to what they eat); the powerful, digging front legs and claws in such burrowing animals as moles, and flippers in swimming animals such as seals. If they become too specialised, however, they may not be able to survive a sudden change (e.g. in climate) and may become extinct. There are fears for the survival of the panda, which is highly specialised and adapted in terms of its habitat and diet (because this consists solely of bamboo shoots).

adaptive radiation the separation of SPECIES through evolutionary process and natural selection (*see* S&T Darwin and natural selection) into many descendant species that are able to exploit a variety of different habitats. An example is the vast numbers of different amphibians that have evolved since their early ancestors moved on to land.

Agnatha a vertebrate CLASS that contains lampreys and hagfishes (ORDER Cyclostomata). These are aquatic, eel-like animals belonging to a very ancient group. Their characteristic feature is a lack of jaws, and they have a sucking mouth with horn-like teeth. They are scavengers or parasites on larger fish.

alga (*plural* **algae**) the common name for a simple water plant that lacks roots, stems and leaves but is able to photosynthesise. Algae range in size from single cells to plants many feet in length.

amoeba *see* PROTOZOAN.

Amphibia a vertebrate CLASS of which salamanders, newts, frogs and toads are members. Amphibians were the first vertebrates to colonise land, about 370 million years ago. Modern amphibians tend to be highly specialised and not typical of their fossil ancestors, and many of their characteristics are adaptations for life on land. Most must return to water to breed, however, and the young (larvae *see* S&T larva) are aquatic and breathe through gills. To become adults they undergo metamorphosis. Adult amphibians breathe through nostrils that are linked by a passage to the roof of the mouth and also through their skin, which is kept moist.

anaconda *see* SQUAMATA.

Angiospermae a class of flowering plants. Complex and highly developed plants that are able to live in a great many different habitats as they have evolved various specialisations. The female reproductive cell, or gamete, is formed within a structure called an *ovule*, itself protected by a closed sheath known as the *carpel*. After fertilisation, the ovule develops into a seed, and seeds may be contained by fruits (*see also* S&T flowers, plants).

Annelida an invertebrate PHYLUM to which ragworms (CLASS Polychaeta), earthworms (class Oligochaeta), and leeches (class Hirudinea) belong. These familiar animals have an outer layer, or cuticle, usually composed of *collagen*-like proteins. The body is cylindrical in shape and divided into segments, each bearing stiff bristles (*chaetae*) made of chitin (a hydrocarbon with nitrogen). The body cavity is called the *coelom* and is fluid-filled. It provides a firm base (*hydrostatic skeleton*), against which muscles that are present in the body wall can contract to cause movement. A simple nervous system (*see* S&T nervous system) consisting of a pair of *nerve cords* with *ganglia* (swellings) is present. Some worms live in the soil and leaf litter whereas others inhabit marine or freshwater habitats. Earthworms are a vital part of the cycle of decay by eating soil, which passes through the gut, food substances being absorbed along the way. Waste material passes out of the body as *castings*. The activity of earthworms helps to till and aerate the soil and the castings improve the texture. Hence they are of great value to farmers, gardeners and horticulturists.

apes *see* PRIMATES.

Arachnida an invertebrate CLASS to which spiders, scorpions, mites, ticks, king crabs, harvestmen, etc, all belong.

Some animals in this group, especially spiders, are very familiar to, and hold a special fascination for, human beings. Most arachnids are terrestrial animals and, unlike insects, they have a head and thorax (middle region of the body) that are not divided from one another. These are formed from eight segments and make up a structure called the *prosoma*. The rest of

the body is made up of 13 segments and is called the *opithosoma*. In the head region there are two pairs of projections, or *appendages*. The first are called *chelicerae* and are adapted for piercing and grasping prey, as most arachnids are carnivorous. The second pair are called the *pedipalps*, and these can be specialised to perform a variety of different functions as sense organs, for copulation, or noise production. Behind these are four pairs of walking legs and on the *opithosoma* there may be other specialised appendages, e.g. for silk spinning (spinnerets in spiders) or for injecting poison (as with scorpions). Ticks and mites are parasites on other animals but most arachnids are free-living.

Archaeornirthes *see* AVES.

Arthropoda the largest PHYLUM of invertebrate animals containing over one million known SPECIES that occupy many different habitats. They are often highly specialised and include such CLASSES as the CRUSTACEA (lobsters, crabs, shrimps), INSECTA (insects), ARACHNIDA (spiders, mites, scorpions) and MYRIAPODA (millipedes and centipedes).

Artiodactyla a mammalian ORDER that includes cattle, camels, hippopotamuses, pigs, deer, antelope, goats, sheep and llamas. These animals are even-toed, with the third and fourth toes equally developed to support the whole weight of the body. They are one of the two orders of mammals that make up the group commonly called the ungulates, the other being the Perissodactyla (horses, tapirs, rhinoceros and zebra).

Aves (*birds*) a CLASS of vertebrates that evolved from flying reptiles and still show some features of their ancestry. The most notable of these is the production of reptilian-like eggs and the presence of scales on the legs. Typically, the body of a bird is highly modified for flight, with a lighter skeleton than that of other vertebrates. Some organs may even be absent to reduce weight, e.g., females possess only one ovary. The front limbs are developed as wings that are aerodynamically specialised for flight. Birds are covered with feathers, those of the wings being modified for flight while others provide insulation. The breastbone of the skeleton is well developed and has a structure, called a *keel*, to which the large flight muscles are attached. Birds lack teeth but grind up food in a special part of the gut called the *gizzard*. The jaws are developed to form a beak or bill, and a great many different sizes and shapes occur, enabling birds to exploit numerous different habitats and foods.

There are two subclasses of the class Aves, the Archeornirthes and the Neornirthes. The former are the early birds, which are now extinct, while of the latter there are two super orders: the Paleognathae and the Neognathae. The Paleognathae are the large, usually flightless birds, e.g., the ostrich and emu. The Neognathae are the flying birds, of which there are numerous orders, including the Passeriformes (e.g. songbirds), the Psittaciformes (e.g. parrots) and the Falconiformes (e.g. eagles, hawks, vultures).

Bacillariophyta the division to which *diatoms*, a type of ALGA, belong. They are simple, single-celled plants that sometimes form chains or colonies and live in both marine and freshwater environments. They are vital organisms in plankton (*see* S&T food chain) and, since they photosynthesise, form the basis of food chains (*see* S&T food chain).

They have beautiful and unique glassy cell walls made of silica and are important fossils. Enormous accumulations of their cell walls are mined as *diatomaceous earth* (or kieselguhr) which has various uses in industry. Planktonic diatoms store food as oil and this has contributed to the petroleum reserves that are extracted and used today.

barrier reef a reef of coral built up in a line running parallel to the shore but at some distance from it so as to create a lagoon. A good example is the Great Barrier Reef, Australia, which is almost 1250 miles (2000 kilometres) long. A barrier reef usually provides a rich and varied habitat and is home to many different kinds of plants and animals.

bat *see* Chiroptera.

beaver *see* Rodentia.

benthos all the plants and animals living in or on the bottom of the sea, a lake,

or river. The organisms are described as *benthic*, and they may burrow, crawl or remain attached.

biome a geographical area that is characterised by particular ecosystems of plants, animals and microorganisms. It is created by and related to climate and is usually mainly distinguished by the form of vegetation that it supports. Examples of biomes are desert, savanna, tropical forest, chaparral (scrubland), temperate grassland, temperate deciduous forest, taiga (coniferous or boreal forest) and tundra. (*See* G&G grassland.)

bionomics *see* ecology.

biosphere the region of the Earth's surface (both land and water) and its immediate atmosphere, which can support any living organism.

birds *see* Aves.

Bivalvia a class of the phylum Molluska to which many species of shellfish, called bivalves, belong e.g. mussels, oysters, scallops and clams. These animals are characterised by having a body enclosed within a shell, divided into two halves (*bivalve shell*), that is flattened and hinged along the midline. They have a smaller head than that of most other molluscs and usually do not move around, living on the bottom of lakes or the sea. More mobile kinds such as scallops occur, however, and also burrowing ones such as the shipworm and razorshell.

boa *see* Squamata.

bony fishes most fishes have a bony skeleton containing calcium phosphate and a body covered with overlapping scales. These are the bony fishes, or class Osteichthyes, and include many familiar freshwater and marine species. They have jaws (*compare* Agnatha), gills covered by a protective flap called the *operculum*, and they often possess an air sac, called a *swim bladder*, for buoyancy. They usually lay large numbers of eggs that are fertilised externally, and examples include cod, haddock, salmon, trout and sticklebacks.

Brachiopoda a phylum of ancient marine invertebrate animals. Brachiopods, also called lampshells, along with two other phyla, possess a special structure, called a *lophophore*, that is used for feeding and

RESPIRATION. They have a bivalve shell (*see* BIVALVIA) and a stalk, known as a *peduncle*, that attaches the animal to the surface on which it lives. Brachiopods are important index fossils, characterising and delimiting a geological zone, and one kind, *Lingula*, has survived to the present day little changed from the Ordovician geological period, 500–440 million years ago.

brackish water water that occurs in estuaries (*see* ESTUARY) and is intermediate in saltiness between sea and fresh water.

Bryophyta the division of the plant kingdom to which mosses belong. These simple plants commonly thrive in shady, wet conditions and have a waxy, outer layer (*cuticle*) that helps to prevent them from drying out. Mosses lack true roots but may be attached to a surface by hairs (*rhizoids*) or use other plants for support. The hornworts and liverworts are other simple plants that are commonly included in the Bryophyta, although this is now considered to be scientifically incorrect. The three types, although sharing several common features, are probably not closely related.

Bryozoa *see* MOSS ANIMALS AND SEA MATS.

butterflies *see* LEPIDOPTERA.

camels *see* ARTIODACTYLA.

camouflage a kind of colour pattern or body shape that helps to disguise an animal and enable it to blend into its background. This is useful for both predators and prey animals and can be seen in many different SPECIES from invertebrates to large MAMMALS. Patterns of camouflage have evolved through the processes of natural selection (*see* S&T Darwin and natural selection) and may be quite intricate and complex. Examples include moths patterned to look like bark or possessing false eye spots, preying mantis, many fishes and animals such as tiger and zebra.

capybara *see* RODENTIA.

Carnivora an ORDER of mammals that are largely flesh-eaters, including both predators and carrion-eaters and those that combine the two. Many of these animals show ADAPTATIONS of the jaws and teeth. They possess a powerful bite and large piercing and shearing teeth. They often have retractile claws, and two suborders

are recognised, the toe-footed carnivores (Fissipedia), such as wolves, dogs, cats, racoons, weasels and badgers, and the fin-footed carnivores (Pinnepedia), e.g., walruses, sea lions and seals.

carnivorous plants a plant that is able to trap and digest insects and other small animals. There are about 400 different SPECIES of carnivorous plants, usually insectivorous. They often grow in poor conditions that would not normally supply enough minerals and nourishment, so they have specially adapted to attract, trap, and digest prey in ingenious and highly effective ways. For example, *sundews* secrete a sticky substance on their leaves that holds insects fast. *Pitcher plants* have modified leaves forming a water-filled trap with smooth sides into which an insect falls and drowns. *Venus flytraps* have hinged leaves with spines at the edges that snap shut over an insect. Once an insect (or other small prey) is caught, these carnivorous plants release digestive ENZYMES and eventually dissolved food substances are absorbed.

cartilaginous fishes a CLASS of fishes, called the Chondrichthyes, which are highly specialised, having a skeleton composed entirely of cartilage (*see* S&T cartilage). The most familiar examples are the rays, sharks and skates (belonging to the subclass Elasmobranchii) and also the ratfish, subclass Holocephali (chimeras).

cat *see* CARNIVORA.

caterpillar *see* LEPIDOPTERA.

cattle *see* ARTIODACTYLA.

centipede *see* MYRIAPODA.

Cephalopoda a CLASS of marine molluscs to which the nautilus, squid, cuttlefish, octopus and the (extinct) fossil ammonite belong. It is the most advanced group in the PHYLUM Mollusc.

The ammonites had well-developed spiral shells with the animal living inside the last chamber, but the *nautilus* is the only living SPECIES that has this structure. In the modern species the shell is much reduced, as in the squids, or is inside the body, as in cuttlefish, or absent altogether, as in octopuses. Cephalopods are mainly marine predators, with a well-developed head surrounded by a ring of tentacles used to seize their prey. They swim by jet propulsion—expelling water from the body using muscular action. They have complicated eyes and excellent vision and a well-developed nervous system that makes them the most intelligent invertebrate animals. Cuttlefish are able to show remarkable colour changes, possibly as a means of communication.

Cestoda a class of the PHYLUM Platyhelminthes. Cestodes are the parasitic tapeworms that live inside the gut of a vertebrate. They have a head with suckers and hooks that attach the animal to the intestinal lining of its host. Behind the head there is a series of sacs (called *proglottids*) that give the appearance of segments. Each of these has male and female sex organs, and these animals are *hermaphrodite*. The outer surface is protected from the digestive juices of the host's gut by a tough, outer cuticle. Tapeworms do not have a gut but dissolved food substances are absorbed over the whole body surface. The life cycle requires both a primary and secondary host.

In one tapeworm that affects people, *Taenia saginata*, the beef tapeworm, the primary host containing the adult animal is man and the secondary hosts are cattle. Human beings are infected by eating poorly cooked meat containing cysts (immature worms with a protective shell) that develop into adults once they have been eaten.

Cetacea an ORDER of marine mammals comprising the dolphins and whales. They are characterised by having forelimbs developed as *flippers*, a powerful, flattened tail with two *flukes*, and a dorsal fin. These animals are excellent swimmers and have a thick layer of blubber (fat) beneath a nearly hairless skin, serving as insulation and a food store. Air is drawn into the lungs through a blowhole on the upper surface that can be shut off when the animal dives. Dolphins, killer whales and toothed whales are predators belonging to the suborder Odontocetti. Many of the great whales, e.g., the blue whale, are plankton-feeders belonging to the suborder Mysticetti. They filter vast quantities of seawater through whalebone plates in order to extract their food. The blue whale is the largest known living animal, in excess of 150 tons in weight and 100 feet (30 metres) in length.

chameleon *see* SQUAMATA.

Chelonia an ORDER of the class Reptilia (*see* REPTILE) comprising the turtles, terrapins and tortoises. Their bodies are encased in a bony shell covered by horny plates. Both marine and land-dwelling species occur, and they have jaws developed as horny beaks without teeth. This is a very ancient group of reptiles, apparently little changed throughout its evolutionary history.

chimera *see* CARTILAGINOUS FISHES.

Chiroptera the mammalian ORDER to which bats belong, the main characteristic of which is flight. Chiropterans have membrane-like wings spread between elongated forelimbs and fingers and the hind limbs and, occasionally, the tail. Most bats are nocturnal insect-eaters, catching their prey on the wing. They have large ears adapted for ECHO-LOCATION by means of which they locate prey and sense their surroundings. Some are nectar-feeders, others eat fruit and vampire bats suck blood.

Chlorophyta the division of organisms to which green ALGAE, the largest and most varied group of algae, belong. They possess chlorophyll and are able to photosynthesise. They are mainly aquatic in both marine and fresh water but can live on land in damp conditions.

Chondrichthyes *see* CARTILAGINOUS FISHES.

class in scientific classification, a group or groups into which a PHYLUM is divided, made up of one or more ORDERS.

Cnidaria or **Coelenterata** the PHYLUM of aquatic invertebrates to which hydras, jellyfish, sea anemones and corals belong. These simple animals have two body forms, an attached stalk called a *polyp* and a free-swimming bell called a *medusa*. Depending upon the SPECIES, one or other body form may predominate or one may succeed another in what is known as an 'alternation of generations'. These animals are carnivorous, with stinging cells that immobilise their prey and tentacles around the 'mouth'. (*See* ACTINOZOA and HYDROZOA.)

cobra *see* SQUAMATA.

cockroach *see* ORTHOPTERA.

coelacanth a type of bony fish, belonging

to the ORDER Coelacanthiformes, suborder Crossypterygii, the flesh-finned fishes. All were thought to be extinct but a living representative was discovered in 1938. Living coelacanths are members of the genus *Latimeria* and have a characteristic three-lobed tail fin. They are large fish, living at great depths on the floor of the Indian Ocean and 'walk' on their crutch-like pectoral fins. Coelacanths give birth to live young and do not possess lungs. They are a remnant of numerous kinds of lobe-finned fishes that were present in the Devonian geological period (408–360 million years ago). The extinct forms were freshwater animals with lungs and some were the ancestors of the amphibians.

Coelenterata *see* CNIDARIA.

Coleoptera a vast ORDER (the largest in the animal kingdom) of the CLASS Insecta to which beetles and weevils belong. There are about 500,000 known SPECIES, found in a great number of different habitats, some feeding on vegetation, others on decaying material. The rest are predatory and carnivorous. They have two pairs of wings, but the first are protective sheaths (called *elytra*) that are hard and, when folded, meet precisely in a line along the middle of the back. They protect the delicate, membranous hindwings that are used for flying (but are reduced or not present in other species). The mouth parts are often enlarged for biting, and both young (larvae) and adult beetles of certain species can be serious economic pests of crops, timber and stored food. Many beetles are beautifully coloured and patterned.

colony a group of individuals of the same SPECIES, living together and to some extent dependent on one another. In some cases the individuals may actually be joined, as in corals, and function as one unit. In others, e.g., social insects such as bees and ants, they are separate individuals but have a complex organisation with specialised functions.

commensalism *see* S&T symbiosis.

conservation the means of managing the environment in such a way as to preserve the natural resources of plants, animals and minerals, etc, and to minimise the impact of people. The natural environment is in a constant state of change, and SPECIES become extinct and landscapes and climate alter, but this is usually over a long period of time. Human activities are often devastating and whole ECOSYSTEMS can be lost very rapidly (e.g. clearance of the tropical rainforest). The environment that is left after such activities is usually significantly poorer and people's gains tend to be short-lived. Conservation therefore involves planning ahead, preservation, restoration and reconstruction, all the while minimising damage. This may be on a small scale or global, and conservation is now recognised to be of vital importance to the survival and quality of the lives of human beings as well as those of plants and animals.

Copepoda a large subclass of the CLASS CRUSTACEA to which tiny marine and freshwater invertebrate animals belong. They are all between 0.0195 and 0.079 inches (0.5 and 2 millimetres) long and do not have a shell (carapace) or compound eyes. They have five or six pairs of swimming legs and are very important SPECIES in the plankton. Some may be free-living filter-feeders while others (e.g. the fish louse) are parasitic. A well-known freshwater type has one simple eye (*ocellus*) in the midline and is called *Cyclops*.

corals *see* ACTINOZOA.

cricket *see* ORTHOPTERA.

Crustacea a CLASS of the PHYLUM ARTHROPODA to which lobsters, crayfish, crabs, shrimps, pill bugs, prawns, barnacles, water fleas and copepods belong. They have a well-defined head and the body (thorax and abdomen) is divided into segments although these may not be obvious. Various projections, called appendages, are used for a variety of different purposes, e.g., swimming, feeding and as gills for respiration (*see* S&T respiration).

cyanobacteria the commonly named 'blue-green ALGAE' which are now regarded as bacteria. They may be single-celled or occur in colonies or as filaments. They are found in all aquatic environments and are often very specialised, growing, for example, in hot springs. They possess the ability to photosynthesise and some are able to trap nitrogen and are important in soil fertility. Some kinds occur in plankton, others form *symbiotic* (*see* S&T symbiosis) relationships with other organisms (e.g., lichens). Blooms of some species in freshwater lakes that have been enriched with agricultural fertilisers can be a problem, as toxins are produced that are lethal to fish and other animals.

cyclostomata *see* Agnatha.

Decapoda the order of the class Crustacea to which prawns, shrimps, lobsters and crabs belong. These animals possess five pairs of walking legs, the first pair of which (in the crawling varieties) are modified to form powerful pincers. The others are used for feeding or swimming.

decomposers organisms that break down dead organic matter, such as plants, animals and animal waste in order to obtain energy, leaving behind simple organic or inorganic waste. Carbon dioxide is produced and heat is released during decomposition. The main organisms involved are bacteria and fungi but also earthworms (*see* annelida) and other invertebrates.

deforestation the felling and removal of trees from an area of natural forest. It usually has a devastating effect on the environment. It is carried out to provide wood for fuel (for local people) or for the timber trade, or to clear land for agriculture. Often the soil is very low in minerals and its fertility is soon exhausted. On slopes the soil can be washed away by water gushing down, leading to erosion and landslides. The end result of deforestation can be the creation of near desert conditions.

deer *see* Artiodactyla.

diatoms *see* Bacillariophyta.

dinosaurs a large group of reptiles that flourished some 190 to 65 million years ago during the Jurassic and Cretaceous geological periods (*see* G&G geological timescale). They showed a tremendous variety of body shape and size, and included flying species. It was once thought that they were all slow, cold-blooded creatures but now scientists believe that many were fast-moving and able to keep their bodies warm by metabolic activities.

The climate in the Cretaceous period changed considerably. For reasons that are still not absolutely clear, the vast majority of the dinosaurs disappeared in a mass extinction occurring over 5 to 10 million years at the end of the Cretaceous period.

Diptera a large insect order that contains about 80,000 species including flies. These are called the true or two-winged flies, but the back pair is modified to form knobs (*halteres*) used for balance. The mouth of a fly is adapted to pierce, lap, or suck, and they feed on sap, nectar and rotting organic matter. Some, e.g. mosquitoes, feed on blood. The larva (maggot) eventually forms a pupa and becomes an adult through metamorphosis (*see* S&T larva).

dog *see* Carnivora.

dolphin *see* Cetacea.

earthworm *see* Annelida.

Echinodermata a phylum of marine invertebrates to which starfish, brittle stars, sea urchins, sea cucumbers, sea lilies and sea daisies belong. They have existed for a very long time, as fossil forms have been found in rocks 500 million years old. They commonly have five arms radiating from a central disc, which is the body. The arms bear many tiny tube feet that act like suction pads and are used for movement, feeding and respiration. They have an external shell of plates containing calcium, often with bumps or spines, and some are able to regenerate lost arms.

echo-location the use by animals of high-pitched pulses of sound that bounce off surrounding objects, allowing the location of these to be determined. Nocturnal animals, such as bats, and aquatic mammals, like dolphins, produce these sounds, and echo-location enables them to make sense of their environment and to locate prey.

ecology or bionomics the study of the relationship between plants and animals and their environment. Ecology is concerned with, for example, predator-prey relationships, population changes (in the species present), and competition between species.

ecosystem all the biological life and non-biological components (e.g. minerals in the soil) within an area and the inter-reactions and relationships between them all. Thus an ecosystem includes all the organisms in a community and the geology, chemistry, and climate, and it may be a lake, forest, region of tundra, etc. Various cycles operate within an ecosystem. Energy, in the form of sunlight, is converted to chemical energy by green plants and is then consumed by animals and released as heat. Food substances, or nutrients, are returned to the cycle as wastes.

Ectoprocta *see* MOSS ANIMALS AND SEA MATS.

Elasmobranchii *see* CARTILAGINOUS FISHES.

elephant *see* PROBOSCIDEA.

environment the area that surrounds and supports an organism, including all the other living creatures that share the area as well as all the inorganic elements (e.g., minerals contained in the soil).

epiphyte a plant that grows up on another plant purely for support and is not rooted in the ground. Common examples are mosses, lichens and some tropical orchids.

estuary a coastal inlet that is affected by marine tides and freshwater in the form of a river draining from the land. An estuary is usually a drowned valley created by a rise in sea level after the last ice age (*see* G&G ice age). Estuaries usually contain a lot of sediment (sand, silt, etc) washed from the land, and the tidal currents may produce channels, sandbanks and sand waves. Organisms that inhabit an estuary are adapted to cope with the changes in the *salinity* (saltiness) of the water. They often provide rich feeding grounds, especially for birds, e.g. waders, ducks and geese.

eutherian the term used to describe mammals that have a placenta with which to nourish their embryos within the womb of the mother and belong to the subclass Eutheria.

eutrophic the term used to describe a body of water, usually a lake or slow-moving river, that is over-rich in nitrogen and phosphorus because of contamination by agricultural fertilisers or sewage. This leads to rapid growth of ALGAE (*algal blooms*), which use up the oxygen available to other SPECIES by bacteria decomposing dead algae. The final outcome is the death of fish and other organisms. The process is known as *eutrophication*.

Falconiformes *see* AVES.

family in scientific classifications, a group of individuals more comprehensive than

a GENUS and less so than an ORDER.

fanworm *see* POLYCHAETA.

Fissipedia *see* CARNIVORA.

Foraminifer a PHYLUM of small marine animals (PROTOZOANS) that have hard shells made of calcium carbonate or silica and are important in the fossil record. Sedimentary rocks such as chalk may contain many foraminiferan fossils and modern SPECIES are often found in deepsea oozes.

fossil *see* G&G fossil.

frog *see* AMPHIBIA.

fungus (*plural* **fungi**) any one of a number of kinds of simple plants without the photosynthetic pigment chlorophyll (*see* S&T chloroplast, chlorophyll). Fungi cause decay in fabrics, timber and food and diseases in some plants and animals. They may be single-celled or form strands called filaments and are used in biotechnology in baking, brewing, and to make antibiotics.

Gastropoda a CLASS of the PHYLUM Molluska to which invertebrate animals, typically (but not always) with a shell, such as limpets, whelks, conches, snails, and slugs, belong. They have a large muscular foot used for movement (hence *gastropod*), a distinct head with eyes and a coiled or twisted shell. Most are marine but some live in freshwater and others are adapted for life on land.

gene therapy the articificial insertion of a normal functioning gene into the cells of a person suffering from a disease or hereditary condition caused by a defective, malfunctioning gene, in order to effect a cure. This normal gene must be introduced by a vector or carrier. This is usually a genetically altered virus into which the human DNA (gene) has been inserted.

genus (*plural* **genera**) a division of plants and animals below a FAMILY and above a SPECIES.

gila monster *see* SQUAMATA.

goats *see* ARTIODACTYLA.

grasshopper *see* ORTHOPTERA.

greenhouse effect the greenhouse effect describes a natural cycle that controls the fate of solar energy when it reaches the Earth's atmosphere (*see* G&G atmosphere). Some of the energy is immediately radiated back out into space as soon as it hits the layer of gases that form the atmosphere. However, a proportion of it passes through and reaches the surface where it is absorbed and causes warming. This energy is then radiated back upwards as heat, which rises into the atmosphere. While some of it escapes back out into space a percentage is absorbed by *greenhouse gases* that are naturally present in the atmosphere. Greenhouse gases re-emit the heat they have absorbed and while some escapes into space, the rest is re-directed downwards to the surface. The energy is *trapped* and it causes a warming effect that would not otherwise occur, maintaining the global temperature at an estimated 30º C (54º F) higher than would be the case if the system did not operate. It is this vital process that enables life to be sustained, allowing water to exist in liquid form and equable temperatures that have facilitated the evolution of plants and animals. Scientists believe that there is a natural, in-built balance in the system, which would normally lead to stability for long periods of time. However, it is further believed that human activity, specifically industrial processes and the burning of fossil fuels has altered the natural balance by causing an entirely artificial build-up of greenhouse gases in the atmosphere. This has resulted in more heat becoming trapped and hence global warming *(see* G&G climate change, global warming).Scientists have predicted that during the next 100 years, the planet will warm by 1.4°C–5.8°C. While some rise is now held to be inevitable and indeed is already being experienced, the extent of the change will depend upon the success or failure of humanity to alter its behaviour and drastically reduce emissions of the principle greenhouse gas, *carbon dioxide* (*see* S&T carbon dioxide).

growth rings the rings seen if you cut through the woody stem of a plant, e.g., the trunk of a tree. Each ring represents a year's growth and by counting the number of rings, the age of the tree can be discovered. Also, each ring is different and comparison of dead and living trees provides a dating method (and information about past climates) for periods within the past eight thousand years. This is known as *dendrochronology* (*see* S&T dendrocronology).

Gymnospermae the CLASS (or subdivision) of the division Spermatophyta, seed plants, to which conifers, cycads and ginkgos belong. They have an ancient history as fossils and are found in rocks dating back to the Devonian geological period (408–360 million years ago). They produce *naked seeds* (hence *gymnosperm*) that are not enclosed by a protective sheath (*carpel*). *Compare* ANGIOSPERMAE.

habitat the place where a plant or animal normally lives, e.g. river, pond, seashore.

hagfish *see* AGNATHA.

halophyte a plant that can tolerate a high level of salt in the soil. Such conditions occur in salt marshes, tidal river estuaries (and on freeway verges and central reservations), and a typical SPECIES is rice grass (*Spartina*).

hedgehog *see* IINSECTIVORA.

Hemiptera the ORDER of the CLASS Insecta to which bugs belong. This is a very large group and includes leaf hoppers, scale insects, bed bugs, aphids, cicadas and water boatmen. The typical body shape is a flattened oval with two pairs of wings folded flat down on the back of the resting insect. Their mouths are tubes adapted for piercing and sucking; some are herbivorous, others carnivorous and yet others parasitic. Some are serious agricultural pests, transmitting plant diseases by feeding on sap.

herbaceous (*herb-like*) the term used to describe a plant with little or no woody stem in which all the green parts die back at the end of each season. Either the whole plant dies (having produced and dispersed seeds), as in *annuals*, or parts of the plant (the roots) survive beneath the ground and grow up again the following year, as in *perennials*.

hibernation an ADAPTATION seen in some animals in which a sleep-like state occurs that enables them to survive the cold winter months when food is scarce. Some marked changes occur, notably a drop in body temperature to about 34.25°F (1.24°C) above the surrounding air, and a slowing of the pulse and metabolic rate to about 1 per cent of normal. In this state the animal's energy requirements are reduced and it uses up stored body fat. Bears, bats, porcupines, some fish, amphibians and reptiles are examples of animals that hibernate.

hippopotamus *see* ARTIODACTYLA.

holocephali *see* CARTILAGINOUS FISHES.

homeothermy or homiothermy warm-bloodedness, that is, the ability of an animal to keep up a constant body temperature, independent of the heat or cold of its ENVIRONMENT. It is a typical feature of birds and mammals, and various metabolic processes are involved (*see also* POIKILOTHERMY).

home range *see* TERRITORY.

homing the ability of animals to find their way home, especially in birds. Many bird species fly thousands of miles over land and sea during annual migrations to return to the same area year after year. It is thought that they navigate by means of the sun and stars and by using magnetic fields.

hominid a member of the PRIMATE FAMILY Hominidae, which includes modern man as well as fossil hominids that may have evolved around 3.5 million years ago. All belong to the GENUS *Homo*. Their main physical characteristic is the ability to walk upright (known as *bipedalism*), and there are also changes in the shape of the skull and teeth compared to those of other primates. They have (or had) complex social and cultural behaviour patterns.

horse *see* PERISSODACTYLA.

human *see* HOMINID.

humus material that makes up the organic part of soil, being formed from decayed plant and animal remains. It has a characteristic dark colour and its composition varies according to the amount and type of material present. It holds water, forming a physical state known as a *colloid* (*see* S&T colloids), which can then be used by growing plants and helps to prevent the loss of minerals from the soil by leaching. Hence it is very important in determining soil fertility. Humus may be more acidic (*mor*), as in the soil of coniferous forests, or alkaline (*mull*), as found in the soil of deciduous woodlands and grasslands.

Humus contains numerous microorganisms and invertebrate animals, and its presence is of obvious economic importance in the cultivation of food crops.

hydroponics or hydroculture the cultivation of plants or crops without the use of soil as a growing medium. The roots of the plants are surrounded by a mineral-enriched substrate which is either a solution or an inert material that has been impregnated with all the elements necessary for growth.

hydrothermal or deep sea vents ('black smokers') vents in the Earth's crust on the deep ocean floor that occur in geologically active areas where tectonic plates are either converging or moving apart. Volcanic eruptions take place through the vents, appearing like black smoke pouring from a chimney, but these are not the same as those that occur on the surface. Seawater under enormous pressure is forced down into the cracks and fissures where it is super-heated by magma within the crust and also becomes saturated with minerals such as manganese. This water spews out as a dark, chemical 'soup' at a temperature 360°C. Some of the dissolved minerals are precipitated around the mouth of the vent and over a period of time, these build up to form a chimney-like structure. When deep sea vents were first studied in the late 1970s, a remarkable and exciting discovery was made. It was realised that they formed the basis of a unique ecosystem that was completely independent of any energy input from the sun. Far from being a hostile, sterile environment, a remarkable web of life flourishes around the vents, relying upon bacteria that are able to metabolise *hydrogen sulphide.* Around 300 species have been documented and perhaps the most unusual are the giant, red-tentacled tube worms that can grow to be 12 feet (3 metres) tall. Other animals include mussels, giant clams, shrimps, crabs and brittle stars.

Hydrozoa the CLASS of the PHYLUM CNIDARIA to which corals known as millepore corals, hydras and such animals as the Portuguese man-of-war (*Physalia*) and *Vellela* belong. These are mostly marine invertebrates although freshwater types (e.g. *Hydra*) do occur. Many are colonial so that what appears to be a single animal is, in reality, made up of numerous small individuals, as with *Physalia* and *Vellela*. *Physalia* is a colony of dozens or perhaps hundreds of individuals. Some form the gas-filled float, others are for feeding, having tentacles and a mouth, yet others are protective, possessing stinging cells, and some are for reproduction.

Hymenoptera the ORDER of the CLASS INSECTA to which bees, wasps, ants, sawflies and ichneumon flies belong. These insects have a narrow 'wasp waist' and usually possess wings. The mouth parts are adapted in a variety of ways for biting, sucking, or lapping. A structure called an *ovipositor* at the hind end of the body is used for egg laying. It may be adapted for piercing, sawing or stinging and is often long and looped forward.

Some are social insects living in colonies, notably the ants and some bees and wasps. Honeybees have always been an important SPECIES to man.

ichneumon fly *see* HYMENOPTERA.

iguana *see* SQUAMATA.

Insecta a very important CLASS of invertebrate animals belonging to the PHYLUM Arthropoda, with over three-quarters of a million SPECIES known. They inhabit a wide variety of HABITATS both on land and in water, and there are 26 ORDERS, including beetles (Coleoptera), flies (Diptera), bees and ants (Hymenoptera), butterflies (Lepidoptera), grasshoppers (Orthoptera) and dragonflies (Odonata). The body of an insect is divided into three regions, known as the head, thorax and abdomen. The head often bears projections, called *antennae*, that are sense organs, and eyes and mouth parts adapted to feed on various food substances. The thorax bears three pairs of legs and also possibly wings and is composed of three segments. The abdomen or rear part of the body is made up of 11 segments.

Insectivora the ORDER of small mammals to which moles, shrews and hedgehogs belong. Insectivores are mainly nocturnal, with long snouts bearing sensitive hairs that respond to touch and tweezer-like (incisor) teeth. Their diet is mainly insects

although other foods are taken. They are quite a primitive group of animals that seem to have changed very little since their emergence in the Cretaceous geological period about 130 million years ago.

Isopoda the ORDER of the CLASS CRUSTACEA to which woodlice, fish lice and pill bugs belong. Isopods are familiar invertebrates that inhabit marine, freshwater and terrestrial ENVIRONMENTS, and many are parasites. Woodlice are important DECOMPOSERS, living in damp places under stones and near the soil surface.

kangaroo *see* METATHERIA.

killer whale *see* CETACEA.

king crab *see* ARACHNIDA.

koala bear *see* METATHERIA.

lamprey *see* AGNATHA.

lampshell *see* BRACHIOPODA.

leaf hopper *see* HEMIPTERA.

leech *see* ANNELIDA.

Lepidoptera the ORDER of the CLASS INSECTA to which moths and butterflies belong. The body, wings and legs of the adult insects are covered with numerous minute scales and the mouth parts are in the form of a long tube (called a *proboscis*) that is often held coiled beneath the head. This is uncoiled and extended to enable the insect to feed on nectar. Two large pairs of fine wings, often brightly coloured, are characteristic of this group and are held vertically in resting butterflies whereas moths hold their wings in various positions. The immature insects are called *caterpillars*, and they have a well-defined head with chewing mouth parts and a segmented body, usually with each segment bearing a pair of legs. Many caterpillars are serious economic pests of food crops and trees and may transmit plant diseases. The caterpillar becomes an adult by undergoing metamorphosis via a *pupa* or *chrysalis* (*see* S&T larva). The pupa may be surrounded by a silk cocoon produced by the caterpillar from special silk glands. Others use leaves or similar material to construct a cocoon.

lichen a plant-like growth formed from two organisms that live together in a symbiotic relationship (*see* S&T symbiosis). The two organisms involved are a FUNGUS and an ALGA. A lichen forms a distinct structure that is not similar to either partner on its own. Usually most of the plant body is made up of the fungus with the algal cells distributed within. The fungus protects the algal cells and the alga provides the fungus with food through photosynthesis (*see* S&T photosynthesis, transpiration). A lichen is typically very slow growing and varies in size from less than an inch to several feet across. It may form a thin, flat crust, be leaflike or upright and branching. Often, lichens are found in conditions that are too cold or exposed for other plants, such as in the Arctic and mountainous regions. Reindeer moss and Iceland moss are lichens that provide an important food source in Arctic regions. Other lichens contain substances that are used in dyes, perfumes, cosmetics and medicines as well as poisons.

limpet *see* GASTROPODA.

littoral a term for the shallow water ENVIRONMENT of a lake or the sea that lies close to the shore. In the sea, the littoral zone includes the tidal area between the high and low water marks. Sunlight is able to penetrate so that rooted aquatic plants can grow and usually there is a wide variety and abundance of organisms.

llama *see* ARTIODACTYLA.

lobster *see* DECAPODA.

locust *see* ORTHOPTERA.

lugworm *see* POLYCHAETA.

Malacostraca the subclass of the CLASS CRUSTACEA to which prawns and other similar marine and freshwater animals belong. They typically have compound eyes on stalks and numerous legs or appendages used for a number of different functions, including swimming, and a hard shell or carapace.

mamba *see* SQUAMATA.

mammal any animal of the vertebrate CLASS Mammalia, which contains approximately 4500 SPECIES. Mammals have a number of distinguishing characteristics. They have hair; four different types of teeth (*heterodont*); small bones in the middle ear that conduct sound waves; they are warm-blooded and able to regulate their body temperature and produce sweat as a cooling mechanism. The heart is four-chambered and keeps oxygenated and deoxygenated blood separate, and a layer of muscle, called the diaphragm, is used to fill the lungs with air. The young of mammals develop within the body of the mother and fertilisation of the egg is internal. Mammary glands produce milk with which to feed the young once they are born. Mammals possess very complex sense organs and larger brains than other vertebrates of a similar size. They are adaptable and are found in almost all HABITATS.

mammoth *see* PROBOSCIDEA.

marsupial *see* METATHERIA.

Metatheria the subclass of the CLASS Mammalia to which marsupial MAMMALS belong. The distinctive feature is that the female has a pouch on the lower part of the body (abdomen) called the *marsupium*. Marsupials are born at a very early stage of development and crawl into the pouch and fix on to a teat. Here they complete their development until they are able to leave their mother's pouch. Familiar marsupials, including kangaroos, koala bears and opossums, are found only in Australia and America. The group evolved about 80 million years ago during the late Cretaceous geological period. The break-up of early landmasses meant that the spread of marsupials was restricted. As a result, and especially in Australia, the marsupials have adapted to occupy habits and lifestyles that might otherwise have been filled by placental mammals.

mice *see* RODENT.

migration the seasonal movement of animals, especially birds, fish and some MAMMALS (e.g. porpoises). Climatic conditions usually trigger off migration, when perhaps lower temperatures result in less food being available. Some animals, particularly birds, travel vast distances, e.g. golden plovers fly 8000 miles (12,000 kilometres) from the Arctic to South America. Migrating animals seem to use three mechanisms for finding their way. Over short distances an animal moves to successive familiar landmarks (*piloting*). In *orientation*, a straight line path is taken, based upon the animal adopting a particular compass direction. *Navigation* is the most complex process because the animal must first determine its present position before taking a direction relative to it. It seems that some birds use the sun, stars (often the North Star, which moves very little) and an 'internal clock' that makes allowances for the relative positions of these heavenly bodies. Even when the sun is hidden by cloud, many birds are able to continue their migration quite accurately by plotting their direction with respect to the Earth's magnetic field.

millepore coral *see* HYDROZOA.

millepede *see* MYRIAPODA.

mimicry a resemblance in which one SPECIES has evolved to look like another species. Mimicry occurs in both the plant and animal kingdoms but is mainly found in insects. There are two main types of mimicry. The first is called *Batesian mimicry* (named after the British naturalist H. W. Bates). In this, one harmless species mimics the appearance of another, usually poisonous, species. A good example is the nonpoisonous viceroy butterfly mimicking the orange and black colour of the poisonous monarch butterfly. Predators learn to avoid the harmful butterfly and leave the mimic alone as well because of the close resemblance. The second type is *Mullerian mimicry* (named after the German zoologist J. F. T. Müller). In this, different species that are either poisonous or just distasteful to the predator have evolved to resemble each other. The resemblance ensures that the predator avoids all the similar looking species so all achieve protection.

mites *see* ARACHNIDA.

mole *see* INSECTIVORA.

Molluska the PHYLUM of invertebrate animals to which many with shells, such as slugs and snails (CLASS GASTROPODA), mussels and oysters (class BIVALVIA) and cuttlefish, squids and octopuses (class CEPHALOPODA) all belong. Most molluscs are marine but there are freshwater and land-living varieties, and it is a large group of animals including over 50,000 SPECIES.

monitor lizard *see* SQUAMATA.

monkey *see* PRIMATE.

mosquito *see* DIPTERA.

moss animals and sea mats (PHYLUM Ectoprocta or Bryozoa) a group of marine invertebrate animals, many of which are important reef-builders. Individual animals are tiny, only about 0.039 inches (1 millimetre) across, and resemble the polyps of the phylum CNIDARIA, but they form colonies that may extend for over 19.5 inches (half a metre). There are around 5,000 SPECIES, many with a hard external skeleton containing calcium into which the body can be withdrawn. They have a mouth surrounded by tentacles that waft in water and trap food particles.

moths *see* LEPIDOPTERA.

Myriapoda the CLASS of the PHYLUM ARTHROPODA to which centipedes (subclass Chilopoda) and millipedes (subclass Diplopoda) belong. These familiar invertebrate animals have a distinct head with antennae and a long segmented body. Centipedes have one pair of legs per segment and are carnivorous. Millipedes have two pairs of legs on each segment and are herbivorous.

nautilus *see* CEPHALOPODA.

nekton animals that swim in the PELAGIC zone (*see also* G&G oceans) of the sea or a lake, such as jellyfish, fish, turtles and whales.

Nematoda the PHYLUM of invertebrate animals to which roundworms belong. They have a characteristically rounded body that tapers at each end, and some are only about 0.039 inches (1 millimetre) in length while others may reach 39.37 inches (1 metre). There are numerous species and they may inhabit water, leaf litter and damp soil and also occur in plant tissues and as parasites in animals (*see* S&T parasite). They have muscles running only lengthways (longitudinally) down the body, a unique feature of roundworms. Some free-living species are of vital importance as DECOMPOSERS in the soil but others are significant economic pests, attacking the roots of crop plants. Yet others are serious parasites of man and animals. Humans can be affected by over 50 nematode species, e.g. threadworms.

Neognathae, Neornirthes *see* AVES.

neritic zone the shallow water marine zone near the shore that extends from low tide to a depth of approximately 656 feet (200 metres). Most *benthic* organisms (*see* BENTHOS) live in this zone because sunlight can penetrate to these depths.

Sediments deposited here are sand and clays, and those laid down in ancient seas (now sandstones and mudstones) preserve features such as ripple marks and fossils of marine organisms.

newt *see* AMPHIBIA.

niche all the ENVIRONMENTal factors that affect an organism within its community. These factors include living space, available food, climate and all the conditions necessary for the survival and reproduction of the SPECIES. Although many species exist side by side, each occupies a specific niche within a community with circumstances that apply uniquely to it.

octopus *see* CEPHALOPODA.

Odonata the ORDER of the CLASS INSECTA to which dragonflies and damselflies belong. These familiar large insects are carnivorous both as adults and *nymphs* (*see* S&T larva). Eggs are laid in or near water and the aquatic nymphs that hatch out have gills for breathing. They are skilful and voracious hunters with biting mouth parts that are on a plate or *mask* held beneath the head. This is shot out suddenly to seize the prey, which includes invertebrates and even small fish. The nymph crawls up the stalk of a reed or other plant, right out of the water, just before its final moult. The adult that emerges has a pair of large compound eyes and two pairs of large wings with conspicuous veins. In dragonflies the wings are always held out horizontally at right angles to the body in the resting insect. In damselflies, the resting insect holds its wings folded over its back. These insects have very good eyesight and are excellent hunters, catching insect prey in flight with their legs. They are often brightly and beautifully coloured and are a very ancient group. Some fossil species found in rocks from the Carboniferous era had wingspans of over 19.5 inches (half a metre).

Oligochaeta the CLASS of the PHYLUM ANNELIDA to which earthworms and some other worm SPECIES belong. They are distinguished by having very few bristles (*chaetae*) that are not borne on special structures called *parapodia*.

opossum *see* METATHERIA.

order in biology, any of the groups into which a CLASS is divided, made up of one or more families.

Orthoptera the ORDER of the CLASS INSECTA to which grasshoppers, crickets, locusts, preying mantises and cockroaches belong. This is a large order of insects containing many familiar SPECIES. They are usually large and mainly herbivorous with biting mouth parts. Two pairs of wings may be present, but some species are wingless. The two hind legs are often large and modified for jumping. Many produce sounds by rubbing one part of the body against another (often wings and hind legs), using special *stridulatory* organs to produce noise which is called *stridulation*. Some species, especially locusts and cockroaches, are pests of crops or buildings.

Osteichthyes *see* BONY FISHES.

paramecium *see* PROTOZOA.

Paleognathae, Passeriformes *see* AVES.

pelagic the term used to describe any organisms swimming and living in the sea between the surface and middle depths, including many fish, marine mammals and plankton. Pelagic sediments (called *ooze*) are deep-water deposits made up of the shells of minute organisms and small quantities of fine debris.

Perissodactyla the ORDER of the CLASS Mammalia to which herbivorous grazing MAMMALS such as horses, zebras, rhinoceroses and tapirs belong. These animals characteristically have hoofed feet and an odd number of toes. The teeth are specialised for grinding and the gut adapted for the digestion of cellulose. This was a distinct mammalian line 60 million years ago in the Eocene geological period.

photic zone the uppermost, surface layer of a lake or sea where sufficient light penetrates to allow photosynthesis to take place (*see* S&T photosynthesis and transpiration). The extent varies according to the quality of the water (e.g. cloudy because of suspended particles), but it can extend to a depth of 656 feet (200 metres).

phylum (*plural* **phyla**) one of the major divisions of the animal or vegetable kingdoms containing one or more CLASSES.

Physalia *see* HYDROZOA.

pig *see* ARTIODACTYLA.

Pinnepedia *see* CARNIVORA.

pitcher plant *see* CARNIVOROUS PLANTS.

plankton *see* S&T plankton.

Plasmodium *see* SPOROZOA.

Platyhelminthes the PHYLUM to which flatworms, of which there are about 20,000 SPECIES, belong. There are four CLASSES in this group: the Turbellaria (free-living worms), Cestoda (tapeworms), Trematoda (parasitic flukes) and Monogenea (flukes).

platypus *see* PROTOTHERIA.

poikilothermy cold-bloodedness, a feature of all animals except MAMMALS and birds. The body temperature of these animals varies according to that of the surrounding environment, but they adjust by seeking sun or shade as required. The blood flow to some body tissues is also adjusted according to whether heat needs to be lost or conserved (*see also* HOMEOTHERMY).

pollution contamination of the natural environment with harmful substances that have usually been released as a result of the activities of people. The substances that cause the pollution are called *pollutants* and include chemicals from industry and agriculture, gases from the burning of fossil fuels, industrial and domestic waste in landfill sites and sewage. Pollution is a serious problem because of the threat it poses to the health not just of humans but of all animals and plants. Many countries have now introduced stringent regulations in order to control pollution levels.

Polychaeta the CLASS of the PHYLUM ANNELIDA to which worms such as the ragworm (*Nereis*), lugworm (*Arenicola*) and fan worm (*Sabella*) belong. These characteristically possess a protruding pair of bumps or lobes on each segment, each having numerous bristles or chaetae. Most of these worms are marine animals and live in tubes constructed from pieces of shell and sand. Lugworms and ragworms make burrows in mud or sand. Most species have a distinct head, often with jaws and eyes.

polyp *see* ACTINOZOA.

population a group of individuals that belong to the same SPECIES. Populations may be genetically isolated, rarely breeding with other members of the same species outside their particular area, or one dense population may merge with another.

Usually a population is affected by such factors as birth and death rates, density (numbers), immigration and emigration.

population dynamics the study of the changes that occur in POPULATION numbers, whether plant or animal, and the factors that control or influence these changes. Distinction is made between factors that are dependent or independent of population density. For example, a natural occurrence such as a flood is an independent factor while food supply is dependent.

Porifera the PHYLUM of invertebrate animals to which sponges, of which there are about 9000 SPECIES, belong. Most sponges are marine and live attached to rocks or other surfaces. They have a hollow, sac-like body punctured with holes and an internal skeleton made up of tiny spines (spicules) of calcium carbonate, silica, or protein. Sponges are filter-feeders, taking particles of food from the water and digesting them. They are very simple animals with no muscle or nerves and are able to regenerate lost parts of their body structure.

Portuguese man-of-war *see* HYDROZOA.

prawn *see* MALACOSTRACA.

praying mantis *see* ORTHOPTERA.

Primates the MAMMALIan ORDER that includes monkeys, lemurs, apes and human beings. Evidence suggests that primates evolved from tree-dwelling INSECTIVORES late in the Cretaceous geological period. Characteristic features are manual dexterity (permitted by thumbs and big toes that can touch and grasp), good binocular vision and eye-to-hand coordination. The brain is large and the primates are highly intelligent. There are two suborders, the Prosimii (lemurs) and Anthropoidea (monkeys, apes and humans).

Proboscidea the ORDER of placental MAMMALS to which elephants belong, characterised by having a trunk (proboscis) and tusks that are modified incisor teeth. The order evolved during the Eocene geological period and had a greater number of SPECIES than now, including, for example, the extinct mammoths. There are just two modern species, the African and Indian elephants.

Prototheria the subclass to which two groups of MAMMALS, the monotremes, that is, the platypuses and spiny anteaters (Echidnas), belong. These are the only living MAMMALS that lay eggs, and today they are found only in Australia and New Guinea. The monotremes resemble reptiles in the structure of their skeleton and in the laying of eggs. They are warm-blooded although the body temperature is variable and lower than that of most other mammals. It is thought that the monotremes originated about 150 million years ago, early in the development of the mammals.

protozoan formerly the term for any of the members of a PHYLUM of small, single-celled (mainly) microorganisms but now a general word for the Protista (*see* S&T Protista). Included are such organisms as *Amoeba* and *Paramecium*, widely distributed in aquatic and damp terrestrial HABITATS. Some feed on decaying organic material (*saprophytes*) while others are parasites, e.g. *Trypsanosoma*, which causes sleeping sickness.

Psittaciformes *see* AVES.

pteridophyte any of the ferns belonging to a division of the plant kingdom called the Pteridophyta. There are about 12,000 SPECIES of ferns, which emerged as far back as the Carboniferous geological period. Ferns are just about all terrestrial. Most are in tropical regions. The leaves are usually called *fronds*, each made up of numerous smaller leaflets. They are considered to be a fairly primitive group of plants. Many of the extinct ferns grew to an enormous size and are well preserved as fossils.

quadrat a small sampling plot, usually 10.8 square feet (one square metre), that is chosen at random. The organisms found within it are counted and studied, providing a 'window' into the area as a whole, revealing the types of animals and plants to be found there. Sampling may be done in relation to a particular SPECIES or several different types of organisms.

race a group of individuals that is different in one or more ways from other members of the same SPECIES. They may be different because they occupy another geographical area, perhaps showing a variation in colour, or they may exhibit behavioural, physiological or even genetic differences. The term is sometimes used in the same

way as subspecies. Usually, animals from different races are able to interbreed.

racoon *see* CARNIVORA.

Radiolaria the ORDER to which the tiny, marine PROTOZOAN animals present in plankton belong (*see* S&T plankton). These organisms have a spherical body shape and characteristically possess a beautiful intricate skeleton often composed of silica. This is perforated with holes, making a large variety of patterns, many in the form of a lattice of spheres, one inside the other. Often there are many spines or hooks projecting outwards. When radiolarians die, their skeletons, which are highly resistant to decay, settle on the ocean floor to accumulate as *radiolarian ooze*. When compressed into rock it forms *flint* and *chert*. Radiolarian fossils are very important to geologists and are among the few found in the most ancient rocks from the Precambrian geological period (more than 590 million years old).

ragworm *see* POLYCHAETA.

rat *see* RODENTIA.

rattlesnake *see* SQUAMATA.

ray *see* CARTILAGINOUS FISHES.

reindeer moss *see* LICHEN.

Reptilia (reptiles) a CLASS of vertebrates that were the first animals to truly colonise dry land and to exist entirely independently of water. They often live in extremely hot conditions such as semi-desert. They have a dry skin covered with horny scales that protect them from drying out. Reptiles usually lay eggs in holes that they excavate in sand or mud. The eggs are covered by a protective shell that is porous and allows the passage of air. Some reptiles retain the eggs inside the body until they hatch. Reptiles are cold-blooded (*see* POIKILOTHERMY) but are able to maintain an even body temperature by behavioural means, such as basking in the sun. There is evidence that some extinct reptiles (e.g. some of the DINOSAURS) were warm-blooded. Modern reptiles include snakes, lizards, turtles, tortoises and crocodiles.

rhinoceros *see* PERISSODACTYLA.

rice grass *see* HALOPHYTE.

Rodentia a widespread and successful ORDER of MAMMALS containing rats, mice, squirrels, capybaras and beavers. The upper and lower jaws contain a single pair of long incisor teeth that grow continuously throughout the animal's life. These are adapted for gnawing, and the absence of enamel on the back means that they wear to a chisel-like cutting edge. Rodents are herbivorous or omnivorous and tend to breed rapidly. Some, notably rats, are serious pests, spoiling food, and are responsible for the spread of diseases.

roundworm *see* Nematoda.

salamander *see* Amphibia.

sawfly *see* Hymenoptera.

sea anemone *see* Actinozoa.

sea cucumber, sea daisy, sea lily, sea urchin *see* Echinodermata.

sea lion and seal *see* Carnivora.

sea snake *see* Squamata.

scale insect *see* Hemiptera.

scorpion *see* Arachnida.

shark *see* Cartilaginous fishes.

sheep *see* Artiodactyla.

shrimp *see* Malacostraca.

skate *see* Cartilaginous fishes.

slug or snail *see* Gastropoda.

snake *see* Squamata.

species (*plural* **species**) a group of animals or plants that bear a close resemblance to each other in the more essential features of their organisation and produce similar progeny, several species uniting to form a genus.

spiny anteater *see* Prototheria.

Sporozoa a class of protozoan organisms that are parasites of higher animals, some causing serious diseases in people. An example is *Plasmodium*, which causes malaria and is transmitted by the mosquito.

Squamata the order of the class Reptilia to which lizards and snakes belong. They are covered by horny scales, and male animals are unique in possessing a paired penis. Lizards possess movable eyelids, and most have four limbs, e.g. iguanas, monitor lizards, chameleons and gila monsters. Snakes lack movable eyelids and are able to dislocate their lower jaw in order to swallow large prey. Some are constrictor types, such as boas, pythons and anacondas, while others may be venomous, such as cobras, vipers, mambas, rattlesnakes and sea snakes.

squid *see* Cephalopoda.

squirrel *see* Rodentia.

starfish *see* Echinodermata.

sundew *see* Carnivorous plants.

tapeworm *see* Cestoda.

tapir *see* Perissodactyla.

terrapin *see* Chelonia.

territory a specific area that animals, whether singly or in groups, defend to exclude other members of their species. A territory may be used for feeding, mating or breeding or all these activities, and the size varies greatly, from the small nesting territory of sea birds to the large areas used by red squirrels. Many mammals mark their territories with scent while birds use song. Territory differs from *home range*, this being the area in which an animal roams but which it does not defend.

tick *see* Arachnida.

toad *see* Amphibia.

tortoise *see* Chelonia.

trypanosome *see* Protozoan.

Turbellaria the class of the phylum Platyhelminthes to which flatworms such as *Planaria* belong. These are simple, small animals, mostly marine, although planarians are common in freshwater streams and ponds. They are carnivorous and move by undulating the body in a wavelike way or by means of small hairs, *cilia*, on their underside.

turtle *see* Chelonia.

ungulate *see* Artiodactyla; Perissodactyla.

vampire bat *see* Chiroptera.

variation the differences between individuals of the same population or species.

Venus flytrap *see* Carnivorous plants.

Vertebrata a major subphylum that includes all the animals with backbones: fishes, amphibians, reptiles, birds and mammals (*see* individual entries).

viper *see* Squamata.

walrus *see* Carnivora.

water boatman *see* Hemiptera.

weevil *see* Coleoptera.

whelk *see* Gastropoda.

zebra *see* Perissodactyla.

Science and Technology

absolute zero *see* TEMPERATURE.

acceleration *see* VELOCITY.

accumulator *see* BATTERY.

acid rain *see* NH acid rain.

acids and bases *acids* are chemical compounds in a liquid form that, depending on their strength, may occur naturally in foods as very weak acids (e.g. citric acid in lemons) or may form corrosive liquids (e.g. sulphuric acid) which have many industrial uses. Most acids have a sour taste, although it is not advisable to taste them as many are poisonous and can burn skin. Acids turn litmus paper from blue to red (*see* INDICATOR) and an acidic solution has a pH lower than 7. To aid digestion, our bodies produce acids to break down food. Some examples of acids:

citric	$C_3H_2O(COOH)_3$; found in lemons and fizzy drinks
hydrochloric	HCl; occurs in the stomach, used a lot in the oil, food and chemical industries
sulphuric	H_2SO_4; a strong acid used to make dyes, fertilisers, explosives, iron and steel; also used in car batteries
nitric	HNO_3; used to make dyes, fertilisers and explosives
formic	HCOOH; an organic acid found in stinging nettles

A mixture of concentrated nitric and hydrochloric acids (in the ratio 1:4) is called *aqua regia* (royal water) because it will dissolve the noble metals such as gold.

Bases are the opposite of acids, and if a base is reacted with an acid in the correct proportions, the two are cancelled out (*neutralised*), producing water and a salt. Nevertheless, bases can be highly reactive and corrosive. Bases turn red litmus paper blue. Some examples of bases:

lime/calcium hydroxide	$Ca(OH)_2$; used industrially and in cement production
caustic soda/sodium hydroxide	Na(OH); used to make other chemicals; also in paper, soap, aluminium and in petrochemicals manufacture.
magnesium oxide	MgO; used in antacid preparations

If a compound (usually the oxide -O, or hydroxide -OH of a metallic element) can function as an acid *or* as an alkali (a soluble base) it is said to be *amphoteric*, i.e. it can combine with an acid or a base to form a salt.

acoustics *see* SOUND.

acrylic *see* SYNTHETIC FIBRES.

actinozoan *see* NH Actinozoa.

active transport *see* MEMBRANE.

adaptation *see* NH adaptation.

adhesion *see* SURFACE TENSION.

adhesive a material that will bond (stick) solids together through initially wetting the surfaces to be joined and then solidifying to form a joint. Some adhesives, or *glues*, can be made from natural materials such as bones, horn and hides by boiling and simple chemical treatment. Glues made in this way are a mixture of proteins. Adhesives made from chemicals are called *synthetic*, and these tend to be stronger than the natural forms. There are several types of synthetic adhesive, including thermosetting resins, thermoplastic resins and epoxy resins, the last being among the strongest. Synthetic adhesives have numerous uses, including in the manufacture of furniture, textiles, windscreens, electrical products and also in construction. In recent years, 'superglues' have been introduced, which, it is claimed, are capable of sticking together most surfaces. Great care has to be taken when working with these compounds as they can also stick fingers together and can be dangerous if they come into contact with eyes, etc.

admixture *see* CONCRETE.

aerial *see* RADIO.

aerodynamics the study of the movement and control of solid objects such as aircraft, rockets, etc, in air. As objects move through the air there is a resistance, or *drag*, that works against the direction of movement, and the drag increases with speed. All machines used in transport, e.g. aircraft, cars, trains, lorries, etc, are designed with streamlined bodies to reduce drag to a minimum. This involves smooth curved shapes rather than angular shapes.

The aerodynamics of an aircraft wing

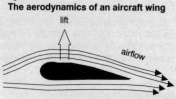

lift

airflow

Another important aspect of aerodynamics is *lift*, which is an upward force vital in the take-off and flight of aircraft. All aircraft have wings with a curved top surface and a flatter lower surface. This feature is based upon *Bernoulli's theorem*, which applies to both liquid and air and which proves that when the flow of air speeds up, the air pressure is reduced. The characteristic *aerofoil* shape of a wing means that air travelling over the top, curved surface has to travel farther than air beneath the wing. It therefore moves faster, causing a reduction in air pressure, and the wing is lifted or pushed upwards.

The aerofoil shape is not only used on aircraft, the same principle is applied to rudders, vanes on a windmill, and even to racing cars, although in the latter case it is to keep the car on the racetrack.

aerosol a fine mist or fog consisting of liquid or solid particles in a gas. It also refers to a pressurised container with a spray mechanism for dispersal of a fine mist of fluid droplets. This system is used for deodorants, paints, insecticides and other chemicals. Within the can is the liquid to be sprayed and a propellant gas that is under pressure. When the valve is opened by pressing the button, the gas forces (propels) the contents out through the nozzle. Until recently, the propellants used were commonly CFCs or chlorofluorocarbons, but because it has been proven that these chemicals damage the ozone layer (*see* G&G ozone layer), alternative compounds have been sought. An *atomiser* is another way of creating an aerosol that does not require a propellant gas.

ageing all the changes that take place in an animal as it grows older. Animals age at different rates, from some adult insects which live for only a day (mayflies) to elephants (up to 70 years) and tortoises and parrots, which may have a life span of well over 100 years. Ageing is perhaps best understood and most studied in human beings. In people, the cells that make up the different parts of the body age at different rates, and while most are renewed, some are not (e.g. brain cells), so the whole process is very complicated. As ageing occurs, noticeable physical changes take place, which include wrinkling of the skin, greying hair, deterioration in sight, hearing, taste, smell and memory and stiffening of limbs and joints. However, there is a great difference between individual people in the ways in which they are affected by these processes depending upon their inherited (genetic) make-up and their lifestyle and environment.

agnathan *see* NH Agnatha.

alcohols organic compounds containing carbon, oxygen and hydrogen and with a particular structure where a hydroxyl group (oxygen and hydrogen, OH) is linked to a carbon. Alcohols are mainly liquids and are used in a variety of ways:

Alcohol	Formula	Uses
methanol	CH_3OH	solvent; manufacture of paints, varnishes, etc
ethanol	CH_3CH_2OH	alcoholic drinks; solvent; food industry; perfumes
propanol	$CH_3CH_2CH_2OH$	solvent
butanol	$C_4H_{10}O$	solvents; artificial flavourings (4 different forms)

The alcohols are produced by various chemical reactions, but ethanol occurs naturally by fermentation in which yeast converts sugar to alcohol with carbon dioxide being the side product.

alkane, alkene, alkyne *see* HYDROCARBON.

allotropy *see* SULFUR.

alluvium *see* G&G alluvium.

alpha particles *see* RADIOACTIVITY.

alternation of generations *see* PLANTS.

alternative or renewable energy any of several technologies which generate electricity or provide fuel from a renewable source, the utilisation of this energy producing little or no addition to atmospheric levels of CARBON DIOXIDE. These technologies are held to be one of the main answers to global CLIMATE CHANGE. They include:

- biomass
- geothermal
- hydropower
- solar power
- tidal/wave power
- wind power

alternator *see* GENERATOR.

alumina *see* SYNTHETIC FIBRES.

amino acid *see* LIVER; PROTEIN AND AMINO ACIDS.

amplitude *see* WAVE.

anion *see* ION.

antifreeze a liquid added to the water in the cooling systems of car engines. The antifreeze lowers the freezing point of the water, helping to prevent freezing in the winter. The main component of antifreezes is ethylene glycol, although alcohols may be used.

antimatter *see* S&A antimatter.

aldehydes or alkanals a group of organic compounds containing carbon, hydrogen and oxygen that have a particular group, CHO, joined to another carbon atom. The oxygen is joined to the carbon by a double bond, the hydrogen by a single bond. Aldehydes are mainly colourless liquids or solids with typical odours and wide uses:

Aldehyde	Formula	Uses
formaldehyde	HCHO	as a solution in water for its germicidal action; also for sterilising instruments and storing specimens in pathology
acetaldehyde	CH_3CHO	as a stepping stone in the manufacture of other chemicals
propanal	CH_3CH_2CHO	a chemical intermediate

alga *see* NH alga.

algebra the use of symbols, usually letters, to help solve mathematical problems where the object is to find the value of an unknown quantity or to study complex theories. In its simplest form it may involve the determination of an unknown in an equation such as:

$$3x + 1 = 16$$

where x is obviously equal to 5. Albert Einstein used a very advanced form of algebra in deriving the equations for his general theory of RELATIVITY. The formal rules were developed in the 9th century by al Khuwrizmi, an Arab mathematician.

algorithm a set of rules that together form a mathematical procedure that allows a problem to be solved in a certain number of stages. Each rule is very carefully defined so that, theoretically, a machine can undertake the process.

An algorithm is a way of reaching the right answer to a difficult problem by breaking the problem down into simple stages. The stages allow the action to be successfully achieved without necessarily understanding fully the whole process. To be an algorithm, a list of instructions must have an end and be short enough to allow each to be completed and the process must end at some point. Computer programs contain algorithms, but simpler more everyday examples include making a telephone call and following a recipe. Long division is another example.

alimentary canal *see* DIGESTION.

alkali a base (*see* ACIDS AND BASES) that when dissolved in water produces a solution with a pH over 7, e.g. Na_2CO_3, $Ca(OH)_2$. These are alkaline solutions. Hydroxides of the metallic elements sodium and potassium (NaOH and KOH respectively) produce strong alkalis, as does ammonia in solution (as ammonium hydroxide, NH_4OH).

alloy a mixture or compound containing two (or more) metals, or a metal with a non-metal, e.g. iron-carbon where the metal is the larger component. Alloys tend to have properties that are described as metallic, but alloying is a means of increasing a particularly useful property, such as strength or resistance to corrosion or high temperatures. *Bronze* was probably the first man-made alloy, made of copper and tin, and it was used for weapons, pans and ornaments. Other common alloys are *brass*, which is copper and zinc and *steel*, which is iron and carbon. There are hundreds of alloys, each created for a particular use, from coins to aircraft parts. This is shown by the different types of brass and bronze now available. Brass may also contain aluminium, iron, nickel, tin, lead, or manganese while the term bronze is now applied to alloys of copper not containing tin, e.g. aluminium bronze (corrosion-resistant), beryllium bronze (high hardness) and manganese bronze (high strength).

A special type of alloy is an *amalgam*—an alloy of a metal with mercury. Mercury is an unusual metal because it is a heavy, silver liquid at room temperature and most metals will mix with it to form an amalgam. For many years dentists used such an amalgam, with silver, for fillings in teeth, but modern materials are now being used more often.

aluminium a silvery-white metallic element that in air forms a protective coating of aluminium oxide which prevents further corrosion. It is ductile and malleable (*see* DUCTILITY), and a good conductor of electricity and is used for the manufacture of a large number of things, from drinks cans and foil to pans, cars and aircraft. Aluminium is the commonest metallic element in the Earth's crust and the third most common overall (at about 8 per cent). It is extracted from the mineral *bauxite* (aluminium hydroxides formed by weathering of aluminium-bearing rocks in tropical conditions) by ELECTROLYSIS. Salts of aluminium are important in the purification of water and as catalysts (*see* CATALYSIS). The oxide is important in the production of cement, abrasives (*corundum*), refractories and ceramics.

Aluminium occurs in a number of drugs and medications but there is a body of opinion that feels that an excess of aluminium in some form may damage the brains of old people or the very young.

amalgam *see* ALLOY.

ammonia a colourless gas made up of nitrogen and hydrogen (NH_3), a very useful chemical compound. It has a

sharp, pungent smell, is lighter than air and is very soluble in water. It is used in the manufacture of nitric acid, nylon, plastics, explosives and fertilisers. It is also used in refrigeration equipment as a coolant. Ammonia gas can be turned into a liquid by cooling to $-33.5°C$ ($-28.3°F$), and when it becomes gas again, it takes a lot of heat from the surroundings, thus producing the cooling effect.

Ammonia occurs naturally in some gases given off at hot springs, and it results from the breakdown of proteins and urea by bacterial action. It is manufactured industrially by the *Haber process*, which involves the reaction of nitrogen with hydrogen under very high temperature ($500°C/932°F$) and pressure (300 atmospheres) and in the presence of a catalyst (*see* CATALYSIS).

amoeba *see* NH protozoan.

ampere the SI UNIT used for measuring electric current, usually abbreviated to *amps*, which was named after the French physicist André Ampère who did much important work in the early 19th century. Machines and appliances use differing currents and, with a mains supply of 240 volts, an electric fire will use between 4 and 8 amps. The ampere has a very specific definition, created in 1948, relating to the force produced between two wires in a vacuum when current is passed. Prior to that the unit related to the amount of silver deposited per second from a silver nitrate solution when one ampere was passed.

amphibian *see* NH Amphibia.

analogue *see* DIGITAL AND ANALOGUE.

analysis in chemistry, the use of one, or a combination of several, analytical techniques and pieces of equipment to identify a substance or a mixture of substances. *Qualitative analysis* is when the components are identified, and *quantitative analysis* involves the determination of the relative amount of constituents, usually elements, making up a sample. Qualitative analysis of inorganic substances (*see* CHEMISTRY) can be done using a variety of *reagents* (a known substance or solution that produces a characteristic reaction) and/or one of several physical methods of analysis, such as X-RAY analysis or SPECTROSCOPY. Spectroscopy (infrared, ultraviolet and also nuclear magnetic resonance) and mass spectrometry are used in organic qualitative analysis, and in addition the compound type can be identified by specific reactions that produce known products. Further methods are adopted for quantitative analysis, including the use of certain reactions to precipitate a compound that is then weighed accurately: physical techniques, such as spectroscopy, and others that relate to a particular property, e.g. electrical and optical; and *volumetric analysis*, which involves *titrations*. Titration is when measured amounts of a solution are added progressively to a known volume of a second solution until the chemical reaction between them is complete (shown by an indicator), thus enabling the unknown strength of one solution to be calculated. CHROMATOGRAPHY is very useful in separating the components of a mixture prior to analysis.

Chemical analysis is used widely in areas such as chemistry itself, medicine, food technology, geology, environmental control, drug testing in sport, forensic science and many more.

anatomy the scientific study of the structure of living things, which enables an understanding to be built up of how different parts of a plant or animal work. Anatomical study often involves dissection of dead specimens.

angiosperm *see* PLANTS *and* NH Angiospermae.

animal kingdom modern biologists usually group animals together in the biological kingdom called *Animalia*, which contains many different *phyla* (*see* CLASSIFICATION). The simplest animals are the sponges (phylum *Porifera*) and the most complicated, including human beings and other mammals, belong to the phylum *Chordata*. These animals are constructed of many cells (multicellular), which perform a variety of functions and which, unlike those of plants, do not have outer cell walls. Animals cannot manufacture their own food but must take it in from the outside in some way. Also, animals possess nerves and muscles that vary greatly in complexity among the different groups. Most animals reproduce by means of sexual reproduc-

tion and store CARBOHYDRATES as an energy reserve in the form of glycogen (a compound made up of glucose units). In plants, carbohydrate is stored as starch.

annelid *see* NH Annelida.

annual *see* PLANTS.

anodising a process for depositing a hard, very thin layer of oxide on a metal. The metal is usually ALUMINUM or an ALLOY and the oxide layer provides a non-corrosive coating of aluminium oxide (Al_2O_3), which is resistant to scratches and which protects the underlying metal. Anodising is achieved by ELECTROLYSIS, and the metal made is the *anode*, often in a bath of sulphuric, chromic, or oxalic acid. Such metals are used in many ways, e.g. for window frames and in trains and aircraft. The oxide coating may be rendered decorative by the use of a dye during electrolysis. Anodised items can be made to retain their natural brightness by the use of very high purity aluminium or an aluminium-magnesium alloy, because in these cases the oxide layer formed is transparent.

anthozoan *see* NH Actinozoa.

anther *see* POLLEN.

Anthophyta *see* PLANTS.

antibody, antigen *see* IMMUNE SYSTEM.

aqueous humour *see* SIGHT.

aquifer *see* G&G aquifer.

arachnid *see* NH Arachnida.

Archimedes' principle a law of physics, named after the 3rd-century BC Greek mathematician, Archimedes. It states that when a body is partly or totally immersed in a liquid, the apparent loss in weight equals the weight of the displaced liquid. Archimedes was a prolific inventor and investigator. He did much scientific work with LEVER and PULLEY and invented the *Archimedean screw,* which is essentially a hollow screw that, with its base in water, when turned, lifts water to a higher level. The device is still used for irrigation if pumps are not available.

argon *see* INERT GAS.

arithmetic the science of numbers, which includes addition, subtraction, division, multiplication, fractions, decimals, roots, etc. Arithmetic was first used by the Babylonians about 4,000 years ago but the system currently used is that of Arabic numerals. The Romans used a different system in which letters represent quantities:

Roman	Arabic	Roman	Arabic
I	1	VIII	8
II	2	IX	9
III	3	X	10
IV	4	L	50
V	5	C	100
VI	6	D	500
VII	7	M	1,000

artery *see* CIRCULATION; LUNGS AND GILLS.

arthropod *see* NH Arthropoda.

artiodactyl *see* NH Artiodactyla.

asbestos *see* SYNTHETIC FIBRES.

asexual reproduction any form of reproduction in which a new individual is produced from a single parent without the production or fusion of sex cells (gametes). It occurs in plants, microorganisms and some of the simpler animals, often alternating with a sexual phase. Different types of asexual reproduction occur, one of which is by division of a single cell into two, known as *fission,* as seen in *Amoeba,* a member of the kingdom *Protista*. Another method is *fragmentation*, in which parts of the plant or animal separate off or the whole breaks up, with new individuals being formed from the portions. This is seen in some invertebrate animals, particularly earthworms. *Budding* is another form of asexual reproduction that occurs in such animals as hydras, sea anemones, and corals. A small bud is produced from the parent, which may break off and form a new animal or remain attached. Asexual reproduction is also seen in plants, e.g. in the production of bulbs, corms and tubers, known as *vegetative propagation*. Such plants as ferns and mosses may have an asexual stage, producing spores, and this is known as the *sporophyte generation*.

astatine *see* HALOGENS.

asteroid *see* S&A asteroid.

astronaut *see* S&A astronaut.

astronomy *see* S&A astronomy.

atmosphere *see* G&G atmosphere.

atom the smallest particle that makes up all matter and yet is still chemically representative of the ELEMENT. Atoms are less than microscopic in size and yet they are made up of even smaller particles. At the centre of an atom is a relatively heavy *nucleus* containing *protons* and *neutrons*. The protons are positively charged and they are offset by an equal number of electrons with negative charge that occupy *orbitals* around the nucleus. The atom is overall electrically neutral, and the various elements in the PERIODIC TABLE each have a unique number of protons in their nucleus. The electron weighs a little more than one two thousandth part of a proton. Orbitals provide a means of simplifying and expressing *atomic structure* and related processes such as bonding (*see* BONDS). The theory put forward by Niels Bohr, the Danish physicist, proposed that electrons circled the nucleus in definite orbits. This was discovered to be too simple and the new theory visualised a charge cloud, or orbital, that represents the likely distribution of the electron. There are various types of orbital, each with a different cloud shape around the nucleus (dependent on atomic structure), and these orbitals interact, merge and change when chemical bonds are formed. The precursor to this picture of atomic structure began several hundred years BC. In the 19th century John Dalton put forward theories to explain the structure of matter and was the first to calculate the weights of some atoms.

Elements that have more than 83 protons are unstable and decay radioactively, while those with over 92 protons occur only in the laboratory, as a result of high-energy experiments. Atoms of an element that have differing numbers of neutrons are called ISOTOPES.

atom bomb *see* NUCLEAR FISSION.

atomic number (*symbol* Z) the number of protons in the nucleus of an ATOM. All atoms of the same ELEMENT have the same number of protons but may have differing numbers of neutrons (producing ISOTOPES). *Atomic weight* or *relative atomic mass* is the ratio of the average mass of an element (i.e. the average for the mixture of isotopes in a natural element) to one twelfth of the mass of carbon-12 atom. Chemical notation places the atomic number as a subscript before the symbol for the element, e.g. chlorine has 17 protons - $_{17}$Cl.

ATP *see* MITOCHONDRION.

atrium *see* CIRCULATION.

audiotape *see* RECORDING MEDIA.

aurora *see* S&A aurora.

autotrophism *or* **self-feeding** the situation in which an organism manufactures the materials it requires for life from inorganic substances (*see* CHEMISTRY). Plants are *photoautotrophs*, using light as an energy source and carbon dioxide, minerals and water from the air and soil. Some bacteria are *chemoautotrophs*, obtaining energy from chemical reactions using such substances as ammonia and sulphur.

average in statistics, a general term for *mean*, *median* and *mode*. The arithmetic mean is the value obtained from a set of figures by adding all the values in the *data set* (collection of numbers) and dividing by the number of readings. The median is the middle reading, so if there are nine readings for temperature, height, weight, or a similar quantity, arranged in order, the median is the middle, i.e. the fifth, value. The mode is the value that occurs most frequently in a set of readings, so in a range of temperatures such as 17, 18, 12, 17, 21, 16, 19, 17, the mode is 17.

axle *see* MACHINE.

axon *see* NERVOUS SYSTEM.

bacteria (*singular* **bacterium**) single-celled organisms belonging to the kingdom Monera. They have a unique type of cell, called *procaryotic* (*procaryote*) and were the first organisms to exist on Earth. Their activities have always been extremely significant as they are important in all life processes. Bacteria may have a protective, slimy outer layer, called a capsule and in some 'hairs', known as filaments, are present, which cause movement. Two types of bacteria, each having a different cell wall structure (*Gram-positive* or *Gram-negative*), are recognised by a test known as *Gram's stain*. Bacteria show a number of different shapes and forms that help to distinguish between the various types. These are *spiral* (spirilli, spirillus), *spherical* (cocci, coccus), *rod-like* (bacilli, bacillus), *comma-shaped* (vibrio) and *corkscrew-shaped* (spirochete). They may require an environment containing oxygen, in which case they are described as *aerobic*, or exist in conditions without oxygen, when they are known as

anaerobic. Bacteria are vitally important in the decomposition of all organic material (*see* CHEMISTRY) and are the main agents in the chemical cycles of carbon, oxygen, nitrogen and sulphur. Most bacteria obtain their food from decaying or dead organic material (*saprotrophs*). Others are parasites and some are *autotrophs* (*see* AUTOTROPHISM), obtaining energy from chemical reactions using inorganic materials such as sulphur and ammonia. Bacteria usually reproduce asexually (*see* ASEXUAL REPRODUCTION) by simple fission but some have a form of sexual reproduction. Some are responsible for serious diseases in animals, plants and people, e.g. typhoid, syphilis, diphtheria and cholera.

Bakelite *see* PLASTICS.

ballistics the study of the flight path of projectiles (i.e. an object that has been projected into the air) under the influence of gravity. The trajectory is the path taken by an object and is usually a particular length, distinguishing it from an orbit. A *ballistic missile* is a missile fired from the ground that follows a flight path shaped like a parabola and that is powered and guided only during the first phase of flight. Ballistics is a term applied to bullets, rockets, missiles and similar objects.

bar code a series of black bars printed on a white background that represent codes that can be scanned and interpreted by a reader and computer. Bar codes are found on most products in supermarkets, on books and other items, and they contain a product number and maker's identification number. As the product is dragged past an optical scanner at the checkout, or a light pen is moved over the bar code, the computer matches the product with the price list in its memory. In addition to speeding up the process of adding up items, the use of bar codes helps an accurate analysis of stock to be made, allowing restocking to be undertaken before a product line is exhausted. It also facilitates the output of a detailed, itemised receipt.

barometer an instrument used to measure atmospheric pressure, i.e. the pressure that the atmosphere exerts on the Earth. The principle of the barometer was discovered by Torricelli, a 17th-century

Italian physicist. It is used to help predict forthcoming weather changes that result from changes in atmospheric pressure. A *mercury barometer* is a thin tube, closed at one end, which is almost filled with mercury and the open end is stood in a mercury-filled container or reservoir. The vertical height of the mercury column that can be maintained by the atmospheric pressure pushing down on the reservoir is taken as the value of atmospheric pressure at the time of reading. The column is usually about 760 millimetres high. The mercury barometer is the most accurate but a more compact device is the *aneroid barometer* (meaning 'without liquid'). This consists of a small metal box-like chamber (with a thin corrugated lid) that is evacuated (to create a vacuum). Subsequent changes of pressure move the lid and this movement is magnified and translated on to a dial.

barrier reef *see* NH barrier reef.

baryon *see* ELEMENTARY PARTICLES.

bases *see* ACIDS

bat *see* NH Chiroptera.

battery a device, usually portable, in which a chemical change is harnessed to produce electricity. Many batteries are to all intents and purposes non-rechargeable and are called primary cells, the most important being the *Leclanch type*. One of the commonest arrangements is a positive electrode made up of a rod of carbon surrounded by a mixture of manganese dioxide and powdered carbon in a case and the whole thing stands in an *electrolyte* (*see* ELECTROLYSIS) of ammonium chloride in the form of a paste. The outer case of zinc acts as the negative electrode. When the battery is connected, a current flows as the result of reactions and the movement of ions between the various components, thus creating a voltage.

The other important type of battery is the *secondary cell*, which can be recharged, e.g. the lead *accumulator*, or car battery. In this cell, plates of lead and lead oxide are suspended in sulphuric acid and on charging there are chemical changes (because of *electrolysis*), which are complete when it is charged. When the terminals are wired up, the chemical changes are reversed

and current flows until the battery is discharged. The sulphuric acid used has to be of a certain relative density and discharge should not be continued beyond a certain point because insoluble salts build up on the plates. Other types of accumulator include nickel-iron, in which the nickel oxide plate is positive and the iron is negative, in a solution of potassium hydroxide; zinc-air, sodium/sulphur and lithium/chlorine. Although the last two are higher energy cells than most accumulators, they require high operating temperatures.

bauxite *see* ALUMINUM.

Beaufort scale *see* G&G Beaufort scale.

beaver *see* NH Rodentia.

behaviour all the activities that an animal (or person) carries out during its life and a major area of scientific study. Those who study behaviour wish to find out why an animal acts in a particular way and what factors might affect this. Behaviour can be divided into three categories. These are known as *reflex*, *instinctive* and *learned*. Reflex behaviour is totally spontaneous and does not involve any conscious act of the will. For example, if you accidentally touch something hot, your hand is immediately and rapidly withdrawn from the source of heat. Instinctive behaviour is inborn and does not need to be learned, being present in all members of a species. The classic example is the male three-spined stickleback fish protecting his territory. Male sticklebacks have a red belly, and this acts as a trigger for the defensive behaviour. A male stickleback will attack models that only vaguely resemble a rival fish provided that the red coloration is present. More realistic stickleback models without a red underside are ignored. Much animal behaviour is learned, i.e. it is changed by experience, and this can be seen especially in the young of a species as they play and experiment in the environment that surrounds them. Various types of learned behaviour are recognised. It is generally agreed that all behaviour is a mix of instinct combined with learning and modified by environmental conditions.

benthos *see* NH benthos.

benzene a hydrocarbon that is toxic and carcinogenic (may cause cancer). At room temperature it is a colourless liquid with a characteristic smell and it has the formula C_6H_6. The six atoms of carbon form a ring with bond angles of 120°. The ring structure is very stable because although the convention is to show benzene with three double bonds, the bonding electrons are not localised and are spread around the ring.

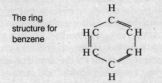

The ring structure for benzene

Benzene was isolated by Michael Faraday, the British physicist, in 1825. He distilled coal tar, and the lightest fraction obtained was condensed to form benzene liquid. Benzene is currently manufactured from petroleum. The benzene ring forms the basis for a large branch of chemistry that deals with *aromatic* hydrocarbons, and benzene is used principally as the starting point for production of other chemicals, e.g. phenol, styrene and nylon.

becquerel *see* SI UNITS.

beta rays *see* RADIOACTIVITY.

big-bang theory *see* S&A big-bang theory.

bimetallic strip a bar with strips of two different metals welded together. Because of the different rates of expansion, each expands (or contracts) by a different amount when subjected to heat (or cold), and the bar bends (the metal on the outside being the one that expands more). The two metals used are often brass and invar (an iron-nickel alloy), the brass expanding about twenty times more than invar. This property enables bimetallic strips to be used in thermostats, thermometers and thermal switches. The indicator bulbs in a car flash because of a small bimetallic strip.

binary numbers a system of numbers that uses a combination of two digits, 0 and 1, expressed to the base 2, thus beginning with the value 1 in the right-hand column, each move to the left seeing an increase to the power of 2:

1×2^5	1×2^4	1×2^3	1×2^2	1×2^1	1×2^0	origin of binary numbers
32	16	8	4	2	1	binary numbers
1	0	1	1	1	0	example

In the example, the figure is $32 + 8 + 4 + 2 = 46$.

The binary number system is the basis of code information in computers, as the digits 0 and 1 are used to represent the two states of on or off in an electronic switch in a circuit.

binary star *see* S&A binary star.

biochemistry the scientific study of the chemistry of biological processes occurring in the cells and tissues of living organisms. Chemical compounds are the building blocks of all plants and animals, and studying the ways in which these react with one another and how they contribute to life processes is the realm of biochemistry. Biochemists are involved in a wide variety of scientific studies including the search for cures of serious diseases such as cancer and AIDS.

biological control a means of controlling pests by using their natural enemies rather than chemicals that might prove harmful to the environment. The control is artificially brought about, in that large numbers of the 'predators' are introduced in order to control the pests. The method can be effective, e.g. the successful control of the spread of the prickly pear cactus in Australia by the introduction of the cactus moth, whose caterpillars fed on and destroyed the young plant shoots. All the biological implications have to be thoroughly researched in advance as sometimes the attempted control has gone wrong. An example of this was the introduction of large Hawaiian toads into Australian sugar cane plantations in the belief that these would eat the beetles that damaged the crop. In fact, the toads did not eat the cane beetles but proved seriously damaging to other animals and are now a great problem in themselves. Another method of biological control used with insect pests (especially some that carry disease, such as the tsetse fly) is to use natural chemicals, called *pheromones*, which attract them so that they can be caught. Sometimes the males are caught and radiation is used to make them sterile and then they are released to mate with females. No offspring are produced from these matings and so the number of insects decreases.

biology the scientific examination of all living things, including plants, animals and microorganisms, which is further subdivided into specialised areas of study.

bioluminescence the production of light by living organisms, which is seen in many sea-dwelling animals, e.g. deep-sea fish (angler fish), hydrozoans such as *Obelia*, molluscs, e.g. squids and some crustaceans. It is also seen in some land-dwelling insects, e.g. fireflies and glow-worms, and in some bacteria and fungi. Some animals have bacteria living with them (SYMBIOSIS) and it is these that actually produce the light. The light may be given out continuously, as in bacteria, or 'switched' on and off, as in fireflies. The light may be used to attract prey or a mate, or as a warning. A special protein (called a *photoprotein*) known as luciferin combines with oxygen and during this chemical reaction light is produced.

biomass a collective name for all organic material (that which is derived from plants or animals). In recent years, several new methods have been developed to utilise biomass as a source of fuel and energy, although many of these are based on old technologies that have been in use throughout the course of human history.

Wood can be burnt in stoves to produce direct heat or to heat water and this can be used either in the home or on a larger scale. Wood can also be burnt in a combustion plant to provide electricity, generally by using it to heat water and produce steam that is then harnessed to produce power. In order for wood to be neutral in terms of CO_2 emissions, it has to come from a renewable source hence trees must be continually planted to replace those that are cut down for fuel.

Energy crops are those that are grown specifically for the purpose of providing a source of fuel. They include poplar and willow trees that are quick to mature and these are grown on a short-rotation, coppice system. Material from the trees is harvested every 3 or 4 years. *Switch grass* and *Micanthus* are examples of grass

crops that are grown to provide biomass for fuel. Oil seed rape is a slightly different example in that the crop is grown to provide a liquid fuel, *biodiesel*, that can be used in vehicles. Other vegetable oils can be utilised in a similar way, as a direct substitute for fossil fuel diesel, but the engines of conventionally powered cars may require initial modification. Vehicles running on biodiesel or vegetable oils still produce some emissions but this is counterbalanced to a certain extent by the fact that the crop absorbs CO_2 during its growth period. However, critics of crop-based fuels point to the fact that large areas of valuable agricultural land need to be sacrificed for this purpose when it is needed to grow food for an expanding world population.

Agricultural waste may be either 'wet' or 'dry'. Dry waste such as straw can be combusted in a similar manner to wood to produce energy. Wet waste such as chicken manure and animal slurry can also be utilised, either by 'digestion', utilising anaerobic BACTERIA to produce METHANE, or by combustion. In many countries, dried animal dung is combusted as a source of domestic fuel.

biome *see* NH biome.

bionomics *see* NH ecology.

biophysics a combination of biology and physics in which the physical properties of biological mechanisms are the subject of study. The laws and techniques of physics can be used, for example, in the study of how the heart and muscles work, or in the mechanisms of respiration and blood circulation.

biosphere *see* NH biosphere.

biota *see* ORGANISM.

biotechnology the use of living organisms to manufacture useful products or to change materials. Examples include the fermentation of yeast to produce alcohol and for use in bread making and the growth of special fungi to make antibiotics. Biotechnology mainly uses microorganisms, especially bacteria and fungi. In recent times, genetic engineering, which alters the genes (*see* CHROMOSOMES AND GENES), or 'building blocks', that determine the nature of an organism, is increasingly being used in the field of biotechnology.

biotic *see* ORGANISM.

bird *see* NH Aves.

birth *see* GESTATION AND BIRTH.

bivalve *see* NH Bivalvia.

black hole *see* S&A black hole.

bladder *see* OSMOREGULATION.

blast furnace a furnace comprising a large vertical tower used mainly for the smelting of iron from iron oxide ores. The tower is made of steel plates lined with refractory bricks (firebricks) to withstand the very high operating temperatures (in excess of 1600°C/2912°F). After some time, about three years, the lining wears out and the furnace is then shut down to allow the bricks to be replaced.

The furnace is fed from the top with ore, coke and limestone ($CaCO_3$). From near the base of the tower is introduced a high pressure blast of very hot air that ignites the coke, producing carbon monoxide (CO), that then reacts with the iron oxide to produce iron (molten) and at the same time the limestone breaks down to form lime (CaO) and carbon dioxide (CO_2). The lime subsequently combines with impurities from the ore to form a molten slag. As the iron is formed it collects at the base of the furnace and the slag floats on top. Each is run off periodically, the iron to form bars of 'pig iron' (CAST IRON) containing about 4.5 per cent carbon. Blast furnaces can also be used for smelting copper.

The slag also finds a use as *ground granulated blast-furnace slag* (ggbfs) in which it is granulated, ground and then mixed with Portland cement for use in construction. Cements made with ggbfs improve workability and resistance to deleterious reactions and although it is slower to harden, it heats up less than most cements.

block and tackle *see* PULLEY.

blood *see* CIRCULATION.

boiling point the temperature at which a substance changes from the liquid to the gaseous state. This occurs when the vapour pressure of a liquid is equal to atmospheric pressure. This explains why at high altitudes, water boils at a lower temperature because air pressure decreases. Boiling points of liquids are therefore quoted as the value at standard atmospheric pressure (one atmosphere). When a substance is dissolved in a solvent such as water, the boiling point of the solvent is raised. Called the *molecular elevation of boiling point*, this is caused by a lowering of vapour pressure (because fewer solvent molecules escape from the liquid), hence the temperature has to be higher.

bonds forces that hold atoms together to form a molecule, or molecules and ions to form crystals or lattices. Bonds are created by the movement of electrons and the type of bond depends on the atoms involved and their *electronegativity* (a measure of an atom's attraction for electrons within a molecule). Three basic bond types are recognised:

1 *ionic* or *electrovalent*, where one atom loses an electron to another atom, as in NaCl, which becomes Na^+ (positive ion or *cation*) and Cl^- (negative ion or *anion*). Such compounds dissociate (split) into ions in solution and therefore are able to conduct electricity.

2 *covalent* bonds, where electrons are shared, often one from each participating atom, although the sharing is equal only when the atoms are identical. Covalent bonding is common in organic compounds.

3 *metallic bonding*, where electrons are shared among many nuclei, thus facilitating conduction of electricity.

bone the hard material that forms the skeleton of most vertebrate animals and contains living cells, called *oestoblasts* and *oestocysts*, which are responsible for the formation and repair of bones. Bone is made up of hard connective tissue, itself consisting of a tough protein called collagen and bone salts (crystals of calcium phosphate hydroxyapatite) which both make it strong. The skeleton of an adult human being has 206 bones, some of which are fused together while others are very small.

bone marrow a soft and spongy tissue that is found in the centre of the long bones (e.g. those of the leg and arm) and also within the spaces of other bones. The bone marrow produces blood cells, especially in young animals. In older animals only some bone marrow, known as red marrow and mainly found in the vertebrae, pelvis, ribs and breastbone, produces blood cells. It contains special (*myeloid*) tissue in which are found cells, known as *erythroblasts*, that develop into red blood cells or *erythrocytes*. The cells of the myeloid tissue also develop into *leucocytes*, or white blood cells, an essential part of the body's immune system.

bony fishes *see* NH bony fishes.

botany the scientific study of all aspects of the life of plants, *compare* ZOOLOGY.

boulder clay *see* G&G boulder clay.

Bowman's capsule *see* OSMOREGULATION.

brachiopods *see* NH Brachiopoda.

brackish water *see* NH brackish water.

brain *see* NERVOUS SYSTEM.

brass *see* ALLOY.

breathing *see* RESPIRATION.

breeding and hybrid breeding is the production of offspring and usually refers to the interference by people to produce animals or plants with particular desirable characteristics. The results of breeding are particularly noticeable in farm animals, such as cattle or dogs, which look very different from their wild ancestors. Selective breeding has given us animals that provide more milk, wool, or meat and crops that produce more grain or larger, juicier fruits and succulent leaves. A *hybrid* animal is the offspring of parents that are of two different species (*see* CLASSIFICATION). A familiar example of this is the mule—the offspring of a female horse and a male donkey. Hybrid animals are usually sterile. **N.B.** hybrid has a different meaning in genetics where the differences in the parents are at the gene (*see* CHROMOSOMES AND GENES) rather than the species level.

bridge a structure used in civil engineering to cover a gap, whether over a road, water, or railway. For short *spans* (i.e. the distance between supports) of 300 to 600 metres, steel arches, suspension or cantilever bridges are suitable. Above 600 metres, a steel *suspension bridge* is often used. In such bridges, the bridge deck (i.e. the floor that carries the load to the beams and supports) is hung from vertical rods or wire ropes connected to cables that go over the towers and are anchored in the ground.

A *cantilever bridge* is usually symmetrical,

comprising three spans. The two outer spans are anchored at each shore and then extend beyond the supporting pier to cover one third of the remaining span. This gap is then bridged by another element that rests on the arms of the two cantilevers.

Other types of bridge have particular functions, e.g. swing bridges that rotate on a pivot to allow vessels to pass (often used over canals).

bromine a typical member of the HALOGEN group (*see also* PERIODIC TABLE). It is a dark red liquid with noxious vapours. It occurs naturally as bromide compounds in sea water and salt deposits, and also in marine plants. When sea water is evaporated, and after sodium chloride ('salt') crystals have precipitated out, the remaining fluid (or *bittern*) contains magnesium bromide.

Bromine is very reactive and has numerous industrial uses, including in the manufacture of disinfectants, fumigants, anti-knock agents for petrol and in photography.

bronchus *see* LUNGS AND GILLS.

bronze *see* ALLOY.

Brownian movement the erratic and random movement of microscopic particles when suspended in a liquid or gas. The movement is caused by the continuous movement of molecules in the surrounding gas or liquid which then impact with the particles. This phenomenon accounts for the gradual dispersal of smells and the mixing of fluids that happen with time and that are accelerated if the gas or fluid is hot. As the particles become larger, there is a greater chance of impacts from all sides cancelling each other out and so the movement can no longer be observed. This occurs when the particles are 3–4 microns or micrometers (μm), equal to 3–4 millionths of a metre. Brownian movement is named after its discoverer, Robert Brown, a Scot. He was a botanist and first observed this movement when studying pollen. It is taken as evidence that kinetic energy applies to all matter and exists even when it cannot be seen.

bryophyte *see* NH Bryophyta.

bubbles a small amount of a gas within a liquid, e.g. air in water, or air surrounded by a thin soap film, as with soap bubbles.

Detergent or soap in water creates good bubbles because the detergent molecules form a stable alignment. The shape of a soap bubble results from a balance between the pressure inside trying to blow it apart and the surface tension of the liquid trying to contract the bubble. The pressure inside a bubble decreases as the size of the bubble increases, so smaller bubbles have greater pressure inside than larger ones.

bud a compact and immature plant shoot made up of many folded and unexpanded leaves or flower petals. These are tightly folded or wrapped around one another and may be enclosed in a protective, sometimes sticky sheath. When the bud opens, the petals or leaves grow and expand, a process that marks the onset of spring moving into summer.

budding *see* ASEXUAL REPRODUCTION.

building and construction the activities that are central to the development of countries and their economies and to the operation of almost all aspects of everyone's daily life. There are many professional people—planners, surveyors, civil and structural engineers, architects, builders and more—involved, and the major parts of the construction process are planning, design, construction, for new projects, maintenance and refurbishment, and restoration of existing buildings.

There are a great variety of projects, from railways, houses, hospitals, offices, schools, roads, harbours to dams, airports, bridges and tunnels. Each requires numerous specialists to take a project from the drawing board in a design office to completion. Large projects in particular, which may cost many millions of dollars, have to be planned and organised as near to perfection as possible to ensure smooth progress and to make best use of time, people and resources. The basic constructional materials used most often are concrete and steel, but, of course, brick, timber, stone, etc, are also important.

Bunsen burner *see* LABORATORY.

buoyancy *see* FLOTATION AND BUOYANCY.

burning *see* COMBUSTION.

butterfly *see* NH Lepidoptera.

caffeine and tannin *caffeine* is an *alkaloid*

(basic organic substance found in plants) and *purine* that occurs in tea leaves, coffee beans and other plants. It acts as a *diuretic* (a substance that increases urine formation) and as a weak stimulant to the central nervous system. It is also found in cola drinks, up to 10 per cent in some cases.

Tannins are a large group of plant substances of use in the treatment of hides. The term is misused in connection with tea, however, because tannic acid is not present and tannin is simply a general collective term. Tea does contain *polyphenols*, which in some mixtures may resemble tannin in their chemical structure.

calculator a device that performs mathematical calculations. They are not a recent invention only the inclusion of integrated circuits on silicon chips has been a recent and revolutionary step. They began as mechanical devices in the 17th century and were, inevitably, laboriously slow. The first electronic calculator was produced in 1963 but its scope was limited, and calculators became generally available in the early 1970s. The first calculator that could be programmed to solve mathematical problems was made by Hewlett-Packard in 1974. Now there is an enormous variety of calculators available, some as small as credit cards.

calculus a large branch of mathematics that enables the manipulation of quantities that vary continuously. The techniques of calculus were developed by two scientists at the same time, the German Gottfried Leibniz and Isaac Newton in Britain. It had its origin in the study of falling objects. *Differential calculus* concerns the rate of change of a dependent variable and involves the gradient, maxima and minima of the curve of a given function. *Integral calculus* deals with areas and volumes and methods of summation, and many of its applications developed from the study of the gradients of tangents to curves.

calcium a soft silver-white metal at room temperature that tarnishes very quickly in air and reacts violently with water. Calcium compounds are very widely distributed: as calcium carbonate ($CaCO_3$) in limestone and chalk; as calcium sulphate ($CaSO_4$) in gypsum; within silicates occurring in minerals, and there are many other occurrences. In biological systems, calcium ions (Ca^{2+}) are vital to life as constituents of bone and teeth. Calcium is also important industrially as lime (CaO), as $CaCO_3$ in the production of iron from its ores, and in the preparation of certain transition element metals, (*see* PERIODIC TABLE).

calendar *see* S&A calendar.

calendering *see* PAPER.

calyx *see* FLOWERS.

camels *see* NH Artiodactyla.

camera *see* PHOTOGRAPHY.

camouflage *see* NH camouflage.

cancer a DISEASE of animal cells in which there is a rapid and uncontrolled rate of growth and reproduction. A collection of cancer cells is known as a *tumour*, which is termed *benign* if it remains localised in one place. A *malignant* tumour spreads, invades and destroys surrounding healthy tissue. It spreads via the bloodstream and produces secondary cancers in other parts of the body by a process known as *metastasis*. These malignant cancers can often prove fatal as they disrupt the normal functioning of cells in the affected tissues. The search for the cure and causes of various kinds of cancer is a vast area of scientific and medical research. The treatment and life expectancy of people affected by most kinds of cancer have greatly improved in recent years. Some substances and environmental factors (*carcinogens*) are known to increase the risk of cancer developing, the best known being cigarette smoke. Cancer treatment involves surgery, radiotherapy (the use of radiation to destroy tumours), chemotherapy (the administration of drugs to destroy tumours), and the giving of more specialised drugs (cytotoxic) that attack the malignant cells in a special way.

candela *see* SI UNITS.

capacitor a device for storing electric charge, in its simplest form comprising two plates separated by air but usually by an insulating material called a *dielectric*. Commercial capacitors have foil plates separated by a dielectric, such as Mylar, forming a sandwich that is rolled up into a cylindrical shape. This gives a large area of plate in a small device. Other dielectrics include mica, certain plastics and aluminium oxide. Capacitors are used a great deal in electrical circuits in televisions, radios and other electronic equipment. The capacitor works by a charge on one plate inducing an equal charge on the opposite plate, and a change in the charge is mirrored between plates.

capillary *see* CIRCULATION; LUNGS AND GILLS.

capillary action a phenomenon related to surface tension in liquids in which there is an attraction between the sides of a glass tube and water molecules. The result is that water is pulled up a very thin glass tube (a *capillary tube*), and it will move farther the thinner the tube. This action happens with other liquids including alcohol, but mercury moves in the opposite way. Many occurrences involving the movement of water involve capillary action, e.g. tissues soaking up water, walls taking in water, producing damp.

capsule a widely used term in biology that describes a structure found in flowering plants, mosses and liverworts, bacteria and animals.

1 in flowering plants, a capsule is a dry fruit containing seeds, which splits when ripe. The splitting and releasing of the seeds occurs in different ways, e.g. splitting into different parts, known as valves, in the iris, through holes or pores as in the snapdragon, or through a lid as in the scarlet pimpernel.

2 in plants called bryophytes (*see* NH Bryophyta), which includes liverworts and mosses, a capsule contains spores and is produced on the end of a thick stalk (seta). It is known as a sporophyte.

3 some bacteria produce an outer sheath of gelatinous material surrounding the cell wall, which is protective and is called a capsule.

4 in vertebrate animals a connective tissue sheath known as a capsule surrounds some of the joints in the skeleton. Also, a membrane or fibrous connective tissue sheath called a capsule encloses and protects some vertebrate organs, e.g. the kidney.

carat *see* GOLD.

carbide a compound of metal with carbon that in many instances results in hard, refractory materials with very high melting points. *Tungsten* or *tantalum carbide* is used for tools, as are mixtures with cobalt and nickel. *Titanium carbide* resists molten metals, has a high melting point and is used for parts in reactors, in gas turbine blades and in coatings on rocket components. *Chromium carbide* is chemically inert and is used for electrodes and for parts for use with corrosive chemicals.

carbohydrate a chemical compound made up of carbon, hydrogen and oxygen, forming a large and important group of substances. The most familiar ones are sugars, STARCH AND CELLULOSE and carbohydrates are manufactured by green plants during the process of PHOTOSYNTHESIS. Carbohydrates are a vital food source for animals as they are broken down within the body to provide the energy required for all the various life processes.

carbon a non-metallic ELEMENT that occurs as the element in two forms, graphite and diamond, and in numerous compounds. Carbon is unique in the enormous number of compounds it can form both in inorganic form, e.g. carbon dioxide, and in being the basis of organic CHEMISTRY. Carbon is *allotropic*, i.e. it exists in several elemental forms in addition to graphite and diamonds, each differing in its crystalline structure and thus its properties. Carbon is used extensively, e.g. in steel making, for motor brushes and cathode-ray tubes, and *active carbon* is used as a purifying agent in the removal of air pollutants, in water treatment and the purification of chemicals, and as CARBON FIBRES. Carbon is the standard for measuring atomic masses (*see* ATOMIC NUMBER) and the radioactive carbon-14 is used in radiocarbon dating (*see* G&G dating method).

carbonate a compound containing carbon and oxygen as CO_3, e.g. calcium carbonate.

carbon capture or sequestration any of several technologies whereby the carbon dioxide that is emitted from power stations that burn fossil fuel is isolated and trapped before it can escape into the atmosphere. One such technology employs amine scrubbers that are fitted to coal-fired power stations, in which a chemical process is utilised to trap CO_2. However, the installation and use of this technology itself has an energy cost in terms of CO_2.

carbon dioxide a colourless gas at room temperature that *sublimes* at –78.5°C (*sublimation* is when a solid substance changes to the vapour phase *without* first becoming liquid). It occurs naturally in the atmosphere and is the source of CARBON for plants, playing a vital role in plant and animal respiration and metabolism (since it is exhaled by animals and absorbed by plants during PHOTOSYNTHESIS). It forms when coal, wood, etc, are burned and is a byproduct of fermentation. It is produced industrially from *synthesis gas* (a mixture of hydrogen and carbon monoxide) used in the production of ammonia. Its physical properties make it a useful refrigerant, and it is dissolved in mineral waters and fizzy drinks, creating bubbles. Also, since it is heavier than air and does not support combustion, it is used in fire extinguishers.

carbon fibre fibres consisting of oriented carbon chains that produce a material that is very strong for its weight. Carbon fibres are manufactured by heating polyacrylonitrile $((CH_2.CHCN)_n)$ fibres initially at low temperatures to stabilise the fibre and then at high temperatures (2,500°C) and under tension to orientate the graphite along the fibre. The resulting fibres are usually 8–11μm in diameter and are not generally totally crystalline, with graphite crystals in amorphous carbon. The fibres are used as a reinforcing material in resins and ceramics, producing strong materials able to withstand high temperatures and with a higher strength-to-weight ratio than metals. Comparative strengths of carbon fibre and selected materials are shown below:

Material	Density	Tensile strength	Temperature of use (°C)
aluminium	2.7	0.06	600
steel	7.9	2.0	1,200
oxide fibre	4.0	2.0	800
carbon fibre	1.9	2.3	2,500
glass	2.5	0.07	700
silicon fibre	2.2	5.8	750
magnesium	1.74	0.04	200

carbon footprint an estimate of the impact of human activity on the global environment, measured in the quantity of CARBON DIOXIDE that is produced. A carbon footprint may be 'personal', referring to the amount of CO_2 emissions for which an individual is responsible or 'corporate', measuring the output of a company, business or other larger group. A personal carbon footprint has two components, comprising direct or primary and indirect or secondary emissions, with some overlap between the two. But it is the sum of these components which makes up the 'size' of the footprint.

Primary/direct factors include: personal fuel consumption (gas, oil, electricity), both in the home and for work and leisure activities, as well the energy cost of the food and drink we require in order to survive.

Secondary/indirect factors covers the cost in terms of CO_2 emissions of all the items that we use, including the manufacture of the products and their eventual decay.

The personal carbon footprint of anyone living in a Western, developed country is at least $2^1/_2$ times greater that that of a person in a poorer part of the world. There are many ways in which a person living in the West can seek to reduce his or her carbon footprint. These include:

- installing low energy light bulbs in the home
- improving home insulation to retain heat
- turning down central heating/ heating devices
- wearing more clothes
- installing solar panels/ micro wind turbine at home
- reducing frequency of individual car use/ increasing use of bus and train
- reducing personal air travel
- reducing use of electrical appliances/ turning off all equipment in 'stand-by' mode
- washing clothes at lower temperature
- choosing food and clothes produced and manufactured in or near home country to reduce 'air miles' and rejecting products with excess packaging
- changing goods in home less frequently/ recycling items and compost household waste
- not tarmacking or paving garden areas and allowing plants to flourish and trees to grow as these will utilise CO_2.

carbon monoxide a colourless gas with no smell that is formed when coke and similar fuels are burnt in a limited supply of air, i.e. incomplete combustion. It also occurs in the exhaust emissions of car engines. It is used industrially because of its reducing properties (*see* OXIDATION AND REDUCTION), e.g. in metallurgy. One of its most important properties is its toxicity. It is poisonous when breathed in because it combines with haemoglobin in the blood, which reduces the capacity of the blood to carry oxygen (*see* CIRCULATION).

carbon storage refers to any technological process by which carbon can be stored but mainly the pumping of CO_2 into 'reservoirs' within SEDIMENTARY ROCKS beneath the sea.

carbon trading and carbon offsetting *carbon trading* refers to a theoretical concept which could possibly be employed to stabilise the CARBON DIOXIDE emissions of a developed country at an agreed, acceptable level. It involves issuing each citizen with an allocation of *carbon credits* that he or she would then use to buy energy. Anyone using less than their allocation would be free to sell the surplus to people who have exceeded their share. It is believed that such a scheme would provide incentives for energy saving and would also be of direct, financial benefit to poorer people in society, who currently consume less energy than those who are more prosperous.

Carbon offsetting refers to the practice by which an individual can seek to 'offset' the carbon cost of a particular activity by paying a sum of money to an environmental scheme which reduces CO_2 emissions, (generally planting trees). It is increasingly being used by people in Western, developed countries, usually to offset the emissions cost of a particular journey by air or a foreign holiday. Critics of the scheme do not believe that it is effective in reducing carbon emissions.

carcinogen *see* CANCER.

carnivore any animal that eats the flesh of other animals, often referring to mammals belonging to the order *Carnivora* (*see* NH Carnivora). Some highly specialised plants are carnivorous, and these usually trap insects or small frogs, etc and secrete enzymes that break them down, enabling the products of digestion to be absorbed (*see* NH carnivorous plants).

carotenoid *see* PIGMENT.

carpel *see* FLOWERS; POLLINATION; REPRODUCTION.

cartilage a special type of connective tissue that, together with bone, forms the skeleton of vertebrate animals. It is composed of proteins and carbohydrates, especially *collagen*, which is a fibrous substance that makes cartilage tough and elastic. Cartilage is found in various parts of the skeleton, e.g. between the vertebrae of the backbone and around joints. It is also present in rings around the windpipe (trachea) and in the ears and nose.

cartilaginous fishes *see* NH cartilaginous fishes.

cast iron or pig iron the impure form of iron produced in a BLAST FURNACE. It contains 2–4.5 per cent carbon in a form called *cementite* (Fe_3C) and other ELEMENTS such as silicon, phosphorus, sulphur and manganese. Cast irons are often too brittle to use but additions of other metals can improve their workability. *Wrought iron* is made by melting cast iron and scrap iron in a special furnace, removing most of the impurities. Cast iron melts at 1,200°C (2192°F), whereas wrought iron softens at 1,000°C (1,832°F) and melts at 1,500°C (2732°F) (*see also* STEEL).

catalysis the use of a *catalyst* to alter the rate of a chemical reaction. A catalyst usually increases the speed at which a chemical reaction proceeds but is itself unchanged at the end of the reaction. In practice the catalyst may be changed physically if not chemically. Catalysts are used a great deal in the chemical industry, iron and platinum being common examples. Metal oxides are also used (copper, zinc, aluminium, titanium), and *zeolites* have become more important over recent years. In biological systems, enzymes are the natural organic equivalent of catalysts.

A *catalytic converter* is fitted to new cars to reduce the volume of exhaust gases produced. The gases pass over a honeycomb structure (which greatly increases the surface area) that is coated with a catalyst such as platinum or palladium and reactions produce water vapour and carbon dioxide.

Zeolites are natural or synthetic alumina silicates of sodium, potassium, calcium and barium that contain cavities filled with water. The water can be removed by heating and the cavities then occupied by other molecules. With small amounts of platinum or palladium they are used in the catalytic cracking of hydrocarbons.

caterpillar *see* NH Lepidoptera.

cathode-ray tube an evacuated tube in which *cathode rays* are produced and strike a fluorescent screen; it forms the basis of a television and a *cathode-ray oscilloscope*, which is used in laboratories and radar systems. At one end of the tube is an assembly (*electron gun*) that produces a beam of electrons that can be focused. The beam passes between two sets of plates, each of which can deflect the electron beam when a voltage is applied to the plates. The resulting beam then impinges upon the screen which is coated with zinc sulphide and fluoresces where the electrons strike.

cat *see* NH Carnivora.

cation *see* ION.

cattle *see* NH Artiodactyla.

caustic soda chemically, sodium hydroxide (NaOH), a whitish substance that gives a strongly alkaline (*see* ALKALIS) solution in water and will burn skin. It is *deliquescent*, i.e. it picks up moisture from the air and may eventually liquefy. It is used a great deal in the laboratory and is an important industrial chemical, being used in the manufacture of pulp and paper, soap and detergents, petrochemicals, textiles and other chemicals. Sodium hydroxide is itself manufactured by the ELECTROLYSIS of sodium chloride solution, chlorine being the other product, or by the addition of hot sodium carbonate solution to quicklime (calcium oxide, CaO).

cell in biology, the smallest and most basic unit of all living organisms. A cell is able to perform the main functions of life, which are METABOLISM, growth and REPRODUCTION, and there are two main types, PROCARYOTE and EUCARYOTE. BACTERIA and blue-green ALGAE are procaryotes and all other animals and plants are eucaryotes. The simple organisms consist of a single cell and are termed *unicellular*, e.g. bacteria. However, most living creatures are formed of vast numbers of cells that congregate together to form highly specialised tissues and organs. A typical cell has an outer layer or membrane surrounding a jelly-like substance called *cytoplasm*. Various structures called organelles (*see* ORGAN) are contained within the cytoplasm which are responsible for a number of different activities. The largest structure present is the nucleus surrounded by a (nuclear) membrane that contains the CHROMOSOMES AND GENES. Plant cells differ from animal ones in having an outer wall composed of a carbohydrate substance called CELLULOSE. These walls may be thick, giving strength and shape to the structure of the plant. Substances pass into and out of cells across the cell membranes, e.g. food materials, oxygen and carbon dioxide.

A typical cell

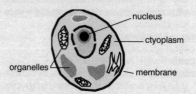

The term 'cell' is also used in chemistry (*see* BATTERY) and physics (*see* CELLULAR COMMUNICATIONS).

cell division the formation of two daughter cells from one parent cell, with the nucleus dividing first by a process known as *mitosis*. The end result is that the nucleus of each daughter cell contains the same number of CHROMOSOMES (carrying the genes) as the original parent cell. The chromosomes are in the form of strands of material that come together in pairs. These eventually arrange themselves across the centre of the nucleus and the nuclear membrane disappears. Each member of a pair is now composed of two strands, known as *chromatids,* which are joined at a single point called a *centromere*. As mitosis progresses, the centromeres split and one chromatid from each of the pairs moves to opposite ends. A nuclear membrane forms around each group of chromatids, now the new chromosomes and then the cytoplasm itself divides to form two daughter cells, each with its own nucleus.

Another type of cell division occurs in the formation of sex cells (sperm and eggs), and this is known as *meiosis*. In meiosis, the stages of mitosis are repeated again after a resting phase. The end result is that four daughter cells are produced, each with half the number of chromosomes of the parent cell, a condition known as *haploid*. At fertilisation, two haploid cells (a sperm and an egg) fuse together so that the new individual has the full number of chromosomes, half from each parent, and this condition is known as *diploid*. Most cells are diploid with only the sex cells (*gametes*) being haploid. *See also* FERTILIZATION, REPRODUCTION, CHROMOSOMES AND GENES.

cellular communications radios and particularly telephones that can be used almost anywhere (car phones, portable telephone) and linked to exchanges and standard telephone lines by means of an almost countrywide network. The network is divided into *cells*, and when a user with a portable or car phone makes a call, it is transmitted to a base station and then to a telephone exchange. From the exchange the signal is then directed to the recipient either via a landline or through a similar route of cells. Each cell has a relay station to deal with all calls in that cell and when a user moves to another cell another station takes over. Mobile phones are now universal and rapidly developing technology (particularly miniature digital components) enables functions in addition to standard voice transmission, such as sending emails, Internet access and the sending of photographs and videos.

cellulose a type of carbohydrate (known as a *polysaccharide*) that is composed of chains of glucose (sugar) units. It makes up the cell walls of many plants and has a fibrous structure that gives strength. Cellulose is not easily digested, so some herbivores have evolved a strategy for dealing with this in that they possess a four-chambered stomach containing bacteria that are able to break down cellulose. These are known as *ruminant* animals. In humans, cellulose is important as dietary fibre.

Celsius scale *see* TEMPERATURE.

cement any compound or mix that binds materials together, especially Portland cement which is used in BUILDING AND CONSTRUCTION in CONCRETE. Cement is manufactured from chalk or limestone with clay, which provides the necessary lime, silica and alumina. The mix is crushed and heated in a kiln to form a *clinker* (a partly melted, dense ash) that contains calcium silicates and aluminates. The clinker is finely ground and gypsum (calcium sulphate, $CaSO_4$) added. The cement product then goes through complex *hydration* (combination with water) reactions that eventually result in a hard stone-like material.

There are now many different cements that have particular properties depending upon their composition. These include ordinary Portland cement, rapid-hardening cement, Portland BLAST-FURNACE cement, sulphate-resistant cement and micro-silica cement.

cementite *see* CAST IRON; STEEL.

centigrade scale *see* TEMPERATURE.

centipedes *see* NH Myriapoda.

centre of gravity the point through which the total effect of gravity acting upon all parts of a body are effectively concentrated. This usually coincides with the *centre of mass* and is the point at which the weight or downward force caused by gravity acts. When applied to everyday objects, this means that some will fall over more easily than others. The stability of an object can be increased by lowering its centre of gravity, perhaps by enlarging its base. A good example is in transport where large tall loads are unstable (because of a high centre of gravity) whereas racing cars are designed to have a low centre of gravity to allow them to move at high speeds.

centrifuge a machine for separating out particles suspended in a liquid. It com-

prises two arms about a central pivot, each arm holding a tube. When the arms are rotated rapidly about the central point the suspended particles are forced outwards to the bottom of the tubes, different particles separating at different speeds depending upon their size and mass. An *ultracentrifuge* rotates at very high speeds (up to 60,000 rpm) and is used for determining the masses of polymers and proteins. In industry, centrifuges are used for separating mixtures and in the production of cream and sugar.

centripetal force the force necessary to move an object in a circular path, such as a ball on the end of a rope. The ball follows a circular route because there is a force in towards the centre of the circle —the centripetal force. If the rope is released, the ball continues in the direction at the time and moves off at a tangent. The force can be felt easily when some weighty object is swung around and the person holding the rope stays in the same place, and an object will only move in a circle if the centripetal force is provided. Centripetal force applies when a car corners, the friction between tires and road providing the force, and in some fairground rides. The same applies to a satellite orbiting the Earth where gravitational attraction between the bodies supplies the centripetal force.

centromere *see* CELL DIVISION.

cephalopods *see* NH Cephalopoda.

ceramics the term generally applied to items manufactured from clays, including *pottery* and *porcelain* where a moist clay is moulded to shape and fired in a kiln until it hardens. Decorative glazes can be added, and many domestic and commercial items are produced in this way. These are *traditional ceramics*, made of 50–60 per cent clay to which animal bone is added (to control the porosity), producing a non-porous *china*. The mineral *feldspar* can be added in place of bone, producing porcelain goods, e.g. insulators. Clay minerals with no additions are used to produce bricks, tiles, pipes and similar construction materials.

Considerable advances have been made in recent years in the field of materials technology and many ceramics or *com-*

posites (a mix of materials, often as fibres of one material in a different matrix) have been developed.

cereals important food crops derived from wild grasses that have been grown for many thousands of years. Cereals are grown for their seeds, which are usually ground to produce flour and contain important nutrients such as carbohydrates, proteins, vitamins and calcium. Over the centuries farmers have selectively cultivated cereal crops, sowing only the seeds from the best and biggest plants and those that produced the most grain. This is an example of plant BREEDING and the end result is that cultivated cereals now look very different from the wild grasses that are their 'ancestors'.

cestodes *see* NH Cestoda.

cetaceans *see* NH Cetacea.

chain reaction *see* NUCLEAR ENERGY; NUCLEAR FISSION.

chalk *see* G&G chalk.

chameleon *see* NH Squamata.

chelonians *see* NH Chelonia.

chemical reaction the interaction between substances (*reactants*) producing different or altered substances (*products*) in which the BOND elements are broken and reformed. Reactions may proceed at normal pressure and temperature or special conditions may be necessary, e.g. high pressure or the presence of a catalyst (*see* CATALYSIS). Some terms refer to typical reactions; e.g. *hydrolysis* is the breakdown of a substance by water. The *heat of reaction* is the heat given out or required when certain amounts of substances react under constant pressure. Other heat quantities of a similar nature include:

heat of combustion: the heat evolved when one mole (SEE MOLECULE) of a substance is burned in oxygen.

heat of dissociation: the heat required to dissociate (splitting a molecule into simpler fragments) one mole of a compound.

heat of formation: the heat given out or required when one molecule of a substance is formed from its constituent elements at standard pressure and temperature.

chemistry the study of the composition of substances, their reactions and effects upon one another and the resulting changes. There are three main branches: physical, inorganic and organic. *Physical chemistry* deals with the link between chemical composition and physical properties and the physical changes brought about by reactions. *Inorganic chemistry* is the study of the ELEMENTS and their compounds (excluding the organic compounds of carbon) and the group and period characteristics as arranged in the PERIODIC TABLE. *Organic chemistry* is the study of CARBON compounds, of which there is an enormous number, and many are compounds with hydrogen, the hydrocarbons. Organic chemistry also deals with compounds of significant benefit to people—drugs, vitamins, antibiotics, polymers and plastics and many more. The study of chemistry really began in the 17th century when Robert Boyle, an Irish scientist, introduced the idea of elements. Since then many scientists have become famous for diverse discoveries —from the discovery of hydrogen by Henry Cavendish (1766) and the synthesis of an organic compound from inorganic substances by Friedrich Wöhler (1828), to the determination of the structure of DNA by James Watson and Francis Crick in 1953.

chemotherapy *see* CANCER.

chiropteran *see* NH Chiroptera.

chlorine the second ELEMENT in the HALOGENS group, is a yellow-green choking gas that is harmful if inhaled. It occurs as the chloride, mainly sodium chloride (NaCl), but also magnesium chloride and others. It is manufactured by the ELECTROLYSIS of brine (which also produces sodium hydroxide, NaOH) and stored as a liquid. It is a very important material in the chemicals industry and its powerful oxidising properties are utilised in bleaches and disinfectants. It is also used in the production of hydrochloric acid and numerous organic chemicals. Compounds derived from chlorine are used in water sterilisation, paper manufacture, solvents, PVC and other polymers, refrigerants and more. Hydrocarbons containing chlorine account for a very large proportion of chlorine derivatives.

chlorofluorocarbons or CFCs organic

compounds that contain chlorine and fluorine (both HALOGENS). Although CFCs have in the past had numerous industrial uses as aerosol propellants and in refrigerants, and are produced when manufacturing foam plastics, their use is now being curbed and much reduced because of their harmful environmental effect. Although CFCs are stable for a long time, they eventually break down and release their chlorine, which reacts with ozone in the atmosphere (*see* G&G ozone layer), producing oxygen and chlorine oxide. This reduction in ozone then has direct detrimental effects upon plants and animals.

chlorophyll *see* CHLOROPLAST AND CHLOROPHYLL.

chlorophyte *see* NH Chlorophyta.

chloroplast and chlorophyll *chloroplasts* are the organelles (*see* CELL) present within the cells of green plants and algae, e.g. *Spirogyra*, which are the site of PHOTOSYNTHESIS. They contain chlorophyll, which is the pigment that gives the plant its green colour. *Chlorophyll* is essential in photosynthesis as it traps energy from sunlight and helps the plant to manufacture its food from carbon dioxide and water. The chloroplasts (and chlorophyll) are mainly found in the leaves but also in the stems of green plants.

cholesterol a type of fatty substance that occurs naturally and is produced within animal bodies. In mammals such as man it is made mainly in the liver, carried in the bloodstream, and stored within cell membranes. Cholesterol is used to make some hormones and also a substance known as bile that is important in digestion.

Cholesterol can cause a problem in some people when too much is present in the blood. It may build up on the inner walls of arteries (a condition known as *arteriosclerosis*), causing them to become narrow and more easily blocked by a blood clot which can lead to a heart attack (*see* CIRCULATION).

chromatid *see* CELL DIVISION.

chromatography a technique used in chemical and biological ANALYSIS in which the constituents of a mixture can be separated. There are numerous closely related techniques but each depends upon one principle—the differing rate at which components of a mixture move through a stationary phase because of the presence of a mobile phase. The simplest case is that of a piece of blotting paper dipped into water. A drop of ink placed on the blotting paper will move up as the water ascends the paper, and in so doing will be separated into its component pigments. In this case the water is the mobile phase and the paper is the stationary phase, and this is essentially a form of paper chromatography. Other chromatographic techniques include:

gas chromatography: where a gas is the mobile phase. Used for complex mixtures of organic materials.

high performance liquid chromatography: passage of the sample through a column by means of a liquid mobile phase under pressure.

thin layer chromatography: separation by solvent movement across a flat surface of special paper, powdered cellulose, silica gel, alumina (aluminium oxide), or other stationary phase. It is used widely in qualitative analysis.

ion-exchange chromatography: separation of ionic materials by a solution passing over the surface of a resin which contains ions that can be exchanged. It is used in inorganic chemistry to separate metal mixtures or to separate amino acids.

gel permeation chromatography: where materials are separated by molecular size by a solution passing through a porous polymer gel in which small molecules are trapped while larger molecules move.

chromium *see* CARBIDE.

chromosomes and genes *chromosomes* are threads of material that are found within the nucleus of each living cell. They consist mainly of chains of DNA (composed of a substance called nucleic acid), and parts of these are called *genes*, which are the 'blueprints' or plans that determine everything about the organism. Each living organism has a particular number of chromosomes, which contain very many genes.

Human beings have 23 pairs of chromosomes, 22 of which look the same in both males and females. The 23rd pair are the sex chromosomes, which in males look like an XY and in females an XX. Although the chromosomes look similar in all individuals belonging to a particular species, the genes that they carry are all slightly different, hence each one is totally unique. *See also* HEREDITY and MUTATION.

chrysalis *see* LARVA AND METAMORPHOSIS.

circuit an electrically conducting path that when complete allows a current to flow through it. A circuit may be very simple consisting merely of a battery connected by copper wire to a bulb and then back to the opposite terminal of the battery. When cells and batteries were first made (in the early 1800s by the Italian scientist, Count Alessandro Volta), how charge moved around a circuit remained a mystery. The convention became that current flowed as a positive charge from the positive terminal around to the negative terminal. This is contrary to what actually happens since electrons flow in the opposite direction, but the convention remains (*see also* ELECTRICITY).

A simple circuit diagram

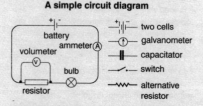

circulation (of the blood) the process by which blood is moved around an animal's body by the pumping action of the heart. The blood carries oxygen and food to all the cells of the body and also takes carbon dioxide from them to the lungs where it is eliminated. Blood that contains oxygen (*oxygenated blood*) is pumped through blood vessels called *arteries* by the left side of the heart. As the arteries reach the tissues and organs they become very tiny (*arterioles* and *capillaries*). Here blood releases its oxygen (becoming *deoxygenated*), and this is picked up and used by cells. Cells release carbon dioxide into the deoxygenated blood as it passes through more capillaries. The blood is now transported through tiny vessels (*venules*) that

become larger *veins* and then it passes back to the right side of the heart. From here it passes to the lungs where carbon dioxide is released and oxygen is picked up before it returns to the left side of the heart once again.

This type of blood circulation is described as 'double'. The heart is divided into two sides, each acting as an independent pump with no communication between them. Each side is further divided into two chambers, the upper one is called the *atrium* and collects incoming blood, passing it to the lower *ventricle*. This is a strong, muscular pump that contracts and pumps blood out either to the body or to the lungs. Arteries always carry oxygenated blood, except for the pulmonary artery which takes blood from the heart to the lungs. Veins always transport deoxygenated blood, except for the pulmonary vein which takes oxygenated blood from the lungs to the heart.

Systemic and pulmonary circulation

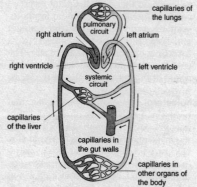

class *see* CLASSIFICATION.

classification a means of grouping living organisms together according to how similar they are to each other. For the early biologists, the physical similarities between organisms were the most important feature, but increasingly in modern times the similarities between organisms at a genetic level have become more important in understanding their relationships.

One main method of classification is most commonly recognised, and this was originally devised by a Swedish naturalist, Carolus Linnaeus, and is known as the *Linnaean system*. In this, all living things belong to a particular species and very similar species are grouped together in a *genus* (plural *genera*). In biology, each living organism has a double-barrelled name, first its generic (genus) and then its specific (species) 'label' which are given in Latin. Examples are *Lumbricus terrestris* (the earthworm), *Rana temporaria* (the common frog), *Homo sapiens* (a human being) and, among plants, *Quercus robur* (the common oak), *Primula vulgaris* (the primrose), and *Taraxacum officinale* (the dandelion). Genera that show similar features are grouped into *families* and these in turn into *orders*. Numbers of orders are put into *classes* that are grouped into a *phylum* (plural *phyla*). Finally, phyla are placed together in a *kingdom*. In plants, the grouping *division* usually replaces phylum but otherwise the classification is the same.

climate *see* G&G climate.

clinker *see* CEMENT.

clone a living organism that is an exact genetic copy of another individual and is produced from a single cell by an asexual process (*see* ASEXUAL REPRODUCTION).

cloning an artificial process much used in the breeding of plants (e.g. cuttings). In 1997 a research team in Scotland announced that they had successfully produced a ewe, which they named Dolly, that had been cloned from another adult ewe. It was later conceded, however, that there was a very remote possibility that Dolly might have been cloned from foetal cells circulating in the ewe's bloodstream.

cloud *see* G&G cloud.

cnidarian *see* NH Cnidaria.

coal *see* G&G coal.

cockroach *see* NH Orthoptera.

coelacanth *see* NH coelacanth.

coelenterate *see* NH Cnidaria.

cohesion *see* SURFACE TENSION.

coleopteran *see* NH Coleoptera.

collagen *see* CARTILAGE.

colloid originally, a substance in solution that could not get through a dialysis (semi-permeable) membrane. The definition of a colloid now is one of particle size—when the size range is 10^{-4} to 10^{-6} millimetres, and it therefore falls between a coarse suspension and a true solution. Most substances can now be prepared to exist in this state, and many exist naturally as colloids. Common examples of colloidal solutions include starch and albumen, butter and cell cytoplasm.

An *emulsion* is a colloidal solution of one liquid in another; generally one is water or a solution in water and the other is an oil or a similar liquid that does not mix with water. Emulsions are used widely in industry in food and pharmaceuticals, cosmetics, paints and lubricants.

colony *see* NH colony.

combustion or burning a chemical reaction that occurs quickly and involves the high-temperature oxidation of a substance, i.e. it combines with oxygen to produce heat, light and flame and, of course, ashes (oxides). Combustion of fossil fuels is the source of most energy used in homes, factories and offices. When coal or a similar fuel is burned, the carbon is converted to carbon dioxide or carbon monoxide and the hydrogen to water vapour. Combustion is a vital industrial process and although it generally refers to burning in oxygen, it is used on other occasions when, for example, a substance is burnt in hydrogen.

comet *see* S&A comet.

commensalism *see* SYMBIOSIS.

compact disc a disc used to hold music, graphics or data for replaying. The disc has a layer of aluminium, and music is recorded as very small pits etched into the surface. The pits are tiny—about half a micrometre (μm) wide and one to three micrometres wide. Each track is about 1.5 micrometres from the next. The music is replayed by focusing a laser beam on the disc. The beam is partially reflected, depending upon whether or not it strikes a pit, and the reflected beam is detected as a series of pulses that are changed back into a copy of the original recording. Because there is no physical contact between the disc and the playing medium, compact discs should last much longer than the earlier magnetic tapes and vinyl records.

compound when two or more elements

combine chemically in a substance and in definite proportions to produce molecules held together by chemical BONDS. The formation of a compound necessitates a chemical reaction and the elements cannot be separated physically. Also, the same compound is formed irrespective of its origin, so one molecule of water is two atoms of hydrogen and one of oxygen no matter how it is made.

The above can be regarded as the specific definition of a compound but there are instances when the boundaries are blurred. For example, many silicate minerals, e.g. the feldspars, have varying compositions, as do many polymers although all are chemically combined. Indeed materials such as glass and steel are not mixtures and yet they do not fall readily into the definition of compound.

concentration see SOLUTIONS.

Concorde see MACH NUMBER.

concrete a building material comprising a mixture of sand, cement, stone and water, which when set becomes very hard. Concrete is used in vast quantities for all types of BUILDING AND CONSTRUCTION and often steel rods or meshes are set into the concrete to increase its strength—*reinforced concrete*. *Prestressed concrete* is when the concrete is under compression, achieved by stretching the reinforcing rods and keeping them in tension after the concrete has set. Prestressed concrete is useful for large spans or where beams have to be as light as possible. There is a whole technology surrounding concrete, with a variety of types and numerous compounds and materials that can be added to a mix to confer particular properties. *Aerated concrete*, made up solely of cement, water and gas bubbles, is used for its insulating properties; *lightweight concrete* utilises lightweight aggregates (synthetic or natural) to form an insulating and lighter concrete; *high strength concrete* has obvious benefits, while a denser concrete for protective shields can be made by using barytes, iron or lead shot in place of stone. Additives to concrete (*admixtures*) are used to alter the properties of the mix or the hardened material and include water reducers, accelerators, plasticisers, corrosion inhibitors and many others. This variety of concrete type renders it one of, if not the most, versatile building material.

condensation the process by which a substance changes from the gaseous state to the liquid state, in doing which energy is lost, i.e. it is cooled. There are many everyday examples of condensation—water forming on a pan lid when vegetables are cooking; water droplets on a cold tap in the bathroom; the steam from a kettle, which is actually the hot water vapour condensing as tiny water droplets in the cooler air. *Cloud* (*see* G&G cloud) is another example that is caused by warm air saturated with water vapour being cooled. The physical process of condensation is used in the chemicals industry when substances are purified by DISTILLATION. In chemistry a *condensation reaction* is the reaction of one molecule with another and the elimination of a simple molecule such as water.

conduction and convection *conduction* of heat is a process of heat moving through a material and is caused by molecular vibrations. When a material is heated, the molecules vibrate rapidly and knock into neighbouring molecules, which transfers the heat (or thermal energy) along the material. Metals, e.g. copper and aluminium, are the best conductors of heat while liquids and gases are progressively poor conductors. In a gas or liquid that is free to move, *convection* is the process that moves heat from one part to another. As water in a tank is heated, the hot water rises and cooler water sinks. This establishes a *convection current*. Convection is used to great effect in the hot water systems in houses. A similar effect is seen with gases, and when air is warmed, this sets up currents that, on a large scale, create onshore and offshore winds at the coast. On a smaller scale, radiators warm the air in a room by convection.

conductor and insulator electric *conductors* are materials that allow a flow of electrons, producing an electric current. As with CONDUCTION of heat, metals form the best electrical conductors because electrons around the outside of the atoms are loosely held and can move freely. Poor conductors include water, glass and air—i.e. most non-metals. A material that does not conduct electric charge is called an *insulator*. Plastics, rubber, glass and air form insulators because their electrons are not usually free to move.

cone *see* SIGHT.

conifer *see* DECIDUOUS AND EVERGREEN.

connective tissue a type of tissue that is commonly found in the bodies of animals. It is further divided into a variety of different sorts depending upon the materials from which it is composed. It is usually composed of a non-living core containing various fibres in which a number of cells are spread.

conservation *see* NH conservation.

constellation *see* S&A constellation.

construction *see* BUILDING AND CONSTRUCTION.

continent *see* G&G continent.

contraction and expansion when a solid is heated and its molecules vibrate more because of the input of thermal energy, the result is that the molecules move apart a little and the solid *expands* almost imperceptibly. When the reverse happens, the solid *contracts*. Although the expansion in a solid may be negligible, the resulting force can be very large. In CONSTRUCTION particularly, account has to be taken for the expansion of steel and concrete and all BRIDGES have expansion joints to avoid damage that would otherwise be caused. Railways lines have a similar feature, but in this case line ends have overlapping joints. The property of expansion also has its useful aspects and it can be applied to numerous devices that contain a BIMETAL STRIP.

Liquids generally expand more than solids, producing an increase in volume. Water is a notable exception to this, its behaviour being quite complex. As water cools from boiling, it contracts a very small amount until it reaches 4°C (39°F), at which point it expands a little. At 0°C (32°F) it forms ice and expands a great deal but on further cooling it contracts more. At 4°C (39°F) water has its least volume and therefore its greatest density and it will sink beneath colder or warmer water. This is the reason for ponds freezing on the surface while fish can survive in the slightly warmer water at depth.

convection *see* CONDUCTION AND CONVECTION.

copepod *see* NH Copepoda.

copper a red-brown metal that is very malleable and ductile (*see* DUCTILITY) and has numerous uses. It occurs as native copper (as the metal itself, often with silver, lead and other metals) and in a variety of mineral forms, e.g. malachite ($CuCO_3.Cu(OH)_2$), bornite ($CuFeS_3$) and chalcopyrite ($CuFeS_2$). The ores are concentrated and copper is extracted by smelting and refining by electrolysis. Copper has been an important metal for thousands of years in its ALLOYS, brass and bronze, and it is now used in coins as an alloy with nickel. Pure copper is an excellent electrical conductor and is used in wiring, and a significant proportion of copper production is taken in electrical applications. It is also used for pipes in plumbing, although plastics are being used increasingly in this context. Copper is also employed in fungicides, paints, pigments and printing.

coral *see* NH Actinozoa.

cornea *see* SIGHT.

corona *see* S&A corona.

corrosion the process of metals and alloys being attacked chemically by moisture, air, acids, or alkalis. If it is left to continue, the metal will be gradually worn away. Corrosion may occur uniformly or it may be concentrated at weak points or joints. It may also produce an oxide layer, as on aluminium, which protects against further attack. More serious effects are seen in corrosion where some moisture is present as this sets up an electrolytic process, and with underground corrosion the soil acts as the electrolyte (*see* ELECTROLYSIS). Corrosion can be prevented or slowed by applying protective layers (paint, anodising, or plating with zinc, nickel, chromium, etc). *Cathodic protection* is also used in the protection of underground structures (e.g. pipelines) by making the object/structure in question the cathode in a CIRCUIT that has a voltage higher than the estimated voltage of corrosion. The anode in this circuit may dissolve away and be replaced when necessary. Steel reinforcement (*see* CONCRETE) can be cathodically protected providing it is electrically continuous.

cosmic rays *see* S&A cosmic rays.

coulomb the SI UNIT of electrical charge, defined as the charge passing a point in a CIRCUIT when a current of 1 ampere flows for 1 second, thus a charge of 8 coulombs passes if a current of 2 amperes flows for 4 seconds. One coulomb is equal to the charge on approximately 6.25×10^{18} electrons.

cracking *see* PETROCHEMICALS.

crickets *see* NH Orthoptera.

critical mass *see* NUCLEAR FISSION.

crustaceans *see* NH Crustacea.

crystal *see* G&G crystal.

cyanobacteria *see* NH cyanobacteria.

cyclone *see* G&G cyclone.

cyclotron *see* PARTICLE ACCELERATOR.

cryogenics *see* HELIUM.

crystal a solid material with a regular ordered structure having faces that are usually flat on several sides.

cytology the branch of biology devoted to the scientific study of cells, including both their structure and function, which depends very much on the use of the light and electron microscope.

cytoplasm *see* CELL.

Darwin and natural selection Charles Darwin was a famous naturalist who devised the theory of evolution (known as *Darwinism*) to explain the great variety of plants and animals that he saw around him. He arrived at his theories during a five-year voyage around the world (the voyage of HMS *Beagle*). When he returned to England in 1859 he published a scientific paper with the title *Origin of Species* in which he proposed that some individuals in a species are more successful than others (they have a greater degree of 'fitness'). In the competition for food or for a mate they are more likely to be successful and these characteristics are inherited by their offspring, which means that eventually these features become more widespread. He called this 'survival of the fittest'. Because of it, plants and animals were gradually able to change and adapt to new conditions and environments, so new species eventually evolved from an original, ancestral stock. Darwin's theories were not accepted at the time and caused outrage because they questioned the Biblical version of God's Creation as a one-off event. They are largely accepted now, however, and have been expanded by the modern study of genes and inheritance. Darwin's theory can be summarised as follows: from organisms that have the ability to change, new species can emerge that will adapt to new environments. Old species that are no longer suited to the surrounding environment will eventually die out.

dating method *see* G&G dating method.

day length *see* S&A day length.

decagon *see* POLYGON.

decapod *see* NH Decapoda.

decibel *see* SOUND.

deciduous and evergreen *deciduous* plants shed their leaves at the end of the growing season, which is the fall in temperate regions such as Britain and Northern America. Examples include familiar trees such as the oak and sycamore. *Evergreen* plants, on the other hand, keep their leaves all through the year, and these include the cone-bearing coniferous trees (*conifers*) such as Sitka spruce.

decimal numbers the most commonly used number system, based on powers of ten. The *decimal point* is the dot that divides the number's whole part from the fractional part (i.e. that which is less than one). However, numbers need not contain a decimal point: 789 is also a decimal number. A decimal is itself less than one and is written after the decimal point, e.g. 0.789 and 0.00987. Decimal numbers are written within the *place-value system*, i.e. the value given to a digit depends upon its position in the number, and with the decimal system each column has ten times the value of the column to the right, thus the number 7891 is really:

seven 1000s	eight 100s	nine 10s	and one 1
(10^3)	(10^2)	(10^1)	(10^0)
7	8	9	1

A common fraction such as $\frac{1}{4}$ can be changed into decimal form by dividing the 1 by 4 to give 0.25.

decimal multiples *see* SI UNITS.

decomposers *see* NH decomposers.

deer *see* NH Artiodactyla.

deforestation *see* NH deforestation.

dehydration in a chemical reaction or process the removal by heat of water held in a molecule or compound. Sometimes a catalyst (*see* CATALYSIS) is used or a dehydrating agent such as sulphuric acid (H_2SO_4). Dehydration is used a great deal in the food industry in the production of coffee, soups, sauces, mashed potato, milk, etc. It arrests the processes of natural decay as there is no moisture available for microorganisms to survive and chemical reactions are slowed or stopped. Of course, dehydration produces a reduction in volume, and particularly weight, which is useful for storage and transport.

In medicine, dehydration is the excessive, often dangerous, loss of water from body tissues, accompanied by loss of vital salts. The average daily intake of water is about two litres but lack of water for just a few days can be dangerous because the heart can be affected.

dendrite *see* NERVOUS SYSTEM.

dendrochronology a technique of dating past events using the growth rings of trees. Each year a new ring of wood is added to the trunk just beneath the bark, and this is called an *annual ring*. It is possible to date the rings in living trees by working back year by year and then this pattern of rings can be used to date fossil trees or specimens of wood found at archaeological or other sites. The longest-living trees are the most useful, the standard one being the bristle cone pine, which can live for up to 5,000 years and be used to date specimens older than that.

density the mass of a substance, per unit volume, given by the following equation:

$$\text{density (d)} = \frac{\text{mass (M)}}{\text{volume (V)}}$$

It is measured in kilograms per cubic metre (kg/m^3), although it may be more convenient on occasion to use grams per cubic centimetre (g/cm^3). Density varies with temperature, only a little in the case of solids and liquids, which usually expand and therefore become less dense. With gases the density varies a great deal depending upon its container and the surrounding pressure.

Relative density is the density of a material compared to that of water, given by the following equation:

$$\text{relative density} = \frac{\text{density of a substance}}{\text{density of water}}$$

Relative density used to be called *specific gravity*. It has no units but is the same value as the density when measured in g/cm^3. Some typical densities:

	kg/m³	g/cm³
air	1.3	0.0013
soft wood	450	0.45
hard wood	800	0.80
petrol	800	0.80
water	1,000	1.00
hardened cement	2,200	2.2
granite	2,600	2.6
aluminium	2,700	2.7
diamond	3,500	3.5
steel	7,700	7.7
lead	11,400	11.4
mercury	13,600	13.6
gold	19,300	19.3

dentine, dentition *see* TEETH.

depression *see* G&G cyclone.

desalination one of several technologies that are employed to remove dissolved salts from sea water, generally so that it can be used as drinking water for people or animals. Technologies include DISTILLATION or evaporation, ion exchange, reverse osmosis and electro-dialysis. Electro-dialysis uses an electrical current to filter dissolved IONS from sea water but the energy demands of the process are high. *Reverse osmosis* is a promising new technology in which sea water is forced through a special membrane under high pressure. The process allows fresh water to pass through and be trapped, while concentrated salt water is left behind.

desert *see* G&G desert.

detergents and soaps cleaning agents that remove grease and dirt and hold it in suspension for washing away. *Soap* acts as a detergent but there are now many synthetic detergents derived from petroleum. The *detergent* molecules contain two distinct groups: one that gives the molecule solubility in water, e.g. a sulphate, and long hydrocarbon chains that enable it to dissolve oily materials. When detergent molecules come into contact with grease, the hydrocarbon chains that are *hydrophobic* (water-hating) attach to the grease, and the other end of the molecule, which is *hydrophilic* (water-loving), is in the water. The grease is then enclosed and can be removed from the garment. Detergents are made in many forms: washing-up liquids, powders, shampoo, etc.

Soaps are sodium and potassium salts of *fatty acids* (a type of organic acid of animal or vegetable origin) that are heated in large vats with dilute sodium hydroxide (caustic soda) to effect *hydrolysis* (*see* CHEMICAL REACTION). Sodium chloride is then added to precipitate the soap from the solution. The soap may then be treated with perfumes before being made into bars or flakes.

Metallic soaps are a very different group of compounds, being insoluble in water. They are metal salts (metals such as lithium, aluminium, calcium and zinc) of long carboxylic acid chains (organic acids with one or more carboxyl, -COOH, groups) and are used in cosmetics and pharmaceuticals and as fungicides and lubricating oils.

dialysis a method for separating small molecules from larger ones in a solution. Dialysis occurs in the kidneys of all vertebrate animals and is the process that cleans the blood of the waste products of METABOLISM. *See also* OSMOREGULATION.

diamond *see* CARBON.

diaphragm *see* LUNGS.

diatom *see* PLANKTON and NH Bacillari-ophyta.

dicotyledon *see* PLANTS.

dielectric *see* CAPACITOR.

differentiation a mathematical operation used in CALCULUS for finding the derivative of a function. Depending upon the complexity of the function, there are different methods of differentiation. The simplest relates to the common function:

$$f(x) \text{ or } y = x^n$$

This has the derivative (or differential coefficient):

$$f'(x) \text{ or } dy = \frac{nx^{n-1}}{dx}$$

Thus, for example, if

$$y = 4x^3, dy = \frac{12x^2}{dx}$$

and for

$$y = 3x^3 + 4x^2, dy = \frac{9x^2}{dx} + 8x$$

diffraction the bending of waves around an obstacle and as they pass through a narrow gap. This applies to all waves—water, sound, light and electromagnetic—and can be detected by a change in the shape of the wavefront and by *interference* patterns. When a beam of light passes through a narrow slit it is diffracted, but the slit has to be very narrow indeed (less than 0.01 of a millimetre) to have any effect. If *monochromatic* (one wavelength) light is used and the diffracted light is passed through two further slits, then an interference pattern of light and dark fringes is created. In 1801, Thomas Young, the physicist, used an experimental procedure such as this to measure the wavelength of light. The fact that sound can be diffracted is easily shown because it is possible to hear around corners.

diffusion the process that occurs in gases and liquids whereby one liquid is spread throughout the body of another, e.g. an ink drop in water, because of the molecular motion of the water (*see* BROWNIAN MOTION), producing a more uniform concentration. The same process occurs with gases and accounts, for example, for the smell of a gas leak filling a room. The molecular movement of gases is more vigorous than liquids and the molecules distribute themselves equally within the volume in which they are enclosed.

Diffusion also occurs across cell membranes, and a similar mechanism is used in DIALYSIS as a means of separating certain molecules.

digestion the process by which organisms break down solid food into small particles that can be used by the body. In human beings, the digestive process starts in the mouth where food is cut up into smaller particles by the teeth. The food is mixed with saliva containing an enzyme that breaks down starch into sugar. The food is then swallowed and passes, via a tube called the *oesophagus*, into the stomach. In the stomach a fluid, the gastric juice, is released which contains hydrochloric acid and enzymes. The stomach has muscular walls and is able to expand and contract and further manipulate the food. Proteins are broken down and eventually a semi-solid acidic mass (known as *chyme*) is passed into the small intestine. Alkaline fluid from an organ called the *pancreas* (pancreatic juice) is added here, and this contains more enzymes that break the food down further. Also, *bile*, a thick fluid produced by the liver and stored in the *gall bladder* located nearby, is added to the food in the intestine. This contains bile salts, bile pigments and cholesterol and aids in the digestion of fatty substances. As the food passes along the highly coiled length of the small intestine it continues to be broken down into minute particles (molecules) that can be absorbed into fine blood vessels present in the intestinal wall. The blood circulation carries the food to all parts of the body where it is used by cells to perform all the functions of life and to provide energy.

Any food substances that cannot be digested, such as fibre, are passed to the large intestine, which is the final part of the alimentary canal or digestive system.

The human digestive system

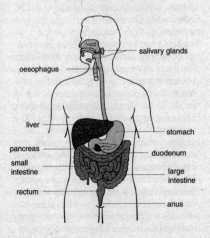

salivary glands
oesophagus
liver
stomach
pancreas
duodenum
small intestine
large intestine
rectum
anus

Here water is removed and reabsorbed into the body, and the final waste product (*faeces*) is passed to the outside through the anus.

digital and analogue two different ways of measuring a value—a *digital* system uses distinct units, e.g. electrical pulses, while *analogue* is a quantity that is similar to another quantity (e.g. a thermometer where the column of liquid represents a temperature). The digital system uses BINARY NUMBERS, which renders it admirably suited for use in computers. Numbers and letters are coded by groups of the digits 1 and 0, and each digit is represented in an electronic circuit by a component being on or off, e.g. passing or not passing current. In a magnetic system it could be magnetised or not magnetised, and that produces the on/off effect.

dinosaurs *see* NH dinosaurs.

diode a device with two terminals that allows current to flow in only one direction. Modern varieties are *solid state* (electronic devices made up of solids with no moving parts, filaments, etc) and usually are made up of a special *silicon chip*. Silicon is a SEMICONDUCTOR used to make diodes. A crystal of silicon with phosphorus and boron added to opposite halves (a process called *doping*) has a poorly conducting junction, called the *depletion layer*, between the two halves. The phosphorus increases the number of electrons available to move through the material and the boron makes holes into which electrons can move. Depending upon the current flow in the CIRCUIT, the diode passes current easily when the depletion layer is thin but when the current is reversed the depletion layer thickens and no current is passed. This property of diodes means they can be used to turn alternating current into a direct current, a process called *rectification*. Then the diode is called a *rectifier*. The diode may be used for *half-wave rectification*, in which it simply blocks the backward half of the current, or with a more complex arrangement of diodes, *full-wave rectification* can be achieved in which the blocked half of the alternating current is reversed and flows through as direct current. This is the principle employed in radios and tape recorders that can use a mains adapter, or batteries.

dipteran *see* NH Diptera.

diploid *see* CELL DIVISION; PLANTS.

disease any illness that affects an organism, which, in people, is caused in two main ways. Often diseases are caused by infectious microorganisms, e.g. bacteria, viruses and fungi (*see* FUNGUS). Bacteria can be killed with antibiotic drugs such as penicillin, and examples of bacterial diseases are cholera, tuberculosis and typhoid. Viruses are not susceptible to antibiotics so the illnesses they cause have to be fought off by the body's immune system, although protection can be given against some of these by means of vaccination. The common cold is a viral disease, and those that can be prevented by vaccination include mumps and measles. The second group of diseases are caused by the failure of the body's system to work properly. This may be an inherited disorder, e.g. cystic fibrosis, or occur at some stage in a person's life for an unknown reason. A common example is diabetes mellitus, which occurs when an organ called the pancreas fails to produce enough of the hormone insulin, itself responsible for the breakdown of sugars in food.

distillation the separation of a liquid mixture into its components. The liquid is first heated to a vapour, which is then cooled so that it condenses and can be collected as a liquid. The mixture can then be separated if the component liquids have different boiling points, each one vaporising at a different temperature. Distillation is one of the most common separation processes in industry, permitting a high degree of separation. It is performed in a large column within which there are a number of trays (or plates) at different levels. The liquid is fed in through a heater, and a constant flow is maintained between the ascending vapour and descending liquid. The vapour is then taken out at the top of the column through a condenser. *Fractional distillation* is the term applied to this process and the column is the *fractionating column*. Whiskey is distilled in this manner and crude oil is refined by the same means. *Flash distillation* involves the rapid

removal of solvent by moving the liquid from high to low pressure so that part turns immediately to vapour and is condensed. This technique is used in the desalination of sea water, i.e. the removal of salts from sea water to provide fresh water.

division *see* CLASSIFICATION.

DNA (abbreviation for deoxyribonucleic acid) the material of which the CHROMOSOMES AND GENES are composed. It occurs as strands in the nucleus of each cell and contains all the instructions that determine the structure and function of that cell. One of the most exciting discoveries of this century occurred in 1953 when two scientists, James Watson and Francis Crick, worked out and demonstrated the structure of DNA. They found that it occurs as two spiral threads coiling round each other (a double helix) with 'bridges' across at intervals connecting the two, as in a ladder. Four types of molecules (known as bases) occur on the 'rungs' of the ladder, and these pair up in particular ways (*base pairing*). These four molecules store all the genetic information by being built up in different combinations. In CELL DIVISION, the two DNA threads split apart and each reproduces the missing half to rebuild the double helix. Sometimes the copying does not occur properly and can result in a mutation. Many mutations are lethal but minute changes can occur in this way and this is the genetic basis for evolution and species change.

dogs *see* NH Carnivora.

dolphins *see* NH Cetacea.

Doppler effect the change in the observed frequency or wavelength of a wave when the source producing the wave is moving. If the source, e.g. a vehicle, is moving towards the listener, the frequency increases (and the wavelength decreases) and the opposite happens as it moves away. The result is that the pitch of the sound changes as the vehicle approaches, passes and moves away. The principle applies to all electromagnetic radiation, including light. The light from a moving object appears more red when it is moving away from the observer. This is taken to mean that stars in distant galaxies are moving away from us when they exhibit the *red shift*.

drag *see* AERODYNAMICS.

dragonfly *see* NH Odonata.

drainage *see* G&G drainage.

drugs and pharmacology *drugs* are substances that, when introduced into an animal's body, produce some kind of effect or response. Most drugs are given to help cure illnesses or other medical conditions and there are a great number of different kinds. *Pharmacology* is the name of the scientific study of all aspects of drugs and medicines, including their preparation, uses, properties and effects. Drugs may be given in a variety of different ways: by mouth (orally) as capsules, tablets, or in liquid form; by injection; as a cream or ointment applied to the skin; by inhalation (sometimes using an inhaler); by means of skin patches or insertion just beneath the skin; and as suppositories, which are placed via the anus into the end of the digestive tract (the rectum). All new drugs are rigorously tested before their use is allowed but many occur naturally in plants. CAFFEINE (in coffee and tea) and alcohol are examples of drugs that are in widespread use.

drupe *see* FRUIT.

ductility and malleability *ductility* is the property of metals or ALLOYS that allows them to be drawn out into a thin wire and, although their shape is permanently changed, they retain their strength and do not crack. *Malleability* is similar but is the property that allows metals and alloys to have their shape altered by hammering, rolling, or a similar process into thin sheets. Most metals are ductile, notable examples being copper and gold. The same metals are very malleable, and gold can be produced as very thin gold leaf which is 2 micrometres thick. The high ductility and malleability of metals is because of their molecular structure, in which the lattice can be greatly altered before the atoms are torn apart and the metal breaks.

duodenum *see* PANCREAS.

dyes or dyestuffs substances with a strong colour that can be fixed to material to be dyed, such as fabrics and fibres, plastics, etc. The synthetic dye manufacturing industry began in 1857 when Perkin & Sons set up a factory to produce mauveine. At that time the wool and cotton trade was undergoing vast expansion and demand for dyes was heavy. Before that, dyes had been made mainly from plants but mauveine was soon followed by the production of other synthetic dyes. Alizarin appeared in 1869, Congo red in 1884 and indigo in 1897. Now dye production is a vast industry undertaken in complex chemical plants. In some cases when a dye does not fix to the material, a *mordant* may be necessary. This is a compound (aluminium, chromium and iron hydroxides) that impregnates the fabric and then the dye reacts with the mordant to ensure stability. There are many types of dye, which are categorised according to application.

dynamics *see* MECHANICS.

dynamite *see* EXPLOSIVE.

ear *see* HEARING.

Earth *see* S&A Earth.

earthquake *see* G&G earthquake.

earthworms *see* NH Annelida.

ecdysis and moulting *ecdysis* is the process of shedding skin. It is undergone by a group of invertebrate animals, enabling them to grow. It is a characteristic of arthropods, such as insects, spiders and crabs, which possess a tough, outer shell. At the start of ecdysis a hormone is released under the influence of which the new shell (or *exoskeleton*) begins to form beneath the old one. In addition some materials are reabsorbed from the old exoskeleton and these can then be used again. Eventually, the old exoskeleton splits and the animal extracts itself from its former covering. To begin with, the new exoskeleton is very soft and the animal is often rather vulnerable at this stage. The new exoskeleton expands, often involving the animal taking in air or water to increase its body size, and it hardens by the incorporation of a special substance called *chitin* (or calcium salts in crabs). The animal is thus larger than it was before and may undergo this process several times during the course of its life (*see also* LARVA). *Moulting* is a term that is sometimes used to describe ecdysis. More familiarly, it is applied to the loss of fur, hair, or feathers, which takes place in vertebrate animals, especially in the spring.

ECG *see* ELECTROCARDIOGRAM AND ELECTRO-ENCEPHALOGRAM.

echinoderms *see* NH Echinodermata.

echo a reflected sound that is heard a short time after the original sound was made. There is a delay between making a sound and hearing its echo because it takes the sound waves a little time to travel the distance (light travels so quickly that it does not exhibit this phenomenon). The time delay can be used in echo-sounding machines to locate the sea bed or submerged objects. SONAR (Sound Navigation Ranging) is such a device that operates with high frequency sound, collecting the returning waves that have been reflected from submerged objects. In all such cases, the distance can be calculated from the time taken for the sound to return. Echo-sounding equipment is used in ships and boats and *radar* is a similar principle but uses microwaves.

In small spaces, particularly rooms and halls, the echo time may be very short and the echo is not heard but becomes mixed up with the original sound, and the whole sound seems to be extended. This is called *reverberation* and may be a problem in concert halls where walls and ceilings may have to be modified to reduce the effect.

echo-location *see* NH echo-location.

eclipse *see* S&A eclipse.

ecology *see* NH ecology.

ecosystem *see* NH ecosystem.

EEG *see* ELECTROCARDIOGRAM AND ELECTRO-ENCEPHALOGRAM.

E factor *see* FOOD ADDITIVES.

egg or ovum (*plural* **ova**) the female reproductive cell. An egg may have a hard outer shell, as in birds and turtles, and is usually surrounded by one or more protective layers called membranes. After the egg is fertilised by a male sex cell (*sperm*), it divides into several cells, which become an embryo. The embryo is nourished by a supply of food from the yolk within the egg. Some eggs contain very little yolk whereas others, such as those of birds, have a large amount, which enables a chick to grow quite large before it hatches. Eggs may be extremely small, as in female mammals, which keep the developing embryos inside their bodies. The young of mammals are supplied with all they need from the body of the mother

and grow until they are ready to be born. There are two exceptions to this, the duck-billed platypus and spiny anteater, which are unique among mammals in that they lay eggs (*see* REPRODUCTION).

elasticity the property of any material such that it stretches when forces are applied and recovers its original form when the forces are removed. To stretch a spring or other elastic material a stretching force must be applied to both ends. As the force is increased, the extension becomes greater and up to a certain point the extension is proportional to the force. However, there is a limit to this proportional response and beyond a material's *elastic limit*, it is permanently stretched and will not return to its original length. *Hooke's law* records this physical relationship but applies only to materials if the elastic limit is not exceeded. All materials are elastic to some extent but in many cases the extension is a very small amount.

electricity a general term to cover the energy associated with electric charges, whether static or dynamic. In a simple circuit the *potential difference* between the BATTERY terminals (i.e. the difference in potential) causes a current to flow. Current is measured in AMPERES and potential difference in VOLTS. Batteries supply *direct current* but the electricity supply to homes and offices is *alternating current*. Power stations generate electricity by means of massive alternators (*see* GENERATOR) driven by turbines that are themselves driven by steam from coal, gas, or oil-fired boilers (or heat from a nuclear reactor). The alternators generate a current of 20,000 amps at a voltage of 25,000 volts, which passes through a transformer and then into overhead power cables at a reduced current but a higher voltage, up to 400,000 or 400 kilovolts. The current is reduced to minimise the power losses resulting from heating in the long cables. The cables feed the nationwide network (*the grid*), and power from the grid is distributed by substations where transformers reduce the voltage to 240 volts for ordinary consumption. Heavy industry uses supply at 33,000 volts and light industry 11,000 volts. *See also* STATIC ELECTRICITY.

electrocardiogram (ECG) and electro-encephalogram (EEG) records of the electrical activity in the heart and brain respectively. The ECG is recorded on an electrocardiograph connected through leads to pads on the chest and legs or arms. It often indicates abnormal heart activity and is therefore a useful diagnostic tool. The EEG records the brain's electrical activity on an electroencephalograph. Electrodes placed on the scalp record activity, or brain waves, of which there are four types associated with particular phases of activity or rest.

electrolysis the chemical decomposition (breaking down) of a substance in solution or molten state when an electric current is passed. The solution is called an *electrolyte* and it permits the passage of a current because it forms ions in solution. A strong electrolyte, e.g. sulphuric acid, undergoes complete ionisation. When the current passes through the solutions the ions move to the electrodes of opposite charge; the *cathode* being negatively charged and attracting positively charged ions (*cation*); the *anode* being positively charged and attracting *anions*, which are negatively charged ions. At the electrodes the ions give up their charges to form atoms or groups. Gases are liberated and solids deposited. Electrolysis is used a great deal in industry to extract and purify metals and also to electroplate objects. *Electroplating* consists of metal salts dissolved in a solution into which are put the electrodes. The cathode has the metal plated onto it, and the anode dissolves into the solution, replacing the metal ions. This technique is used to plate with chrome, nickel, gold, silver and other metals, and also to anodise (*see* ANODISING).

electromagnet a magnet created by passing a current through a coil of wire that is wound round a soft iron core; the core becomes a magnet while the current is on. The coil of wire is called a *solenoid*. This magnetic effect of electric current was discovered by H. C. Oersted, a Danish scientist. There is a cumulative magnetic effect because, in producing a magnetic field, the coil magnetises the core, which produces a magnetic field that can be about a thousand times stronger than the field from the core alone. Electromagnets are clearly useful because the magnetic field generated can be controlled easily. They are used in televisions to control the electron beams in the cathode-ray tube, and also in devices such as switches, electric bells, loudspeakers and in the earpiece of a telephone.

An associated phenomenon is that of *electromagnetic induction* in which an electric current is produced in a conductor when it is moved through a magnetic field (*see also* GENERATOR).

electromagnetic waves come from a number of sources and are the effect of oscillating electric and magnetic fields. Their wavelength varies but all travel through free space (a vacuum) at approximately 3 x 10^8ms^{-1} (300,000 kilometres per second), which is the speed of light. The *electromagnetic spectrum* contains waves from low frequency/long wavelength radio waves (long wave) through microwave, infrared and the visible spectrum to ultraviolet X-rays and the short wavelength/high frequency gamma rays.

Approximate wavelengths and frequencies for electromagnetic waves

	Wavelength (m)	Frequency (Hz)
gamma rays	10^{-13}–10^{10}	10^{19}–10^{21}
X-rays	10^{-10}–10^{-8}	10^{17}–10^{19}
ultraviolet radiation	10^{-8}–10^{-7}	10^{15}–10^{17}
visible light	10^{-7}–10^{-6}	10^{14}–10^{15}
infrared radiation	10^{-6}–10^{-2}	10^{11}–10^{14}
microwaves	10^{-2}–10^{-1}	10^{10}–10^{11}
radio waves	10^{-1}–10^{4}	10^{5}–10^{10}

Electromagnetic waves are generated when particles with an electrical charge change their energy, e.g. when an electron changes orbit around a nucleus. It also happens when electrons or nuclei oscillate and their kinetic energy changes. A large change in energy produces high frequency/short wavelength radiation.

Radio waves are the longest in the spectrum and are used to transmit sound and pictures. *Microwaves* have wavelengths of a few centimetres and have numerous uses. *Infrared* (IR) *waves* are generated by the continuous motion of molecules in materials and hot objects give out most. When an electric fire is switched on the infrared radiation is felt in the heat. As objects become hotter and hotter, their molecules vibrate more rapidly and the wavelength of the radiation becomes shorter. Eventually it impinges on the visible spectrum and the object appears 'red hot'. *Ultraviolet* (UV) radiation occurs beyond the violet end of the visible light spectrum, is a component of sunlight and is emitted by white-hot objects. Ultraviolet light from the sun converts steroids in the skin to essential vitamin D but an excess of UV light can be harmful. However, much of the sun's ultraviolet radiation is stopped by the Earth's ozone layer (*see* G&G ozone layer). *Gamma rays* are very short wavelength radiation released during radioactive decay and are the most penetrating of all radiation.

electron *see* ATOM; ELEMENTARY PARTICLES.

electronics an important area of science and technology that deals with electrical circuits using SEMICONDUCTORS, DIODES, TRANSISTORS and other devices in which the movement of electrons is controlled to create switches and other components. Technology has advanced so much in recent years that electronic circuits can fit onto a single *silicon chip* and highly complex circuits are constructed on *printed circuit boards* in which individual components are linked by metal traces printed on the board and through which the current flows.

The use of such boards and microelectronic components is widespread and they are found in computers, cars, watches, televisions, spacecraft and many other machines and pieces of equipment.

electroscope an instrument used in physics for the detection of small electrical charges. It consists of a metal cap joined to a rod that projects down into a case. At the bottom of the rod is a gold leaf. When a charged object touches the cap, some charge is transferred to the rod and gold leaf and because like charges repel each other, the gold leaf rises. When it is charged, the electroscope can be used to determine whether the charge on an object is positive or negative.

electroshock weapon (stun gun/taser) an electronic gun that delivers a high voltage, electrical pulse by means of electrodes, causing temporary immobilization. The weapon fires small electrodes with attached metal wires and these adhere to the skin or clothing of the target. The maximum range of the gun is about 10 metres or 30 feet and versions of these weapons are used by many police forces throughout the world. In normal circumstances the weapon is non-lethal but fatalities have been recorded, usually when the victim has been suffering from a heart condition.

element a pure substance that comprises atoms of the same kind and which cannot be broken down into simpler substances in ordinary chemical reactions (nuclear reactions can, however, alter elements). There are 112 elements known to us, of which 92 occur naturally and the rest have been created in the laboratory (*see* table on page 93). Indeed, scientists continue to experiment and occasionally claim the existence of another element.

Elements combine together to form COMPOUNDS, and under normal conditions all but two elements (bromine and mercury) are either a solid or a gas. The elements are classified by their atomic number into the PERIODIC TABLE, which comprises groups and periods with similar properties and behaviour.

elementary particles or fundamental particles or subatomic particles the basic particles and building blocks of which all matter is made. The three key particles in all atoms—electrons, neutrons and protons—have now been supplemented by new particles. Essentially two types are thought to exist, *leptons* and *hadrons*, and these are identified by the different ways in which they interact with other particles. Leptons include the electron and the *neutrino*, the latter having no charge and virtually no mass. The neutrino was originally proposed on the basis of theory, to preserve the physical laws of mass, energy and momentum, and its existence has since been established experimentally. The proton and neutron are called hadrons, although they are not truly elementary particles, and it is now thought

Elements and their symbols

element	symbol	atomic number	element	symbol	atomic number
actinium	Ac	89	mercury	Hg	80
aluminium	Al	13	molybdenum	Mo	42
americium	Am	95	neodymium	Nd	60
antimony	Sb	51	neon	Ne	10
argon	Ar	18	neptunium	Np	93
arsenic	As	33	nickel	Ni	28
astatine	At	85	niobium	Nb	41
barium	Ba	56	nitrogen	N	7
berkelium	Bk	97	nobelium	No	102
beryllium	Be	4	osmium	Os	76
bismuth	Bi	83	oxygen	O	8
boron	B	5	palladium	Pd	46
bromine	Br	35	phosphorus	P	15
cadmium	Cd	48	platinum	Pt	78
caesium	Cs	55	plutonium	Pu	94
calcium	Ca	20	polonium	Po	84
californium	Cf	98	potassium	K	19
carbon	C	6	praseodymium	Pr	59
cerium	Ce	58	promethium	Pm	61
chlorine	Cl	17	protactinium	Pa	91
chromium	Cr	24	radium	Ra	88
cobalt	Co	27	radon	Rn	86
copper	Cu	29	rhenium	Re	75
curium	Cm	96	rhodium	Rh	45
dysprosium	Dy	66	rubidium	Rb	37
einsteinium	Es	99	ruthenium	Ru	44
erbium	Er	68	samarium	Sm	62
europium	Eu	63	scandium	Sc	21
fermium	Fm	100	selenium	Se	34
fluorine	F	9	silicon	Si	14
francium	Fr	87	silver	Ag	47
gadolinium	Gd	64	sodium	Na	11
gallium	Ga	31	strontium	Sr	38
germanium	Ge	32	sulphur	S	16
gold	Au	79	tantalum	Ta	73
hafnium	Hf	72	technetium	Tc	43
helium	He	2	tellurium	Te	52
holmium	Ho	67	terbium	Tb	65
hydrogen	H	1	thallium	Tl	81
indium	In	49	thorium	Th	90
iodine	I	53	thulium	Tm	69
iridium	Ir	77	tin	Sn	50
iron	Fe	26	titanium	Ti	22
krypton	Kr	36	tungsten	W	74
lanthanum	La	57	uranium	U	92
lawrencium	Lr	103	vanadium	V	23
lead	Pb	82	xenon	Xe	54
lithium	Li	3	ytterbium	Yb	70
lutetium	Lu	71	yttrium	Y	39
magnesium	Mg	12	zinc	Zn	30
manganese	Mn	25	zirconium	Zr	40
mendelevium	Md	101			

that these are composed of real elementary particles called *quarks*. Quarks have become part of a highly elaborate theory of hadron structure in which hadrons occur in two forms, *baryons* and *mesons*, the first comprising three quarks and the latter two plus a quark and its antiquark (*see* S&A antimatter). In addition, quarks have properties termed 'flavour' and 'colour charge', producing a highly complex character for each particle. Although this theory seems to be generally accepted by physicists, quarks have yet to be confirmed experimentally.

elephant *see* NH Proboscidea.

embryo the stage in the development of a new plant or animal that follows on from the fertilisation of an egg by a sperm. It is most often used to describe the young of a mammal before birth while they are developing within the mother and, in birds, to the growing chick while it is still inside the egg. Doctors define an 'embryo' as the stage in the development of a human being, from two weeks after fertilisation until two months, and after this the word *foetus* is used (*see* REPRODUCTION).

embryology the branch of biological or medical study that is concerned with all aspects of the growth and development of embryos.

emulsion *see* COLLOID.

enamel *see* TEETH.

endocrine system the name given to a network of small organs (known as *glands*) within the body of an animal, which are responsible for the production of chemical signalling substances called HORMONES. A hormone is released into the bloodstream and travels in the body until it reaches its target cells or organ somewhere else, where it causes a response to occur. There are several endocrine glands in the body of a human being, including the *pituitary gland* (at the base of the brain), the *thyroid gland* (in the neck), and the paired *adrenal glands* (one above each kidney). The male and female sex organs (the *testes* and *ovaries*) are also endocrine glands that produce hormones that are responsible for the changes that occur at puberty, and control fertility. *See also* REPRODUCTION.

energy the capacity to do work. There are many different forms of energy: light, heat, sound, electrical, kinetic, potential and more, and all are measured in joules (J). *Kinetic energy* is possessed by moving objects and for a mass m, with a constant speed v, the kinetic energy is $\frac{1}{2}mv^2$. So a ball kicked by a footballer has kinetic energy that it loses when it hits the net of the goal, pushing the net outwards. Objects have *potential energy* by virtue of their position, i.e. they have been moved and when released can do work. Hence a stretched spring, a car at the top of a hill, or a weight on a shelf all have potential en-

ergy. The energy is defined as mgh where m is the mass which is raised through a height, h and g is the acceleration of free fall. *Thermal energy* (sometimes called *heat energy*) is that kinetic and potential energy possessed by an object's molecules, and it rises with an increase in temperature. *Electrical energy* is that stored in batteries and *electromagnetic waves* and sound waves also possess energy.

The law of conservation of energy states that energy cannot be created, nor can it be destroyed, but it can be changed from one form to another. This means that in any action all energy can be accounted for. This may be a simple procedure, such as throwing a ball, where chemical energy in the arm launches the ball, which then has kinetic energy. Depending upon the throw, it may have potential energy if the ball stops momentarily before falling, again with kinetic energy. Then when it hits the ground the kinetic energy becomes sound and thermal energy.

Society today requires vast amounts of energy to survive, and this is supplied as electricity, from oil, gas, coal, etc. The primary source of energy is the sun, however, and this energy is stored in plants that in turn provide energy either as food or as fuels. In addition to burning fuels for energy, alternative and renewable sources are being exploited such as tidal, wind, solar and hydroelectric energy.

engine a machine that converts energy into work, and fuel undergoes COMBUSTION to supply the energy. Petrol and diesel engines use the chemical energy from their fuels and electric motors use electrical energy stored in a BATTERY or from a GENERATOR. The human body is also an engine and food is the fuel.

There are essentially two types of engine: those in which the combustion is internal, as in the *internal combustion* engine, and those where the fuel is burned outside the engine itself—*external combustion*. Engines are used to power all sorts of vehicles such as boats, aeroplanes and cars, and although the internal combustion engine is not particularly efficient, it does provide a means of turning fuel into mechanical work very rapidly indeed. In the 1940s a

British engineer, Frank Whittle, invented the gas turbine or *jet engine*. Air enters the front of the engine, is compressed and then enters a combustion chamber where liquid fuel is burnt. The energy produced expands the gas and shoots it out, where it provides both thrust for motion and energy to drive the turbine that operates the compressor.

The *efficiency* of an engine is a ratio of the work provided for the energy put in. In general, most systems that burn fuels are very inefficient because so much energy is lost as heat. As a percentage, the efficiency of petrol and diesel engines is 25 and 35 per cent respectively, while power stations are only around 30 per cent efficient in producing electrical energy. Although electric motors are in themselves about 75 per cent efficient, the process supplying the electrical input energy is only around 30 per cent efficient.

entomology the specialised branch of biology that is concerned with the study of insects. A person who studies insects is known as an *entomologist*.

entropy a measure of the disorder or randomness of a system that tends always to increase. The increase is because at every stage of ENERGY transfer, some energy is wasted and the greater the disorder, the higher is the entropy. One result of entropy is that heat always flows from a hot to a cold body—the basis of the second law of THERMODYNAMICS, which can be rewritten as: any system will always undergo change so as to increase the entropy.

environment *see* NH environment.

enzymes naturally occurring protein molecules that are found in all living things and that act as catalysts (i.e. they speed up and activate chemical reactions, *see* CATALYSIS) within cells. Enzymes are very specialised and each acts only on a certain substance. Also, conditions of temperature and acidity or alkalinity have to be just right or the reaction will not take place. This is one of the reasons why a stable body temperature is maintained in mammals. Some enzymes are involved in breaking down processes, e.g. digestive enzymes such as *ptyalin*, which is present in saliva and breaks down starch to sugar. Others are involved in reactions to build up more complex molecules from simpler ones as in tissue growth.

epiphyte *see* NH epiphyte.

epithelium *see* SMELL.

equilibrium when a system, whether chemical or physical, remains the same over time. In physics an object is *in equilibrium* if all the forces acting on it are equal and opposite. However, there are three equilibrium states. If a system returns to equilibrium position after being moved slightly, then it is in *stable equilibrium*, e.g. tipping slightly a box with a wide base. *Unstable equilibrium* is when the system moves from equilibrium when moved slightly, e.g. a pencil 'stood' on its point, and *neutral equilibrium* is when a movement results in a new equilibrium position, as with a ball. In chemistry equilibrium is reached in a CHEMICAL REACTION when the proportion of reactants and products is constant, as the rate of the forward and reverse reactions is the same. Equilibrium is affected by changes in temperature, pressure, or concentration of the reactants.

erosion *see* G&G erosion.

erythroblast and erythrocyte *see* BONE MARROW.

escape velocity *see* S&A escape velocity.

estrous cycle *see* REPRODUCTION.

estuary *see* NH estuary.

eucaryote the type of cell found in all plants and animals—but not bacteria or blue-green algae (cyanobacteria)—in which the nucleus is bound within a membrane. *See also* PROCARYOTE.

eutherian *see* NH eutherian.

eutrophic *see* NH eutrophic.

evaporation the process that occurs when a liquid turns into a vapour. Heat accelerates the process, which happens because some molecules near the surface of the liquid gain sufficient kinetic ENERGY to overcome the attractive forces of the liquid's molecules and escape into the surrounding atmosphere. During the process of evaporation from a container, the temperature of the liquid falls until heat is replaced from heat in the surroundings. This is the reason why swimmers feel cold when leaving the water, because heat energy is taken from the body, converted into kinetic energy, enabling some water molecules to escape.

Evaporation is occurring all around us as rainwater puddles dry in the sun or as moisture evaporates from lakes, rivers, etc, eventually to form cloud and then rain. The principle is also used in industry, where solutions are made more concentrated by evaporating off the solvent, and also in cooling and refrigeration systems. In a refrigerator, a volatile liquid evaporates and its vapour is pumped away. As it evaporates, it draws heat from the stored food. The pump then compresses the vapour back to liquid, and heat is given off via the cooling fins at the back of the refrigerator.

evaporite *see* G&G evaporite.

evolution the gradual change, over a long period of time, of one species of animal or plant. The organisms eventually acquire characteristics that are different from those of the ancestral species. This is able to occur, firstly, if there has been genetic mutation that allows for different information to be passed on from a parent to its offspring. Secondly, if the offspring (one or several) that received the different characteristic proves better suited to its environment than other members of the species then it is more likely to survive and reproduce. In this way the new characteristic tends to be preserved while those individuals not possessing it are more likely to die out. These changes are very small and take place slowly over many thousands of years, but it is thought that all living organisms have evolved from different ancestors in this way. The study of fossils (*see* G&G fossils) has helped in the understanding of how this may have taken place in particular species. *See also* DARWIN; CHROMOSOME; DNA.

excretion the name given to the process by which an organism gets rid of the waste products of METABOLISM and eliminates them from its body. It differs from the process of getting rid of food waste, which is called *egestion* and is concerned with eliminating material that has been taken in. Excretion gets rid of waste products manufactured within the organism itself. The main waste products are carbon dioxide, water and nitrogen-containing substances from the breakdown of protein.

One way that these are disposed of is by DIFFUSION or leakage to the outside (in plants and simple animals), either from a single cell or through the body. Higher animals have developed specialized organs for excretion of waste products, and these include gills, lungs and kidneys.

expansion *see* CONTRACTION AND EXPANSION.

expansion theory *see* S&A expansion theory.

explosive a substance or mixture that, when heated or subjected to a shock or a blow, releases a very large amount of energy very violently. The chemicals are actually undergoing rapid decomposition, producing large volumes of gas and quantities of heat. Explosives have numerous uses, both military and civil. In CONSTRUCTION they are used for clearing land and blasting new cuttings through rock, in mining, quarrying and tunnelling, and also to demolish large structures, e.g. old cooling towers or multistory buildings.

There are basically three groups of explosives. *Propellants* are compounds that burn at a steady speed and can be detonated (set off) only under very specific conditions, e.g. as used in rockets. *Initiators* (or primary explosives) are extremely sensitive to heat and shock and are used in very small quantities to initiate explosions in large masses of less sensitive explosive. Compounds such as mercury fulminate $(Hg(ONC)_2)$ and some metallic azides, e.g. lead azide, $Pb(N_3)_2$, are initiators. *High explosives* are very powerful yet more stable and are used in bombs and shells.

Dynamite is a mixture of nitroglycerine with other compounds, while TNT (trinitrotoluene) is a very violent explosive made from toluene with nitric and sulphuric acids. Plastic explosives can be moulded by hand and are made of a high explosive such as cyclonite mixed with an oil binder.

extinction the event when a plant or animal species dies out completely. It has occurred many times to thousands of plant and animal species in the course of the Earth's history. There have been times of mass extinctions, e.g. at the end of the Palaeozoic geological era (*see* G&G geological timescale), about 248 million years ago, when it is thought about 90 per cent of species ceased to exist. A further similar event took place some 65 million years ago, in the early Tertiary period, when the dinosaurs became extinct. Until the appearance of modern man, which was recent in terms of geological time (about 100,000 years ago), extinctions could be described as 'natural', occurring because of the processes of evolution. Mass extinctions were probably brought about by climatic (especially temperature) changes, volcanic activity and possibly collision of asteroids with the Earth. Man's impact upon the Earth has been enormous as whole environments have been changed by tree felling, the development of modern agriculture and industry, and by pollution. Sadly, the extinction of many species that used to inhabit the Earth has been brought about by the destructive activities of human beings.

extrusion a manufacturing process used in the production of shaped metal and particularly plastic goods. It is the most economical of plastic-shaping methods, and the products are simple in shape and have features in just two dimensions so that they can be extruded in the third, continuous dimension. Pipes and gutters, strips, tubes, fibres can all be produced in this way. The essence of the process is a large screw that receives grains or pellets of plastic that have been heated and compressed, and the melt is then forced out through a die, which gives the section its shape. PVC foam can also be produced by extrusion. In the extrusion of metal, a block is forced by a ram out through a die. Some metals are extruded while cold but most are heated to increase the malleability (*see* DUCTILITY AND MALLEABILITY).

eye *see* SIGHT.

Fahrenheit scale *see* TEMPERATURE.

family *see* CLASSIFICATION.

farad *see* SI UNITS.

fats a group of naturally existing compounds known as *lipids*. They are composed of combinations of one molecule of a substance called GLYCEROL and three of fatty acids. They are found widely in plants and animals and are very important as long-term energy stores, having twice the number of calories as carbohydrates. In mammals there is a layer of fat deposited beneath the skin that provides insulation, preventing heat loss from the body. This is a vital provision for many animals, enabling some to inhabit the coldest regions of the Earth, e.g. seals, polar bears and penguins. These fat reserves enable some animals, e.g. bears, to hibernate through the cold winter months, and when they emerge in the spring they must immediately replenish their fat stores. The layer of fat beneath the skin helps to cushion the body against injury and at deeper levels it is stored as fatty (adipose) tissue.

faults *see* G&G folds.

feedback effects of global warming as global temperatures rise, it is believed that certain feedback effects are likely to come into operation which may further accelerate warming. The overall influence of these effects is quite difficult to predict as they themselves may be counterbalanced or lessened by other processes that may be triggered. One such feedback process is called the *Ice Aledo* effect. The whiteness of snow and ice acts as an effective reflector of solar energy. Melting of polar ice and less winter snow cover will result in more dark-coloured land being exposed and hence more heat being absorbed, thus accelerating the rate of warming and melting. Additionally, even at the higher altitudes where ice may persist, its thickness will be reduced due to melting and this lessens the ability of new ice to form during the polar winter. However, if ice recedes and land is exposed, there is a possibility of future colonisation by plants, which will then remove CO_2 from the atmosphere. Also, in those areas of the world where plant growth is currently restricted by cold temperatures and a short growing season, warming may produce more equable conditions. Increased plant growth in these regions will again result in a greater utilisation of atmospheric CO_2 and hence be of some benefit.

Alternatively, if thawing occurs in TUNDRA regions, large quantities of trapped methane will be released, boosting the GREENHOUSE EFFECT. Warming may also enable methane trapped within the sea bed to be released. At present, about 50 per cent of the CO_2 generated by human activity is absorbed by the oceans but it is thought that if sea temperatures rise, this process will become less effective so leading to an additional greenhouse effect. Although water vapour is not generally considered to be a GREENHOUSE GAS, it nevertheless exerts a considerable effect. Clouds prevent heat ascending from the earth's surface from escaping, but they also provide a barrier that stops some solar energy from getting through. As global temperatures rise, there will be greater evaporation from both the oceans and land-based bodies of fresh water, hence increasing cloud formation. However, the overall effect of this is a matter of some debate.

fermentation a process carried out by certain microorganisms, e.g. yeast, bacteria and moulds, which break down organic substances (those containing carbon, hydrogen and oxygen) into simpler molecules, producing energy. Alcoholic fermentation is a process that has been harnessed for centuries. In it, yeast converts sugar to alcohol and carbon dioxide, and it is used to produce such drinks as wine, beer and cider. Fermentation is one of the processes now used in BIOTECHNOLOGY and is important in the manufacture of cheese, yoghurt and bread. Also, and most importantly, it is used in the production of DRUGS such as antibiotics.

fertilisation the fusion or joining together of the male (sperm) and female (egg or ovum) sex cells, which is the essential part of sexual reproduction. Fertilisation describes the process in which the two cells come together to become one, and it sets in motion a chain of events (involving further cell division and growth) that eventually gives rise to a new individual. It is a common event in both plants and animals and enables genetic 'mixing' to occur as the new organism receives its characteristics from each parent. In many animals, e.g. most fish, fertilisation is described as *external* as the eggs are laid outside the body and sperm are shed over them. In many

other animals, e.g. mammals, fertilisation is *internal* as the male sex cells are released inside the body of the female.

fertilisers chemicals added to the soil to improve crops and their yield and the growth of plants and flowers. Fertilisers replace the nutrients in the soil that are extracted by growing plants. Modern farming is very intensive and natural processes are unable to provide all the necessary nutrients required. In addition to carbon, hydrogen and oxygen, there are other *essential elements* such as nitrogen, phosphorus, potassium, calcium, magnesium and sulphur. Plants require *trace elements* (perhaps in parts per million quantities), such as iron, boron, manganese, zinc, copper, molybdenum and chlorine. Artificial fertilisers make up a lot of the deficits in these elements.

Ammonium sulphate is an important nitrogenous fertiliser (i.e. nitrogen-supplying), and other chemicals used include sodium nitrate, urea and ammonia. *Superphosphates* contain phosphorus, the chemical used being calcium hydrogen phosphate, $Ca(H_2PO4)_2$.

It is essential that fertilisers are used correctly and that they are not overused as the excess nutrients can have detrimental effects on land and particularly on streams and rivers. As the nutrients drain into water they encourage the growth of algae and surface plants, which choke the stream, resulting in a lack of oxygen in the water that eventually kills animal and plant life beneath the surface.

foetus *see* EMBRYO; REPRODUCTION.

filters and filtration a *filter* is a device for separating solids or particles suspended in solution from the liquid, and *filtration* is the separation process. It may also involve removing particles from a gas. There are numerous materials that are used as filters: filter paper, a pure CELLULOSE paper used in laboratories; cloth and paper filters are used in engines to clean oil and air; crushed charcoal and sand are used in industry; and in medicine DIALYSIS machines use membranes as filters to cleanse the blood of patients with defective kidneys.

The *filtrate* is the clear liquid that results from filtration while the solid particles left are called the *residue*. *See also* OSMOREGU-LATION.

firedamp *see* METHANE.

flashpoint the lowest temperature at which certain liquids give off sufficient flammable vapour to produce a brief flash when a small flame is applied. The term is used particularly for products such as petrol which vaporise very easily, because it is for all practical purposes the temperature at which petrol burns. It is important to be aware of this when petrol is used, transported, or stored. The same applies to industrial solvents such as toluene, benzene, ethanol, etc, which have flashpoints up to 13°C (55.4°F). Benzene has a melting point of about 5°C (41°F) but will generate an explosive vapour while solid.

flight a few specialised groups of animals possess particular features that enable them to fly, and these include insects, such as beetles, flies, dragonflies and butterflies, and birds and bats. The forewings in beetles are hardened and form protective covers for the rear pair of flying wings, which are moved in coordination, and these are the most ancient group known to have possessed flight. Bees and wasps also have two pairs of flying wings that are hooked together and move as one. Similarly, in butterflies, the two pairs of wings are overlapped and move as a single pair and are covered with numerous minute scales. Insect wings are extensions of the outer covering (*cuticle*) of the middle part of the body (*thorax*) behind the head. They are membranes with veins running through them and are moved by large flight muscles that bend the thorax out of shape. As they move up and down, the angle of the wings alters in relation to the body, which allows for lift on both the up and down strokes of the beat.

In birds and bats the wings are modified forelimbs or arms. In bats the membranous wings are a layer of skin spread between the long forelimbs and fingers and the body and hind limbs. Birds possess several adaptations for flight, including a lighter skeleton than other vertebrate animals, fewer organs, to reduce weight, and aerodynamic wings with modified flight feathers.

flood *see* G&G flood.

floodplain *see* G&G floodplain.

flotation and buoyancy *buoyancy* is the upward thrust felt by an object in a fluid and is equal to the weight of the fluid displaced (*see* ARCHIMEDES' PRINCIPLE). An object in water experiences this upthrust because although the object is under pressure on all sides from the liquid, the pressure is greatest where the water is deepest, i.e. underneath the object. Hence an object will float if the upthrust is more than its weight and the *law of flotation* states that a floating object will displace its own weight of the fluid in which it floats. Thus if a block is floated in water and then in a less dense fluid, it will float lower in the less dense fluid to displace a greater volume.

This principle applies to ships, and because salt water is denser than fresh water, a ship floats lower in fresh water. Water temperature also affects DENSITY and therefore affects flotation. All ships have a line marked on their side (the *Plimsoll line*), which indicates the point beyond which the ship cannot be loaded. This is particularly important for a ship sailing from cold salt water to warm, less salty water.

flowers the reproductive organs of a group of plants called *Angiospermae* or *Anthophyta* (*see* NH Angiospermae), which are the flowering plants. They vary greatly in size, from the very small and insignificant to the large and magnificent, showing an enormous range of colours and patterns of petals. Before the flower bud opens, it is usually tightly folded and enclosed by green, leaf-like structures called *sepals*. These together make up an outer supporting structure for the flower, called the *calyx*. When the flower bud opens, the coloured petals expand and the sepals may wither and fall off. Petals may attract insects to the flower for pollination, but the actual reproductive parts are contained inside them. These are the *stamens*, which are the male organs, and the *carpels*, which are female and contain egg cells or *ovules*. These structures are supported at the base by a portion of the flower called the *receptacle*. Following fertilisation, the ovules eventually form seeds.

fluids substances that flow easily and readily

alter their shape in response to outside forces. Liquids and gases are both fluids. Liquids have freely moving particles that tend to be restricted to the one mass, but gases expand to fill their containing space and do not maintain the same volume. These properties of fluids are very useful in many ways, particularly in industry where machines utilise fluid- or gas-filled chambers or cylinders to operate mechanisms, e.g. the braking system on a car.

Hydrostatic is the term applied to a machine using fluid pressure, and PNEUMATIC is a system that uses compressed air, e.g. air-brakes, pneumatic drills and other tools.

fluorescent lamp *see* LIGHT BULB.

fluorine *see* HALOGENS.

fog *see* SUSPENSION.

folds *see* G&G folds.

food additives chemicals added to foods by manufacturers to improve a particular property, whether it is colour, shelf-life, taste, or appearance. In addition to colourings and preservatives there are anti-oxidants to stop reaction of the food with oxygen, sweeteners, flavour enhancers (e.g. monosodium glutamate, MSG), emulsifiers, pH adjusters and many more. There is now a regulatory system whereby each additive that can be used in food is given a number and it is then listed on the packaging. Although the vast proportion of these compounds cause no problems, some do create side effects in some people. *Tartrazine*, a well-known example, is a yellow colouring agent that can cause hyperactivity in children and also skin complaints and breathing problems. Other *E factors* may cause dizziness, vomiting, or muscular weakness.

food chain in simple terms, the route by which energy is transferred through a number of organisms by one eating another from a lower level (called a *trophic* level). At the base of the chain are the *primary producers*, which are the green plants. These are able to use energy from the sun to manufacture food substances from carbon dioxide and water. These food substances (glucose, cellulose and starch) are made use of by animals at the next level in the chain. The herbivores that eat the green plants are known as *primary consumers*. These in turn are eaten by carnivores (flesh-eating animals), which are called *secondary consumers*. There may be more than one level of secondary consumer (a flesh-eater may itself be eaten by a larger carnivore), ending up with animals at the end of the chain, e.g. lions, which are not preyed upon and are called the *top predators*. When these and all organisms die, however, they are eaten by scavenging animals and the remains are eventually broken down by microorganisms so that none of the energy is lost but is used again. Food chains are often highly complicated, and all those that exist in a given environment are interlinked and form a *food web*. A food chain should be perfectly balanced, with many more organisms at the lower levels than at the higher ones. Sometimes the natural balances are upset, and this may be the result of human interference. For example, in Britain there are no large carnivores such as wolves because they were hunted and killed off during the Middle Ages. In Scotland red deer numbers are too high and (although the situation is complicated) these would, at one time, have been hunted by wolves.

food preservation the prevention of food spoilage by chemical decomposition and the action of microorganisms. It is generally achieved by sterilising the food, which destroys any BACTERIA, by heating it in sealed containers (canning) or by pickling, drying, freezing, smoking, etc. Pickling, drying and salting are methods that were used over history, and these kept foods fresh through the use of agents (acid, i.e. vinegar and smoke) in which bacteria would not survive or by the removal of water (essential to the growth of bacteria) as in drying. These established methods have been supplemented by modern techniques such as canning and freezing and also *freeze-drying*. Freeze-drying is used for numerous foods, notably coffee and perishable foods (and it has been used for some time in the medical, veterinary and pharmaceutical fields). The process involves freezing, producing ice from the liquid content of the material, and then *sublimation*, i.e. the ice is extracted as vapour at low pressure and temperature. Foods preserved in this way can be kept for very long periods.

Another recent innovation is that of *irradiation*, in which food is subjected to ionising radiations (RADIOACTIVITY) to kill microorganisms. The technique is still under scrutiny and not everyone is fully convinced that it is suitable.

foraminifer *see* NH Foraminifera.

force the push or pull upon a body which may cause it to move, stop moving, or alter direction of motion. Force is defined as the mass of a body multiplied by its acceleration. If the mass is in kilograms and the acceleration in metres per second per second (m/s^2) then the force is in *newtons*. An object will continue to move at a constant speed and in a straight line unless another force acts upon it. For example, a craft in space under the influence of no forces will maintain the same speed in the same direction and would need a force to change its direction. This is the basis of *Newton's first law of motion*, which states that an object will continue in a state of rest or uniform motion in a straight line unless an external force acts upon it. The second law of motion relates to momentum, and the third law can be given concisely as to every action there is an equal, opposite reaction.

On Earth, we have to contend with friction and gravity but objects can move at a constant velocity or be at rest if forces acting on them are balanced. So an aeroplane can maintain a constant air speed because lift and weight are balanced, as are thrust and air resistance. Should any of these constituent forces change, however, then the velocity of the airline would change.

formula (*plural* **formulae**) in mathematics or physics, a law or relationship denoted by symbols and figures, and possibly expressed in algebraic (*see* ALGEBRA) form.

In chemistry, it is a type of shorthand notation that enables a substance to be written in terms of ELEMENTS and MOLECULES, using letters to represent the elements (*see* SYMBOLS). There are three types of chemical formula: an *empirical formula* shows the simplest ratio of atoms present in a compound, e.g. butane has the empirical

formula C_2H_5, although it is really C_4H_{10}. The number and type of atoms present is shown in the *molecular formula*, in the case of butane, C_4H_{10}, which means there are four carbon and ten hydrogen atoms in every molecule. The *structural formula* indicates the structure of a molecule and shows the bonds between atoms.

fossil fuels *see* G&G fossil fuels.

fossils *see* G&G fossils.

fragmentation *see* ASEXUAL REPRODUCTION.

freezing the change in a material's state from liquid to solid, brought about by reducing its temperature. The temperature at which this change occurs is called the *freezing point*. For pure substances the freezing point is the same as the *melting point*. The freezing point varies enormously between materials as the following table shows:

hydrogen	−259°C	(−434°F)
mercury	−39°C	(−38°F)
argon	−189°C	(−308°F)
oxygen	−218°C	(−360°F)
water	0°C	(32°F)
silicon	1410°C	(2570°F)
nitrogen	−210°C	(−346°F)
sodium	98°C	(208°F)
carbon	3,550°C	(6,422°F)

Impurities reduce the freezing point, e.g. salt reduces the freezing point of water, and this property is exploited in car engines by adding *antifreeze* to the coolant to avoid freezing in winter.

frequency (*symbol* **f**) the number of complete wavelengths (*see* WAVE) of a wave motion per second. Frequency is measured in hertz (Hz) and is calculated from the formula $c = f$, where c is the speed of the wave and (lambda) is the wavelength. In the *electromagnetic* spectrum there is a large range of frequencies, from low frequency radio waves to very high frequency gamma rays.

Sound waves are very different from light waves, and the human ear can hear sounds with frequencies between 20 Hz and 20, 000 Hz (or 20 kHz). A different frequency is heard as a different sound, with high frequencies being sounds of high pitch. The scientific pitch of middle C on the piano has a frequency of 256 Hz and the Cs below and above are 128 Hz and 512

Hz, although when a piano is tuned these frequencies are changed slightly.

friction the force that acts against motion, trying to stop materials and objects sliding across each other. A moving object will tend to slow down because of friction, and a force has to be exerted to keep it moving. The force required will differ depending on the surface and the nature of the material moving across it. Friction is higher between solids (or a solid and liquid) than between solids and air. The reason for friction is that rough surfaces have minute projections that restrict movement, and also there is a tendency for molecules to stick together under pressure. Friction in solids can be divided into *static friction* and *dynamic friction*. If an object is being pushed across a surface, the static friction is the maximum force, applied just before the object moves, while the dynamic friction is that in action when the object is moving and it is much less than the static friction. There is also *fluid friction*, when an object moves through a liquid or a gas. The effects of friction can be seen all around us—the difficulty of pushing a heavy box across the floor; being able to walk and run because of the friction between our shoes and the ground; a car's tires gripping the road and a train's wheels gripping the rails. In all these cases, friction causes the loss of energy as heat, something that applies to all machines.

frogs *see* NH Amphibia.

fruit a fruit develops from the ovary of a FLOWER and is given the name when it is mature and ripe. It contains the seeds, and there are two main kinds: dry, e.g. an acorn, and succulent or juicy, e.g. a tomato. The fruit is the means by which the seeds, which will become new plants, are protected until they are ready to be dispersed. Most juicy fruits are eaten by animals, and the seeds pass through the digestive system without harm and are scattered in the droppings to grow elsewhere. Dry fruits often split open to release the seeds, which may be shot out explosively, be carried away by wind or water, or may cling to the fur of animals to drop off elsewhere. There are several different kinds of juicy fruit, including a berry (e.g. blackberry),

which is an *aggregate* fruit formed from one flower but with lots of seeds, a pineapple, which is a *multiple fruit* formed from a cluster of flowers, and a cherry, a *simple fruit*, also known as a *drupe*, containing a stone surrounding the seed. Many of the food plants that we think of as vegetables are actually fruits, e.g. peas, beans and marrows. Pears and apples are known as *pomes*, and they and some other kinds of fruit, such as strawberries, are also called *false fruits*. This is because the fruit does not just develop from the ovary of the flower but also from the receptacle.

fuel a material that stores energy and upon combustion will release that energy. Fossil fuels (*see* G&G fossil fuels) are the most widely used and account for most of the world's energy supply, with PETROLEUM being the largest contributor. When these fuels are burnt (oil, gas, coal), energy is released and the other products are carbon dioxide, water and a variety of other gases and solids depending upon the original composition or purity of the fuel. NUCLEAR fuels such as plutonium and uranium are unstable and release large amounts of energy in nuclear reactions.

fuel cell a cell that generates electricity directly by the conversion through electro-chemical reactions of fuels (gas or liquid) fed into the cell. The two components required are a fuel and an oxidant, which are supplied to the electrodes, and invariably a catalyst is used (*see* CATALYSIS). Fuels used include hydrogen (H_2), hydrazine (N_2H_4), ammonia (NH_3) and methanol (CH_3OH), and the oxidant is usually oxygen (O_2) or air. The electrolyte (*see* ELECTROLYSIS) in the cell can be a solution or solid, or special ion-exchange resins that, as the name suggests, contain ions that can be replaced by other ions. Fuel cells have been used on spacecraft. In these, hydrogen and oxygen are combined to produce electricity.

fungicide *see* PESTICIDE.

fungus (*plural* **fungi**) a simple organism that may be one cell or exist as threads (or *filaments*) of many cells. Fungi were once classified as simple plants but as they contain no chlorophyll and cannot photosynthesise, they are now placed in their own kingdom—fungi (*see* CLASSIFICATION and NH fungus). They absorb their food from other organic material and are vital in the breakdown and recycling of organic substances. They are essential in that they make minerals available to the roots of growing plants. Fungi are vital organisms for people, being used in the processes of BIOTECHNOLOGY and FERMENTATION. Some are harmful, causing diseases in plants and animals, others are parasites, and a few are edible, e.g. mushrooms. The scientific study of fungi is called *mycology*.

fuse a very useful, protective device for electrical CIRCUITS. Most electrical appliances have their own fuse in the plug and in addition circuits, whether domestic or industrial, have fuses. In all circuits there is the possibility of a fault developing and too much current flowing, which could damage the circuit or cause a fire. The fuse is placed in the circuit to avoid this possibility. The commonest form of fuse is a short piece of thin wire encased in a small glass tube with metal ends which overheats, melts and breaks if too high a current flows through it. It is placed in the live wire of the circuit so that if a fault develops, the current is switched off. The fuse value is greater than, but as close as possible to, the current that usually goes through the appliance; 3 amp and 13 amp fuses are commonest.

More recently, *circuit breakers* have replaced fuses. These are switches that automatically break the circuit in the event of an overload and they can be reset when the fault has been eliminated.

fusion *see* REPRODUCTION.

galaxy *see* S&A galaxy.

galvanising a process whereby one metal is coated with a thin layer of another, more reactive metal. It is performed to offer protection to the coated metal, and iron and steel are often treated in this way. Galvanising is done in two ways: by dipping into molten zinc or by electrodeposition, i.e. electrolysis. When iron or steel is dipped into zinc, a little aluminium or magnesium is added to prevent a zinc iron ALLOY forming, as this is very brittle.

With electrodeposition, the object to be coated is connected to the cathode (*see* ELECTROLYSIS) and zinc ions from the electrolyte coat the object while current flows. The layer of zinc then protects the underlying metal because corrosion affects it before the iron or steel beneath.

galvanometer an instrument used to measure small currents and often called a *milliammeter* if its scale is calibrated accordingly. It uses the physical property that a wire in a magnetic field experiences a force when a current passes through the wire. The current to be measured passes through a coil in a magnetic field and as a result the coil turns, and in turn it moves a pointer across the scale. Not surprisingly, this is called the *moving coil galvanometer*. The movement of the coil is resisted by springs, and it comes to rest when the force generated by the coil in the magnetic field is balanced by the springs. The higher the current, the greater the force generated and the farther the pointer moves across the scale. The sensitivity of the meter (i.e. giving more pointer movement for a particular current) can be increased in several ways, and some galvanometers use a light indicator in place of the pointer. A beam of light is shone on to a mirror positioned on the coil and any movement deflects the beam along the scale. Although galvanometers are used a lot and can be converted for use as ammeters or voltmeters, many modern versions are digital instruments.

gamete *see* CELL DIVISION; POLLEN; REPRODUCTION.

gametophyte generation *see* PLANTS.

ganglion *see* NERVOUS SYSTEM.

gas the fluid state of matter (SOLID and LIQUID being the others). Gases are capable of continuing expansion in every direction because the molecules are held together only very loosely. A gas will therefore fill whatever contains it, and because the molecules move around rapidly and at random, they bump into each other and the walls of the container, which results in a PRESSURE being exerted on the walls. If a certain amount of gas in a container is put into another container half the size, the pressure doubles (if the temperature is constant). Heating a gas in a container also increases the pressure. It can be seen therefore that the temperature, pressure and volume of a *fixed mass* of gas are all related. Many years ago early experimentation with gases resulted in three *gas laws*, which when combined can be stated as:

For a fixed mass of gas, $\dfrac{pv}{T}$ is constant

where p is pressure, v is volume and T is temperature. The three laws individually are:

$\dfrac{p}{T}$ = constant if v is unchanged (the pressure law)

$\dfrac{v}{T}$ = constant if p is unchanged (Charles' law)

PV = constant if T is unchanged (Boyle's law)

Only an *ideal gas* obeys these laws exactly, and no gas can be considered ideal in this sense, although many approach this point at medium pressures and temperatures.

gaseous exchange *see* LUNGS AND GILLS.

gastropod *see* NH Gastropoda.

gas turbine a type of internal combustion ENGINE, used in aircraft and ships, which is often called the *jet engine* because it involves the production of a jet of hot gas that provides the propulsion. It was invented by Frank Whittle, a British engineer, in the 1940s. The jet engine produces a forward force by thrusting out gas behind and it takes in large quantities of air for this purpose. The air also supplies the oxygen needed for COMBUSTION of the fuel. The air intake is therefore at the front of the engine, and behind is the compressor, which consists of a number of blade-like fans. The compressor forces air under high pressure into the combustion chamber where the fuel (kerosene) burns to produce a hot gas that expands and is thrust out of the rear of the engine, creating a forward thrust on the engine. This gas passes through the turbine before being expelled, providing the rotational force to turn the compressor.

Geiger counter (Geiger tube or Geiger-Müller tube) an instrument that can detect and measure ionising radiations, mainly alpha, beta and gamma rays. It was named after the German physicist Hans Geiger. It is made of a sealed and enclosed tube with a fine wire down the centre of the tube. The tube is filled with argon gas at low pressure, and the wire is the anode and the tube forms the cathode. The end of the tube is covered by a mica window through which the radiations pass. When a particle with a charge (or gamma ray) enters the tube, the argon is ionised into electrons and positive ions, which move to their respective and opposingly charged electrodes and for a moment the gas conducts and a small current flows in the circuit. This is registered by a *ratemeter* (or *scaler*) and can be converted to a series of clicks.

generator a machine that produces an electric current from mechanical motion. It is based on the principle of electromagnetic induction (*see also* ELECTROMAGNET). If a coil in a magnetic field is rotated, a current is generated (induced) as the coil cuts through the magnetic field. As the coil completes its rotation, it cuts the field in the opposite direction and an induced current flows in the opposite direction. This is the basis of an alternating current generator, or *alternator*. To enable the coil to continue turning, carbon brushes form the connection between the coil and the outside circuit by rubbing against slip rings fixed to the ends of the coil. To generate direct current from a generator, the device is fitted with a *commutator* and instead of having two slip rings the generator has one ring that is split (i.e. the split ring, or commutator) and the coil ends connect to each half. Then every time the coil passes the split, the connections are reversed and current flows in a constant direction to the outside circuit.

Cars have alternators for charging the battery (after the supply has been turned into direct current), and enormous versions are used in power stations for generating mains electricity.

genes *see* CHROMOSOMES AND GENES.

genetics and genetic engineering *genetics* is the name given to the branch of science that deals with the study of CHROMOSOMES AND GENES and the way in which characteristics are passed on from parents to offspring (called *heredity*). It is one of the most important areas of modern scientific study, especially in helping us to gain an understanding of how certain hereditary diseases and disorders are passed on. It also enables new strains of organisms with useful characteristics to be bred more easily. *Genetic engineering* is the term given to the modification by human beings of an organism's genetic make-up, which is done in two main ways. Firstly, DNA from one organism might be transferred to another where it would not normally occur. This has been carried out in the fight against various diseases and is a technique within BIO-TECHNOLOGY. An example is the gene that codes for the HORMONE insulin in human beings, which has been inserted into the cells of certain BACTERIA. The bacteria have been harnessed to produce insulin, which is then used to treat diabetes. Secondly, DNA from two different organisms has been combined to produce an entirely new species. It is this second area of research that has caused a great deal of concern and raised fears that harmful organisms might be produced. It is therefore subject to extremely strict regulation and controls so that all the organisms involved remain securely within the laboratory.

genus *see* CLASSIFICATION.

geochemistry *see* G&G geochemistry.

geochronology *see* G&G geochronology.

geography *see* G&G geography.

geological timescale *see* G&G geological timescale.

geology *see* G&G geology.

geomagnetism *see* G&G geomagnetism.

geometry a branch of mathematics that deals with the properties of lines, curves and surfaces. It includes the study of planar (flat) figures such as the circle and triangle and also three-dimensional figures such as the sphere and cube. Geometry (meaning measurement of the Earth) was first used in the measurement of land areas and today it is the basis of much calculation undertaken by engineers, builders and architects.

Coordinate geometry is where points, lines and shapes are represented by algebraic (*see* ALGEBRA) expressions. In two dimensions the plane containing a point is represented by x and y axes at right angles to each other that meet at the origin, O.

The position of a point can then be defined by two distances, one along the x and one along the y *axis*, which intersect at the point in question. Lines are represented by equations, whether straight or curved. The values given to the particular position of a point are its *Cartesian coordinates*.

A well-known *theorem* (a rule proven by reasoning) in geometry is *Pythagoras' theorem*, which states that in a right-angled triangle the (area of the) square on the hypotenuse (the longest side opposite the right angle) equals the sum (of the areas) of the squares on the other two sides.

geomorphology *see* G&G geomorphology.

geophysics *see* G&G geophysics.

geothermal energy geothermal energy technologies harness the heat that exists within the surface of the Earth for domestic and industrial purposes. Strictly speaking, *ground source heat pumps* extract and utilise SOLAR ENERGY that has heated the immediate surface layers of the ground but other technologies harness the deeper, geothermal heat generated by molten rocks within the Earth's crust. Most commonly, this involves tapping into reservoirs of super-heated water or steam as in Iceland, where this resource is widely used to provide heat, power and hot water for buildings. (*See* G&G geothermal energy.)

gestation and birth the period of time in a mammal between fertilisation of the egg and birth of the young, which, in human beings, is also called *pregnancy.* The *gestation* period is characteristic of the species concerned and varies from 18 days in the mouse to 9 months in human beings and 18 to 23 months in the Indian elephant. Usually, larger mammals have longer gestation periods, and their offspring require care for a greater length of time before they can live independently. Following FERTILISATION of the egg in a mammal, cells divide rapidly to become an EMBRYO that becomes attached, by means of a special organ called the *placenta*, to the wall of the *womb* (*uterus*). The placenta allows oxygen and food to pass to the baby through a connecting cord called the *umbilical cord.*

When the gestation period is completed and the baby is ready to be born, the process of *birth* takes place. This is triggered off by hormones that cause the womb to contract by means of the powerful muscles that are present in its wall. The baby is gradually forced through the birth canal (*vagina*) to the outside and afterwards the placenta is also shed. Most mammals eat through the umbilical cord (but it is cut after a human birth), and the portion that is left attached to the baby soon dries, shrivels and drops off, leaving a mark called the *umbilicus* or *navel*.

Animals that give birth to live young as described above are called *viviparous*, whereas those that lay eggs that develop and hatch outside the mother's body (e.g. birds and some reptiles) are called *oviparous*. Some animals keep their eggs inside the body for protection. The young are nourished within the egg and not by the body of the mother and these animals (e.g. some fish, reptiles and insects) are called *ovoviviparous*.

ggbfs *see* BLAST FURNACE.

gills *see* LUNGS AND GILLS.

glacier *see* G&G glacier.

gland *see* ENDOCRINE SYSTEM.

glass the hard transparent material from which windows, bottles, jars and glasses, lenses and laboratory ware is made. There are several types of glass but the essential ingredient in all is silica (SiO_2).

Man-made glasses appeared about 4000 BC in Egypt, and by 1500 BC glass-making had developed into both an art and a technology. Glass science was then not developed until the work of numerous scientists, including Faraday then later Zeiss, Abbé and Schott. Over 30 elements had been used in experimental glasses by the turn of the 20th century and now 70 have been tried, but just three commercial systems account for nearly all glass production (*see* CERAMICS). The raw materials are heated in a furnace to form a red-hot liquid. A blob of this molten glass on the end of a 'blowpipe' can be blown into intricate and beautiful shapes by glass-blowers. However, most glassware is produced from mould (for bottles, etc), and *sheet glass* is made by floating molten glass on a bed of molten tin. Glass is used in many ways, and its properties can be altered by the

processing or addition of other materials. *Toughened glass* is manufactured by cooling glass rapidly under cold air; *laminated glass* has a plastic layer sandwiched by two layers of glass, increasing toughness; and *glass fibres* in a resin form a useful *composite* (i.e. a mix or combination of materials) for making strong but light structures, e.g. boat and car bodies (*see also* SYNTHETIC FIBRES). *Bullet-proof* glass is a very effective composite that consists of several sections with different properties.

glass wool *see* SYNTHETIC FIBRES.

global warning *see* NH greenhouse effect.

glomerulus *see* OSMOREGULATION.

glucose *see* CELLULOSE.

glue *see* ADHESIVE.

glycerol or glycerin a sweet-tasting, viscous liquid with no colour or smell. It belongs to the alcohol group but has a structure similar to a sugar. It is derived synthetically from propane (C_3H_6)—its formula is $HOCH_2CH (OH)CH_2OH$—or as a by-product in the production of soap. It occurs naturally in plants and animals as a component of stored FATS. It is an extremely useful compound, being used in the manufacture of ice cream, sweets and other foodstuffs, toilet preparations, resins and explosives. It also has the useful property that it can absorb up to 50 per cent of its weight of water vapour, which means it can be used as a moisturising agent.

glycogen *see* ANIMALS; PLANTS.

goat *see* NH Artiodactyla.

gold one of the NOBLE METALS, a bright yellow metal and a good conductor of electricity and heat. It is soft and malleable (*see* DUCTILITY) and can be produced as very thin (even see-through) leaf or drawn out into wire and it is very resistant to CORROSION. Its primary use for thousands of years has been in the making of jewellery and coins, and its value has been fundamentally important to the financial stability of the world's currency markets.

Gold occurs as nuggets or veins or smaller particles in quartz or in streams after it has been weathered out of its original site. It is also found in the residue after copper has been purified by ELECTROLYSIS. It is extracted from ore by dissolving the gold in potassium cyanide (KCN) solution (the cyanide process) or by the amalgamation process, which involves treatment with mercury to form an amalgam that is processed further.

In addition to the applications mentioned above, gold is used in dentistry, photography, medicine, and in electrical contacts (in microchips) and conductors. The purity or fineness of gold is measured in *carats*, which are parts of gold in 24 parts of the alloy. Thus pure gold is 24 carat. Jewellery is often made of 9 carat gold, in which the remaining 15 parts are copper.

gonad *see* REPRODUCTION.

Gram's stain *see* BACTERIA.

graph a drawing or picture that represents data and numerical values or shows the mathematical relationship between two or more variables. Often this takes the form of plotting (positioning) points at a certain place, relative to two values measured along axes at right angles to each other (*see Cartesian coordinates* in GEOMETRY). A *histogram* is a type of graph consisting of a number of blocks drawn with reference to two axes such that the area of each block is directly proportional to the value of the frequency. A *bar graph* looks similar to a histogram but the height of the block is then the relevant factor. A *pie chart* is another graphical method of representing data in which a circle is divided into different sized sectors where the angle of the sector is proportional to the size of the sample, expressed as a percentage.

graphite *see* CARBON.

grasshopper *see* NH Orthoptera.

grassland *see* G&G grassland.

gravity or gravitational force the downward pull exerted by the material making up the Earth. A gravitational attraction exists between all objects, and this will increase with their mass and with a lessening of the distance between them. Although this attraction is always present, in most instances it is so very small as to be unnoticeable and the attraction that dominates is that of the Earth, which affects objects on its surface (*see* WEIGHT). If gravity is thought of as a gravitational field exerting a force on a mass, the value of that field strength, g, can be calculated as almost 10 m/s^2 (metres per second per second).

This means that a falling object near the Earth's surface accelerates at 10 m/s^2; alternatively, a mass of 1 kilogram near the Earth's surface has a force acting on it, because of gravity, of 10 N (Newtons). Gravity on the Moon is much less than on Earth—about one-sixth, so although an astronaut's *mass* remains the same, his or her weight is much less.

gray *see* SI UNITS.

greenhouse effect *see* NH greenhouse effect.

greenhouse gases are gases present in the ATMOSPHERE which are responsible for the GREENHOUSE EFFECT. Several gases have been identified and of these, by far the most significant is CARBON DIOXIDE which occurs as a natural component of the atmosphere. Carbon is the building block of all life, being present in both plants and animals. It is also present in FOSSIL FUELS and held in sea water and in the absence of any artificial, human interference, there is a natural transfer or exchange between the various carbon stores which maintains them in a roughly equal balance. The elements of this exchange constitute what is known as *the carbon cycle* and it has several components. One of these is an exchange between the air and the oceans whereby some atmospheric carbon dioxide passes into solution in the surface layers of sea water. A proportion of this then sinks down into the deeper levels of the sea where it is held in store. But it is also released and passes upwards in the opposite direction and the two processes roughly counterbalance one another. Green plants absorb and utilise carbon dioxide during PHOTOSYNTHESIS but when living organisms are subject to death and decay, CO_2 is released. In the natural cycle, there is no net loss or gain of CO_2. However, human activity has upset this balance, mainly due to the burning of fossil fuels which continue to add excess CO_2 to the atmosphere. Additionally, there has been widespread clearance (*deforestation*) of natural forests, and destruction of the *rain forest*, (described as 'the lungs of the Earth') is held to be of particular concern.

Scientists have calculated that the concentration of CO_2 in the atmosphere has risen by a quarter since the start of the industrial revolution in the 1700s. Half of this increase has happened in only the last 3 decades and it is Western countries that have been largely responsible. However, the current economic boom in India and China is soon expected to outstrip that of the West and will further accelerate the rise in emissions unless urgent action is taken in the very near future. About half of the greenhouse effect is directly attributable to CO_2.

METHANE is another important greenhouse gas, the atmospheric level of which is rising, not only due to the burning of coal and natural gas but also because of increased agricultural activity. Methane is released when land is cleared and vegetation burned and it is given off from landfill sites where waste is buried. It is also released from wetland areas cultivated for rice growing. Another important source is animals, especially cud-chewing herbivores such as sheep and cattle but also camels, donkeys and horses. Agricultural activity has increased in step with a rising human population throughout the world and atmospheric methane levels have risen by about 1 per cent per year during the last 4 decades. Methane molecules are additionally relatively long-lived, persisting for about 10 years in the atmosphere.

NITROUS OXIDE (N_2O) is responsible for an estimated 6 per cent of the greenhouse effect. Industrial and agricultural processes, including the utilisation of fossil fuels, the cutting and burning of rain forest and the use of nitrogen-based fertilizers in cultivation are responsible for nearly half of the N_2O released. Another significant source is human sewage and animal waste.

CHLOROFLUOROCARBONS (CFCs) generated by industrial activities exist at low levels in the atmosphere but they are significant for two reasons. CFC molecules are highly effective at trapping heat (about 10,000 times more efficient than molecules of CO_2) and they are long-lived, persisting for about 110 years in the atmosphere before they decay. Hence their contribution to the greenhouse effect is proportionately greater than their concentration would initially suggest.

grid *see* ELECTRICITY; TRANSFORMER.

ground granulated blast-furnace slag *see* BLAST FURNACE.

groundwater *see* G&G groundwater.

growth the process by which living organisms increase in size and often in weight. It is brought about by cells dividing and often becoming more specialised to form the bulk of a particular tissue or *organ*. All organisms have a maximum size that is determined by their genetic make-up, and the growth process is controlled by HORMONES. Once the individual has reached its full size there is no more growth but CELL DIVISION occurs to repair and replace worn-out or damaged tissues. Growth often occurs in spurts, as can be seen in the development of a human child. A baby grows fastest during the first six months of life, and there is a further growth spurt at the time of adolescence.

growth rings *see* NH growth rings.

gymnosperm *see* PLANTS *and* NH Gymnospermae.

Haber process *see* AMMONIA.

habitat *see* NH habitat.

hadron *see* ELEMENTARY PARTICLES.

hair a fine outgrowth from the surface of a plant or animal, found on many living organisms and may be used for a variety of different purposes. The hair or fur of mammals is composed of dead cells in which a substance called *keratin* has been laid down. It is used for insulation to keep the animal warm and may occur in a variety of colours determined by the presence and amount of a certain dye or pigment known as *melanin*.

The base of each hair is embedded in the skin and has a tiny muscle attached to it. In cold conditions the hair is raised by these muscles to stand up straight, and this traps a layer of air, which has a warming effect. People notice this happening when they have 'goose pimples' in response to skin feeling cold.

half-life *see* RADIOACTIVITY.

halogens the elements fluorine, CHLORINE, BROMINE, iodine and astatine, which form a group in the PERIODIC TABLE. They are the extreme form of the non-metals and show typical characteristics forming covalent diatomic molecules, i.e. form molecules of two atoms, e.g. Br_2. At room temperature fluorine and chlorine are gases, bromine is a volatile liquid and iodine a volatile solid. Astatine exists only as short-lived, radioactive isotopes. The reactivity increases from iodine to fluorine, and the latter reacts with all elements except helium, neon and argon to form compounds. Halogens occur naturally in salt deposits and as IONS in sea water.

halophyte *see* NH halophyte.

haploid *see* CELL DIVISION; PLANTS.

hardness of minerals *see* G&G hardness of minerals.

hard water water that does not readily produce a lather with soap (*see* DETERGENTS AND SOAP) because of dissolved compounds (carbonates, sulphates and chlorides) of calcium, magnesium, sodium and iron. The use of soap results in the formation of a scum caused by a chemical reaction between the metal IONS and fatty acids in the soap, producing salts. Water that does produce a good lather is called *soft water*. *Temporary hardness* is one of two types of hard water and results from water passing over carbonate-rich rocks such as chalk or limestone. This produces metal hydrogen carbonates that dissolve in the water. On boiling, these salts form insoluble carbonates that in a kettle results in kettle fur. This leaves the water soft. *Permanent hardness* is caused by metal sulphates (calcium or magnesium sulphates or chlorides) and cannot be removed by boiling. Special ion-exchange water softeners must be used in this case.

haustorium *see* PARASITE; SYMBIOSIS.

hearing the means by which animals are able to receive and decode sound waves, which is usually closely related to balance, especially in vertebrates. Specialised small organs called RECEPTORS, which are often hair-like, vibrate in response to sound waves. This triggers off an electrical impulse in a sensory nerve (one that travels to the brain) which is in contact with the receptor (or receptors.) The information is transmitted to the brain where it is decoded and interpreted as sound. In many invertebrates sound receptors may be relatively simple structures. In other animals such as mammals, however, complex and specialised organs, the ears, are used to detect sound.

The human ear

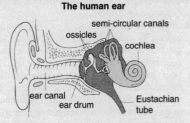

Fish have simpler ears than mammals and also a *lateral line system* that has sensory cells along the body, both of which are used for hearing. Amphibians (frogs and toads), reptiles and birds possess ears with a simpler structure than those found in mammals.

heart *see* CIRCULATION; LUNGS AND GILLS.

heat ENERGY and measured in JOULES. It is stored in materials as vibrations of the molecules and the vibration increases with temperature. Heat travels by CONDUCTION, CONVECTION AND by electromagnetic RADIATION and material states, i.e. whether something is LIQUID, SOLID, or GAS depends upon the heat available. In a solid the molecules are attracted together, and this overcomes the kinetic energy possessed by virtue of the molecules vibrating. If energy is put in and the molecules can be separated enough to become free, then the solid becomes a liquid. The work done in separating the molecules is called the *latent heat of fusion*. Similarly, the *latent heat of vaporisation* is the heat required to turn a liquid into gas. When these changes are reversed, the material gives out heat.

The human body generates heat from food, the liver being a major heat-producing organ. Muscles also generate heat as a byproduct during activity. *See also* CHEMICAL REACTION.

heat exchanger a device used to transfer heat from one fluid (i.e. a liquid or gas) to another without the fluids coming into contact. Heat exchangers are used a great deal to cool machines, e.g. the radiator in a car engine, or to conserve heat in an industrial (often chemical) process so that it can be used elsewhere in the process.

heat shield *see* S&A heat shield.

hedgehog *see* NH Insectivora.

Heisenberger's uncertainty principle *see* QUANTUM MECHANICS.

helium one of the INERT GASES (or noble gases), so called because it has a stable electronic configuration and no chemical reactivity as such. It occurs naturally in very small quantities and being non-inflammable is used as an inert atmosphere for arc welding, for airships and balloons, in gas lasers and with oxygen as the atmosphere for deep-sea divers. Helium liquefies below 4K (–269°C/–452°F) and is used extensively in *cryogenics*—the study of materials at very low temperatures.

Helium has no colour, taste, or smell and was named after *helios*, the Greek word for 'sun'. It is formed in stars such as the Sun as hydrogen nuclei are pressed together in the processes of nuclear fusion (*see* NUCLEAR FISSION AND FUSION).

hemipteran *see* NH Hemiptera.

haemoglobin *see* IRON.

henry *see* SI UNITS.

herbaceous *see* NH herbaceous.

herbicide *see* PESTICIDES.

herbivore any animal that feeds on plants, e.g. the familiar grazing mammals such as cows, sheep and horses.

heredity the passing on of characteristics from parents to offspring, which is accomplished through the transfer of genes (*see* CHROMOSOMES AND GENES). Some of the basic laws of heredity were studied and worked out by an Austrian monk, Gregor Mendel, who carried out experiments with pea plants. He noticed that some characteristics were dominant over others, e.g. tallness is dominant over shortness in these plants. The study of GENETICS in the 20th century established that there are *dominant* and *recessive genes* for many characteristics, and this is particularly important in some inherited DISEASES. A dominant gene is one that will always be seen in the offspring. A recessive gene will be seen only if it is present as a 'double dose'. i.e. one from each parent. *See also* DNA.

hertz *see* FREQUENCY; SI UNITS.

hexagon *see* POLYGON.

hibernation *see* NH hibernation.

hippopotamus *see* NH Artodactyla.

histogram *see* GRAPH.

holography a method of recording and then projecting a three-dimensional image using light from a LASER but without the need of a camera. A single laser beam is split into two by a special mirror, with half the beam continuing straight through the mirror on to photographic film. The other part of the beam is reflected by the mirror on to the object in question and then on to the film. The two beams produce an interference pattern, or *hologram*, on the film, which, when illuminated with laser light, recreates a three-dimensional image of the object. A screen is not required and the light forms an image in mid-air.

There are now holograms that do not need laser light to produce an image, e.g. some credit cards have holograms that work with reflected daylight.

homeothermy *see* NH homeothermy.

homing *see* NH homing.

hominid *see* NH hominid.

homiothermy *see* NH homeothermy.

Hooke's law *see* ELASTICITY.

hormone an organic substance produced in minute amounts by special cells within plants and animals that acts as a 'chemical messenger', causing a powerful response somewhere else in the body. In mammals, hormones are produced and released (*secreted*) by special small organs called glands (the *endocrine* glands) and travel in the bloodstream. The site at which they produce a response is called the *target* (*see* ENDOCRINE SYSTEM).

horse *see* NH Perissodactyla.

horsepower a measure of power that originated in the time when steam engines began to replace horses. The name was coined by James Watt, the British engineer, and one horsepower is equivalent to about $^3/_4$ kilowatt (kW) or, more accurately, 746 watts (W). It has become the standard practice to measure engine power in *brake horsepower*. This is horsepower measured by means of the resistance offered by a brake and shows the useful horsepower that can be produced by an engine. A typical car develops around 90–100 brake horsepower (bhp) while an articulated lorry develops 400 or 500 bhp.

horticulture the cultivation of all kinds of garden and greenhouse plants, including flowers, vegetables and fruit. Horticulture is concerned with the breeding of new varieties of plants by propagation and seed production. Many of our food plants, especially fruit and vegetables, result from the techniques of horticulture.

humidity *see* G&G humidity.

humus *see* NH humus.

hurricane *see* G&G hurricane.

hybrid *see* BREEDING.

hydration *see* CEMENT.

hydraulics the study of fluid flow and the practical application of the dynamics of liquids in science and engineering. It is an important subject as it is relevant to the design of harbours, canals and dams and the study of the flow of water in pipes. *Hydraulic machinery* is operated and the power transmitted using the pressure of a liquid. Such machines use the properties of liquids that they cannot, for all practical purposes, be squashed and that when pressure is applied to a confined liquid, the pressure applies to all parts of the liquid. The transference of a force through the liquid is arranged in such a way as to produce a greater force in the machine, e.g. in a hydraulic car jack.

Most car braking systems use this hydraulic principle. When the brake pedal is pushed, a piston in a cylinder forces brake fluid through narrow pipes that go to the wheels. At the wheels, the fluid pressure pushes pistons in cylinders which then move the brakes which are in the form of pads or shoes which move against the drum or disc attached to the wheel.

hydride *see* HYDROGEN AND THE HYDRIDES.

hydrocarbon an organic compound (*see* CHEMISTRY) that contains only CARBON and HYDROGEN. There are many different hydrocarbon types and they form one of the most important groups of organic compounds. There is a fundamental division into two groups based on structure: *aliphatic hydrocarbons* comprise carbon atoms in open chains and in addition to the main groups such as alkanes (the paraffins), this term includes all compounds made by the replacement of atoms in a molecule. *Aromatic hydrocarbons* are characterised by a ring structure made up of six carbon atoms as found in BENZENE (C_6H_6). These are also called *closed-chain* or *cyclic compounds*.

Aliphatic hydrocarbon groups include the *alkanes*, with a general formula CnH_{2n+2}, e.g. ethane C_2H_6. The first four compounds in the series are gases, then liquids and the higher members (above $C_{16}H_{34}$) are waxy solids. Alkanes are the main components of PETROLEUM and in general they are quite resistant to chemical action. The *alkenes* have the formula C_nH_{2n} and resemble the alkanes, but are more reactive. They are used as fuels and in the manufacture of other substances, e.g. alcohols and glycerols. The *alkynes* (or acetylenes) have triple bonds between two carbons, and a general formula of C_nH_n. Acetylene is a well-known member of this series.

hydroelectricity ELECTRICITY that is generated from water moving from a high to a low level. If a river or lake is dammed to form a large reservoir then the water is held back, high above the original river level, the body of water has enormous *potential* ENERGY. To turn this into electrical energy, the vast concrete dam contains a tunnel down which water can be directed and at the foot of the tunnel, before the water rejoins the river, the force of the flow is used to turn the blades of a large turbine linked to a GENERATOR, thus creating electricity.

Some power plants of this nature are called *pumped storage schemes*, in which water flows through the day from a high level to a low level reservoir to generate electricity and at night when demand for electricity is low, water is pumped back up to the higher level ready for supply the next day.

Hydroelectric schemes are an alternative, or 'green' energy source because they do not cause pollution. However, they can affect the local environment considerably because they alter the balance of plant and animal life around the dam, particularly when a valley is flooded to create the reservoir.

hydrogen and the hydrides *hydrogen* is the lightest ELEMENT and forms molecules comprising two atoms, H_2. It occurs free and is widely distributed in water (H_2O), organic matter (HYDROCARBONS and CARBOHYDRATES) and minerals. The ordinary hydrogen atom has a nucleus of one proton, with one electron. There are other ISOTOPES, and in addition to *protium*, there is *deuterium*, which contains one neutron, and *tritium*, containing two neutrons.

Hydrogen is manufactured by the ELECTROLYSIS of water and is produced in the treatment of PETROLEUM with catalysts (*see* CATALYSIS). It is explosive over a wide range of mixtures with oxygen and because of this is no longer used in ballooning (it has been replaced by HELIUM). It is used in numerous industrial processes, including the production of methanol and ammonia, and in metallurgy.

Hydrogen reacts with most elements to form *hydrides*, of which there are several different types. Some are ionic and salt-like while most of the non-metals form covalent compounds (*see* BONDS), e.g. methane, CH_4. There are then many more complex compounds. Hydrides are often used as catalysts in hydrogenation reactions, i.e. the addition of hydrogen to a substance, frequently used in the refining of PETROLEUM.

hydrology *see* G&G hydrology.

hydrolysis *see* CHEMICAL REACTION.

hydrometer an instrument used for measuring the relative DENSITY of a liquid. It is a quick and convenient tool, although not as accurate as some other methods. The hydrometer consists of a tubular stem with a weighted bulbous base. It floats in the liquid to be measured and the density can be read from the graduated scale on the stem. The narrow stem ensures that small changes in density create readily visible changes in the reading.

Hydrometers are used in checking the quality of beer and also in testing the level of charge in a car battery, because the relative density of the acid in a battery varies with the available charge.

hydropower technology that harnesses the energy of fresh, flowing water in order to generate electricity. The technology utilises the kinetic energy of the moving water to drive turbines, which then generate power. Hydro schemes have generally been on a large, industrial scale often involving the building of dams to control water flow. However, it is now recognised that there is a place for smaller scale, local projects to generate power from rivers and streams.

hydrostatic *see* FLUIDS.

hydroxides compounds that contain the OH group, which is present as the hydroxyl ion OH$^-$. ALKALIS are the hydroxides of metals and are strongly basic. Hydroxides such as caustic soda (NaOH), potassium hydroxide (KOH) and ammonium hydroxide (NH_4OH) are commonly used in industry in the production of soap, detergents, bleaches, paper and many other items.

hydrozoan *see* NH Hydrozoa.

hymenopteran *see* NH Hymenoptera.

hypersonic *see* MACH NUMBER.

hypertonic and hypotonic a *hypertonic* solution is one that has a higher *osmotic* pressure (*see* OSMOSIS) than another or a standard with which it is being compared. *Hypotonic* is the opposite, i.e. a hypotonic solution has a lower osmotic pressure than the solution to which it is compared. *Isotonic* solutions are those with the same concentration. These concentration differences are important in cells (*see* OSMOREGULATION).

ice age *see* G&G ice age.

igneous rocks *see* G&G igneous rocks.

iguana *see* NH iguana.

immune system the natural defence system that operates within a vertebrate animal to protect it from infections caused mainly by such microorganisms as BACTERIA and VIRUSES. The cells that operate the immune system are the white blood cells or *leucocytes*, of which there are a number of different types. The immune system is provoked into action by the presence of 'foreign' PROTEIN substances, which are called *antigens*.

Many substances are antigens but they are commonly found on the surface of bacteria and viruses. When the white blood cells encounter antigens in the body, they produce special proteins, called *antibodies* that trap the foreign material. The antibody and antigen are locked together like two pieces of a jigsaw puzzle and are eventually 'eaten up' by other cells of the immune system called *macrophages*. More antibodies are rapidly produced by the cells and will always recognise, and be ready to bind to, the antigens. In this way, the animal becomes *resistant* to a particular disease and this is the basis of *vaccination*. This is the use of a *vaccine*, a modified preparation of a virus or bacteria, to kill a virus or bacteria or make them harmless by provoking the production of antibodies (an immune response) when the vaccine is injected into the bloodstream. These antibodies are then always available to attack any live microorganisms of that type which the animal might encounter in the future.

Particular antibodies are produced to each kind of antigen and the immune system operates in two ways. Firstly, there is *inborn* or *natural immunity*, which is present from birth and is not specialised, operating against almost any substance that threatens the body. Secondly, there is *acquired immunity*, which is the situation described above and which is brought about by an encounter with a particular foreign substance.

implosion *see* S&A implosion.

inclined plane *see* MACHINE.

indicators substances used to detect the presence of other chemicals. Most often an indicator is used in the laboratory to show the pH of a liquid, i.e. its acidity or alkalinity. Indicators are used in *titrimetry*, which is the fast reaction of two solutions to an end point determined by a visual indicator, and the two solutions are commonly an ACID and a base.

The simplest indicator is *litmus paper*, which shows red in acid and blue in alkali. *Universal indicator* is a mix that shows a gradual series of colour changes over a range of pH. However, most such indicators operate over a narrower pH range, e.g. methyl orange is red below pH 3.1 and changes to orange and then yellow as the pH reaches 4.4. Other indicators in acid-base reactions include:

indicator	low pH colour	high pH colour	range
thymol blue	red	yellow	1.2–2.8
methyl red	red	yellow	4.2–6.3
bromothymol blue	yellow	blue	6.0–7.6
phenol red	yellow	red	6.8–8.4
phenolphthalin	colourless	red	8.3–10.0
alizarin yellow	yellow	orange	10.1–12.0

Another group, called *redox indicators*, show different colours depending upon whether they are oxidised or reduced (*see* OXIDATION AND REDUCTION). The change occurs over a narrow range of electric potential within the system under study.

inductance the property of a circuit carrying an electric current characterised by the formation of a magnetic field. Similarly a current can be made to flow when the position of the magnetic field moves relative to the circuit (*see* ELECTROMAGNET, GENERATOR). The unit of inductance is the henry (H), named after the American physicist Joseph Henry who was a pioneer in this field. Because of inductance a change in the current within one circuit can cause a current to flow in a nearby circuit. This is because if current flows through a circuit containing a coil, a magnetic field is created and an adjacent coil, in a separate circuit but within the magnetic field, experiences an *induced current*.

inert gas or noble gas any of the gases in group 0 of the PERIODIC TABLE. These are helium, neon, argon, krypton, xenon and radon, and they make up approximately 1 per cent of air by volume, with argon the most abundant. As their name suggests, these ELEMENTS are chemically unreactive because of their stable electronic configuration. They can be extracted from liquid air by fractional DISTILLATION, and helium occurs in natural gas deposits. Their stability makes them useful in many applications, e.g. helium and argon are used as inert atmospheres for welding and in light bulbs and fluorescent lamps. Helium in its liquid form is important in low temperature research.

hydroelectricity the property of a body that causes it to oppose any change in its velocity even if the velocity is zero. An object at rest requires a FORCE to make it move, and a moving object requires a force to make it slow down or accelerate or change direction. Newton called this resistance to a change of velocity inertia. The greater the mass of a body, the higher is its inertia.

infection and toxin an *infection* is a disease or illness that is caused by the invasion of a microorganism, which, because it is able to do this, is called a PATHOGEN. In animals and people most pathogens are BACTERIA or VIRUSES but in plants a wide range of fungi are pathogenic. A high standard of hygiene is the best means of preventing infections from occurring, and sometimes people who are sick with an infectious disease require special isolation, nursing and care.

There are a number of ways in which a pathogen can enter a body. It might be breathed in; it may enter the bloodstream through a cut or wound; it might be carried by a blood-sucking insect, such as a mosquito, that passes the pathogen on when it bites or stings; it may be present on food (called contaminated), which is then eaten, or in drinking water, particularly that which is contaminated by sewage; or it may enter through sexual intercourse—a sexually transmitted disease. Often the illness is caused not by the microorganism itself but by a poison, known as a *toxin*, that it produces, and this is especially true of bacteria.

infinity (*symbol* ∞) the term used to describe a number or quantity that has a value that is too large to be measured. For example, outer space is regarded as infinite since it has no limits. By convention, infinity is the result of dividing any number by zero. If a value is so small as to be incalculable, it is called *infinitesimal* and can be written as negative infinity (−∞).

infrared and ultraviolet *see* ELECTROMAGNETIC WAVES.

infrared astronomy *see* S&A infrared astronomy.

initiator *see* EXPLOSIVE.

injection moulding an industrial process, similar to EXTRUSION, used for the production of plastic mouldings. Granular or powdered plastic is fed into a hopper that feeds into a screw mechanism. The heat generated by the screw and outside heaters produces a plastic melt by the time it reaches the end of the screw. The melt is then injected or forced through a nozzle into a cool mould and pressure is maintained while the entrance to the mould is blocked by solidified melt. The moulding is then released and the process is repeated. Most injection moulding machines run automatically and large quantities of products can be produced at low cost, including small boats, buckets and bowls, crates, telephone handsets and small gears.

insect *see* NH Insecta.

insecticide *see* PESTICIDES.

insectivore *see* NH Insectivora.

instinct *see* BEHAVIOUR.

insulation the means of preventing the passage of heat or heat loss by CONDUCTION, CONVECTION, or RADIATION (it also applies when an electric current is prevented from passing). There are many ways of providing thermal insulation, the commonest example being insulating materials used in houses to reduce heat loss. Cavity walls can be filled with foam, roof spaces lined with fibreglass or polystyrene beads, and windows can be double-glazed.

A vacuum prevents conduction and convection and this property is utilised in a vacuum flask to retain heat in hot drinks. There are several examples of natural insulation, notably the fur and feathers of mammals and birds respectively.

insulator *see* CONDUCTOR.

intelligence the ability of animals to learn and understand and so to be able to live effectively in their surroundings. Human beings are considered to be the most intelligent of animals, and this ability depends upon GENETIC make-up and environment. The potential for developing a person's intelligence is considered to be at its greatest during childhood, especially in the early years. It is also thought to be important to use intellectual abilities throughout life in order to exercise intelligence to its full power.

interstellar medium *see* S&A interstellar medium.

invar *see* BIMETAL STRIP.

invertebrate an animal 'without a backbone' or, rather, one that lacks an internal skeleton. They make up 95 per cent of animal species and show many different kinds of specialisation, allowing them to adopt all sorts of lifestyles and habitats.

iodine see HALOGENS.

ion an atom or molecule that is charged because of the loss or gain of an electron or electrons. A *cation* is positively charged and an *anion* negatively charged.

Ionization is the process that results in ions, and it can occur in a number of ways, including a molecule breaking down into ions in solution or the production of ions resulting from the bombardment of atoms by RADIATION. During ELECTROLYSIS, ions are attracted to the electrode with an opposite charge.

ionosphere see RADIO.

iris see SIGHT.

iron a metallic ELEMENT in group 8 of the PERIODIC TABLE, which in its pure form is silver-white. It is a common component of minerals in clays, granites and sandstones and is a dominant element in meteorites. It occurs naturally as several minerals: magnetite (Fe_3O_4), hematite (Fe_2O_3), limonite ($FeO(OH)_nH_2O$), siderite ($FeCO_3$) and pyrite (FeS_2). In combination with copper it occurs as chalcopyrite, $CuFeS_2$. Pure iron melts at 1535°C (2795°F) and is extracted from its ores by the BLAST FURNACE process.

Iron is a widely used metal, in combination with other metals. Cast and wrought iron (see CAST IRON) are both used extensively but most iron goes into the production of STEEL.

Iron is also of biological significance because it is essential to the red blood cells. These contain the pigment *haemoglobin*, which is made up of the iron-containing pigment heme and the protein globin. Haemoglobin is responsible for the transport of oxygen around the body, hence if there is insufficient iron in the diet anaemia may result.

irradiation the exposure of an object to RADIATION, which may be electromagnetic radiation such as X-rays or gamma rays. The radiation may also come from a radioactive source. Above a certain level radiation harms organisms, and this principle is adopted when using irradiation as a technique for FOOD PRESERVATION. Very specific irradiation is used in medicine when obtaining an X-ray or in the use of ionising radiations to treat cancer.

irrigation see G&G irrigation.

isobar see G&G isobar.

isomers chemical compounds with the same molecular formula, i.e. same composition and molecular weight, but which differ in their chemical structure. This property is called *isomerism*, of which there are two types. *Structural isomers* differ in the way that their atoms are joined together, whether it be changes in the arrangement of carbon atoms in the chain or the position of a group or atom on the chain or ring. *Tautomerism* is a special case of structural isomerism, which is termed dynamic. This is because a compound exists as a mixture of two isomers in equilibrium and removal of one isomer results in conversion of the other to restore the equilibrium. The other type of isomerism is *stereoisomerism*, in which isomeric compounds have atoms bonded in the same way but arranged differently in space. One type of stereoisomerism is *optical isomerism*, resulting from asymmetry of the molecules, and in this case the isomers differ in the direction in which they rotate a plane of polarised light (*see* POLARIZATION OF LIGHT).

isopod see NH Isopoda.

isotonic see HYPERTONIC AND HYPOTONIC.

isotope one of several atoms of the same ELEMENT that have the same ATOMIC NUMBER (i.e. same number of protons) but differing numbers of neutrons in the nucleus (affecting their atomic mass). The chemical properties of isotopes are therefore the same, only physical properties are affected by mass differing. Most elements exist naturally as a mixture of isotopes but can be separated on their slightly different physical properties. For laboratory purposes MASS SPECTROMETRY is often used. *Radioisotopes* are isotopes that emit RADIOACTIVITY and decay at a particular rate, e.g. carbon-14.

Chemical symbols can be used to show the different configurations of isotopes; thus for hydrogen there are three isotopes:

	protium (ordinary hydrogen)	deuterium	tritium
protons	1	1	1
neutrons	0	1	2
electrons	1	1	1
symbol	^1_1H	^2_1H	^3_1H

When deuterium replaces hydrogen in a water molecule, the resulting compound is called *heavy water*.

jaw *see* TEETH.

jet engine *see* ENGINE; GAS TURBINE.

jet stream *see* G&G jet stream.

joule (*symbol* **J**) the SI UNIT for measurements of ENERGY and WORK. It is equal to a force of one NEWTON moving one metre. It is named after the British physicist James Prescott Joule who investigated the link between mechanical, electrical and heat energy. One thousand joules is called a *kilojoule*. Energy used to be measured in *calories*, one calorie being 4.1868 joules.

Jupiter *see* S&A Jupiter.

kangaroo *see* NH Methatheria.

Kelvin scale *see* TEMPERATURE; SI UNITS.

kidney *see* OSMOREGULATION.

kiln a furnace or large oven that has many uses. The most obvious is its use for drying, baking and hardening clay objects such as plates, cups, and similar domestic items but also bricks and other building components. Kilns vary greatly in size depending upon their use, and modern versions are heated by gas or electricity.

The mineral extraction industry also uses kilns for drying ore, driving off carbon dioxide from limestone or roasting sulphide ores to remove sulphur as sulphur dioxide prior to further processing.

kilogram *see* SI UNITS.

kinematics *see* MECHANICS.

kinetic energy *see* TEMPERATURE.

kingdom *see* CLASSIFICATION.

koala bear *see* NH Methatheria.

krypton *see* INERT GAS.

laboratory any room or building that is especially built or equipped for undertaking scientific experiments, research, or chemicals manufacture. The study of physics, chemistry, biology, medicine, geology and other subjects usually involves some work in a laboratory and each is equipped with special instruments. A chemical laboratory typically contains balances for weighing samples, bottles of chemicals including dangerous acids, a vast array of glassware (test tubes, flasks, etc) and bunsen burners. The bunsen burner is a gas burner consisting of a small vertical tube with an adjustable air inlet at the base to control the flame. The flame produced by burning the hydrocarbon gas/air mix has an inner cone where carbon monoxide is formed and an outer fringe where it is burnt. When the gas is burnt completely the flame temperature is very high, around 1450°C (2642°F). The burner was invented by Robert Wilhelm Bunsen, a German scientist. Most laboratories nowadays are also equipped with computers, spectrophotometers, polarising microscopes, or electron microscopes, and other specialist equipment depending on the area of research.

lactic acid *see* RESPIRATION.

laminate a material produced by bonding together under pressure two or more different materials. Plastics are commonly used in this way, bonded to chipboard or another building board to make kitchen units and worktops and other items of furniture. Wood, such as *plywood*, is made of veneers bonded together, which is in effect a laminate. Laminated plastics are composites made up of plastics and reinforcing or strengthening materials, e.g. carbon fibres, glass fibres. Glass sheet can also be made in laminated form with layers of glass joined by tough plastic, and these are used for security glass, sound insulation, fire resistance, etc. The overriding feature of laminates is that the combination of materials, albeit in thin sheets, produces a composite material that is much stronger than the individual components alone.

larva and metamorphosis a *larva* is a young or immature form of an animal that looks and often behaves differently from the adult. There may be several larval stages, and this is a common feature of invertebrate animals. Familiar larvae are those of butterflies and moths (caterpillars), those of flies (maggots), and those of many marine animals, huge numbers of which make up PLANKTON. Larvae can feed and lead an independent life but (with one or two exceptions) are not able to reproduce. Usually an animal passes through several larval stages before undergoing the process known as *metamorphosis* to become an adult. In insects, the final larval stage is a *pupa* or *chrysalis*, during which all activities such as feeding and walking cease. The body is enclosed within an outer case and, under the influence of HORMONES, it gradually changes to become an adult. Usually, there is a breakdown of some of the larval tissues, which are then reused, and some of the cells that were inactive in the larva divide to form the body of the adult. When the process is complete, the pupal case splits and the adult emerges.

laser (an acronym for *l*ight *a*mplification by *s*timulated *e*mission of *r*adiation) a device that produces an intense beam of LIGHT of one wavelength (*monochromatic*) in which the waves are all in step with each other (*coherent light*). In its simplest form a ruby crystal shaped like a cylinder is subjected to flashes of white light from an external source. The chromium atoms in the ruby become excited through absorbing photons of light, and when struck by more photons, light energy is released. One end of the cylinder is mirrored to reflect light back into the crystal and the other end is partially reflecting, allowing the escape of the coherent light. The ruby laser produces pulses of laser light and is called a *pulse laser*.

Lasers have also been constructed using INERT GASES (helium and neon mixed, argon alone) and carbon dioxide. These are called *gas lasers* and produce a continuous beam of laser light. Lasers are being used for an increasing number of tasks, including printing, communications, compact disc players (*see* CD TECHNOLOGY), for cutting metals, HOLOGRAPHY, and for an ever-widening range of surgical techniques in medicine. Lasers are also used in shops at the checkout to read BAR CODES.

latitude *see* G&G latitude.

lava *see* G&G lava.

learning *see* BEHAVIOUR.

Leclanché *see* BATTERY.

leech *see* NH Annelida.

lens a device that makes a beam of rays passing through it either converge (meet at a point) or diverge. Optical lenses are made of a uniform transparent medium such as glass or a plastic and they refract the light (*see* REFRACTION). They are either convex (thickest in the middle) or concave (thickest at the edges) in shape, and lenses can be made with combinations of these profiles or one side may be flat (plane). Light rays that pass through a convex lens are bent towards the *principal axis* (or optical axis—the line joining the centre of curvature of the two lens surfaces) and away from the axis with a concave lens. The *focus* is where the light rays are brought together at a point and the focal length is the distance of the focus from the centre of the lens.

A convex lens forms a small image of the object that is inverted (upside down) and on the opposite side of the lens. This is called a *real image* and can be seen on a screen. As an object in the distance is brought nearer to a convex lens, the image moves away from the lens and becomes larger. The image formed by a concave lens is always upright, smaller than the object, and it is a *virtual image*, i.e. it cannot be projected because although the rays of light appear to come to the observer from the image, they do not actually do so.

Lenses can be found in many optical instruments including the camera and the telescope and also in the human eye (*see* SIGHT).

lepidopteran *see* NH Lepidoptera.

lepton *see* ELEMENTARY PARTICLES.

leucocyte *see* BONE MARROW; IMMUNE SYSTEM; LYMPH SYSTEM.

lever a simple MACHINE that, at its simplest, consists of a rigid beam that pivots at a point called the *fulcrum*. A load applied at one end can be balanced by an *effort* (a FORCE) applied at the opposite end. There are three classes of lever depending on the position of fulcrum, load, and effort. The fulcrum may be between the effort and load (sometimes called a first-class lever); if the load is between the fulcrum and effort, it is second-class; and a third-class lever has the effort between the fulcrum and load. Examples of these are pliers, a wheelbarrow, and the shovel on a mechanical digger. Although the work done by both effort and load must be equal, it is possible by moving a small effort through a large distance to move a very large load, albeit through a small distance.

lichen *see* NH lichen.

lift *see* AERODYNAMICS.

light ELECTROMAGNETIC WAVES of a particular wavelength that are visible to the human eye. Objects can be seen only if light reflected from them or given off by them reaches the eye. Light is given out by hot objects, and the hotter the object the nearer to the blue end of the spectrum is the light emitted. The Sun is our primary source of light, the light travelling at almost 3×10^5 (300,000) kilometres per second (km/s) through space. The light waves are made up of packets or quanta (*singular* quantum) of energy, called *photons*. Every photon can be considered to be a particle of light energy, the energy increasing as the wavelength shortens.

White light is actually made up of a range of colours. This can be shown by passing a narrow beam of light through a prism. Because the individual colours have different wavelengths, they are refracted by differing amounts and the resulting *dispersion* produces the characteristic *spectrum*. A beam of light can often be seen, particularly if a torch is shone on a misty night or in a dark room where there is smoke or if sunlight highlights dust particles. In each case the edge of the beam indicates that light travels in straight lines, and because of this a shadow forms when an object is placed between a light source and a flat surface.

light bulb a glass bulb within which is a filament of tungsten. When a current is passed, the tungsten glows white hot, giving out light. Tungsten is used because it has a very high melting point (3410°C or 6170°F) and because the thin wire of the filament would burn up quickly in air. The bulb contains argon and/or nitrogen to provide an inert atmosphere. Only a small proportion of the energy of is given out in the form of visible light. Fluorescent lights are often used because to achieve the same illumination, they use only a third of the

power. *Fluorescent lamps*, or *strips*, contain a vapour, e.g. mercury, under low pressure. Electrons from an electrode bombard the mercury atoms, making electrons move into a higher orbit around the mercury nuclei. When the electrons move back into their normal orbit, ultraviolet light is given off, which causes a coating on the tube to glow. Neon and other INERT GASES are used for this purpose, as is sodium.

lightning *see* G&G lightning.

lightning conductor a device invented by the American Benjamin Franklin made of a metal rod (often copper) attached to the top of a building that is then connected by cable to a metal plate buried in the ground. If and when lightning strikes, the lightning conductor provides a suitable path for electrons to move to the ground without causing damage to the building. The ground, or as it is known, the *earth*, has an unlimited capacity to accept electrons. A lightning conductor may also help reduce the possibility of lightning striking. This is because there is a flow of IONS from the point of the conductor which lowers the charge induced on the roof by the thundercloud. The result is that some of the charge on the cloud is cancelled out, lowering the risk of a strike.

light pipes *see* OPTICAL FIBRES.

light year *see* S&A light year.

limestone *see* G&G limestone.

limpet *see* NH Gastropoda.

linear acceleration (linacs) *see* PARTICLE ACCELERATOR.

linear equation an equation in which the variables in the equation are not raised to any power (squared, etc) but may have a coefficient. Thus

$$y = mx + c$$

is a linear equation, and the slope of the line plotted has a gradient *m*, and *c* is the value where the line crosses the y-axis. This is known as the *intercept*. Sets of linear equations are used in engineering to describe the behaviour of structures.

linear motor or linear induction motor a form of electric motor that relies essentially upon the principle of ELECTROMAGNETIc induction, i.e. when current flows through a coil, magnetic forces cause the coil to spin. In the linear motor, electro-magnets are laid flat, and when a current is passed, a metal bar skims across them, i.e. it becomes a method of propulsion. Linear motors are now used in trains that do not run on conventional rails but 'float' over a guiding rail because of the magnetic fields generated.

Linnean system *see* CLASSIFICATION.

lipid *see* FATS; LIVER.

liquid a fluid state of matter that has no definite shape and will take on the shape of its container. A liquid has more kinetic energy than a SOLID but less than a GAS, and although it flows freely the molecules stick together to form drops, unlike gases which continue to spread out whenever possible. Liquids can form solids or gases if cooled or heated, but many substances such as oxygen, nitrogen, and other gases will form liquids only if cooled a great deal or put under pressure.

liquid crystals liquid substances that on heating become cloudy, and in this state they show alignment of molecules in an ordered structure, as in a crystal. At higher temperatures still there is a transition to a clear liquid. The applica-tion of a current disrupts the molecules, causing realignment and optical effects, darkening the liquid, and this property has been exploited for use in displays. *Liquid crystal displays* are used in calculators and watches and also in thin thermometers that work by laying a strip containing the liquid crystals on a child's forehead—the temperature is shown by the segments of crystal changing colour.

littoral *see* NH littoral.

liver a large and very important organ present in the body of vertebrate animals, just below the ribs in the region called the ABDOMEN. It is composed of many groups of liver cells (called *lobules*) which are richly supplied with blood vessels. The liver plays a critical role in the regulation of many of the processes of METABOLISM. A vein called the hepatic portal vein carries the products of digestion to the liver. Here any extra glucose (sugar) that is not im-mediately needed is converted to a form in which it can be stored, known as glycogen. This is then available as a source of energy

for MUSCLES. PROTEINS are broken down in the liver and the excess building blocks (amino acids) of which they are composed are changed to ammonia and then to urea, a waste product that is excreted by the kidneys. Lipids, which are the products of the digestion of fat, are broken down in the liver, and CHOLESTEROL, an essential part of cell membranes, some HORMONES and the NERVOUS SYSTEM, is produced. Bile, which is stored in the gall bladder and then passed to the intestine, is produced in the liver. In addition, poisonous substances (toxins) such as alcohol are broken down (detoxified) by liver cells. Important blood proteins are produced and also substances that are essential in blood clotting. VITA-MIN A is both produced and stored in the liver and it is a storage site for vitamins D, E and K. IRON is also stored, and some hormones and damaged red blood cells are processed and removed.

lizard *see* NH Squamata.

llama *see* NH Artiodactyla.

lobster *see* NH Decapoda.

lobule *see* LIVER.

locust *see* NH Orthoptera.

logarithm (*abbreviation* **log**) a mathemati-cal function first introduced to render mul-tiplication and division with large numbers more simple. The advent of calculators has reduced the former dependency on logs. The basic definition is that if a number x is expressed as a *power* (i.e. the number of times a quantity is multiplied by itself) of another number, y, i.e. $x = y^n$, then n is the logarithm of x to the base y, written as $\log_y x$. There are two types of log in use: *common* (or *Briggs'*) and *Napierian* or *natural*. Common logs have base 10, $\log_{10} x$. Addition of the logs of two numbers gives their *product,* while subtraction of the logs of two numbers is the means of division. Natural logs are to the base e where e is a constant with the value 2.71828. The two logs can be related by the function:

$$\log_e x = 2.303 \log_{10} x$$

longitude *see* G&G latitude.

loudspeaker a device for turning an electric current into sound, found in radios, televi-sions, and many other pieces of equipment that output sound. The commonest design is the *moving-coil loudspeaker*. This consists of a cylindrical magnet with a central south pole surrounded by a circular north pole producing a strong radial magnetic field. There is also a coil sandwiched between the two poles of the magnet that is free to move forwards and backwards and a stiff paper cone that is fastened to the coil. Because the wire of the coil is positioned at right angles to the magnetic field, when current flows through the coil it moves. When an alternating current passes through the coil it moves forwards and backwards and the paper cone vibrates, resulting in sound waves.

low *see* G&G cyclone.

lubricants a vital group of materials used in modern industry to make surfaces slide more easily over each other by reducing FRICTION. Without *lubrication*, surfaces grind against each other, producing wear, which can shorten the working life of a machine or engine. In the main, lubricants are liquid in form and are made from oil, but there are other liquid lubricants (vegetable and mineral oils), some plastic lubricants (fatty acids, soaps), and also some solids, such as graphite and talc. Oil is used as a lubricant in vehicle engines and synthetic fluids are used in turbines for aircraft. The main synthetic lubricants are silicones, polyglycols, esters, and halogenated (*see* HALOGENS) HYDROCARBONS.

Greases made from a liquid lubricant with a thickening agent are also used to combat wear where temperature and shearing forces apply. A petroleum oil forms the base, and a soap mixture the thickener, often with additives such as graphite or fatty acids.

lumen *see* SI UNITS.

luminescence when a body gives out light for a reason other than a high temperature. It is caused by a temporary change in the electronic structure of an atom and involves an electron taking in energy and moving to a higher orbit in the atom, which is then re-emitted as light when the electron falls back to its original orbit. The energy required to promote the electron to a higher orbit may come from light (*photoluminescence*) or from collisions of the atoms with fast particles (*fluorescence*).

When materials continue to give out light after the primary energy source has been removed, this is called *phosphorescence*.

This phenomenon of luminescence is put to use in the CATHODE RAY TUBE of TELEVISIONS. It also occurs in nature and is called BIOLUMINESCENCE.

lungs and gills *lungs* are the sac-like organs that are used for RESPIRATION in air-breathing vertebrate animals. In mammals, a pair of lungs are situated within the rib cage in the region of the body behind the head, known as the thorax. Each lung is made of a thin, moist membrane that is highly folded, and it is here that oxygen is taken into the body and carbon dioxide is given up. The lungs do not have muscles of their own but are filled and emptied by the muscular movement of a sheet-like layer dividing the thorax from the abdomen, known as the *diaphragm*. The diaphragm flattens, which reduces the pressure in the thoracic cavity, enabling the lungs to expand and fill with air (*inhalation*). When the diaphragm muscle relaxes, it arches upwards, forcing air out of the lungs (*exhalation*). This is accompanied (and the effect made greater) by outward and inward movement of the ribs, which are controlled by other (*intercostal*) muscles. *Gills*, which are present in many invertebrate animals and also in fish, are organs that fulfil the same function as lungs.

In mammals such as human beings, air enters through the nose (and mouth) and passes into the windpipe, or *trachea*, which itself branches into two smaller tubes called *bronchi* (singular *bronchus*). Each bronchus goes to one lung and further divides into smaller, finer tubes known as *bronchioles*. Each bronchiole is surrounded by a tiny sac called an *alveolus* (plural *alveoli*) formed from one minute fold of the lung membrane. On one side of the membrane there is air and on the other there are numerous tiny blood vessels called *capillaries*. Deoxygenated blood, i.e. blood that contains little oxygen, is brought via a branch of the pulmonary artery to each lung. The artery divides many times, eventually forming capillaries surrounding the alveoli. In the same way, other capillaries unite and become larger, eventually forming the pulmonary veins that take oxygenated blood back to the heart. The heart pumps it around the body. Carbon dioxide passes out from the capillaries across the alveoli into the lungs, and oxygen passes into the blood in the opposite direction, this process being known as *gaseous exchange*. The numerous folds of the membrane forming the alveoli increase the surface area over which this is able to take place.

The human respiratory system

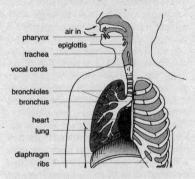

pharynx
air in
epiglottis
trachea
vocal cords
bronchioles
bronchus
heart
lung
diaphragm
ribs

drain into two major lymphatic vessels that empty into veins at the base of the neck. The circulation of lymph is by muscular action rather than by the beating of the heart, and it is essential in the transport of digested fats as well as in the immune system. In children, white blood cells are produced in the thymus gland, which shrinks as adulthood is reached. In adults, white blood cells are produced in the BONE MARROW, spleen and lymph nodes.

The lymph system

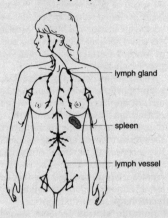

lymph gland
spleen
lymph vessel

lux *see* SI UNITS.

lymph system a network of fine tubules occurring throughout the body of a vertebrate animal. In places the tubules are swollen to form lumps of tissue known as *lymph nodes* or *glands*. This network transports the lymph a colourless, watery fluid that is mainly water but also contains white blood cells (called *leucocytes* and *lymphocytes*), PROTEIN and digested fats. The lymphocytes are an essential part of the body's IMMUNE SYSTEM and collect in the lymph glands and nodes. In the event of an infection, these cells multiply rapidly, often causing a swelling that can be felt through the skin. (An example of this is the adenoids and tonsils, which often become enlarged in the case of an infection of the nose or throat.)

Lymph, which contains waste matter from cells, drains into the tubules from all the tissues of the body. It is filtered when it reaches the lymph nodes, where BACTERIA and other foreign and waste material are destroyed. The lymph tubules finally

machine basically, a means of overcoming resistance at a point by applying a FORCE at another point. Although a machine does not reduce the amount of work to be done to achieve a task, it does allow the work to be done more conveniently.

There are six *simple machines* in the study of physics. These are the *wheel* and *axle*, *wedge*, LEVER, PULLEY, SCREW, and the *inclined plane*. Each in its own way can be used for a particular task—the lever or pulley to raise a load, the wheel to transport a load, and so on. More complex machines usually involve the input of energy either for modification or for driving a mechanism to achieve a task.

The *mechanical advantage* of a machine is the ratio of the load moved to the effort put in to achieve the movement. The *velocity ratio* is the distance moved by the effort, divided by the distance moved by the load. An inclined plane, or *ramp*, doesn't appear much like a machine, but it is because it enables a load to be taken gradually to a height to which the load could not have been lifted vertically. In this case the velocity ratio is essentially the length of the ramp over the height of the ramp.

Mach number the speed of a body expressed as a ratio with the speed of sound. It was named after an Austrian physicist Ernst Mach. If the Mach number is below 1, then the speed is *subsonic*; above 1 is *supersonic*, and as an aircraft increases its speed to go over Mach 1, it is said to *break the sound barrier*. *Hypersonic* is when speeds are in excess of Mach 5. Most airliners travel subsonically but Concorde flies at Mach 2. Certain military planes reach over Mach 3.

The noise associated with breaking the sound barrier is a *sonic boom*. A subsonic aircraft produces pressure waves in front of itself and these waves travel at the speed of sound. A supersonic aircraft overtakes the pressure waves, creating a shock wave like a cone with the point of the cone at the nose of the aircraft. The shock wave creates a typical double bang that can be strong enough to damage buildings.

macrophage *see* IMMUNE SYSTEM.

Magellanic clouds *see* S&A Magellanic clouds.

magma *see* G&G magma.

magnetic field the region of space in which a magnetic body exerts its force. They are produced by moving charged particles and represent a FORCE with a definite direction. There is a magnetic field covering all the Earth's surface, which is believed to be a result of the iron-nickel core.

magnetic tape *see* RECORDING MEDIA.

magnetism the effective force that originates within the Earth and behaves as if there were a powerful magnet at the centre of the Earth, producing a MAGNETIC FIELD. This has its north and south poles pointing approximately to the geographic north and south poles, and a compass needle or freely swinging magnet will align itself along the line of the magnetic field. With the correct instrument it can also be seen that the magnetic field dips into the Earth, increasing towards the poles.

A *bar magnet* has a north and south pole,

so named because the pole at that end pointing to the north is called a north-seeking pole, and similarly with the south pole. When dipped in a material that can be magnetised, such as iron filings, the metal grains align themselves along the magnetic field between the poles of the magnet. Some materials can be magnetised in the presence of a magnet, e.g. iron and steel. Iron does not retain its magnetism but steel does. These are called *temporary* and *permanent magnets*. A more effective way to produce a magnet is to slide a steel bar into a solenoid (coil) through which current is passed, inducing magnetism in the steel (*see* ELECTROMAGNET).

In addition to iron, cobalt, and nickel can also be magnetised strongly, and these materials are called *ferromagnetic*. Non-metals and other metals such as copper seem to be unaffected by magnetism, but very strong magnets do show some effect.

The origin of magnetism is actually unknown, although it is attributed to the flow of electric current. On the electronic scale within magnetic materials it is thought that electrons act as minute magnets (because electrons carry a charge) as they spin around their nuclei in ATOMS. In some ELEMENTS, this electron spin is cancelled out but in others it is not and each atom or molecule acts as a magnet contributing to the overall magnetic nature of the material.

magnetometer an instrument for measuring the strength of a MAGNETIC FIELD. The *deflection magnetometer* consists of a long magnetic pointer pivoted on a short magnet. The pointer swings along a scale, allowing small deflections of the magnet to be measured. Other versions have a small coil that generates a voltage on moving through a magnetic field. More complex and sensitive magnetometers are used for special purposes, e.g. it is possible to tow a magnetometer behind an aircraft to detect changes in the Earth's magnetic field that may be caused because of mineral deposits, including oil.

magnification the ratio of the size of the image to the object in an optical magnifying system. Magnification of an object can be achieved by simple means, e.g. a hand lens or *magnifying glass*, which is merely a convex LENS. A far greater magnification can be achieved by using a *compound microscope*, which consists essentially of two convex lenses with a short focus, called the *objective*, and the eyepiece. The two lenses are at opposite ends of a tube beneath which is a stage upon which the sample (object) is placed. Magnifications of several hundred can be obtained with this microscope. For greater magnification still (above 1500) an *electron microscope* is used. This uses a beam of electrons striking the object. In the *transmission electron microscope* (*tem*) the electron beam passes through a thin slice of the sample and the resulting image is formed by the scattering of the beam, which is enlarged and focused on a fluorescent screen. The *scanning electron microscope* (*sem*) actually scans the surface of the sample and the image is created by secondary electrons that are emitted from the sample. Scanning does not magnify the object as much as transmission electron microscopy, but the image is three-dimensional. Magnifications up to 200,000 can be achieved with tem.

Microscopes are used throughout science and engineering, often with modifications to fulfil a particular role. They are used for studying samples of plant and animal tissue, rock samples to determine minerals and structures present, metals and non-metals to determine structure, and much more.

malacostracan *see* NH Malacostraca.

malleability *see* DUCTILITY.

mammal *see* NH mammal.

mammoth *see* NH Proboscidea.

map *see* G&G map.

Mars *see* S&A Mars.

marsupial *see* NH Metatheria.

maser (an acronym for *m*icrowave *a*mplification by *s*timulated *e*mission of *r*adiation) a microwave amplifier/oscillator that works in a similar way to the LASER and, after it was discovered, prompted the research that resulted in the laser. An atom already in an excited state, because of absorption of energy, gives out a photon because of absorption of further energy. The 'active' material of the maser is therefore built up to an excited state

and enclosed to generate a wave of just one frequency. The microwaves produced can also be used in a clock because of their very precise frequency.

mass *see* WEIGHT.

mass number the total number of *protons* and *neutrons* in the nucleus of an ATOM. Atoms of a particular element may have differing mass numbers because of different numbers of neutrons in the nucleus, i.e. they are ISOTOPES.

mass spectrometry a technique to analyse samples to determine the ELEMENTS in a COMPOUND or the various ISOTOPES in an element. The *mass spectrometer* bombards the sample with high energy electrons, producing charged IONS and fragments that are neutral. The ions are then deflected in a MAGNETIC FIELD that separates them according to their mass and then pass through a slit to a collector. The output is a printed chart (a *mass spectrum*) containing a series of lines or peaks where each peak corresponds to a particular ion and its mass. If isotopes are being identified, the mass spectrometer provides the mass and relative amount of each isotope. Mass spectrometry is used for the identification and structural analysis of organic compounds and the determination of elemental traces in inorganic materials (*see* CHEMISTRY).

mathematical symbols as well as the well-known symbols of ARITHMETIC such as = (equals), – (minus), + (plus), x (multiplied by), and ÷ or / (divided by), there are many other useful symbols that permit the shorthand writing of scientific formulae, equations, and statements. These are used in mathematics, physics, chemistry, astronomy, geology, and other scientific and engineering disciplines. A sample is shown below:

± plus or minus	Σ the sum of
> greater than	α proportional to
< less than	≈ similar or equal to
≥ greater than or equal to	∫ equivalent to
≤ less than or equal to	∴ therefore
= equal by definition	∵ because

mathematics the science of relationships that involve numbers and shapes and has been around for thousands of years since the ancient Egyptians used GEOMETRY in construction. It is divided into two main categories—*pure* and *applied mathematics*. Pure mathematics includes ALGEBRA, ARITHMETIC, GEOMETRY, TRIGONOMETRY, and CALCULUS. Applied mathematics verges on to other subjects or parts of subjects and includes STATISTICS, MECHANICS, computing (*see* CT), and mathematical aspects of topics such as THERMODYNAMICS and astronomy (*see* S&A).

matrix (*plural* **matrices**) an array of elements, i.e. numbers or algebraic symbols set out in rows and columns. It may be a square or a rectangle of elements. Matrices are very useful for condensing information and are used in many ways, e.g. in solving simultaneous LINEAR EQUATIONS (simultaneous equations are two or more equations with two or more unknowns that may have a unique solution). The order of a matrix refers to the number of rows and columns, thus:

$A = \{2\ 1\ 3\}$ has one row and three columns

while

$B = \left\{\begin{matrix} 2\ 6 \\ 1\ 4 \end{matrix}\right.$ has two rows and two columns

Matrices with one row are called *row vectors*, and similarly *column vectors* are so named because they have just one column.

Only matrices of the same order can be added or subtracted, and to be multiplied the second matrix must have the same number of columns as the first has rows. The multiplication is carried out by combining the rows and columns of each matrix to form a new matrix where the various elements are the products of the rows of the first and the columns of the second matrices. Thus if

$A = \left.\begin{matrix} a\ b \\ c\ d \end{matrix}\right\}$ and $B = \left.\begin{matrix} w\ x \\ y\ z \end{matrix}\right\}$

then

$AB = \left.\begin{matrix} aw + by \\ cw + dy \end{matrix}\right\} \left.\begin{matrix} ax + bz \\ cx + dz \end{matrix}\right\}$

matter any substance that occupies space and has mass (*see* WEIGHT) and the material of which the universe is made.

Matter exists normally in three states: GAS, LIQUID, and SOLID. Most substances can be made to exist in all three states at different temperatures, thus by cooling a gas it eventually becomes liquid and then a solid. *Plasma* is considered a fourth state and consists of a high temperature gas of charged particles (electrons and ions). Although it contains charged particles, a plasma is neutral overall, but it can support an electric current. Stars are made of plasma, but it finds applications in the study of controlled NUCLEAR FUSION (*see also* NUCLEAR FISSION).

mean *see* AVERAGE.

mechanics the part of physics that deals with the way MATTER behaves under the influence of FORCES. It involves:

dynamics: the study of objects that are subjected to forces that result in changes of motion.

statics: the study of objects subjected to forces but where no motion is produced.

kinematics: the study of motion without reference to mass or force but which deals with VELOCITY and acceleration of parts of a moving system.

Newton's law of motion (*see* FORCE) forms the basics of mechanics except at the atomic level, when behaviour is explained by QUANTUM MECHANICS.

median *see* AVERAGE.

megaparsec *see* S&A megaparsec.

meiosis *see* CELL DIVISION.

melting point *see* FREEZING.

membrane a thin sheet of tissue widely found in living organisms. It covers, lines, or joins cells, organelles (small organs), organs, and tissues, and consists of a double layer of lipids (FATS) in which protein molecules are suspended. Water and fat-soluble substances are able to pass across a membrane but sugars cannot. Other substances or IONS are actively carried across a membrane by a complex system known as *active transport*.

memory a function of the brain in animals that enables information to be stored and brought back for use later. Several areas of the brain (such as the temporal lobes) are involved in memory, and although, in humans, this function has been widely studied it is not entirely understood. Placing information in the memory involves three stages—registration, storage and recall. The information is committed either to the *short-term memory* or the *long-term memory*. It tends to fade quickly from the short-term memory if not needed but, if used often, is transferred to the long-term memory. Information is usually lost (forgetfulness) during the process of retrieval or recollection. Sometimes this can be helped if the circumstances in which the information was registered can be recreated. This is a technique that is used by the police when they are trying to gain information (that might have been only fleetingly seen) from witnesses at the scene of a crime.

meniscus *see* SURFACE TENSION.

menstrual cycle *see* REPRODUCTION.

Mercury *see* S&A Mercury.

mercury *see* ALLOY; CAPILLARY ACTION.

meridian *see* G&G latitude.

meson *see* ELEMENTARY PARTICLES.

metabolism the name given to all the chemical and physical processes that occur in living organisms. These are of two kinds: *catabolic* (or breaking down), as in the digestion of food; and *anabolic* (or building up), as in the production of more complicated MOLECULES from simple ones. All these processes require energy and ENZYMES in order to take place. Plants trap energy from the sun during PHOTOSYNTHESIS and animals gain energy from the consumption of food. The metabolic rate is the speed at which food is used or broken down to produce energy, and this varies greatly between different species of animals. In people, children have a higher metabolic rate than adults, and more energy is required by someone doing hard work than by someone who is at rest.

metal a material that is generally ductile, malleable (*see* DUCTILITY), dense with a metallic lustre (or sheen), and usually a good conductor of heat and electricity. There are about 80 metals in all, some of which occur as the pure metal, but most are found as compounds in rocks and deposits. Pure metals are used for certain applications (e.g. GOLD in jewellery and copper in electrical goods) but it is usually the case that mixtures of metals (ALLOYS) provide the properties required for specific applications. *Metallic elements* are generally electropositive, i.e. they give up electrons to produce a cation (e.g. Na^+) in reactions. When reacting with water, bases are produced. Elements that show some features of both metals and non-metals are called **metalloids** or *semimetals*, e.g. arsenic, bismuth, and antimony.

metal fatigue the structural failure of metals because of repeated application of stress, which results in a change to the crystalline nature of the metal. *Stress* is FORCE per unit area, and when it is applied to a material, a *strain* is developed, i.e. a distortion. Minor defects in the surface of a metal may provide points where stress can build up and a crack may form. This is particularly important in the design and construction of aircraft, bridges and buildings to ensure that there is not a sudden catastrophic failure.

metallurgy the scientific study of METALS and their ALLOYS. It includes the extraction of metals from their ores and their processing for use. *Extractive metallurgy* deals with production of the metals from their ores and *physical metallurgy* is the study of the structure of metals and their properties. Metals are studied in the laboratory using a microscope to allow small flaws and cracks to be seen. Such studies are important in designing to avoid or minimise METAL FATIGUE.

metamorphic rocks *see* G&G metamorphic rocks.

metamorphosis *see* LARVA.

metastasis *see* CANCER.

metatherian *see* NH Metatheria.

meteorite *see* S&A asteroid.

meteorology *see* G&G meteorology.

methane the first member of the alkane (*see* HYDROCARBONS) series, with the formula CH_4. It is a colourless, odourless gas and the main component of coal gas and a byproduct of decaying vegetable matter. It is the primary component of natural gas and occurs in coal mines where, mixed with air, it forms highly explosive *firedamp*. It is highly flammable and is used in the manufacture of hydrogen, ammonia, carbon monoxide, and other chemicals.

metric system a system of measurement of weights and measures based on the principle that levels of units are related by the factor 10, i.e. it is a decimal system that began with the metre. There are now seven basic units of measurement: metre, second, kilogram, ampere, Kelvin, candela (light) and mole, and each has a standard value and is defined very precisely. *See also* SI UNITS.

mice *see* NH Rodentia.

microbiology and microorganism *microbiology* is the scientific study of all aspects of the life of microorganisms or microbes. These organisms are so called because they can be seen only with a microscope. They include BACTERIA, VIRUSES, yeasts and moulds, many of the (largely single-celled) organisms called protozoa (*see* PROTISTA), and some algae and fungi. Many of these organisms are highly significant because of their use in BIOTECHNOLOGY and also because some cause DISEASES of various kinds. The study of microbiology has advanced significantly, along with the technological development of microscopes, particularly the electron microscope and also with the availability of more advanced LABORATORY facilities.

microphone a device for changing sound into electric current. It is essentially the reverse process to that which happens in a LOUDSPEAKER. In a moving coil microphone, sound waves cause vibration in a diaphragm made of paper or plastic, and this moves a small coil that rests in the field of a cylindrical magnet. A small current is *induced* in the coil by moving it through the magnetic field, and this can be amplified and output through a loudspeaker. A variety of microphones are now in use: *carbon microphone* where the diaphragm changes the resistance in a carbon contact; *condenser microphone* and a *crystal microphone* which relies upon the PIEZOELECTRIC EFFECT in crystals.

microscope *see* MAGNIFICATION; MICROBIOLOGY.

microwaves electromagnetic WAVES with wavelengths of a few centimetres or less. Microwaves are used for communications, e.g. via satellites, and intense beams are produced in a MASER. They are easily deflected and as they have a shorter wavelength than radio waves, they are suitable for use in radar systems because they can detect small objects. HEAT is produced when microwaves are absorbed, and this is utilised in microwave ovens. A unit called the MAGNETRON generates the microwaves and these impart their energy to the water in the food, producing heat and the cooking effect.

migration *see* NH migration.

Milky Way *see* S&A Milky Way.

milliammeter *see* GALVANOMETER.

mimicry *see* NH mimicry.

mineralogy *see* G&G mineralogy.

minerals *see* G&G minerals.

mirror an object or surface that reflects light. Mirrors are made from glass coated with a thin metallic layer, but polished metal surfaces have the same effect. When light strikes a mirrored surface, it is reflected in a particular way according to the laws of REFLECTION. A *plane mirror* has a flat surface that bounces back light, creating an image 'behind' the mirror. *Curved mirrors* are convex or concave. *Concave mirrors* produce a magnifying effect if the object is sufficiently near to the mirror but distant objects are smaller and inverted. *Convex mirrors* produce upright images that are smaller than the object. Concave mirrors are used in car headlights while convex mirrors are often used for driving mirrors because they produce a wide angle of view.

mite *see* NH Arachnida.

mitochondrion (*plural* **mitochondria**) a type of rod-shaped organelle found in the cytoplasm (CELL contents except for the nucleus) of EUCARYOTIC cells, which is surrounded by a double membrane. Mitochondria have been called the 'power houses' of the cell as they are very important in the generation of energy in a form called ATP. ATP production is the end result of cellular respiration and provides energy for all metabolic processes. As mitochondria are the sites where this takes place, they are especially abundant in cells that require lots of energy, such as those of muscles. Mitochondria contain a form of DNA, structures called ribosomes in which proteins are manufactured with numerous enzymes, each specific to a particular metabolic process.

mitosis *see* CELL DIVISION.

mode *see* AVERAGE.

Mohs scale *see* G&G hardness of minerals.

molar *see* TEETH.

mole (1) *see* MOLECULE AND MOLE; SI UNITS.

mole (2) *see* NH Insectivora.

molecule and mole a *molecule* is the smallest chemical unit of an element or compound that can exist independently. It consists of ATOMS bonded together in a particular combination, e.g. oxygen, O_2, is two oxygen atoms and carbon dioxide, CO_2, is one carbon and two oxygen atoms. Molecules may contain thousands of atoms. Gases, organic compounds, liquids, and many solids consist of molecules but some materials, e.g. metals and ionic substances, are different and comprise charged atoms or IONS.

The *mole* is the unit of substance that contains the same number of elementary particles as there are in 12 grams of carbon. One mole of a substance contains 6.023×10^{23} molecular atoms, or ions, or electrons.

mollusc *see* NH Mollusca.

moulting *see* ECDYSIS AND MOULTING.

momentum the property of an object defined as the product of its VELOCITY and mass (*see* WEIGHT) and it is measured in kilograms per second (kgm/s). Momentum is related to FORCE as follows:

force = the rate of change of momentum.

Changes in momentum occur mainly because of the interaction between two bodies. During any interaction the total momentum of the bodies involved remains the same, providing no external force, such as FRICTION, is acting. Newton's second law of motion states that the rate of change of momentum of a body is directly proportional to the force acting and occurs in the direction in which the force ends. If a body is rotating around an axis then it has *angular momentum*, which is the product of its momentum and its perpendicular distance from the fixed axis. Momentum can be seen around us all the time, but one of the most obvious examples is the collision of balls on a pool table.

Monera the biological kingdom (*see* CLASSIFICATION) in which all the organisms have PROCARYOTIC cells and are the BACTERIA and cyanobacteria (formerly called blue-green algae). *See* PROCARYOTE.

monkey *see* NH Primates.

monocotyledon *see* PLANTS.

monomer *see* POLYMER.

monsoon *see* G&G monsoon.

Moon *see* S&A Moon.

moraine *see* G&G boulder clay; glacier.

Morse code *see* TELEGRAPH.

mosquito *see* NH Diptera.

moss *see* NH Bryophyta.

moss animals *see* NH moss animals.

moth *see* NH Lepidoptera.

motors (electric) the basic principle behind most common electric motors is that when current is passed through a coil in a MAGNETIC FIELD, a turning effect is produced. In a DC (direct current) motor a coil rotates between the poles of a permanent magnet and is connected to a BATTERY via carbon brushes that contact a split ring or *commutator*. The commutator reverses the current direction every half-turn of the coil, ensuring that the coil continues to rotate (*see also* GENERATOR). Motors are used in many different devices and pieces of equipment, such as hair-dryers, mixers and food processors, drills, and so on. Such motors operate from an AC (alternating current) supply, and in this case an electromagnet is used because it can match the change in current and yet maintain a constant turning effect. In addition, the smooth and reliable running of these motors is ensured by: the incorporation of several coils at different angles, each connected to a set of commutator pieces; several hundred turns of wire in each coil, on a soft iron core (as *armature*) which becomes magnetised, increasing the strength of the magnetic field; the poles of the magnet are shaped into a curve, creating a magnetic field that is almost radial, giving a constant turning force (*see also* INDUCTANCE).

mountains *see* G&G mountains.

muscle a special type of tissue that is responsible for movements in the body of an animal and often works by pulling against the hard SKELETON. Muscle cells are elongated and arranged as bundles (called *fibres*). In mammals there are three types controlled by different parts of the nervous system. *Voluntary* or *striated muscle* operates limbs and joints and is under the conscious control of the will. Each muscle fibre consists of smaller elongated *fibrils* (myofibrils), and these either lengthen and become thinner or shorten and become fatter as they slide over one another, depending on whether the muscle is contracting or relaxing. *Involuntary* or *smooth muscle* is not under conscious control but is regulated by a special part of the NERVOUS SYSTEM (called the *autonomic nervous system*). These muscles work automatically and are responsible for the contractions of the gut and of the uterus at the time of birth. This type of muscle also occurs at various other sites within the body. *Cardiac muscle* is the third specialised kind and is responsible for the beating of the heart, which continues throughout life. This muscle is involuntary but the rate of beat is affected by activity of an important nerve called the *vagus nerve*. The *pacemaker* is a collection of specialised cardiac muscle cells situated in the wall of the right atrium (one of the upper chambers of the heart). These cells are under the control of the autonomic nervous system and produce the contractions that stimulate the rest of the heart to contract.

mutation any change that occurs in the DNA in the CHROMOSOMES of cells. It is one way in which genetic variation occurs and allows natural selection to operate (*see* GENETICS). This is because any alteration in the sex cells may produce an inherited change (mutation) in the characteristics of later generations of the organism. Mutations occur during the time when DNA is copying itself, as in CELL DIVISION, but are relatively rare and most are harmful or lethal. They can occur much more frequently following exposure to certain chemicals and radiation (X-rays), which are known as *mutagens*. A *mutant* is an organism that shows the effects of a mutation.

mutualism *see* PARASITES; SYMBIOSIS.

mycology the name given to the scientific study of all aspects of the life of FUNGI.

myelin sheath *see* NERVOUS SYSTEM.

myeloid tissue *see* BONE MARROW.

myriapod *see* NH Myriapoda.

nanotechnology a broad term that embraces the fields of scientific research and development concerned with matter smaller than one micrometre in size and usually between 1 to 100 nanometres. Many scientific disciplines are involved, concerned with the study, applications and manufacture of 'nano-products'. Nanotechnology has many commercial applications as well as being a subject of pure scientific research. The fields of applied physics, colloidal science, materials science, chemistry and engineering may all be involved in nanotechnology.

natural gas *see* G&G natural gas.

natural selection *see* DARWIN.

nautilus *see* NH Cephalopoda.

navel *see* GESTATION AND BIRTH.

nebula *see* S&A nebula.

nekton *see* NH nekton.

nematode *see* NH Nematoda.

neon *see* INERT GAS.

nephron *see* OSMOREGULATION.

Neptune *see* S&A Neptune.

neritic zone *see* NH neritic zone.

nervous system a network of specialised cells and tissues that is present in all multicellular animals to a greater or lesser degree (with the exception of sponges). The activity of the nervous system consists of electrical impulses that are caused by the movement of chemical (sodium and potassium) IONS. The nervous system includes RECEPTORS, which receive information from the surrounding environment and are called *sensory*. These are concerned with the senses, such as sight, sound, touch, and pressure, and they transmit the information that they detect along nerves (called *sensory nerves*) and these travel to the central nervous system. In the simpler animals such as invertebrates, this often consists of a paired nerve cord with swellings along its length, called *ganglia* (singular *ganglion*). In vertebrate animals, the central nervous system is highly complex and consists of the brain and spinal cord. Within the central nervous system all the information is decoded and, if appropriate, a response is initiated. This often consists of a signal being sent outwards along a nerve (called a *motor nerve*) that travels to a muscle, causing a contraction to occur. In vertebrates, a part of the nervous system is concerned with the control of the involuntary or smooth MUSCLE of the body. This is called the *autonomic nervous system* and consists of two divisions, the *sympathetic* and *parasympathetic*, which act in opposite ways (*antagonistic*). It is sometimes called *involuntary* because its activity regulates the internal environment of the body and it supplies the smooth muscle (heart, gut, etc) and glands with their motor nerve supply.

A *nerve* is made up of numerous nerve cells or *neurons*. Some nerves are sensory, others are motor and yet others are mixed, carrying both types of neurons. Each neuron has a cell body (containing the nucleus) and many fine projections called *dendrites*. Dendrites from surrounding neurons are able to communicate with one another across a gap called a *synapse*. A long, fine projection, called an *axon*, runs out from the neuron cell body. It may be surrounded by a fatty sheath (a 'myelin sheath'), which is restricted at intervals at sites that are known as *nodes of Ranvier*.

neutrino *see* ELEMENTARY PARTICLES.

neutron star *see* S&A neutron star.

newt *see* NH newt.

newton (*symbol* **N**) the SI UNIT of FORCE. One newton is the force required to give a mass of one kilogram an acceleration of one metre per second per second.

niche *see* NH niche.

nitrides compounds similar to CARBIDES that form hard materials with high melting points. Metals such as titanium, chromium, vanadium, zirconium and hafnium are used, resulting in nitrides with high hardness, resistance to molten metals and a high CORROSION resistance. As such they are used in crucibles for melting metal, as protective coatings for moving surfaces, and as cutting tools.

nitrogen a colourless GAS existing as a diatomic molecule, N_2. It occurs in air (75 per cent by weight), and as nitrates, ammonia, and in PROTEINS. It is relatively unreactive at room temperature but reacts with some ELEMENTS on heating. It is used extensively in the production of ammonia in liquid form as a refrigerant (its melting point is –210°C/346°F) and as an inert

atmosphere. It is obtained industrially by the fractionation of liquid air. Nitrogen is a vital element in the life cycle of both plants and animals and there is a regular circulation, called the *nitrogen cycle*. BACTERIA take nitrogen from the atmosphere (*nitrogen fixation*) and plants use nitrate ions (NO_3^-) from the soil. The nitrogen is incorporated into plant tissue that is then eaten by animals. The nitrogen is returned to the soil by the decomposition of dead plants and animals and by excretion.

noble gas *see* INERT GAS.

noble metals metals such as platinum, silver, and GOLD, which are highly resistant to attack by ACIDS and to CORROSION. They tend not to react chemically with non-metals.

noise a random mixture of changing frequencies of sound, e.g. as produced by an electric drill. It is also the term describing the background disturbance registered when a signal of some description is being measured. The effect occurs in electrical circuits and is caused by interference arising from other sources, e.g. lightning, electric motors, or random motion of electrons making up the current. This often happens with a radio receiver, and electronic filtering is often undertaken to improve the signal and reduce the noise.

nose *see* SMELL.

nova *see* S&A nova.

nuclear club the group of countries that have nuclear weapons, which includes USA, Russia, UK, France, India, Pakistan and China. In addition it is believed that Israel has the bomb and North Korea also has the technology. Nuclear weapons are inextricably linked with enrichment, a part of the process to deliver nuclear power. Iran is undertaking enrichment although it denies it has nuclear weapons ambitions, and Brazil is now also able to enrich uranium to generate energy.

nuclear energy the energy produced by the controlled decay of radioactive ELEMENTS. Upon decay, an element such as uranium releases energy as heat that can be harnessed. During radioactive decay the energy given off per atom is thousands and thousands times more than during burning. However, the decay often has to be accelerated by bombarding the material with neutrons.

NUCLEAR FISSION is the splitting of such atoms and is the way in which electricity is generated for nuclear power. In a *nuclear reactor* heat from the nuclear reactions heats water into steam that drives the turbines. The core of a reactor contains the nuclear fuel, which may be uranium dioxide with uranium-235. Neutrons produced by the fission reactions are slowed down by a graphite core to ensure the *chain reaction* continues. The graphite core is called the *moderator*. *Control rods* of boron steel are lowered into or taken out of the reactor to control the rate of fission. Boron absorbs neutrons, and so if rods are lowered there are fewer neutrons available for the nuclear fission, and the reactor core temperature will fall. This is a *thermal reactor*. In a *fast breeder reactor*, low-grade uranium surrounds the core and impact from neutrons creates some uranium-239, which forms plutonium, which itself can be used as a reactor fuel. NUCLEAR FUSION has not yet been harnessed for commercial power production.

Nuclear energy has the benefit of producing a lot of energy from a small amount of fuel. It does not produce gases that contribute to the GREENHOUSE EFFECT, but the waste produced is very dangerous and must be stored or treated very carefully. The waste products are from the reprocessing of used fuel in which unused uranium is separated from the waste and small quantities of plutonium-239 (as produced and used in fast breeder reactors). Plutonium-239 is very hazardous indeed and is used in the production of nuclear weapons. *See* NUCLEAR CLUB.

nuclear fission the splitting process that results when a neutron strikes a nucleus of, for example, uranium-235. The nucleus splits into two and releases more neutrons and a lot of energy. A *chain reaction* develops when the neutrons go on to split further nuclei and the energy released becomes enormous. The splitting of the uranium creates two other nuclei, both radioactive:

uranium-235 + neutron Æ krypton-90 + barium-144 + neutrons + energy

This chain reaction occurs when there is a certain mass of uranium-235, known as the *critical mass*. This was the principle employed in the first *atom bomb* when two pieces of uranium-235 were brought together to exceed the critical mass and produced a destructive force of unimaginable proportions.

nuclear fusion where two nuclei are combined to form a single nucleus with an accompanying release of energy. Ordinarily nuclei would repel each other because of the like electrical charge, and so very high collision speeds have to be used, which in practice means the use of incredibly high temperatures. A fusion reaction may be:

deuterium + tritium → helium + neutron + energy

$$\, _{1}^{2}\text{H} \; + \; _{1}^{3}\text{H} \; \rightarrow \; _{2}^{4}\text{He} \; + \; _{0}^{1}\text{n}$$

It is necessary to raise the temperature of the hydrogen gas to around 100 million K. Because thermal energy has to be supplied before the nuclear reactions occur, fusion is often called *thermonuclear fusion*. Fusion occurs in the Sun and, in an uncontrolled way, in the *hydrogen bomb*, but it is technically very difficult to control in the way that NUCLEAR FISSION is managed. Research into this subject involves the use of a *tokamak*, which employs a MAGNETIC FIELD shaped like a doughnut to trap the hot gas. Thermonuclear reactors could be a solution to energy supply problems because the fuel is readily available and the waste product is not radioactive and it is also inert (unreactive).

nuclear reactor *see* NUCLEAR ENERGY.

nucleus *see* ATOM; CELL; CELL DIVISION.

nuclide *see* RADIOACTIVITY.

numbers our numbers are based on Arabic numerals, which in turn were based on a Hindu system, and the system is constructed upon powers of ten, i.e. the decimal system (*see* DECIMAL NUMBERS). BINARY NUMBERS use the base two and are used extensively in computer programs. *Real numbers* include all *rational numbers* (whole numbers or integers and fractions) and *irrational numbers*, i.e. those that cannot be expressed as an exact fraction, e.g. some square roots such as 2, 5 and values such as the constant π (pi). *Complex* *numbers* are those written in the form *a* + *ib* where *a* and *b* are real numbers and i is the square root of –1.

A *prime number* is a number that can be divided only by itself and 1, such as 2, 3, 5, 7, 11, 13, 17, 19, 23. There is an infinite number of prime numbers, and over the years mathematicians have spent much time trying to find a general method for calculating primes. A *surd* is an expression that contains the root of an irrational number and that can never be expressed exactly, e.g.:

$$\sqrt{3} = 1.7320508 \ldots$$

nylon *see* POLYMER; SYNTHETIC FIBRES.

ocean *see* G&G ocean.

ocelli *see* SIGHT.

octopus *see* NH Cephalopoda.

ohm *see* SI UNITS.

oils greasy liquid substances that are obtained from animal or vegetable matter or mineral sources and are complex organic compounds (*see* CHEMISTRY). There are also many synthetic oils. There are basically three groups of oils: the *fatty oils* from animal and vegetable sources; *mineral oils* from PETROLEUM and coal; and *essential oils* derived from certain plants. Typical vegetable oils are extracted from soya beans, olives, nuts, and maize. The essential oils are volatile (evaporate quickly) and are used in *aromatherapy* and in making perfumes and flavourings. Examples are peppermint oil, clove oil, oil of wintergreen, and rose oil. Mineral oils are actually fossil fuels and come under the general term of petroleum.

oligochaete *see* NH Oligochaeta.

omnivore any animal that eats both plant and animal material, e.g. human beings (*compare* CARNIVORE and HERBIVORE).

opossum *see* NH Metatheria.

optical fibres very thin glass rods that are flexible. When light rays enter one end of the fibre it is reflected completely within the fibres, being reflected from side to side until it emerges at the other end. Bundles of fibres are called *light pipes*, and they have several very important uses. Surgeons use them to see inside the body of a patient, often without the need for an incision. Also the pipes can carry an enormous number of telephone calls, where the calls are coded and sent along the fibres as pulses of LASER light. Another remarkable feature of optical fibres is that the light exits almost as strongly as it entered, even if the path is several kilometres, and this eliminates the need for numerous stations to boost the signal as required with ordinary telephone cables.

orbit *see* S&A orbit.

orbital *see* ATOM; QUANTUM NUMBERS.

order *see* CLASSIFICATION.

ore *see* G&G ore.

organ and tissue a *tissue* is a collection of cells within an ORGANISM, which are specialised to perform a particular function. An *organ* is a distinct and recognisable site or unit within the body of an organism that consists of two or more types of tissue. It is specialised in terms of its structure and function, and, in animals, examples include the kidneys, liver, skin, and eyes. In plants, flowers, stems, roots, leaves, and flowers are all organs. An *organelle* is a structure within a cell that performs a particular function and is surrounded by a membrane to separate it from other cell contents, e.g. the nucleus and MITOCHONDRIA.

organelle *see* ORGAN AND TISSUE.

organism any living creature, including microorganisms, plants, and animals. There are very many different kinds of organism with new species being discovered all the time. At the other end of the scale, over the course of the Earth's history, numerous types of organism have become extinct. *Biotic* is an adjective relating to life or living things (hence *biota*, the plant and animal life of a region). Thus, for any organism, the other organisms around it make up the biotic environment.

orthopteran *see* NH Orthoptera.

osmoregulation any process or mechanism in animals that regulates the concentration of salts (e.g. sodium chloride) and water in the body. Depending on the environment it inhabits, there is a tendency for water to pass into or out of an animal's body by OSMOSIS. Water tends to pass into the body of an animal that inhabits fresh water as the concentration of salts within its body is higher than that outside. Animals have a variety of structures to rid the body of excess water. In simple ORGANISMS (e.g. single-celled ones) an organelle called a *contractile vacuole* fills with water and expels it to the outside through a pore in the cell membrane. In marine animals there is a tendency to lose water from the body to the surrounding environment where the concentration of salts is higher. In vertebrate animals, whether the problem is water gain or loss, the kidneys are the main osmoregulatory organs. In land-dwelling animals, the outer covering of skin or cuticle forms a barrier to excess water gain or loss but many other mechanisms are also at work (including kidneys, sweating, panting, behavioural responses) so that a correct water/salt balance is maintained.

In humans, there is a pair of kidneys situated at the back of the abdomen, and these are responsible for cleaning the blood and removing waste products that are then excreted. The kidney contains numerous tubules called *nephrons*, each with an expanded cup-shaped portion at one end called the *Bowman's capsule*. Behind this there is a folded length of tubule, known as the *proximal convoluted tubule*, then a straight hairpin-shaped loop, the *loop of Henle*, and finally another looped portion called the *distal convoluted tubule*. Blood enters the Bowman's capsules from tiny capillaries that form a knot, called the *glomerulus*, inside the cup. This blood is brought to the kidney by the renal artery. Water and waste substances, such as urea, a breakdown product of protein digestion, pass along the length of the nephrons, and this is known as *filtrate*. Useful substances, including water and salts, are reabsorbed. Many capillaries surround the nephrons, and cleaned or filtered blood eventually leaves the kidney in the renal vein. The distal convoluted tubules, containing the waste products that have not been reabsorbed, empty into a collecting duct and final processing takes place.

The liquid that is left, known as *urine*, enters the ureter, which is a narrow tube leading to the *bladder*. From the bladder another tube, called the *urethra*, leads to the outside. The two kidneys daily receive between 1000 and 2000 litres of blood and process about 180 litres of filtrate. 1.5 litres

of urine is produced and the rest of the filtrate is reabsorbed. If the kidneys fail, their function has to be carried out by a machine, a process known as *dialysis*.

The human kidney

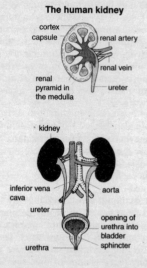

cortex
capsule
renal artery
renal vein
renal pyramid in the medulla
ureter

kidney
inferior vena cava
aorta
ureter
opening of urethra into bladder
sphincter
urethra

osmosis the process whereby molecules of solvent (usually water) move through a semipermeable membrane to the more concentrated solution. This is because of the size of the molecules compared to the holes in the membrane. The holes permit the small water molecules through but not the larger solvent molecules so there is a tendency for the molecular concentrations to approach equality. *Osmotic pressure* is the pressure that must be applied to prevent osmotic flow.

Osmosis is an important mechanism in living organisms in the movement of water across cell membranes, particularly in the uptake of water by plant roots. Certain mechanisms have also evolved to prevent too much water entering cells, causing rupture, or leaving cells, causing shrinkage.

ovary *see* POLLINATION; REPRODUCTION.

oviparous, ovoviviparous *see* GESTATION AND BIRTH.

ovule *see* FLOWERS; POLLINATION; REPRODUCTION.

ovum *see* EGG.

oxidation and reduction processes that occur during CHEMICAL REACTIONS. *Oxidation* is the gain of oxygen or loss of electrons from the reactant. Oxidation can occur in the absence of oxygen as it can also be represented by the loss of hydrogen. Similarly, *reduction* is the loss of oxygen or gain of electrons from one of the reactants and also the gain of hydrogen.

oxygen a colourless, odourless GAS vital for the RESPIRATION of most life forms. It is the most abundant of all the ELEMENTS, forming 21 per cent by volume in air, almost 90 per cent by weight of water and nearly 50 per cent by weight of rocks in the crust. It is manufactured by the fractional DISTILLATION of liquid air and on heating reacts with most elements to form oxides. It is used extensively in industry for steel making, welding, rocket fuels, and in chemical synthesis (forming other chemicals).

ozone layer *see* G&G ozone layer.

pacemaker *see* MUSCLE.

paint a liquid made up of the pigment (the coloured material) in SUSPENSION within a non-volatile and a volatile part. The non-volatile oil or resin holds the pigment in place, while the volatile part enables the paint to be applied easily and it eventually evaporates (and may be water or a HYDROCARBON solvent). When applied to a surface the liquid evaporates, leaving the pigment as an adhesive skin. Many paints are oil-based and are waterproof when dry and may contain additives to speed drying or improve coverage. Linseed oil was used with a thinner and a drier, but synthetic compounds are now commonly used. Paints based on water are emulsions (*see* COLLOID), hence *emulsion paint*. These are often acrylic resins or polyvinyl acetate in water. The earliest examples of paint were obtained from natural materials. Now there are special paints for particular purposes, e.g. anti-fouling paint to stop the growth of barnacles on a ship's hull.

pancreas an important gland present in VERTEBRATE animals, situated behind and just below the stomach. It has two functions as it produces both digestive ENZYMES and the HORMONES insulin and glucagon that regulate the amount of sugar present in the blood. The digestive enzymes produced include trypsin, which breaks down protein, amylase, which digests starch, and lipase, which aids in the digestion of FATS. These are produced in an alkaline fluid that counteracts the acid effect of the stomach's gastric juice. The *pancreatic juice*, with its enzymes, passes through a tube or duct into the first part of the small intestine below the stomach, which is called the *duodenum*.

paper sheets of hydrated CELLULOSE fibres derived from wood pulp. Pulp is made from timber mechanically or chemically. The mechanical method is simpler and more economical but produces weaker, poorer quality papers (e.g. newsprint). Pulp from chemical processes is stronger and brighter but more expensive. The pulp is washed, bleached and broken down and delivered to the paper mill where any fillers, size (a glue), and dyes are added. *China clay* is a common filler, providing bulk and opacity. The pulp is then watered down to make a slurry, treated further, and then output on to a moving wire mesh and through presses that remove most of the water. Heated rollers then dry the paper, which is then smoothed and finished (involving pressing the surface fibres—a process known as *calendering*). The paper is then taken on to rolls for use or for cutting into sheets.

The whole process from pulp to paper can be a continuous process requiring machinery occupying many metres but it can produce sheets of paper in minutes.

parallax *see* S&A parallax.

parasite an organism that obtains its food by living in or on the body of another living organism without giving anything in return. The organism on which the parasite feeds is known as the *host*. Usually, the parasite does not kill the host as its future depends on their mutual survival. However, sometimes a host species can become so seriously ill or weakened by the presence of the parasite that it dies. Parasites are of two kinds: *ectoparasites* attach themselves to the host's surface or skin and examples include the bloodsucking head lice, ticks, and fleas; *endoparasites* live inside the host's body, often within the gut or muscle, and examples are tapeworms, roundworms, and liver flukes. Parasitic plants usually twine themselves around their host. They send projections, called *haustoria* (singular *haustorium*), into the sap of the host to draw up water and food substances. A plant of this type is the dodder, which lacks leaves and CHLOROPHYLL and cannot PHOTOSYNTHESISE. Others, such as the mistletoe, are partial parasites, able to photosynthesise but obtaining minerals and water from the host.

Some other organisms live together in a way that brings mutual benefit rather than harm, and this type of relationship is called *mutualism*. Sometimes one organism benefits while the other remains unharmed; this is termed *commensalism*. These three types of relationship between organisms—parasitism, mutualism, and commensalism usually of two different species—are grouped together and called SYMBIOSIS.

parsec *see* S&A parsec.

particle accelerator a machine for increasing the speed (and therefore the kinetic energy) of charged particles such as protons, electrons, and helium nuclei by accelerating them in an electric field.

Accelerators are used in the study of subatomic particles. To split an atom, particles travelling close to the speed of light are required. There are two types of accelerator, linear and cyclic. *Linear acceleration*, or *linacs*, have to be very long, up to several kilometres, and consist of rows of electrodes separated by gaps. The IONS in the beam accelerate across each gap because of a high frequency potential between alternate electrodes.

Cyclic accelerators use a magnetic field to bend the path of the charged particles. The *cyclotron* is an example in which energies of several million electron volts are imparted to the particles as they travel along a spiral path between D-shaped electrodes. The *synchrotron* is another example. In the cyclic accelerators the stream of charged particles is accelerated to the required level and then deflected out of the ring.

The first accelerator was built by Cockcroft and Walton in 1932, and with it they split the ATOM for the first time. The energies of modern machines are measured in GeV (gigaelectron volts, i.e. billions) and at the Fermi Laboratory in the USA, 800 GeV has been reached. Higher energies can be achieved using a *storage ring*, which is a toroidal (doughnut-shaped) component in some accelerators. Particles enter the ring and can stay there for many weeks or months. A ring 300 metres in diameter in Geneva produces energies up to 1700 GeV.

pascal *see* SI UNITS.

pasteurisation the process, named after French chemist and biologist Louis Pasteur, that involves the partial sterilisation of food, killing potentially harmful bacteria. Milk is an obvious example: heated to 62°C (143°F) for 30 minutes, BACTERIA that could cause tuberculosis are killed, and the shelf life is increased by delaying fermentation because other bacteria have also been killed or damaged. An alternative treatment involves heating milk to 72°C (162°F) for 15 seconds. Higher temperatures still are used to produce 'long-life' milk. Pasteurisation is also used with beer and wine to eliminate any yeast that would create cloudiness in the drink.

pathogen any organism that causes disease in another organism. Most pathogens that affect humans and other animals are BACTERIA or VIRUSES, but in plants a wide range of fungi also act as pathogens.

pathology the medical science and speciality in which the area of study is the causes of diseases and the ways in which these affect the body. Pathology relies on the use of powerful microscopes to study samples and also on the techniques of MICROBIOLOGY.

peat *see* G&G peat.

pelagic *see* NH pelagic.

perennial *see* PLANTS.

periodic table an ordered table of all the ELEMENTS arranged by their ATOMIC NUMBERS, i.e. the number of protons and electrons in an atom. The arrangement means that elements with similar properties are grouped near to each other. The horizontal rows are called *periods* and the vertical rows are *groups*. Elements with the same number of electrons in their outer shell behave in a similar way, and this is the basis of the vertical group. Moving from left to right along

The periodic table

Group																	
1A	2A	3B	4B	5B	6B	7B	8			1B	2B	3A	4A	5A	6A	7A	0
H 1																	He 2
Li 3	Be 4											B 5	C 6	N 7	O 8	F 9	Ne 10
Na 11	Mg 12		←		Transition Elements				→			Al 13	Si 14	P 15	S 16	Cl 17	Ar 18
K 19	Ca 20	Sc 21	Ti 22	V 23	Cr 24	Mn 25	Fe 26	Co 27	Ni 28	Cu 29	Zn 30	Ga 31	Ge 32	As 33	Se 34	Br 35	Kr 36
Rb 37	Sr 38	Y 39	Zr 40	Nb 41	Mo 42	Tc 43	Ru 44	Rh 45	Pd 46	Ag 47	Cd 48	In 49	Sn 50	Sb 51	Te 52	I 53	Xe 54
Cs 55	Ba 56	La* 57	Hf 72	Ta 73	W 74	Re 75	Os 76	Ir 77	Pt 78	Au 79	Hg 80	Ti 81	Pb 82	Bi 83	Po 84	At 85	Rn 86
Fr 87	Ra 88	Ac° 89															

* Lanthanides	La 57	Ce 58	Pr 59	Nd 60	Pm 61	Sm 62	Eu 63	Gd 64	Tb 65	Dy 66	Ho 67	Er 68	Tm 69	Yb 70	Lu 71
° Actinides	Ac 89	Th 90	Pa 91	U 92	Np 93	Pu 94	Am 95	Cm 96	Bk 97	Cf 98	Es 99	Fm 100	Md 101	No 102	Lr 103

the periods corresponds to the gradual filling of successive electron shells and an increase in the size of the atom.

The elements and their symbols are listed on page 95. The periodic table is shown opposite on page 137.

There are various sections within the periodic table, as follows:

alkali metals	Li, Na, K, Rb, Cs, Fr
alkaline earth metals	Ca, Sr, Ba, Ra
chalcogens	O, S, Se, Te, Po
halogens	F, Cl, Br, I, At
inert gases	He, Ne, Ar, Kr, Xe, Rn
rare earth elements	Sc, Y, La to Lu
lanthanides	Ce to Lu inclusive
actinium series	Ac onwards
transuranium elements	elements after U
platinum metals	Ru, Os, Rh, Ir, Pd, Pt

Dmitri Ivanovich Mendeleev (or Medeleyev) was a Russian chemist who constructed the first periodic table but based upon atomic weights. This basic principle, modified to use atomic numbers rather than atomic weights, formed the basis of the modern table and even then, in 1869, allowed Mendeleev to predict the existence of undiscovered elements.

perissodactyl *see* NH Perissodactyla.

permafrost *see* G&G permafrost.

pesticides chemical poisons designed to kill insects (*insecticides*), weeds (*herbicides*), fungi (*fungicides*), and other pests. Until the advent of organic pesticides in the 1930s, the compounds used were inorganic mixtures such as Bordeaux mixture (copper sulphate and lime) and calcium arsenate. Some naturally occurring organic insecticides were also used, such as pyrethrum, produced from the flowers of the chrysanthemum. Now most are organic, save for some well-known examples such as DDT.

Fungicides traditionally contained sulphur or copper or mercury although the toxicity of mercury has led to a decline in its use. Now there are a number of organic compounds, and many are *systemic* i.e. they actually enter the plant. *Herbicides* are the single most important group of pesticides, as they kill weeds that compete with crops for light and nutrients and may be sources of other pests and diseases. Herbicides may be *selective* (killing only certain plants) or total (*nonselective*), and in the main are complex organic chemicals. *Insecticides* are very important in controlling insects that consume or destroy crops and also in limiting diseases spread by insects, such as malaria and sleeping sickness. There are naturally occurring insecticides, e.g. nicotine, derris, and pyrethrum, and synthetic compounds, which form the greater proportion. Synthetic types include organochlorines, organophosphates, and carbamates.

Pesticides do not achieve 100 per cent success, and some individuals, e.g. insects, survive to reproduce. It is possible that successive generations have a greater resistance to a particular pesticide, which is overcome only by using higher concentrations of the pesticide. However, the pest may eventually become resistant to the pesticide, as happened with DDT.

petrochemicals chemicals derived from crude oil (petroleum) and natural gas which are used to manufacture an enormous range of compounds and materials, including plastics, drugs, fertilisers, solvents, and detergents. Over 90 per cent of synthetic organic materials come from these sources. A major factor in the development of petrochemicals was the dramatic rise of the motor car in the early part of the 20th century and the discovery of oil in large quantities. The HYDROCARBONS left from petroleum after the removal of the gasoline meant that producers and governments sought ways of using these chemicals, and consequently production of organic chemicals from these sources grew dramatically.

Petroleum is a complex mixture and *distillation* produces a number of *fractions*:

Petroleum fractions

methane and ethane	natural gas
propane and butanes	liquefied petroleum gases
light naphtha	
naphtha	motor spirit (gasoline)
kerosene	jet fuel
gas oil	diesel fuel
heavy distillates	feedstocks for lubricants, waxes, etc
bitumen/asphalt	

The operations undertaken in a *refinery* to produce lighter fractions are *cracking* and *reforming*. Catalytic cracking, which has replaced the old thermal process, is an accelerated decomposition of middle to higher fractions over a solid catalyst usually consisting of zeolites. Catalytic reforming, which uses a platinum or platinum/rhenium catalyst, is undertaken at about 500°C (932°F) and 7 to 30 atmospheres pressure. Various reactions occur simultaneously, with straight-chain alkanes being converted to ISOMERS and gasoline of a higher octane number being produced. There are other processes, including hydrocracking, steam cracking, and steam reforming, which are implemented to act on a particular feedstock to produce certain chemicals.

petroleum *see* G&G petroleum.

pH a measure of a solution's acidity or alkalinity. It shows the concentration of hydrogen IONS (H^+) in an aqueous solution and is the negative LOGARITHM (to base 10) of H^+ concentration calculated with the formula:

$$pH = log10 \ (1/H^+)$$

The scale ranges from 1 (very acidic, e.g. concentrated hydrochloric acid) through the neutral point of 7 (pure water) to 14 (very alkaline, e.g. CAUSTIC SODA). Since pH is a logarithmic value, one unit of change is equivalent to a tenfold change in the H^+ ion concentration. The pH of solutions is checked by means of INDICATORS.

pharmacology *see* DRUGS AND PHARMACOLOGY.

pheromone a chemical substance that acts as a communication signal between individuals of the same species. Pheromones are found widely throughout the animal kingdom and have a number of different functions, e.g. sexual attraction (common in insects) and marking of territory (used by many mammals, either by urine-spraying, as by dogs and members of the cat family, or by means of special scent glands, often on the head or bottom). Pheromones act as *external hormones* and have been shown to be effective at very low concentrations. They are often organic acids or alcohols, which are usually termed *volatile* because their effect is short-lived. Pheromones are important in techniques of BIOLOGICAL CONTROL.

Pheromones are much rarer in plants, but one of the most important economically and environmentally is produced by a plant called the 'scary hairy wild potato' (*Solanum berthaultii*). The leaves produce a pheromone chemically identical to the warning signal produced by aphids (small insect pests of many garden and crop plants). It is hoped that breeding this aphid-repellent character into cultivated crops will lead to a reduction in aphid damage and less need for chemical insecticides.

phosphorus a non-metal that occurs naturally as compounds and mainly as calcium phosphate ($Ca_3(PO_4)_2$) but also the mineral apatite. Phosphorus has several forms: red, white, and black (a property called *allotropy*), and the white form is the most reactive. It is obtained by heating calcium phosphate with sand and carbon in an electric furnace. Phosphorus is essential to life because calcium phosphate is a vital component of animal bones. It is also important in the compounds that it forms, e.g. phosphates are widely used in fertilisers. Phosphorus compounds are also used in the manufacture of glass and chinaware, matches, detergents, special steels, and foods and drinks.

photic zone *see* NH photic zone.

photocell *see* PHOTOELECTRIC CELL.

photochemistry the study of chemical reactions brought about by light. Only light that is actually absorbed will produce any effects, and it is necessary to determine which parts of the spectrum are appropriate. The essential step in a photochemical reaction is the raising of an atom or molecule to an excited state by the absorbed light. Ultraviolet light is often the vehicle for such reactions and radiation from the far ultraviolet can break chemical bonds. However, the light may not actually produce a reaction directly. The excited molecule may emit the energy absorbed, affecting a neighbouring molecule that then undergoes a reaction.

Absorbed light may act as a catalyst or supply energy that renders a reaction possible. PHOTOSYNTHESIS is an example of a photochemical reaction.

photoelectric cell or photocell a device used for the detection of LIGHT and other radiations. One type of cell, the *photoemissive cell*, makes use of the *photoelectric effect*. This is when light ENERGY striking a substance causes energy to be transferred to electrons in the substance. When light above a certain (threshold) frequency is used, photoelectrons are generated and can create a current in a CIRCUIT. The photoemissive cell is in effect a light-powered electric cell and comprises a metal base and a transparently thin metal layer coated with selenium. Light entering the cell causes electrons to be released from the selenium, and they move across a barrier to the metal layer, setting up a potential difference that can be used to drive a cur-

rent. Cells of this nature can be used on solar cells and in camera light meters.

The other types of photoelectric cell are *photovoltaic* and *photoconductive*, used to detect ultraviolet and infrared radiation respectively.

photography the process of capturing an image on photographic film (or plates) by means of LENSES in a *camera*. The earliest cameras produced images on metal or glass plates. Cameras consist essentially of a box with a variable aperture and a timed shutter through which light enters, after which it is focused by lenses on to the light-sensitive film. The film is coated with an EMULSION containing a silver halide (chloride or bromide); on exposure to light, the silver becomes easily reduced and when the film is developed a black deposit of fine silver gives a negative image. By further exposure of the negative and an underlying paper sensitive to light, a positive image is produced that is fixed and washed, producing a photograph. A *Polaroid camera* is different in that the photograph develops immediately after exposure to light.

The technique of photography is based on the incidental discovery by a German, Dr Schulze, who noticed that a silver nitrate solution on chalk turned black in sunlight. A French inventor, Louis Daguerre, then took the first photographs of a living person over one hundred years later, in 1839. The modern face of photography owes much to William Fox-Talbot, a British scientist who invented the negative-to-positive process, and to the American George Eastman who developed the rolls of film for cameras and who in 1892 founded Kodak. The first moving photographs were made in 1893 by Thomas Edison (US) and Dickson (UK) in the USA, although only one person could view at a time. The French Lumière brothers made the first practical projector—the start of the movies.

photon *see* LIGHT; QUANTUM MECHANICS.

photosynthesis and transpiration *photosynthesis* is the complicated process by which green plants use the energy from the Sun to make CARBOHYDRATES from carbon dioxide and water, releasing oxygen as a result. There are two stages of photosynthesis, known as the *Calvin cycle* and *light reactions*, which are very complex but result in the production of sugars and starch. Photosynthesis can occur only if light-trapping pigments are present, the main one of these being chlorophyll (*see* CHLOROPLAST AND CHLOROPHYLL), which is green-coloured and occurs in stems and leaves. Chlorophyll captures light energy, and this initiates a series of energy transfer reactions that enable simple organic compounds to be made from the splitting of carbon dioxide and water. Photosynthesis is the basis of all life on Earth and regulates the atmosphere, as it increases oxygen concentration while reducing the carbon dioxide concentration.

Transpiration is the loss of water in the form of vapour through pores, known as *stomata*, in the leaves of plants. As much as one-sixth of the water taken up by the roots can be lost in this way. The transpiration rate is affected by many environmental factors, such as temperature, light, and carbon dioxide levels (i.e. whether photosynthesis is taking place), humidity, air currents, and water uptake from the roots. Transpiration is greatest when a plant is photosynthesising in warm, dry, windy conditions.

phototropism the response by plants, in the form of growth movement, to the presence of light. Plant shoots show *positive phototropism* as they grow towards the light but roots tend to display *negative phototropism* because they grow away from the light source. Phototropism is caused by *auxin* (a plant growth HORMONE). The hormone is more abundant on the dark side of the plant, and this side is induced to grow more by elongation of cells, resulting in a curving towards the light.

phylum *see* CLASSIFICATION.

physics the study of matter and energy and changes in energy without chemical alteration. Physics includes a number of topics such as MAGNETISM, ELECTRICITY, HEAT, LIGHT, and SOUND. The study of modern physics also encompasses QUANTUM THEORY, atomic and nuclear physics (i.e. subatomic particles and their behaviour *see* ELEMENTARY PARTICLES), and physics

of NUCLEAR FISSION AND FUSION. As the research into topics has expanded over recent years, so new subjects begin to develop, often on the boundaries of major disciplines. This has happened in geophysics (geology and physics), biophysics (biology and physics), and astrophysics (astronomy with physics).

physiology the study of all the metabolic functions (*see* METABOLISM) of animals and plants, including the processes of RESPIRATION, REPRODUCTION, EXCRETION, working of the NERVOUS SYSTEM, PHOTOSYNTHESIS, etc. It covers all aspects of the life of organisms and may be one specialised area of research or broadly based.

pie chart *see* GRAPH.

piezoelectric effect the effect within certain crystals whereby positive and negative charges are generated on opposite faces when the crystal is subjected to pressure. The charges are reversed if the crystal is put under tension, and the whole effect is reversible, i.e. the application of an electric potential produces an alteration in the size of the crystal. Quartz is the commonest piezoelectric crystal, and very pure crystals grown in the laboratory can be cut to vibrate at one frequency when a voltage is applied. The vibrations are used in watches and enable near perfect time to be kept. The effect is also used in crystal microphones and pickups. Other crystals that show the effect are Rochelle salt (sodium potassium tartrate) and barium titanate.

pig *see* NH Artiodactyla.

pig iron *see* CAST IRON.

pigment a compound that produces colour and occurs naturally in plants and animals. In plants, *chlorophyll* (*see* CHLOROPLAST AND CHLOROPHYLL) imparts a green colour, and animals contain *melanin*, which produces the black or brown colour of hair or skin. *Carotenoids* are plant pigments, orange, red and yellow, that occur in carrots and tomatoes.

Colour	Pigment
white	titanium dioxide, lead carbonate, sulphate, zinc oxide and sulphide
red/brown	iron oxides, red lead, cadmium red

orange, scarlet, yellow	iron oxides, lead, zinc and cadmium chromates
blue	ultramarine (an aluminosilicate with sulphur)
black	carbon

Synthetic pigments are used to colour plastics, textiles, inks, etc. Pigments are different from dyes and tend to be insoluble. They occur as particles and many are inorganic.

pitch *see* SOUND.

pitchblende an important ore of uranium, a mineral called uraninite, made up primarily of uranium oxide. It is also the principal source of radium, an ELEMENT discovered by Marie and Pierre Curie in 1898 (they also discovered polonium from the same source). Pitchblende occurs as a black mass resembling tar, and the uranium in it decays to form radioactive radium and radon gas. Deposits occur in Canada, East Africa, Saxony and Colorado.

placenta *see* GESTATION AND BIRTH; REPRODUCTION.

place-value system *see* DECIMAL NUMBERS.

planet *see* S&A planet.

planetoid *see* S&A asteroid.

plankton very small organisms, often microscopic and including both plants and animals, that drift in the currents of oceans and lakes. The plants (or *phytoplankton*) consist mainly of single-celled algae (*Bacillariophyta*) called *diatoms* that photosynthesise and form the basis of FOOD CHAINS. The animals (or *zooplankton*) include the *larval* stages of larger organisms, some protozoans (PROTISTA), and the small copepods, which are related to crabs (*see* NH Crustacea). Plankton provide food for many larger animals, e.g. whales, and are of vital importance in the FOOD CHAIN.

plants (kingdom *Plantae*) one of the major kingdoms of life (*see* CLASSIFICATION). Plants are distinguished from animals by their ability to manufacture food by PHOTOSYNTHESIS. This type of nutrition is *autotrophic*, whereas that of animals, relying on taking in food from outside, is called *heterotrophic*. The photosynthetic cells of plants contain organelles (*see* ORGAN) called CHLOROPLASTS that contain the pigment chlorophyll, which traps light energy from the sun. Plant cells have walls (absent in animal cells), and the main substance of which these are composed is a CARBODYHYDRATE called CELLULOSE. Plant cells store carbohydrate in the form of STARCH, whereas animal cells store it as glycogen.

There are twelve divisions of the plant kingdom (the same as phyla in animals). In three of these divisions there is no true system of structures or tubes to transport water and food. These are called *nonvascular plants*, and they include mosses, liverworts and hornworts. In the other divisions this *vascular tissue* is present but they are further divided into those that produce *seeds* and those that do not. The *seedless plants* are the horsetails, ferns, club mosses, and whiskferns. The *seed plants* are divided into two groups, the *gymnosperms*, which produce 'naked' unprotected seeds, e.g. the conifers, and the *angiosperms* (or *Anthophyta see* NH Angiospermae), the flowering plants. These are the ones most familiar to us and are the most complex among plants, producing seeds within special protective coverings.

Most plants have sexual REPRODUCTION and many are also able to reproduce asexually. In the plant life cycle an *alternation of generations* occurs, with a SPOROPHYTE generation, which is *diploid* (i.e. has the full number of CHROMOSOMES) producing the *gametophyte generation, which* is *haploid* (half the number of chromosomes). The sporophyte generation is nearly always the most prominent form, and in most plants the gametophyte is represented by very small structures.

Flowering plants are either *monocotyledons*, with one seed leaf, or *dicotyledons*, with two. Some flowering plants are called *annuals* as they grow from seed, produce flowers, and die. Others are *perennials*, which grow up from the same root stock year after year even though the leafy parts die back during the winter.

plasma *see* MATTER.

plastics a group name for mainly synthetic organic compounds that are mostly POLYMERS, formed by polymerisation, which can be moulded when subjected to heat and pressure. There are two types: *thermoplastics* (e.g. PVC or polyvinyl chloride), which become plastic when heated and can be heated repeatedly without changing their properties; *thermosetting plastics*, such as phenol/formaldehyde resins, lose their plasticity after being subjected to heat and/or pressure. Plastics are moulded and shaped while in their softened state and then cured by further heat (thermosetting, e.g. epoxy resins, silicones) or cooling (thermoplastics, e.g. perspex and polythene).

The first synthetic plastic was *Bakelite*, invented in 1908. Since then the plastics industry has become vast, with an enormous range of domestic, leisure, industrial and commercial items now being produced. Plastics can be shaped by blow moulding, vacuum forming, EXTRUSION, and INJECTION MOULDING, and they are used extensively in composite materials and LAMINATES.

plate tectonics *see* G&G plate tectonics.
platyhelminth *see* NH Platyhelminthes.
platypus *see* NH Prototheria.
Plimsoll line *see* FLOTATION AND BUOYANCY.
Pluto *see* S&A Pluto.
plutonium *see* NUCLEAR ENERGY.
plywood *see* LAMINATE.
pneumatics the use of compressed air, usually to power machines. A supply of air is piped to the pneumatic motor, which commonly features a piston within a cylinder. Compressed air pushes the piston one way and a spring or air pressure pushes it back, producing a hammer action used in drills, for mixing or construction. The greatest benefit of pneumatic tools over electrically powered tools is that there is no chance of electric shocks or sparks which could cause a fire or explosion in certain circumstances.
poikilothermy *see* NH poikilothermy.
polarization of light when LIGHT is made to vibrate in one particular plane. Light normally consists of waves vibrating in many directions, and because it is ELECTROMAGNETIC radiation there is an electric and a magnetic field vibrating at right angles to each other. If light is polarised, the electric field vibrations are confined to one plane (*plane polarised light*), called the *plane of vibration*, and the magnetic vibrations

are in another plane at right angles, the *plane of polarisation*. Polarisation occurs when light passes through certain crystals (quartz, calcite) or is reflected from some surfaces (e.g. the sea). A polarise produces polarised light and a Polaroid filter is one such material used in sunglasses. Polarised light also has uses in mechanical engineering to reveal stress patterns in materials. Only transverse waves such as light can be polarised; longitudinal waves such as SOUND cannot.

Polaroid *see* PHOTOGRAPHY; POLARIZATION OF LIGHT.
pollen the male sex cells (*gametes*) of flowering PLANTS. Pollen grains occur in small pollen sacs contained within a structure called the *anther*, which is part of the male reproductive organ of the flower. The anther occurs on the end of a thin stalk called the *stamen*. Pollen grains and their female equivalents, the *embryo sacs*, are the *gametophyte generation* (*see* PLANTS) in flowering plants.
pollination the transfer of pollen from an anther to a *stigma*. This is part of the female reproductive organ of the flower, the other portions being the *style* and *ovary*, which together make up a *carpel*. The ovary contains one or more *ovules*, which develop into seeds. Pollen may be transferred by means of the wind, insects, birds, water, etc, and the grains vary in shape according to the method of pollination used by the plant. Wind-pollinated plants have light, smooth grains while insect-pollinated ones have grains that are rough or spiny. This is called *cross-pollination*, as the pollen is transferred from one flower to another of the same species. *Self-pollination* is where pollen is transferred from an anther to a stigma in the same flower.
pollution *see* NH pollution.
poluchaete *see* NH Poluchaeta.
polyester *see* SYNTHETIC FIBRES.
polygon a term used in GEOMETRY to describe a closed plane figure (i.e. two-dimensional) with three or more straight line sides. Common polygons are figures such as the triangle, quadrilateral and hexagon. A square is a regular polygon where the sides and all the angles are equal.

For a polygon with *n* sides, the sum of the interior angles = 180° (*n*≥2). Except for the triangle and square, polygons are named after the number of their sides, so a ten-sided figure is called a *decagon*. Polygons are common around us, whether natural, as in a honeycomb or the faces of CRYSTALS, or man-made, as with tiles and nuts and bolts.

polymer a large, usually linear molecule that is formed from many simple molecules called *monomers*. Synthetic polymers include PVC, Teflon, polythene and nylon, while naturally occurring polymers include STARCH, CELLULOSE (found in the cell walls of plants) and RUBBER. Early versions of polymers were modified natural compounds, e.g. the vulcanisation of rubber by heating with sulphur. The first fully synthetic polymer to be developed was *Bakelite* (*see* PLASTICS), followed by urea-formaldehyde and alkyd resins in the late 1920s. Polyethylene (i.e. polythene) was first produced by ICI on a commercial basis in 1938 and the Dupont company in the USA produced the first nylon in 1941. Many synthetic polymers are produced from alkenes (*see* HYDROCARBONS) in reactions called *addition polymerisations*, which are rapid and require only relatively low temperatures. *Condensation polymerisation* is another means of producing polymers, e.g. the nylons (polyamides) and the silicones (polysiloxanes) in which some molecule (often water) is removed at each successive reaction stage.

polyp *see* NH Actinozoa.

polypeptide *see* PROTEIN AND AMINO ACID.

polyphenol *see* CAFFEINE AND TANNIN.

polysaccharide *see* CELLULOSE; STARCH.

polythene *see* POLYMER.

population *see* NH population.

population dynamics *see* NH population dynamics.

poriferan *see* NH Porifera.

potassium an ALKALI metal that is silver white and highly reactive. In fact, it reacts violently with water and therefore in nature occurs only as compounds. It occurs widely in silicate rocks as alkali feldspar, in blood and milk and in salt beds and as potassium chloride in sea water. Potassium is an essential element for plants and is added to soil by farmers as FERTILISERS (such as potash). Fertilisers are the primary use of potassium but it is also used in making batteries, ceramics, and glass.

potential difference *see* ELECTRICITY.

power the rate at which WORK is done. It is also regarded as the rate at which ENERGY is converted. The unit of power is the *watt* (*symbol* **W**), which is measured in JOULES per second. Thus if a machine does 10 joules of work every second, it has a power output of 10W. Electrical power can be calculated from the product of the voltage (*see* VOLT) and the current. Power is very important because many routine processes and functions require energy to do work, whether it concerns an engine, a light bulb or our bodies. In most cases, when energy is expended it is not all turned into the useful work required but some escapes or is lost, e.g. engines lose energy in vibrations and heat.

prawn *see* NH Malacostraca.

praying mantis *see* NH Orthoptera.

pregnancy *see* GESTATION AND BIRTH and REPRODUCTION.

premolar *see* TEETH.

pressure the FORCE exerted per unit area of a surface. The pressure of a GAS equals the force that its molecules exert on the walls of its container divided by the surface area of the vessel. The pressure of a gas varies with temperature and volume, the pressure in a LIQUID or in air equalling the weight of liquid or air above the area in question; therefore, as the depth increases, the pressure also increases. This explains why air pressure decreases with height (*see* G&G atmosphere). If force is measured in N (Newtons) and area in m^2 (square metres), pressure is N/m^2 or *pascals* (Pa).

primary cell *see* BATTERY.

primates an order of mammals (*see* CLASSIFICATION) that includes monkeys, lemurs, apes, and human beings. Primates have highly mobile hands and feet because of the presence of thumbs and big toes that can grasp. They also have a large brain (especially the part called the *cerebrum*) and are very intelligent. *See also* NH Primates.

prism a solid figure that is essentially triangular in shape (resembling a wedge) and made of a transparent material. It is used in physics to deviate or disperse a ray in optical instruments or laboratory experiments. If a narrow beam of white light passes through a prism, it is split into a range of colours, the *spectrum*. The light is split because each of the colours is refracted by a different amount because each is light of a different *wavelength* (*see* WAVE).

probability the chance of something happening, or the likelihood that an event will occur, expressed as a fraction or decimal between 0 and 1 (or as odds). If something is absolutely certain, the probability is 1; if it is impossible, then the probability is 0, all probabilities lying within these two figures. Thus if a coin is flipped, there is an equal chance of gaining 'heads' and 'tails', i.e. one chance out of two for heads or tails, giving a probability of $\frac{1}{2}$ or 0.5. The probability of a particular number coming up on rolling a dice is one in six, i.e. $\frac{1}{6}$ or 0.1666, and it is 0.5 for rolling an even number (3 possibilities out of the 6 numbers).

proboscidean *see* NH Proboscidea.

procaryote any organism that has a nucleus that is *not* surrounded by a true membrane. They all belong to the kingdom MONERA and are the BACTERIA and blue-green *algae* (*cyanobacteria*). They have a single chromosome and do not undergo meiosis or mitosis (*see* CELL DIVISION) but reproduce asexually by a method called *binary fission* (*see* ASEXUAL REPRODUCTION). In this, the whole cell divides, and each 'daughter' cell receives a copy of the single parental chromosome. They are very important organisms, vitally involved in all life-sustaining processes. A few are disease-causing organisms, but others are used in BIOTECHNOLOGY. They were the first organisms to evolve, being the only life forms on Earth for about two billion years.

product *see* LOGARITHM.

propellant *see* EXPLOSIVE.

protein and amino acid a *protein* is a type of organic compound (*see* CHEMISTRY) of which there are many different kinds, and it usually contains nitrogen and sulphur. The individual MOLECULES are made up of building blocks called *amino acids* arranged in long chains (known as *polypeptide* chains). There are 20 different amino acids but a huge number of possible arrangements in a polypeptide chain or protein. Most proteins consist of more than one polypeptide.

Protista a biological kingdom (*see* CLASSIFICATION) containing numerous different kinds of simple organisms, most of which are single CELLS. They are the simplest eucaryotic (*see* EUCARYOTE) organisms because they are usually unicellular (single-celled). However, since each protist is able to carry out lots of different functions within its one cell, and many are highly complex, some have the most elaborate of all cells. Most protists have extensions or projections out from the *cytoplasm* of the cell, called *cilia* (singular *cilium*) or *flagella* (singular *flagellum*), which are used for movement. These may not be present at all stages of the life cycle but usually occur at some time or other. All protists can reproduce asexually and some also have sexual reproduction. They are important organisms in the PLANKTON and hence significant in FOOD CHAINS. Most require oxygen for RESPIRATION and so are called *aerobic*. Some are PHOTOSYNTHETIC (i.e. they are *autotrophic* and make their own food), others are *heterotrophic* (i.e. they absorb or ingest food), and yet others combine the two, a condition described as *mixotrophic*. Protists inhabit a wide range of environments. Many are free-living but others live inside cells and tissues of other organisms as PARASITES or in other relationships (known as SYMBIOSIS).

proton *see* ATOM.

prototherian *see* NH Prototheria.

protozoan *see* NH protozoan.

Proxima Centauri *see* S&A Proxima Centauri.

pteridophyte *see* NH pteridophyte.

pulley one of the six varieties of simple MACHINE. It is a wheel with a groove around the edge around which a rope can be passed. An individual pulley suspended on an axle may make lifting a load a little easier, but in general several pulleys are combined in a *block-and-tackle* system to enable the lifting of larger loads that would not normally be feasible. A rope wound around the pulleys in such a system can be pulled a long way to raise a heavy load a short distance.

pulp *see* PAPER.

pulp cavity *see* TEETH.

pulsar *see* S&A pulsar.

pump a machine that moves gases and liquids. A basic pump is the *force* or *reciprocating pump*, in which a piston moves in and out of a cylinder. Fluid or gas is taken into the cylinder on one stroke and pushed out through a valve when the piston moves in the opposite direction. A bicycle pump and a water pump are examples of this type. Another type is the *rotary pump*, which uses some form of spinning blade assembly to push liquid along a pipe.

pupa *see* LARVA AND METAMORPHOSIS.

pupil *see* SIGHT.

PVC *see* POLYMER.

Pythagoras' Theorem *see* GEOMETRY.

quadrat *see* NH quadrat.

quadrilateral *see* POLYGON.

quantum mechanics the system of ME-CHANICS that facilitates an explanation of the structure of the ATOM and the behaviour of small particles within atoms. The electronic structure of the atom comprises a nucleus around which electrons orbit at various levels. Putting energy into an atom causes electrons to move temporarily into a higher orbit through absorption of the energy. When the electron returns to its original orbit, light energy is given off as a *quantum* or *photon*. This principle (called *quantum theory*) was discovered by the German physicist Max Planck, and it was realised that all ELECTROMAGNETIC radiations can be thought of in this way, i.e. a photon is a quantum of electromagnetic radiation. Further developments were made in the subject by another German physicist, Werner Heisenberg, who used quantum mechanics to explain atomic structure and the behaviour of subatomic particles. Essentially he stated that it is not possible to know both the position and momentum of a particle such as the electron *at the same time* (this is called *Heisenberg's uncertainty principle*). Quantum mechanics was gradually superseded by *wave mechanics*, and in the 1920s the Austrian physicist Erwin Schrödinger evolved his wave equation, which describes the behaviour of a particle in a force field. It permitted the description of the electrons in an atom in terms of waves.

quantum numbers a set of four numbers used to describe atomic structures (*see* ATOM and QUANTUM MECHANICS). The principal quantum number (n) defines the shells (or orbits) that are visualised as orbitals (i.e. a charge cloud that represents the PROBABILITY distribution of an electron). The orbit nearest the nucleus has 2 electrons and $n = 1$. The second shell contains 8 electrons (and $n = 2$), and so on, the maximum number of electrons in each shell being defined by the formula $2n^2$. The orbital quantum number (l) defines the shape of the orbits, and these are designated s, p, d, and f, the letters arising purely for historical reasons. The magnetic orbital quantum number (m) sets the position of the orbit within a magnetic field, and s is the spin quantum number. The latter is based upon the assumption that no two electrons may be exactly alike and pairs of electrons are considered to have opposite spin. The quantum numbers n, l, and m are related and allow the electronic structure of any atom to be determined.

quantum theory *see* QUANTUM MECHANICS.

quark *see* ELEMENTARY PARTICLES.

quasar *see* S&A quasar.

race *see* NH race.

racoon *see* NH Carnivora.

radar *see* ECHO; RADIO.

radian *see* SI UNITS.

radiation (thermal) a process by which HEAT is transferred from one place to another. Objects give out infrared waves and hot objects may also emit light into the ultraviolet region. Some surfaces are better emitters and absorbers of thermal radiation. Dull black surfaces are better at absorbing and emitting thermal radiation than white or silver surfaces. The nearer to a silver, mirror-like finish a surface is, the greater will be the reflection and lower the absorption of radiation.

Vacuum flasks, silver body blankets, and greenhouses all make use of this property. In the case of the greenhouse, the glass permits light and short wavelength infrared radiation through from the Sun, which warms the air and the plants. The plants re-emit radiation but of a longer wavelength, and this does not pass through the glass but is reflected back into the greenhouse, helping to maintain the higher temperature.

radio the use of ELECTROMAGNETIC WAVES to send and receive information without wires (hence the former term 'wireless' for the radio). It includes, in its widest sense, radio, television, and radar. Radiowaves are created in an *antenna* or *aerial* by making electrons oscillate. Long and medium waves are sent around the world by bouncing them off the *ionosphere* (a layer of charged particles in the upper atmosphere), but VHF (very high frequency) and UHF (ultrahigh frequency waves for television) waves require a straighter path between the receiver and the transmitting aerial because these waves are not reflected by the ionosphere. Similarly, the longer wavelengths can diffract around hills and other obstacles, unlike the short-wavelength VHF and UHF waves. When a receiver is tuned to the frequency of the appropriate wave sent from the transmitter, it can amplify and rectify the signal to produce a varying current that matches the frequency of the sound wave at the microphone. This current is then used to work a LOUDSPEAKER, thus reproducing the original sound.

radioactivity the radiation that a material naturally gives out while undergoing spontaneous disintegration. The (nuclear) radiation given out by a radioactive material is one of three types: particles (alpha), ß particles (beta) or gamma ( ) rays, and each is a different entity with varying effects.

Radioactivity was discovered in 1896 by Henri Becquerel, who found that uranium salts emitted some form of radiation capable of ionising the air and also capable of affecting a photographic plate through its wrapping. Further work determined the properties of the three types of radiation.

An *alpha particle* is a helium nucleus (2 protons and 2 neutrons, He^{2+}), and it has a strong ionising effect but little penetration, having a range in air of a few centimetres. *Beta particles* are electrons moving at

different speeds, in some cases almost at the speed of light. They have a negative charge, and although their ionising effect is very weak, they are more penetrating, with a range in air of about one metre. Beta particles can be stopped by a few millimetres of aluminium. *Gamma rays* are short wavelength ELECTROMAGNETIC WAVES with little ionising effect but greatest penetration. They are never completely absorbed, but lead 25 millimetres thick reduces their intensity to half. Radioactive materials can give one or a combination of radiation types.

Radioactive decay is the emission of particles by an unstable nucleus, which, in so doing, becomes another ATOM. The decaying nucleus is the parent, the resulting nucleus is the daughter, which together with particles emitted are called the *decay products*. During decay, nuclei disintegrate randomly but at a different set rate for different atoms. The *half-life* of a radioactive *nuclide* (i.e. the radioactive form of an element) is the time taken for half the atom to decay, i.e. for the activity to fall by half. For example, uranium-238 has a half-life of 4.51 x 10^9 years, radium-226 1620 years, sodium-24 15 hours and radon-220 just 52 seconds. Artificial nuclides are used in many ways, e.g. in medicine cobalt-60 for the treatment of cancer. On industrial plants radioisotopes are used to check the flow of fluids and gases, leaks, and residence times in chemical processes, and a variety of isotopes are used. (*See also* DATING METHODS.)

radio astronomy *see* S&A radio astronomy.

radiolarian *see* NH Radiolaria.

radio telescope *see* S&A radio telescope.

radiotherapy *see* CANCER.

radon *see* INERT GAS.

rain *see* G&G rain.

rainbow the characteristic display of the colours of the spectrum, which may form a large arc of a circle. The Sun must be behind the viewer for the rainbow to be seen. LIGHT enters droplets of water in the sky and is refracted and internally reflected. Because the raindrop acts like a PRISM, the light is split up into the constituent colours.

ramp *see* MACHINE.

rat *see* NH Rodentia.

rattlesnake *see* NH Squamata.

rayon *see* SYNTHETIC FIBRES.

reaction *see* CHEMICAL REACTION; CHEMISTRY.

reagent *see* ANALYSIS.

receptacle *see* FLOWERS.

receptor a special type of animal cell that is called *excitable* because it is sensitive to a particular type of stimulus. When the receptor cell is excited, electrical impulses are sent along a (sensory) nerve to the NERVOUS SYSTEM. Some receptors respond to factors or stimuli outside the animal's body and others are present internally. They are sensitive to a variety of different stimuli and are often called after the *sense* that they detect. Examples are *chemoreceptor* (chemicals), *photoreceptor* (light), *mechanoreceptor* (touch), and *proprioreceptor* (pressure, movement, or stretching within the body). Receptors may be grouped together within a special organ, such as the ear, which detects sound waves and also controls balance and posture.

recording media the many ways in which sounds and pictures can be recorded. One medium that has been replaced by new technologies is the vinyl record. These are plastic discs upon which the sound is recorded in a groove cut in the disc. The sound to be recorded is fed via microphones to cutters operated by electromagnets. Thus, when a stylus is placed on the record, it vibrates along the groove, and the vibrations are turned into electric currents to operate loudspeakers. *Magnetic tape* can be used for recording sound (audiotape) or pictures (videotape) and consists of a plastic tape coated with magnetic particles, often iron oxide or chromium dioxide for higher quality. Recordings are made by magnetising the tape in a specific way. It is a flexible medium as it can be reused and edited. More recent media include the COMPACT DISC, a form of LASER disc that has a very large capacity, often used in the storage of computer data, mini disks, and DVDs. Technological developments are rendering many of the older media obsolete and new forms of data recording and storage include mini-discs, memory sticks (known as flash drives), and iPODs and MP3 players both of which are digital audio players utilising either internal hard drives or flash memory.

rectifier *see* DIODE.

red giant *see* S&A red giant.

reduction *see* OXIDATION AND REDUCTION.

reflection LIGHT striking a surface may be reflected, but in most cases the reflections are in all directions. When the surface is smooth, e.g. a mirror, an image is produced. When light is reflected from a surface, it follows certain laws. The incoming (*incident*) ray makes an angle (*angle of incidence*) with the line drawn at 90° to the surface (the normal). This angle is equal to the angle of reflection, which is the angle between the normal and the *reflected* ray. This encompasses the *laws of reflection*.

A *reflector* is any surface that reflects electromagnetic radiation.

refraction the bending of, most commonly, a LIGHT ray when it travels from one medium to another, e.g. air to water. The refraction occurs at the point where the light passes from one material to another and is caused by the light travelling at different velocities in the different media. The incident ray (*see* REFLECTION) passing into a material becomes the refracted ray, and in an optically more dense medium is bent towards the normal to the interface. The two angles—of incidence and refraction—are related by *Snell's Law*, which states that the ratio of the sines (*see* TRIGONOMETRY) of the two angles is constant for light passing from one given medium to another. The value of the ratio of the sines of the angles is called the *refractive index*, measured when light is refracted from a vacuum into the medium.

refrigeration *see* EVAPORATION.

relative atomic mass *see* ATOMIC NUMBER.

relativity the theory developed by Albert Einstein and made up of two parts. The *special theory* states that the speed of light is the same for all observers, whatever their speed, i.e. light from an object travels at the same VELOCITY whether the object is moving or stationary. Nothing may move faster than the speed of light. Further important implications of this theory are that the mass of a body is a function of its speed, and Einstein derived the *mass-energy equation*, $E = mc^2$, where c is the speed of light. As a result of this theory, the concept of *time dilation* was proposed, which essentially means that for someone travelling at very great speed, time passes much more slowly for him or her than it does for a stationary observer.

The *general theory of relativity* relates to GRAVITY. Matter in space is said to cause space to curve so as to set up a gravitational field and gravitation becomes a property of space. The validity of Einstein's theories has been tested with experiments in modern atomic physics.

remote sensing *see* G&G remote sensing.

reproduction the production of new individuals of the same species, either by *asexual* or *sexual* means. The term usually refers to sexual reproduction that involves the joining together (*fusion*) of special sex cells, one of which is female (the egg or *ovum*) and the other is male (e.g. *sperm* in animals and *pollen* in flowering plants). The sex cells of any organism are known as *gametes*. Many organisms produce gametes within special reproductive organs. In the flower of a seed plant, the male sex organs are the *stamens*, which produce pollen. The *carpels* are female and produce *ovules*, which later develop into seeds after FERTILISATION. Gametes are special cells that contain half the number of CHROMOSOMES (called haploid, *see* CELL DIVISION) of the parent. When a male and female gamete join together (*fusion*), fertilisation takes place and a single cell (now called a zygote) is produced that contains the full number of chromosomes (*diploid*). This goes on to produce a new individual, usually by a process of many cell divisions. In mammals (and many other animals), the male sex organs are the *testes* and the female ones are the *ovaries*. These reproductive organs (also called *gonads*), are specialised structures, the cells of which produce the sperm and ova under the influence of hormones. Most adult female mammals have a reproductive cycle, called an *oestrus cycle*, during which time the eggs develop and the animal becomes ready to mate (a period known as *heat* or *oestrus*).

Mating occurs at the time when the animal is most likely to become pregnant. Some mammals have a definite *breeding season* and only one oestrous cycle in a year (*monestrous*). Others have several cycles and are *polyestrous*. In female humans, the *menstrual cycle* replaces the oestrus cycle. Mating usually results in the fertilisation of one or more egg. The cells rapidly divide and become EMBRYOS that grow and develop inside a muscular, bag-like organ called the *uterus* or womb. The animal is now said to be *pregnant*. A special organ of pregnancy, called the *placenta*, develops, and this attaches the embryos to the uterus by a cord called the *umbilical cord*. This provides for the passage of food, oxygen, and some other substances (e.g. vitamins and antibodies) to the embryos while waste products (mainly carbon dioxide and urea) pass in the opposite direction and are removed by the mother's blood circulation. When the young are fully developed they are born, which means that they are pushed to the outside through a passage leading from the womb called the *vagina*. This is brought about by contractions of the muscles in the wall of the uterus under the influence of HORMONES. Immediately after BIRTH, the placenta is also pushed out.

reptile *see* NH Reptilia.

resistance (*symbol* **R**) the potential difference between the ends of a conductor divided by the current flowing, measured in *ohms*. SUPERCONDUCTORS apart, materials resist the flow of current to varying degrees and some of the electrical energy is thereby converted to HEAT. The resistance of a wire depends on the ability of the material to conduct electricity and the dimensions of the wire. In general, a short wire has less resistance than a long one and a thick wire less resistance than a thin one. *Resistors* are devices made to produce resistance and they control the current in a CIRCUIT. They are found in radios, televisions, and similar equipment. A variable resistor is called a *rheostat* and it can alter the current flowing by means of a sliding contact. Wires used in circuits have a low resistance to minimise heat loss, but in some cases thermal energy is required, as in heating elements for electric kettles, fires, immersion heaters, and cookers. Nichrome wire is commonly used for such applications.

resonance the creation of vibrations in a system such that it is vibrating at its natural frequency, because of vibrations of the same frequency being received from another source. Resonance occurs in many instances—the strings of an instrument, columns of air in a wind instrument, and even an engine causing vibrations in a bus or van.

respiration and ventilation *respiration* is often used to mean *breathing* but more correctly it is a metabolic (*see* METABOLISM) process that occurs in the CELLS of an organism. It is the process by which living cells release energy by breaking down complicated organic substances (food molecules) into simpler ones, using enzymes. In most organisms, respiration occurs in the presence of oxygen and is called *aerobic*, with water and carbon dioxide produced as waste products and energy released. Some organisms (e.g. a number of species of BACTERIA and yeasts) do not require oxygen but use alternative CHEMICAL REACTIONS. This is known as *anaerobic respiration*, and it is possible for it to occur for a short time in the muscles of mammals when these are being worked very hard. It is short-lived, however, and results in the build-up of *lactic acid*, which causes muscular *cramps*. *Ventilation* is the actual process of breathing or drawing air in and out of an animal's body. Various mechanisms and structures are involved in different animals, using muscles to pump air in and out (*see also* LUNGS AND GILLS).

retina *see* SIGHT.

reverberation *see* ECHO.

rheostat *see* RESISTANCE.

rhinoceros *see* NH Perissodactyla.

Richter scale *see* G&G earthquake.

rivers *see* G&G rivers.

rocks *see* G&G rocks.

rodent *see* NH Rodentia.

roundworm *see* NH Nematoda.

rubber a high molecular weight POLYMER that occurs naturally, being obtained from the tree *Hevea braziliensis*. It is an elastic solid from the latex (a COLLOID of rubber particles in a watery base) of the tree, which contains about 35 per cent rubber. After being strained, the latex is coagulated and the raw rubber 'compounded', other substances being added to increase strength, and it is then *vulcanised* (heated with sulphur) to increase the cross-linking in its structure. This provides more elasticity, the rubber becoming less sticky. Natural rubber is a form of polyisoprene: $[CH_2.CH : C(CH_3) : (H_2)]n$.

Synthetic rubbers are polymers of simple molecules and include butyl rubber, neoprene, butadiene rubber, and silicone rubber. Butyl rubber is used for the inner tubes of tires, styrene-butadiene for car tires, and silicone rubbers for applications requiring temperature stability, water repellence, and chemical resistance.

salt the common name for sodium chloride, NaCl. It occurs in sea water, and in hot climates shallow ponds of sea water are left to evaporate to dryness, providing deposits of salt. Significant salt deposits were formed in the geological past and are now mined (*see* EVAPORITE). In chemistry, a salt is produced by the reaction of equivalent amounts of an ACID and a base, with the production of water. Salt molecules contain metal atoms with one or more non-metal atoms and are named from the acid and base from which the salt is formed, e.g. hydrochloric acid and sodium hydroxide produce sodium chloride.

satellite *see* S&A satellite.

saturated solution a SOLUTION of a substance (*solute*) that exists in equilibrium when there is excess solute present. Heating a saturated solution allows more to dissolve, producing a *supersaturated solution*. Cooling or loss of solvent will cause some of the solute to come out of solution, i.e. it will crystallise.

Saturn *see* S&A Saturn.

savanna *see* G&G grassland.

screw one of the six varieties of simple MACHINE. It is an extremely effective device and is used extensively for fastening things together. Screws or screw threads are also used in instruments to enable controlled movement, e.g. on a microscope stage or in a micrometer when making accurate measurements. A screwjack is one type of jack for lifting a car to allow a wheel to be changed. This means that a heavy object like a car can be raised relatively easily.

second *see* SI UNITS.

secondary cell *see* BATTERY.

sedimentary rocks *see* G&G sedimentary rocks.

seed *see* FLOWERS; PLANTS.

seismograph *see* G&G seismograph.

semiconductors materials, such as silicon, that can act as a conductor of electricity or an insulator. Pure semiconductors are insulators when cold and allow current to pass when heated although at room temperature they conduct only poorly. However, by *doping* them, with small amounts of other substances, semiconductors can be made to conduct. Depending upon the material used for doping, a p- or n-type semiconductor is created (*see* DIODE).

Semiconductors may be COMPOUNDS or ELEMENTS. In addition to silicon, germanium, selenium, and lead telluride are used. Diodes, rectifiers, and transistors all utilise semiconductors, as do silicon chips used in microprocessors.

sense organ *see* RECEPTOR.

sepal *see* FLOWERS.

sheep *see* NH Artiodactyla.

shooting star *see* S&A asteroid.

siemens, sievert *see* SI UNITS.

sight the sense possessed by many animals that allows them to see. Some simple, single-celled (unicellular) organisms have cells that are sensitive to light but cannot be said to 'see' in the way we understand it. They have *eyespots* that contain PIGMENTS (called *carotenoids*) and these are sensitive to light. They cause the cell or organism to move in a particular way in response to LIGHT. Other invertebrate animals have more complicated eyes, ranging from a fairly simple type called *ocelli* (singular *ocellus*) to a more advanced kind known as a *compound eye*. Compound eyes are a feature of many arthropod invertebrates (spiders, insects, beetles, etc) and give very good vision, especially in some insects, e.g. dragonflies and flies. Squids and octopuses (which are molluscs) have eyes that are similar to those of vertebrate animals and have excellent powers of vision.

The eyes of vertebrates are almost spher-

ical balls filled with fluid and contained within bony sockets in the skull. Light enters the eye through the transparent *cornea* and is bent (or refracted) as it passes through a small space filled with a fluid, the *aqueous humour*. The light passes through the *pupil*, which is a hole in the centre of the coloured *iris*. The light rays pass through the lens and on through a larger cavity filled with fluid called the *vitreous humour*. The lens bends the LIGHT rays and focuses them so that they form an *image* on the layer at the back of the eye, which is called the *retina*. The retina contains the actual light RECEPTORS (photoreceptors). These are pigment-containing cells of two types, *rods* and *cones*. The pigments undergo chemical changes (*bleaching*) in light of different wavelengths, and this generates electrical impulses that travel to the brain along a special sensory *optic nerve*. Cones contain pigments that allow for colours to be detected and there are about 6 million in a human retina. Rods are sensitive in very dim light and allow for night vision but do not detect colour. The human retina contains about 125 million of these. Most mammals are nocturnal and have poor colour vision, but keen night sight is allowed for by the large number of rods that are present.

The human eye

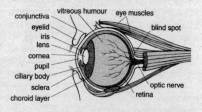

conjunctiva • vitreous humour • eye muscles • eyelid • iris • lens • cornea • pupil • ciliary body • sclera • choroid layer • blind spot • optic nerve • retina

silicon a non-metallic ELEMENT and the second most abundant in the Earth's crust. It does not occur as free silicon but is found in abundance as numerous silicate minerals including quartz (SiO_2). Silicon is manufactured by reducing SiO_2 in an electric furnace but further processing is necessary to obtain pure silicon. When *doped* with boron or phosphorus it is used in SEMICONDUCTORS (*see also* DIODE). Quartz and some silicates are used industrially to produce glass and building materials. Silicon melts at 2570°F (1410°C). *Silicones* are POLYMERS built on SiR_2O groups (where R is a hydrocarbon). Simpler substances are lower melting point oils that are used as LUBRICANTS. More complex varieties are solid and very stable and are used as electrical insulators.

siphon a bent tube, shaped like an upside-down U, used for transferring liquid from a higher to a lower level. One end of the tube is placed in the higher container and the other end is primed by sucking. When the liquid flows through the tube, the end is placed in the lower container and the flow continues even though the suction is no longer there. The liquid flows because of a PRESSURE difference between the two ends of the tube.

Sirius *see* S&A Sirius.

SI units (Système International d'Unités) a system of units agreed internationally. It comprises seven *basic units* and some *supplementary units* with a larger number of *derived units*. It also established the prefixes used for *decimal multiples*, where the practice is to raise to 10 by a power that is a multiple of three.

Basic units		Derived units		
m	metre	Bq	becquerel	(radioactivity)
kg	kilogram	C	coulomb	(electric charge)
s	second	F	farad	(capacitance)
A	ampere	Gy	gray	(ionising radiation)
K	kelvin	H	henry	(inductance)
mol	mole	Hz	hertz	(frequency)
cd	candela	J	joule	(work or energy)
	(light)	lm	lumen	(luminous flux)
		lx	lux	(illuminance – one lumen/m²)
		N	newton	(force)
		Ω	ohm	(resistance)
		Pa	pascal	(pressure)
		S	siemens	(conductance)
		Sv	sievert	(dose equivalent)
		T	tesla	(magnetic flux density)
		V	volt	(electric potential)
		W	watt	(power)
		Wb	weber	(magnetic flux)

Supplementary units

rad	radian	(angular measurement)
sr	steradian	(solid angle)

Decimal multiples

10^{-18}	atto	a	10	deca	da
10^{-15}	femto	f	10^2	hecto	h
10^{-12}	pico	p	10^3	kilo	k
10^{-9}	nano	n	10^6	mega	M
10^{-6}	micro	μ	10^9	giga	G
10^{-3}	milli	m	10^{12}	tera	T
10^{-2}	centi	c	10^{15}	peta	P
10^{-1}	deci	d	10^{18}	exa	E

skeleton the whole structure that provides a framework and protection for an animal's body and within which organs are protected and muscles are attached. In many invertebrates there is an *exoskeleton* which may have to be shed to allow for growth (*see* ECDYSIS AND MOLTING).

Other invertebrates add to the outer edge of their exoskeleton to allow for growth, e.g. molluscs such as snails. Other animals have an *endoskeleton* that lies inside the body. Vertebrate animals have a skeleton made up of numerous bones and cartilage. In mammals, over 200 bones are present, some of which are joined by *ligaments* while others are fused together. Both types of skeleton are flexible because of the presence of joints which allow for the movement of limbs, etc.

Snails have a shell hardened by calcium (*calcareous*); in arthropods the skeleton is hardened by the presence of a substance called *chitin*; and in crabs and lobsters the shell (carapace) is hardened with chitin and calcium salts.

Posterior view of the human skeleton

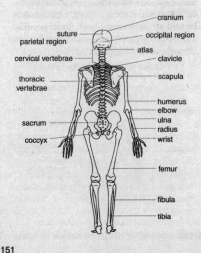

cranium
occipital region
suture
parietal region
atlas
cervical vertebrae
clavicle
scapula
thoracic vertebrae
humerus
elbow
ulna
sacrum
radius
coccyx
wrist
femur
fibula
tibia

skin an important organ that forms the outer covering of a vertebrate animal. There may be a variety of structures protruding from the surface of the skin (i.e. hair, fur, feathers, or scales) depending on the type of animal. The skin provides a protective layer for the body, helping to cushion it in the event of accidental knocks and preventing drying out. Skin also helps to maintain the correct body temperature. When the body is hot, the many blood *capillaries* in the skin widen, allowing more blood to flow through them and heat to be lost to the outside by radiation. Sweat *glands* present in the skin secrete a salty fluid that evaporates from the surface and forms another cooling mechanism. If the body is cold, the capillaries contract to decrease blood flow and conserve heat. The layer of fat in the skin has a warming effect and small erector muscles attached to hair roots contract to raise the hair. The hairs trap a layer of air, which helps to warm the body. Skin is a physical barrier to harmful substances or organisms that might otherwise enter more easily. It contains many RECEPTORS sensitive to pain, touch, pressure, and temperature and these connect with sensory nerves (*see* NERVOUS SYSTEM) relaying messages to the brain. Hence skin is very important in enabling an animal to live within its environment. The outer layer is dead and is continually being shed and replaced by cells from underneath. In amphibians (frogs, toads, etc) the skin has to be kept moist and there is some exchange of gases (oxygen in and carbon dioxide out) through the surface.

Cross-section of human skin

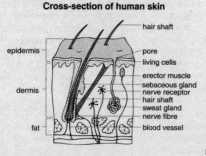

- hair shaft
- epidermis
- pore
- living cells
- erector muscle
- sebaceous gland
- dermis
- nerve receptor
- hair shaft
- sweat gland
- nerve fibre
- fat
- blood vessel

sleep a period of deep rest shown by many animals during which the metabolic rate (*see* METABOLISM) is lowered, awareness is reduced, and the body is relaxed. Most animals sleep but some need more than others. Adult humans require about eight hours sleep each night. Other animals (e.g. some grazing mammals) need only a few minutes sleep at any one time. Many animals are easily and rapidly awakened from sleep, and this is more likely in those that are hunted as prey. There is a change in the electrical activity of the brain of a person entering into sleep, and this can be recorded, producing a trace called an *electroencephalogram* (EEG). *Alpha* brainwaves are produced when an adult person is awake and *delta* waves during sleep. At the onset of sleep, low frequency waves of high amplitude are produced (known as *slow wave sleep*). These are interrupted by short periods of high frequency, low amplitude waves, during which time the person may be restless and show rapid eye movements behind closed eyelids. This is known as rapid eye movement (REM) sleep and it is the time when dreaming occurs. A person who wakens during REM sleep remembers dreams but otherwise these are usually forgotten. The part of the brain especially involved in the control of sleep is called the *reticular formation*.

smell a keen sense of smell or *olfaction* is characteristic of many animals. This is achieved by special RECEPTORS (*chemoreceptors*) that are able to detect chemicals carried in the air or dissolved in water. They may be grouped together within *olfactory organs* such as the *nose* of vertebrates. The lining or *epithelium* of the *nasal cavity* contains *olfactory cells* that respond to chemical molecules dissolved in the moisture of the surface mucous membranes. These cells are neurones (*see* NERVOUS SYSTEM) that connect with branches of the *olfactory nerve* within a special area of the brain called the *olfactory bulb*. The olfactory nerve transmits the information to the *cerebral cortex* of the *brain* where it is decoded and detected as a particular smell.

smoke *see* SUSPENSION.

snake *see* NH Squamata.

Snell's law *see* REFRACTION.

sodium an alkali metal that occurs widely, its principal source being sodium chloride (salt) in sea water and salt deposits. It is obtained by ELECTROLYSIS of fused sodium chloride but does not exist in its elemental form because it is highly reactive. When prepared, the metal is sufficiently soft to be cut with a knife and is a silvery white colour. However, it reacts violently with water and rapidly with oxygen and the HALOGENS. It is essential to life, particularly in the biological mechanism involved in the transmission of nerve impulses.

It forms numerous compounds with diverse uses and is itself used as a heat-transfer fluid in reactors. Compounds and their uses include those below and many more:

hydroxide	numerous uses
benzoate	antiseptic
carbonate	in glass, soap and other manufacturing processes
chlorate	herbicide
citrate	medicinal
hypochlorite	bleaches
nitrite	in dyes

The other alkali metals are lithium (Li), potassium (K), rubidium (Rb), caesium (Cs), and francium (Fr). Francium is radioactive, and caesium is extremely reactive.

sodium hydroxide *see* CAUSTIC SODA.

soft water *see* HARD WATER.

soil *see* G&G soil.

solar cell an electric cell that produces electrical energy from light. It is based upon a SEMICONDUCTOR device, called a PHOTOELECTRIC CELL that creates a small current because of the movement of electrons. Solar cells are ideal for use in spacecraft to power electronic equipment, but to produce an appreciable output cells have to be put into panels. They are used in this way to complement domestic heating systems.

solar energy *see* S&A solar energy.

solar power technology that traps the energy of the sun by means of *solar panels*, either for the generation of electricity or to heat buildings. There are two types of solar panel, *solar electric* (or *photovoltaic*) and *solar water heating panels*. Photovoltaic panels directly convert the heat of the sun

into electricity while solar water heating panels use the energy to heat water.

solar system *see* S&A solar system.

solar wind *see* S&A solar wind.

solenoid *see* ELECTROMAGNET; MAGNETISM.

solid a state of matter in which the component ATOMS, IONS or MOLECULES maintain a constant position relative to each other. Some solids are *crystalline*, with a regular and repetitive arrangement of atoms, while others are totally disordered (*amorphous*—no shape). When solids are heated, their atoms absorb the energy and vibrate more. Eventually the energy intake is sufficient to break down the structure and it melts to form a liquid. A few solids go directly from solid to gas, they *sublime*, e.g. solid carbon dioxide.

solid state *see* DIODE.

solution a mixture of two or more components producing a single, homogeneous phase from which there is no settling out. The term usually applies to a solution of a solid in a liquid and often the liquid is water (producing an *aqueous* solution). However, it is possible to have solutions of gases in liquids, gases in solids, liquids in liquids and solids in solids (a solid solution).

The *solute* is the substance that dissolves to make a solution, and the *solvent* is the substance in which the solute dissolves. The solvent is usually a liquid and water is the commonest. *Solubility* is the concentration of a SATURATED SOLUTION, i.e. the maximum amount of one substance dissolved in another.

A *solid solution* is when two or more elements share a common crystalline framework. The composition can vary, although within limits, and two types of solid solution are found. A *substitutional solid solution* is when atoms of one element are replaced by another, e.g. nickel and copper. An *interstitial solid solution* is when small atoms rest in lattice spaces of the structure, as with carbon in metals. Minerals commonly exhibit solid solutions.

sonar *see* ECHO.

sonic boom *see* MACH NUMBER.

sound the effect upon the ear created by air vibrations with a frequency between 20 Hz (hertz) and 20 kHz (20,000 Hz).

More generally, sound waves are caused by vibrations through a medium (whether gas, liquid, or solid). One of the commonest sources of sound is a LOUDSPEAKER. When it produces sound, the cone vibrates, producing a series of compressions in the air. These are called *longitudinal progressive waves*, i.e. the oscillations occur in the same direction that the wave is travelling. The sound waves so produced enter the ear, causing pressure changes on the eardrum and causing the brain to register the sound. Most items produce sound when they vibrate or are moved or banged together, but sound can only be transmitted through a medium and it cannot travel through a vacuum.

The speed of sound varies with the material it is travelling through, moving most quickly through solids, then liquids and gases. In air, sound travels at approximately 350 metres per second. The speed increases with temperature but is unaffected by pressure. Frequency of sound waves relates to *pitch*; high frequencies produce a sound of high pitch, e.g. a whistle at 10 kHz, while low pitch is caused by low frequencies, e.g. a bass voice at 100 Hz. Sound intensity is measured in *decibels* (db) and it is a logarithmic scale. Ordinary conversation might register 40–50 decibels, traffic 80 and thunder 100, while jet aircraft can exceed 125 dB.

sound barrier *see* MACH NUMBER.

spacecraft *see* S&A spacecraft.

space probe *see* S&A space probe.

space shuttle *see* S&A space shuttle.

space station *see* S&A space station.

space telescope *see* S&A space telescope.

species *see* CLASSIFICATION.

specific gravity *see* DENSITY.

specific heat or specific heat capacity the HEAT required by unit mass to raise its temperature by one degree, i.e. the gain in thermal energy divided by mass and temperature. The units are JOULES per kgK. The specific heat capacity varies with the material, and metals have a much lower value than, e.g. water. This means that much more energy is required to create a 1K ($1°C/1.8°F$) rise in 1kg of water than in 1kg of copper:

water	4,200	joules required per kgK			
ice	2,100	"	"	"	"
aluminium	900	"	"	"	"
glass	700	"	"	"	"
copper	400	"	"	"	"

If the specific heat capacity of a substance is known, and its mass (*see* WEIGHT), it is possible to work out the thermal energy (heat) required to give a certain temperature rise.

spectroscopy the study of *spectra* (singular *spectrum*) using *spectroscopes* (this includes *spectrometers, spectrographs*, etc). LIGHT emitted from a hot object, or given out by a substance upon excitation, can be analysed. The light or radiation passes through an analyser or *monochromator*, which usually incorporates a PRISM to split the light into its components. This enables monochromatic light (light of a specific wavelength) to be studied. An alternative is to use a filter that absorbs unwanted frequencies. The light then passes into a detector. There are many types, some employing a photoelectric cell. *Spectrometry* is used to study light from the stars and also extensively in chemistry. There are numerous techniques, some of which are:

Type	Applications
X-ray fluorescence	determination of most elements in e.g. rock sample
atomic absorption	determination of metals, whether in trace or minor amounts
infrared	identification of organic compounds
mass spectrometry	organic compound identification and structural analysis

Others include spectrometry, ultraviolet, plasma emission, and flame photometry.

spectrum *see* LIGHT; PRISM; RAINBOW; SPECTROSCOPY.

sperm *see* REPRODUCTION.

spleen *see* LYMPH SYSTEM.

spore and sporophyte a *spore* is a small reproductive structure, usually consisting of one CELL only, that detaches from the parent and is dispersed. If environmental conditions are favourable it grows into a new individual. Spores are commonly produced by fungi and bacteria but also occur in all groups of green land plants, especially *ferns, horsetails,* and *mosses.* The *sporophyte* is the phase in the life cycle of a plant that produces spores. The sporophyte is *diploid* but it produces haploid spores (*see* CELL DIVISION). It may be the dominant stage in the life cycle of a plant (as in the seed plants) or be mainly dependent upon the gametophyte structure for both its water and nourishment, as in mosses (*Bryophyta*).

sporophyte generation *see* ASEXUAL REPRODUCTION.

sporozoan *see* NH Sporozoa.

squamate *see* NH Squamata.

square *see* POLYGON.

squid *see* NH Cephalapoda.

squirrel *see* NH Rodentia.

stalactites, stalagmites *see* G&G stalactites.

stamen *see* FLOWERS; POLLEN; REPRODUCTION.

star *see* S&A star.

starch a *polysaccharide* found in all green plants. Polysaccharides are a large group of natural carbohydrates in which the molecules are made from simple sugars (*monosaccharides*) of the form $C_6H_{12}O_6$ (hexoses) or $C_5H_{10}O_5$ (pentoses). Starch is built up from chains of glucose ($C_6H_{12}O_6$) units arranged in two ways, as *amylose* (long unbranched chains) and *amylopectin* (long cross-linked chains). Potato and some cereal starches contain 20–30 per cent amylose and 70–80 per cent amylopectin. Amylose contains 200–1000 glucose units while amylopectin numbers about 20. Starch is formed and broken down in plant cells, is stored as granules, and occurs in seeds. It is insoluble in cold water and is obtained from corn, wheat, potatoes, rice, and other cereals by various physical processes. It is used as an adhesive, for sizing paper, and has many uses in the food industry.

static electricity electricity or electric charges at rest. The structure of the ATOM is visualised as having electrons 'orbiting' a central nucleus, and this means that in some materials electrons can be removed by rubbing with a cloth. When, for example, a Perspex rod is rubbed with a woollen cloth, the cloth pulls electrons away from the rod, becoming negatively charged and leaving the rod positively charged. The reverse happens when the cloth is rubbed on a polythene rod, the rod becoming negatively charged. No charge is created, it is just that charges are separated. Charges on materials can be registered using the gold-leaf electroscope and, as with other phenomena involving charges, unlike charges attract while like charges repel (*see also* VAN DE GRAAFF GENERATOR).

statics *see* MECHANICS.

statistics the part of mathematics that deals with the collection, analysis, interpretation, and presentation of quantitative data. It involves processing data with a view to predicting future outcomes based upon the information available. PROBABILITY plays an important role in statistics. The figures can be presented in numerous graphical ways but it is important to select relevant features to illustrate a point, i.e. statistics can be very misleading, depending upon how they are presented. Statistics are used extensively by manufacturers, in medical research, insurance, and, of course, in politics.

steel IRON that contains up to 1.5 per cent carbon in the form of *cementite* (Fe_3C). The properties of steel vary with iron content and also depend upon the presence of other metals and the production method. *Alloy steels* contain alloying elements while *austenitic steel* is a solid solution of carbon in a form of iron and is normally stable only at high temperatures but can be produced by rapid cooling. *Stainless steel* is a group of chromium/nickel steels that have a high resistance to CORROSION and chemical attack. A high proportion of chromium is necessary (12–25 per cent) to provide the resistance and a low carbon content, typically 0.1 per cent. Stainless steel has many uses: for cutlery, equipment in chemical plants, ball bearings, and many other items of machinery.

steradian *see* SI UNITS.

stereoisomerism *see* ISOMERS.

stigma *see* POLLINATION.

stomata *see* PHOTOSYNTHESIS.

stratigraphy *see* G&G stratigraphy.

stratosphere *see* G&G stratosphere.

stress *see* METAL FATIGUE.

stroboscope an instrument that is used to view rapidly moving objects. By shining a flashing light on to a revolving or vibrating object, the object can be made to appear stationary providing the frequency of the flashes of light match the revolutions or vibrations of the object in question. This technique is used in engineering, e.g. to examine the blades of a propeller or engine part. It is also used to set ignition timing in car engines.

subsonic *see* MACH NUMBER.

sulphur is a yellow, nonmetallic element that exhibits *allotropy*, i.e. exhibits several physical forms. It is widely distributed in both the free state and in compounds (*see* SULFUR COMPOUNDS), forming sulphates, sulphides, and oxides, amongst others. It is manufactured by heating pyrite or purification of the naturally occurring material. The primary use of sulphur is in the manufacture of sulphuric acid (H_2SO_4), but it is also used in the preparation of matches, dyes, fireworks, fertilisers, fungicides, and in the photographic industry.

sulphur compounds compounds with sulphur are very common and include sulphates such as gypsum ($CaSO_4.2H_2O$) and anhydrite ($CaSO_4$). Metal sulphides often form minerals, e.g. FeS_2 iron pyrite (also chalcopyrite, $CuFeS_2$) from which the elements can be separated. Sulphur forms several oxides, including sulphur dioxide (SO_2), one of the primary gases causing acid rain (*see* NH acid rain). Sulphuric acid is the commonest product of sulphur and is a very strong and corrosive acid that is used very widely in the manufacture of dyestuffs, explosives, and many other products.

Sun *see* S&A Sun.

sunspots *see* S&A sunspots.

superconductor a material that shows practically no resistance to electric current when maintained at temperatures approaching absolute zero (–273°C). Each material has a critical temperature above which its behaviour is normal, resistance decreasing with falling temperature. At the critical temperature, the resistance disappears almost to nothing. If a current is induced in a superconducting material by a changing magnetic field, then the current will continue to flow long after its source has been removed. Metals such as aluminium, lead and tin become superconducting, as do some ceramics, and the phenomenon has been applied to ELECTROMAGNETS because large currents can flow without the supply of large amounts of ENERGY. Other potential uses of superconductors include larger and faster computers and the transmission of electricity without heat loss.

supernova *see* S&A supernova.

supersonic *see* MACH NUMBER.

surd *see* NUMBERS.

surface tension the 'tension' created by forces of attraction between molecules in a liquid, resulting in an apparent elastic membrane over the surface of the liquid. This attraction between molecules of the same substance is called *cohesion*, and the result is that it tries to pull liquids into the smallest possible shapes. This can plainly be seen in water, which forms round droplets and also supports the feet of insects on ponds and puddles. The same phenomenon is demonstrated by putting a needle on a piece of blotting paper that is then placed gently on water. When the paper absorbs sufficient water to sink, the needle remains afloat because of the surface tension of the water. Droplets of mercury show the same effect, forming compact globules on a surface. *Adhesion* is when molecules of two different substances are attracted to each other, as shown by water wetting glass. This attraction is also responsible for the *meniscus* formed where water meets glass. The meniscus is the upward-curving surface of the water upon meeting the glass. Mercury forms a meniscus curving down because its cohesion is greater than its adhesion with glass (*see also* CAPILLARY ACTION).

suspension a two-phase system, with denser particles distributed in a less dense liquid or gas. Settling of the particles is prevented or slowed down by the viscosity of the fluid or impacts between the particles and the molecules of the fluid. *Fog* is a suspension of liquid particles and *smoke* a suspension of solid particles.

symbiosis a relationship between organisms, usually two different species, that co-exist to the benefit of at least one of the parties involved. In *mutualism* both parties benefit and neither is harmed. In *commensalism* one party benefits and the other is unharmed but in *parasitism*, one organism thrives at the expense of the other (*see also* PARASITE).

symbol in chemistry, a letter or letters used to represent ELEMENTS, ATOMS, MOLECULES, etc. Each element has its own symbol of one or two letters (*see* PERIODIC TABLE), thus fluorine is F and chlorine is Cl. Symbols are used further in FORMULAE, i.e. the shorthand representation of a compound, e.g. NaCl is sodium chloride. The formulae can then be used in equations to represent chemical reactions and processes, e.g.:

$$NaOH + HCl \quad NaCl + H_2O$$

This formula states that caustic soda and hydrochloric acid, when combined, will react to form sodium chloride and water.

Symbols are used elsewhere, particularly in the sciences, to provide a convenient shorthand, e.g. prefixes in decimal numbers (*see* SI UNITS), concepts in physics, such as *m* for mass and *I* for electric current, and in mathematics where a letter or figure represents a word or sentence (*see* MATHEMATICAL SYMBOLS).

symmetry the property of a geometrical figure whose points have corresponding points reflected in a given line (*axis of symmetry*), point (*centre of symmetry*), or plane. Symmetry is closely related to balance in nature, and many forms exhibit *bilateral symmetry*, human beings included. Symmetry is very evident in crystals that have grown in ideal conditions because then the crystals' faces are apparent and most crystals exhibit several symmetrical features (*see also* CRYSTALLOGRAPHY).

synapse *see* NERVOUS SYSTEM.

synchotron *see* PARTICLE ACCELERATOR.

synthesis gas *see* CARBON DIOXIDE.

synthetic fibres fibres that are made artificially by CHEMICAL REACTIONS. They are used widely in producing cloth and for reinforcements in composite materials. They are manufactured from POLYMERS or modified natural materials, and the first synthetic fibres, e.g. *rayon*, were made from CELLULOSE. Rayon is produced from wood fibre treated with alkali and carbon disulphide and then extruded into a bath of sulphuric acid to harden the fibres.

Completely synthetic fibres include *nylons*, which are used in textiles, insulation, and cables; *polyesters*, which are used in textiles and film, and also for reinforcement in boats etc; *acrylics* and *glass fibres*, which are incorporated in resins to increase strength. There are inorganic fibres such as *alumina* (Al_2O_3) and *glass wool*, many of which are used in insulation and packing. *Asbestos* was used for the production of fire-resistant textiles but it is being replaced because it is hazardous to health.

style *see* POLLINATION.

tannin *see* CAFFEINE AND TANNIN.

tantalum *see* CARBIDE.

tapeworm *see* NH Cestoda.

taste and taste bud *taste* is one of the senses and is enhanced by that of smell. Hence if a person has a cold, he or she is not able to taste things properly.

The organs of taste are called *taste buds* and are situated on the tongue and sides of the mouth. They consist of groups of cells that are able to detect four different tastes—salt, sweet, bitter, and sour. All the flavours that we detect are combinations of these in different proportions, and the taste buds for each are grouped together in various parts of the tongue. Substances can be tasted only if they start to dissolve in the saliva of the mouth, hence certain hard materials have no taste at all.

tautomerism *see* ISOMERS.

teeth the hard structures in the mouth used by animals for biting and chewing food and also for attacking, grooming and other activities such as behavioural displays. In the more advanced vertebrate animals the teeth are collected in the *jaws*, but fish and amphibians (frogs and toads) have teeth all over the *palate* (roof of the mouth). Teeth evolved from the scales of cartilaginous fish and are adapted according to the lifestyle of the animal. In mammals, a tooth consists of a central *pulp cavity* supplied with nerves and blood vessels, surrounded by a layer of *dentine* and an outer thickness of *enamel*. Enamel is extremely hard so as to resist wear and decay. The *root* of the tooth is embedded in a socket in the jawbone. Four different types of teeth are present—molar, premolar, canine and incisor—but the numbers and arrangement differ between animals. This is known as *dentition* and also *jaw of carnivore*—carnivores have well-developed canine teeth for biting and the last *premolars* (upper jaw) and first *molars* (lower jaw) have *cusps* with sharp, cutting edges for shearing through flesh. These are called *carnassial teeth*.

Jaw of herbivore—herbivores have large, ridged premolars and molars for grinding vegetation and incisors for cutting through stems.

Rodent jaw—in rodents the upper and lower jaws contain a single pair of long incisors that grow continuously throughout the animal's life. These are adapted for gnawing and there is an absence of enamel on the back, which means that they wear to a chisel-like cutting edge.

Teflon *see* POLYMER.

telegraph an early device for transmitting messages, first developed in the late 1700s. By the mid-19th century the technique had been refined so that information was sent along a wire as electrical pulses. The American inventor Samuel Morse introduced his code in which each letter of the alphabet was represented by a different set of pulses. Telegraph messages were also used to control train movements and eventually the Post Office formed a network. The telegraph gradually faded into history when it became possible to use the telephone on an international basis.

telephone an instrument that enables speech to be transmitted by means of electric currents or radio waves. It was invented by Alexander Graham Bell in 1876 and a public service was begun three years later after Bell took his invention to the UK. The modern telephone consists of a mouthpiece containing a thin diaphragm of aluminium that moves with the sound of speech. This movement presses carbon granules, producing a surge of current, and in the earpiece of the receiving set, these surges are changed back into sound. An ELECTROMAGNET reacts to the current charges and vibrates a diaphragm, thus reproducing the voice of the speaker. Advances in technology have improved the transmission of telephone calls, and satellites are used for international calls, and

now optical fibres have been introduced as a new medium of transmission. Cellular telephones (mobile phones or cellphones) are operated using networks of cellular radio transmitters.

telescope *see* S&A telescope.

television the transmission of moving images by electrical means. The television set is essentially a complex CATHODE-RAY TUBE. The tube consists of an electron gun and a screen that fluoresces, and the beam of electrons is deflected by magnetic coils. On a black and white screen, the picture is composed of lines as the spot moves across the screen and the spot is also moved down the screen, although at a slower rate. The result is that 25 images per second are shown on the screen, which to the human eye appear to be a moving picture.

Producing colour pictures is much more complex. There are three electron guns for red, green and blue, and the screen is coated with thousands of tiny strips of the same colours which, when struck by electrons, glow in combination to produce a colour picture. Accurate targeting of the strips is achieved by a *shadow mask* through which the electron beams are fired.

The pictures and sounds are converted by cameras and microphones into electrical signals that are sent to transmitting antennas. Receiving antennas then pick up the signal and pass them to the television set where they form pictures and sound.

The signals have hitherto been sent in analogue form but there is now a switch to digital signals which permits a larger number of programmes to be transmitted with a degree of interactivity with the viewer and all at a higher quality. Technical developments also include flatter screens, plasma screens (large flat screens that utilise inert gases that form a plasma to excite phosphor coatings) and HDTV (high definition television). HDTV provides better qualiy in picture and sound and is transmitted digitally.

temperature a measure of an object's overall kinetic ENERGY. When an object is cold, its molecules, atoms, or ions have less kinetic energy—its temperature is lower. Although molecules do not stop moving altogether, at –273°C (–523°F) they possess the minimum possible energy. This is *absolute zero*, and this temperature cannot be exceeded. The temperature scale that has –273°C (actually –273.15°C/523.67°F) as its zero is called the *Kelvin scale*. The degrees are the same size as centigrade degrees but the temperatures are stated as figures without the degree sign. In addition to the centigrade (or *Celsius*) scale, which has water freezing at 0° and boiling at 100°, there is the *Fahrenheit* scale where the respective temperatures are 32°F and 212°F. Fahrenheit can be converted to Celsius using the equation:

$$F = 1.8C + 32$$

and the reverse is:

$$C = \frac{5}{9}(F - 32)$$

tempering the process whereby (usually) steel is heated to a particular temperature and then cooled quickly in oil or water. The heating permits stresses in the metal to be relieved and results in a toughened, less brittle material.

tensile strength the force that is required to stretch a material until it breaks. It is measured using a special machine upon which the 'breaking' force can be read from a dial. Since tensile strength is the force per unit area, the breaking force is divided by the material's cross-sectional area. The units are newtons per square metre.

territory *see* NH territory.

tesla *see* SI UNITS.

testes *see* REPRODUCTION.

thermocouple a device for measuring temperatures, consisting of two different types of metallic wire joined at both ends. The temperature is measured at one join and the other join is kept at a fixed temperature. A temperature difference between the two joins causes the metals to produce a small electric current that can be metered. Thermocouples are used in furnaces because they have a range up to about 1600°C (2912°F). The two metals used are often copper and *constantan*, the latter being a copper/nickel ALLOY that has a constant resistance irrespective of the temperature.

theorem *see* GEOMETRY.

thermodynamics the study of laws affecting processes that involve HEAT changes and ENERGY transfer. Heat transfer from one body to another, the link between heat and work, and changes of state in a fluid all come within the field of thermodynamics; it is the prerequisite to analysis of work by machinery. There are essentially three *laws of thermodynamics*.

The *first law* says that heat is a form of energy and is conserved, and any work energy produced in a closed system must arise from the conversion of existing energy, i.e. energy cannot be created or destroyed.

The *second law* states that the ENTROPY of any closed system cannot decrease and if the system undergoes a reversible process it remains constant, otherwise it increases. The result of this is that heat always flows from a hot body to a cooler one.

The *third law* states that absolute zero (*see* TEMPERATURE) can never be attained.

thermometer an instrument used to measure TEMPERATURE. The basis of a thermometer is a property of a substance that varies reliably with temperature, e.g. expansion. Thermometers that utilise a liquid in glass are based on the property that liquids expand slightly when they are heated. Both mercury and alcohol are used, and when the bulb at the base of the thermometer's stem is heated, the liquid expands up the stem to create a reading. More sensitivity is gained by using a narrower tube. This is the case with *clinical thermometers* where the scale covers just a few degrees on either side of the normal body temperature of 37°C (98.6°F).

In industry, THERMOCOUPLES are used for temperature measurement in furnaces, and other instruments that provide an electrical measurement are used in preference to liquid in glass thermometers, which have a limited range. *Resistance thermometers* are based on the property that the electrical resistance of a conductor normally increases with heat, so it becomes more difficult to pass an electric current. A spiral of platinum wires is used in this case. A *thermistor thermometer* works on the same principle but consists of a SEMICONDUCTOR in which the resistance decreases with a temperature increase, e.g. 100,000 ohms at 20°C (68°F) and just 10 ohms at 100°C (212°F).

thermonuclear fusion *see* NUCLEAR FUSION.

thermostat *see* BIMETAL STRIP.

thunder *see* G&G lightning.

tick *see* NH Arachnida.

tides *see* G&G tides.

time zones *see* G&G time zones.

tissue *see* ORGAN AND TISSUE.

titanium a malleable and ductile silvery-white metal that melts at 1660°C. It occurs as the minerals rutile (TiO_2) and ilmenite ($FeTiO_3$) and is obtained by reducing titanium chloride ($TiCl_4$) with magnesium. It is characterised by its lightness, strength and high resistance to CORROSION and is used in ALLOY form (with aluminium, manganese, chromium, and iron) in the aircraft industry. It is also used in missile manufacture, engines and chemical plants.

Titanium COMPOUNDS have many important uses. Titanium carbide (TiC) is very resistant to chemical attack and is used in tool tips. Titanium dioxide (TiO_2) is used as a white pigment in the production of paints and printing inks and as a filler in paper, rubber, fabrics and plastics.

titration *see* ANALYSIS.

toad *see* NH Amphibia.

tokamak *see* NUCLEAR FUSION.

tornado *see* G&G tornado.

tortoise *see* NH Chelonia.

touch the sense of touch is made possible by specialised sets of RECEPTORS that are located in the SKIN and also in muscles and other internal areas of an animal's body. Touch has different elements, including pressure, pain, and temperature. The receptor cells that detect pain and pressure tend to be concentrated in certain areas (e.g. fingertips) and distributed less thickly elsewhere. Sensory receptor cells are associated with the hairs covering an animal's body so that the slightest movement of air can be detected. The sense organs involved in touch are specially adapted to respond to a particular sensation. Different nerve pathways are used to transmit the information to the brain, where it is decoded and detected.

toxin *see* INFECTION AND TOXIN; LIVER.

trace element in biology, an ELEMENT that an organism requires in very small quantities. These elements may be necessary for the formation or action of VITAMINS, ENZYMES, and HORMONES. In geology, trace elements occur in small quantities in rocks but can be detected by geochemical analysis. Most elements, except the few commonly occurring ones, are present as trace elements, if at all, and in quantities of 1 per cent or less. Often the concentrations are just a few parts per million.

trachea *see* LUNGS AND GILLS.

transformer a device for changing the voltage (*see* VOLT) of an alternating current (*see* ELECTRICITY). It is based on the principle of mutual induction whereby an alternating current passing through a coil (the primary) on a soft iron core induces current flow in another (secondary) coil on the core. The primary and secondary coils form a transformer. Transformers can be made to step up or step down a voltage by varying the number of turns in the coils. For example, if the primary coil has ten times the number of turns compared to the secondary, then the voltage in the secondary is one-tenth that of the supply, and the associated current increases tenfold.

Transformers have many uses but practical versions are not 100 per cent efficient and some ENERGY is lost as HEAT. Huge transformers are used in the mains power supply between the power station and the domestic supply. Current generated at a power station goes through a step-up transformer, creating voltages of up to 400,000 VOLTS at much reduced currents (thus minimising heat loss) for transmission through the power lines of the *grid*. Power from the grid then goes to substations where a series of transformers step the voltage down to 132,000 volts, then 33,000V (for heavy industry), then 11,000V for light industry, and finally 240V for offices and homes.

transistor a SEMICONDUCTOR that can be used for three functions: as a switch, a rectifier, and as an amplifier. A transistor consists essentially of a semiconductor chip of silicon which is doped (*see* DIODE) to form two p-n junction diodes back to back (p-type diode is silicon doped with boron; n-type is doped with phosphorus). Current cannot flow through a transistor unless a small current is applied to the p-type region of the semiconductor, called the *base circuit*, but when this current is applied an enlarged current flows in the *output* or *collector circuit*. A transistor can be used to amplify current changes, and practical amplifiers contain several transistors, as used in RADIO, to increase currents to output a signal through the LOUDSPEAKER. Because a current must flow in the base circuit to allow current to flow in the collector circuit, a transistor can be used as a switch and is turned on and off by a change in the base current.

triangle *see* POLYGON.

trigonometry the branch of mathematics that involves the study of right-angled triangles, including problem solving involving the calculation of unknown sides and angles from known values. It involves the use of the *trigonometrical ratios*, sine, cosine, and tangent. In the right-angled triangle below the ratios are:

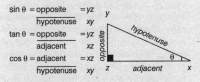

$$\sin \theta = \frac{\text{opposite}}{\text{hypotenuse}} = \frac{yz}{xy}$$

$$\tan \theta = \frac{\text{opposite}}{\text{adjacent}} = \frac{yz}{xz}$$

$$\cos \theta = \frac{\text{adjacent}}{\text{hypotenuse}} = \frac{xz}{xy}$$

Trigonometry is used in surveying and navigation.

trophic level *see* FOOD CHAIN.

tropics *see* G&G tropics.

troposphere *see* G&G troposphere.

tsunami *see* G&G tsunami.

tundra *see* G&G tundra.

tungsten *see* CARBIDE.

turbellarian *see* NH Turbellaria.

turtle *see* NH Chelonia.

UHF *see* RADIO.

ultrasound or ultrasonic waves sound with a frequency beyond the range of human hearing, i.e. around 20,000 Hz. Ultrasound is used extensively in industry and medicine. It is used to detect faults and cracks in metals and to test pipes; it can clean surfaces because of the rapid, small vibrations; it is used in welding, soldering, and machining; and in medicine ultrasound is used to scan a growing foetus and also to destroy kidney stones or gall stones. A recent development is the use of ultrasound in chemical processes to initiate reactions in the production of food, plastics, and antibiotics. Ultrasound can make chemical processes safer and cheaper as it eliminates the need for high operating temperatures and expensive catalysts (*see* CATALYSIS).

umbilical cord, umbilicus *see* GESTATION AND BIRTH; REPRODUCTION.

unconformity *see* G&G unconformity.

universe *see* S&A universe.

Uranus *see* S&A Uranus.

urea *see* LIVER.

urine *see* OSMOREGULATION.

uterus *see* GESTATION AND BIRTH; REPRODUCTION.

vaccination *see* IMMUNE SYSTEM.

vacuum a space in which there is no matter. In practice a perfect vacuum cannot be achieved although interstellar space comes very close indeed. Special equipment in the LABORATORY can also reach very low pressures, but in general vacuum is taken to be air or gas at very low pressure. The vacuum flask uses a vacuum to help keep liquids or gases cold or hot. It was invented by James Dewar at the end of the 19th century and it consists of a double-walled glass bottle. A vacuum is created between the glass walls, and the surfaces are silvered so that, together, transfer of heat by convection and radiation is reduced to a minimum.

vagina *see* GESTATION AND BIRTH; REPRODUCTION.

valency the bonding potential or combining power of an ATOM or group, measured by the number of hydrogen IONS (H^+, or equivalent) that the atom could combine with or replace. In an *ionic compound*, the charge on each ion represents the valency, e.g. in NaCl, both Na^+ and Cl^- have a valency of one. In covalent compounds (*see* BONDS), the valency is represented by the number of bonds formed. In carbon dioxide, CO_2, carbon has a valency of 4 and oxygen 2. The *valency electrons* of an atom are those in the outermost shell that are involved in forming bonds and are shared, lost or gained when a compound or ion is formed, i.e. they determine chemical reactivity.

The *electronic theory of valency* explains bonds through the assumption that specific arrangements of outer electrons in atoms (outer shells of 8 electrons) confers stability (as with the INERT GASES, which have such a structure) through the transfer or sharing of electrons. Thus with the combination of sodium with chlorine, sodium has one electron in the outer shell, which it loses (to form the neon stable structure) to chlorine, giving it also a stable structure, in this case that of argon.

Van Allen belts *see* S&A Van Allen belts.

Van de Graaf generator a machine that provides a continuous supply of electrostatic charge (*see* STATIC ELECTRICITY) and can build up a very high voltage. It consists essentially of a hollow metal sphere supported on an insulating tube. A motor-driven belt of rubber or silk carries charge (positive or negative) from the driving roller up the moving belt to the sphere, where the charge collects. Very high voltages (up to 13 million VOLTS) can be produced, and in conjunction with high voltage X-ray tubes and other equipment, these voltages are used in research to split atoms. The apparatus was named after the American physicist R. J. Van de Graaff.

variation *see* NH variation.

vegetative propagation *see* ASEXUAL RE-PRODUCTION.

veins *see* LUNGS AND GILLS.

velocity the rate of change of an object's position, i.e. the speed at which an object travels. Velocity provides both the magnitude (size) and direction of travel (per unit time) and such is called a *vector quantity*. The units are metres per second (ms^{-1} or m/s). On plotting a graph of distance moved against time, a straight line would represent an object moving at constant velocity. It is usually the case, however, that velocity changes with time, in which case an object is said to be accelerating (or decelerating). *Acceleration* is the gain in velocity of an object divided by the time taken to achieve the gain and the units are metres per second per second. As with velocity, it is a vector quantity. Graphical plots of velocity against time are useful because the gradient of the line plotted is equal numerically to the acceleration and

the area under the graph represents the distance moved. The *terminal velocity* of an object falling through air, for example, is the constant velocity reached when the object's weight is matched by the air resistance.

ventilation *see* RESPIRATION AND VENTILATION.

Venus *see* S&A Venus.

ventricle *see* CIRCULATION.

vertebrate any animal with a backbone, including fish, amphibians, reptiles, birds, and mammals. *See also* NH Vertebrata.

VHF *see* RADIO.

videotape *see* RECORDING MEDIA.

virus the smallest kind of microorganism, which is completely parasitic (*see* PARASITE) and exists and reproduces within the cells of a host organism. Most, but not all, viruses cause DISEASES in plants, animals, and even bacterial cells. Viruses operate by invading and taking over the METABO-LISM of the cells that they inhabit, using the metabolic processes to reproduce. Diseases that are caused by viruses include influenza, herpes, chickenpox, HIV/AIDS, mumps, polio, and possibly some cancers. Recently, concern has been expressed at the potential for viruses that are currently restricted to animals to jump the species barrier and infect humans. This has been prompted in particular by the avian influenza virus H5N1 which has infected vast numbers of birds but has only infected a few people, directly, and even then only those who worked very closely with the animals. No human to human infection has occurred but the fear is that it could, causing a pandemic very similar to the Spanish Flu (which is thought to have been caused by an avian influenza virus) which killed an estimated 40 million after World War 1.

viscosity a property of fluids that indicates their resistance to flow. Oil is more viscous than water, and an object will take much longer when falling through oil than when it falls through water. All fluids show this resistance to shear forces but a perfect fluid would be nonviscous. Viscosity measurements can be used to find the molecular weight of POLYMERS.

vitamins a group of organic substances that are required in very small amounts in the human diet to maintain good health. A lack of a particular vitamin results in a *deficiency disease*. There are two groups of vitamins: those that are fat-soluble, including A, D, E and K, and those that are water-soluble, C (ascorbic acid) and B (thiamine). The six vitamin groups are as follows:

A or retinol
Source: green vegetables, dairy produce, liver, fish oils.
Needed for: the manufacture of rhodopsin—a pigment needed by the rod cells of the eye for night vision and also for the maintenance of the skin and tissues.
Deficiency: night blindness and possible total blindness.

B complex including thiamine, riboflavin, nicotinic acid, pantothenic acid, biotin, folic acid, B_6, pyroxidine, B_{12} (cyanocobalamin), lipoic acid.
Source: green vegetables, dairy produce, cereals, grains, eggs, liver, meat, nuts, potatoes, fish.
Needed for: the manufacture of red blood cells, for enzyme activity and for amino acid production and also for maintaining the fatty sheath (myelin) around nerves.
Deficiency: beri beri (B_1 deficiency), anaemia and deterioration of the nervous system (B_{12} deficiency).

C or ascorbic acid
Source: citrus fruit, green vegetables.
Needed for: maintaining cell walls and connective tissue and aiding the absorption of iron by the body.
Deficiency: scurvy—affects skin, blood vessels, and tendons.

D
Source: fish oils, eggs, dairy produce.
Needed for: control of calcium levels required for bone growth and repair.
Deficiency: rickets in children—deformation of the bones; osteomalacia in adults—softening of bones.

E
Source: cereal grains, eggs, green vegetables.
Needed for: maintenance of cell membranes.
Deficiency: unusual as common in the diet.

K
Source: leafy green vegetables, especially spinach, liver.
Needed for: clotting of blood.
Deficiency: rare as it is also manufactured by bacteria in the gut.

vitreous humour *see* SIGHT.

viviparous *see* GESTATION AND BIRTH.

volcano *see* G&G volcano.

volt (*symbol* **V**) the SI UNIT of potential difference. It is defined formally as the difference of potential between two points on a conducting wire that is carrying a current of one ampere when the power given out between these points is one watt. The *voltage* across BATTERY terminals is a measure of the potential energy given to each coulomb of charge, and a potential difference of one volt exists if each coulomb has one joule of potential energy, so there is a potential difference of 6 volts if each coulomb is given 6 joules of potential energy.

volumetric analysis *see* ANALYSIS.

water the normal oxide of hydrogen, H_2O, found in one form or another in most places on Earth. It can occur in SOLID, LIQUID or GAS phases, forms a large part of the Earth's surface, and is vital to life. Natural water is never absolutely pure but contains dissolved salts, organic material, etc. Pure water freezes at 0°C (32°F) and boils at 100°C (212°F) and has its maximum density of $1gm/cm^3$ at 4°C (39°F). It occurs in all living organisms and has a remarkable combination of properties in its solvent capacity (i.e. its ability to dissolve so many substances), chemical stability, thermal properties, and abundance. Water has an almost unlimited range of uses and can provide power through HYDROELECTRIC schemes.

waterspout *see* G&G tornado.

water table *see* G&G water table.

watt *see* POWER; SI UNITS.

wave a periodic displacement that repeats itself and a mechanism of transferring ENERGY through a medium. In the simple wave form shown, the *amplitude* is the maximum distance moved by a point from its rest position as the wave passes. The *wavelength* is the length of one complete wave. The origin of a wave is vibrating particles that store and release energy while their average position remains constant, as it is only the wave that travels. Waves are either *longitudinal*, with oscillations occurring in the direction of wave travel (e.g. sound), or *transverse* because the oscillations are from side to side, at 90°

to the direction of travel (e.g. light). The *wave equation* relates frequency (*f*) and wavelength (λ):

$$c = f \lambda$$

where *c* is the speed of the wave.

All forms of wave show the properties of reflection, refraction, interference and diffraction. ELECTROMAGNETIC WAVES have these properties but have one additional feature in that they can travel through a VACUUM.

A wave form

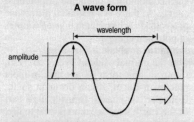

wavelength

amplitude

wave mechanics *see* QUANTUM MECHANICS.

wave and tidal power comprises a range of new technologies seeking to harness the movement of the sea to drive turbines to generate electricity. Many of these technologies are still at the developmental stage or are undergoing trials.

weather *see* G&G weather.

weathering *see* G&G weathering.

weber *see* SI UNITS.

wedge *see* MACHINE.

weight the gravitational force of attraction exerted on an object by the Earth. Although such an attraction exists between all objects, it is so infinitesimally small as to be nonexistent and the Earth is so massive that its attraction dominates. Weight is a force, measured in newtons (N), and is the force that makes an object accelerate downwards when falling to the Earth's surface. The weight of an object is therefore dependent upon its distance from the Earth, and the farther away it is, the smaller the pull of the Earth and the less is the object's weight.

Mass is a measure of the quantity of matter that a substance possesses; it remains constant, but the weight of an object varies. A constant mass will therefore have different weights depending on the gravitational effect of nearby bodies. The weight of a constant mass on Earth is about six times greater than its weight on the Moon and in space the weight of that same mass is zero. Because weight on Earth is directly proportional to mass, any instrument that measures one property also measures the other.

wheel *see* MACHINE.

white dwarf *see* S&A white dwarf.

wind *see* G&G wind.

wind power a technology that harnesses the force of the wind to drive turbines that generate electricity. Wind turbines vary greatly in size and may be large and grouped together as a 'wind farm' or 'wind factory' or small and placed as a single unit on the roof of a building.

work ENERGY expended when something is moved by a FORCE. It is also a transfer of energy, that is energy is changed into a different form when work is done. Work is measured in the unit of energy, the JOULE, and is calculated as the force multiplied by the distance moved in the direction of the force. One joule of work is done when a force of one NEWTON is moved through one metre, *in the direction of the force*.

wrought iron *see* CAST IRON.

xenon *see* INERT GAS.

X-rays ELECTROMAGNETIC WAVES with a short WAVELENGTH (approximately 10^{-10}–10^{-8}m) produced when electrons moving at high speed strike a target and are stopped very quickly and X-rays are emitted. They were discovered in 1895 by the German scientist Wilhelm Röntgen. He found that wrapped photographic plates left near a working CATHODE-RAY TUBE became fogged, as if they had been exposed to light, and he called this unknown radiation X-rays. In fact X-rays were being emitted as electrons hit the anode and walls of the cathode-ray tube. Atoms of all elements give out characteristic X-rays when hit by electrons. The stream of electrons colliding with the atom displaces electrons from inner orbitals and vacant places are then filled by electrons from the outer orbital, which give out energy as they move down. X-rays have the properties of electromagnetic radiation and also penetrate solid matter, cause ionisation (by removal of electrons from atoms), make some materials fluoresce and, as mentioned, they affect photographic film. These properties render X-rays both useful and hazardous. Their ionisation effect damages living tissue, but by using very small doses, they can be used in medicine to take X-ray photographs of the body. The extent to which the rays are absorbed depends on the density and the atomic weight (or relative atomic mass, see ATOMIC NUMBER) of the material; the lower these factors, the more easily will the rays penetrate. The greater density of bone means it is possible to take an X-ray photograph because the flesh appears transparent while the bones are opaque. X-rays are also used in industry for checking joints in metal and examining flaws. They are also used in *X-ray diffraction* (or *X-ray crystallography*), which is an analytical tool in geology, crystallography, and biophysics. X-rays directed at the sample are diffracted off the planes of atoms in the crystal. By repeating the procedure and then calculating the spacing between atomic planes, a representation of the crystal's structure can be determined. In this way the structure of some proteins and nucleic acids has been analysed.

X-ray astronomy *see* S&A X-ray astronomy.

yeast *see* FERMENTATION.

zebra *see* NH Perissodactyla.

zeolite *see* CATALYSIS.

zoology the scientific study of animals.

zygote *see* reproduction.

Art, Music and Literature

A the sixth NOTE of the SCALE of C; it is the note to which instruments of an orchestra are usually tuned (*see* TUNING).

abbandono (*Italian*) 'passionately'.

abbreviations are employed in music for terms of expression, as *dim.* for DIMINU-ENDO, *f.* for FORTE; as arbitrary signs, such as two DOTS on either side of an oblique line for repetition of a group of NOTES; or as numerals, which serve as shorthand symbols for various CHORDS in FIGURED BASS.

absolute music or abstract music instrumental music that exists purely as music and does not attempt to relate to a story or image. It is the opposite of PROGRAMME MUSIC.

absolute pitch or perfect pitch the sense by which some people can exactly identify, or sing without an accompanying instrument, any NOTE they hear.

abstract art art that intentionally avoids representation of the observed world. Abstraction has long been a feature of the decorative arts and to a large degree continues to dominate 20th-century art. There are two distinct trends: one towards an ordered, hard-edged CONSTRUCTIVISM, the other leaning to a freer, more expressionistic reduction of forms.

abstract expressionism art that is based on freedom of expression, spontaneity, and random composition and is characterised by loose, unrestrained brushwork and often indistinct forms, usually on large canvases. The works may or may not be figurative. The term mainly applies to an art movement of the 1940s in New York, although it was first used in 1919 with reference to the early abstract work of Kandinsky. Inspired by SURREALISM, the movement represented a breakaway from the REALISM hitherto dominant in American art and went on to influence European art in the 1950s.

abstract music *see* ABSOLUTE MUSIC.

Absurd, Theatre of the a form of theatre, developed in the 1960s, that characterises the human condition as one of helpless-ness in the face of an irrational, 'absurd' universe. Beckett, Pinter, and Ionesco, whose characters communicate with one another in disjointed, inconsequential language, are among the best-known practitioners of the form, whose roots go back to DADAISM. Absurdist drama reacts strongly against the conventions of naturalism.

a cappella or alla capella (*Italian*) literally 'in the chapel style'. A term that has come to mean unaccompanied choral singing.

accel. the abbreviation for ACCELERANDO.

accelerando (*Italian*) 'quickening'; a term used to indicate a gradual speeding up of pace (abbreviation ACCEL.).

accent emphasis given to specific notes to indicate the RHYTHM of a piece of music.

acciaccatura (*Italian*) an ornamental or auxiliary NOTE, normally the SEMITONE below, played just before, or at the same time as, a regular note. An *acciaccatura* is written in small type before the regular note and has a stroke through its tail. From the Italian *acciacciare*, to crush.

accidental a NOTE in a piece of music that departs by one or two SEMITONES from the KEY SIGNATURE. It is indicated by a SHARP, FLAT, or NATURAL sign before it. An accidental holds good throughout a BAR unless contradicted.

accompaniment music supporting a soloist or CHOIR. An accompaniment may be provided by an orchestra, organ or, most usually, a piano.

accordion a portable REED ORGAN that was invented in Germany in the early 19th century. Air is forced through the reeds by means of bellows that are operated by the player's arms and notes and chords are played by pressing buttons. The *piano accordion* has a keyboard (operated by the right hand) for playing MELODY NOTES, and buttons (operated by the left hand) for simple chords. The accordion is associated with informal or FOLK music, but it has been used by serious composers.

Acmeist group a school of Russian poetry

166

which first emerged as a coherent group in St Petersburg in 1911. In part a reaction to the more obscure aspects of SYMBOLISM, the group proclaimed the virtue of clarity of expression. It was founded by the poet Anna Akhmatova (1889–1966) whose ex-husband was executed by the Bolsheviks in 1921.

acoustics (1) a branch of physics that is concerned with SOUND. The main characteristics of a sound are its PITCH, intensity, RESONANCE, and quality. (2) the characteristics of a hall or auditorium that enable speech and music to be heard without the sounds being distorted. In a concert hall with good acoustics, sounds from the stage can be heard clearly in all quarters.

acrostic a type of poem in which the initial letters of each line form a word reading downwards and used by Roman poets. The Elizabethan poet and statesman Sir John Davies (1569–1626) devised 26 verses, in *Hymns of Astraea* (1599), each spelling the name of Elizabeth I ('Elisabetha Regina').

acrylic paint a versatile synthetic paint that is quick drying and can be used in thick, heavy layers or thin washes on almost any surface. A range of matt or gloss finishes can be achieved by the use of additives.

action (1) the mechanism of a keyboard instrument that links the keyboard to the strings or, in the case of an ORGAN, to the PIPES and STOPS. (2) the gap between the strings and FINGERBOARD of a stringed instrument as dictated by the height of the BRIDGE.

action painting a form of ABSTRACT EXPRESSIONISM in which the paint is applied to the canvas in the course of a series of actions or movements by the artist. This may involve dancing, cycling or rolling about on the canvas to spread and mix the wet paint. In a less random technique the artist paints the silhouette of a model in various poses against the canvas.

act tune or curtain music an instrumental piece of music that is played between the acts of a play while the curtain is down. It is usually associated with 17th- and 18th-century music. *See also* ENTR'ACTE; INTERLUDE; INTERMEZZO.

ad lib. abbreviation for AD LIBITUM.

ad libitum (*Latin*) literally 'at pleasure' and usually abbreviated to AD LIB. In music, the term is used to indicate that, when playing a piece, a performer can: (a) alter the TEMPO or RHYTHM; (b) choose an alternative PASSAGE by the composer; (c) improvise a CADENZA; and (d) include or omit a passage if he or she so chooses.

adagietto (*Italian*) (1) 'slow' but not as slow as ADAGIO. (2) a short composition in an adagio TEMPO.

adagio (*Italian*) (1) literally 'at ease', i.e. at a slow TEMPO. (2) a slow movement.

adagissimo (*Italian*) 'very slow'.

added sixth a frequently used CHORD created by adding the sixth note from the ROOT to a MAJOR or MINOR TRIAD; for example, in the KEY of C major, A is added above the triad of C-E-G.

additional accompaniments new or revised PARTS for extra instruments written by later composers and added to 17th- and 18th-century works in order to increase fullness. In many cases, the additions did not match the quality of the original music, but Mozart once wrote additional music for Handel's MESSIAH when an organ was not available.

a due corde (*Italian*)**or à deux cordes** (*French*) 'on two strings'; when applied to music for stringed instruments, the term means that a piece should be played on two strings, not just on one.

Aeolian harp a type of ZITHER that has strings of similar length but of different thickness. The instrument is not actually played but left outside to catch the wind; different CHORDS are sounded according to the speed of the wind, which makes the strings vibrate faster or slower (*see* VIBRATION). The name is derived from Aeolus, who was the Greek god of the wind.

Aeolian mode a MODE that, on the PIANO, uses the white NOTES from A to A.

Aesthetic movement a cultural movement that developed in England in the late 19th century, characterised by a very affected and mannered approach to life and the arts, a fondness for orientalism and decadence, archaic language and pseudomedievalism. The character Bunthorne in Gilbert and Sullivan's comic opera *Patience* (1881) is a conflation of all the features found ridiculous in the movement by its contemporaries. Oscar Wilde is the most prominent literary figure of merit associated with the movement.

aesthetics an area of philosophy concerning the ideals of taste and beauty and providing criteria for critical study of the arts. The term was coined in the mid-18th century by the German philosopher Alexander Baumgarten and in the 20th century came to include a wider theory of natural beauty.

affettuoso (*Italian*) 'tender' or 'affectionate', i.e. an indication that a piece of music should be played with tender feeling.

agitato, agitatamente (*Italian*) literally 'agitated', 'agitatedly', i.e. an indication that a piece should be played restlessly or wildly.

Agnus Dei (*Latin*) 'O Lamb of God', the concluding part of the Latin MASS. Numerous musical settings have been made for it.

air (1) a simple TUNE or SONG. (2) a melodious BAROQUE composition.

air brush an atomiser, powered by compressed air, that is used to spray paint. It is shaped like a large fountain pen and produces a fine mist of colour, giving delicate tonal gradations and a smooth finish. Its principal use is in the fields of advertising and graphic design.

alabaster a fine-grained type of gypsum that can be translucent, white or streaked with colour. It is soft and easy to carve and is therefore a popular medium for decorative artefacts and statues. It is not as strong or weather-resistant as marble, and is not often used for outdoor works.

Alberti bass a simple accompaniment to a MELODY consisting of 'broken' or spread CHORDS arranged in a rhythmic pattern, so called because the Italian singer, composer, and harpsichordist Domenico Alberti (1710–40) used it in his keyboard SONATAS.

alborada (*Spanish*) literally 'morning song'; a form of popular Spanish music for BAGPIPES and SIDE DRUM.

Albumblatt (*German*) literally 'album leaf', a popular title given by 19th-century composers to short instrumental compositions (often for the PIANO) of a personal nature.

Aldeburgh Festival an annual music FESTIVAL held in June founded by Britten and the tenor Peter Pears at Aldeburgh, Suffolk, England, in 1948. It maintains its strong association with Britten, many of whose works were first performed there.

aleatory music music that contains unpredictable or chance elements so that no two performances of a piece are ever similar. It is a form explored since 1945 by composers such as Cage, in his *Music of Changes*, and Stockhausen.

alienation effect an effect that is supposed to occur upon an audience when it is reminded by action, dialogue, or song that it is in fact an audience watching a play and not, for example, waiting for a bus. The intention is to confront the audience with the artificiality of dramatic representation through devices such as interrupting the action to address the audience or by bursting into song or by stylising the stage set or action. The theory is especially associated with Brecht. 'Alienation effects' of the kind described by Brecht have existed in drama since before Aristophanes, and form an important element in the Theatre of the ABSURD.

alla (*Italian*) 'in the style of'.

alla breve (*Italian*) (1) an instruction that a piece of music should be performed twice as fast as the NOTATION would suggest. (2) 2/2 TIME.

allargando (*Italian*) literally 'getting broader', i.e. an indication that a piece should be played grandly whilst at the same time getting slower.

alla tedesca (*Italian*) an abbreviation of *alla danza tedesca,* meaning 'in the style of a German dance'. *See* ALLEMANDE.

allegory a form of narrative in which the characters and events symbolise an underlying moral or spiritual quality or represent a hidden meaning beneath the literal one expressed. Bunyan's *Pilgrim's Progress* is the greatest English-language example of a sustained allegory.

allegretto (*Italian*) a term indicating light and moderately quick movement but not as fast as ALLEGRO.

allegro (*Italian*) literally 'lively', i.e. in a quick TEMPO, and often used as the title of a bright composition or MOVEMENT.

allemande (*French*) an abbreviation of *danse allemande* or 'German dance'. There are two forms: (1) a moderately slow dance used by 17th- and 18th-century composers as the first MOVEMENT of a SUITE of four contrasting dances; (2) a brisk dance of the 18th and 19th centuries, similar to the WALTZ.

allentando (*Italian*) 'slowing down', i.e. a term used to indicate that the TEMPO of a piece of music should be slowed down.

all' ongarese (*Italian*) 'in the style of Hungarian [gypsy] music'.

alphabet the letters used in music as they occur in the natural SCALE are C, D, E, F, G, A, B. The oldest HARPS and shepherd PIPES are believed to have had seven TONES, to which the Greeks gave the names of letters, A being the lowest. Greek NOTATION became highly complicated with the development of the MODES, and Pope Gregory the Great (540–604) changed church notation, again employing the first seven letters, indicating the lower OCTAVE by capitals and the upper by small letters. NOTES were gradually added to the lower A, and when the modern scale was adopted in the 16th century, the lowest tone had become C instead of A. In addition, Germans use H for B natural, B for B flat.

alphorn or alpenhorn a primitive type of HORN with no valves, traditionally played by Swiss herdsmen to call in their cattle in the evening. Made from wood and bark, alphorns usually have an upturned bell that rests on the ground, and they can be up to 10 feet (3 metres) long.

al segno (*Italian*) 'to the sign' (i.e. to a standard symbol used in musical NOTATION). The term is used in two ways: it can instruct the player either to *go back* to the sign and start again, or to *continue* until the sign is reached.

alt an abbreviation of the Latin phrase *in alto*, which means 'high'. It is used for the NOTES in the OCTAVE rising from G above the TREBLE CLEF; the notes in the octave above that are said to be *in altissimo*.

Altamira the site in northern Spain of prehistoric rock paintings dating from about 13000 BC. In 1879 the first such ever to be discovered. Originally dismissed as forgeries, their age and authenticity were accepted as genuine only in the early 20th century. A variety of animals painted in a lively, naturalistic manner are depicted, including bison, aurochs and wild horses.

altarpiece a decorated wall, screen, or sectional painting set behind the altar of a Christian church, a feature of church decor from the 11th century. There are two forms: a *retable* can be fairly large and complex, rising from floor level; a *reredos* is often smaller and may stand on the altar itself or on a pedestal behind it.

alto (*Italian*) 'high' (1) the highest adult male VOICE, which is now used only in male-voice CHOIRS. (2) an addition to the name of an instrument to indicate that it is one size larger than the SOPRANO member of the family, e.g. alto CLARINET. (3) a low female voice that has a greater compass than the male alto voice (more properly called CONTRALTO).

Amati the name of a famous family of violin-makers who worked in Cremona, Italy, in the 16th and 17th centuries.

Ambrosian chants a collection of CHANTS or PLAINSONG, used in Milan Cathedral, which are named after St Ambrose (*c.* 340–97), Bishop of Milan, who greatly influenced church singing and may have introduced the antiphonal singing of the Syrian church. Despite bearing his name, the earliest surviving chants were composed long after his death.

amen (*Hebrew*) 'so be it'.

American organ or cabinet organ a REED ORGAN, similar to a HARMONIUM except that air is sucked through the reeds instead of being blown through them.

amoroso (*Italian*) 'lovingly', played with warm affection.

amplifier any device, particularly an electric one, which renders a sound louder.

anabasis (*Greek*) a succession of ascending tones.

anacrusis (*Greek anakrousis*, literally 'a prelude') an unstressed NOTE or grouping of notes at the beginning of a musical PHRASE; it can also mean an unstressed syllable at the beginning of a SONG.

Ancients, the a group of Romantic artists working in England between 1824 and the 1830s. Samuel Palmer was a leading member of the group. Their work was mainly pastoral in theme, much inspired by Blake's illustrations of Virgil.

ancora (*Italian*) 'again', 'yet', or 'still', as in *ancora forte* meaning 'still loud', and *ancora più forte* meaning 'yet louder'.

andante (*Italian*) 'going' or 'moving'; it is usually used to indicate a moderate TEMPO or a walking pace. *Più andante* means 'moving more' or slightly faster. Andante is sometimes used as a title for a moderately slow piece of music.

andantino (*Italian*) 'less slow' (i.e. slightly faster) than ANDANTE.

Anfang (*German*) 'beginning'; *Anfangs* means 'from the beginning'.

anglaise (*French*) short for *danse anglaise* or 'English dance', i.e. a lively dance in quick time, such as a HORNPIPE.

Anglican chant a characteristically English way of setting prose, psalms and canticles to music in which the number of syllables per line can vary. To accommodate this irregularity, the first NOTE of each musical PHRASE is a RECITING NOTE, which is timeless and is used to sing as many syllables as necessary before moving on to notes that are sung in time and normally carry one syllable each. It is a simple form of GREGORIAN CHANT.

Anglo-Saxon art a term for works of art produced in England between AD 5 and 1066. The major source of surviving artefacts is the 7th-century excavation site at Sutton Hoo, from which much of the Anglo-Saxon jewellery collection at the British Museum comes. The late 7th and early 8th centuries saw the production of the *Lindisfarne Gospels* in the kingdom of Northumbria. These are famous for their delicate interwoven designs, reminiscent of Irish illuminations, as in *The Book of Kells*.

Angry Young Men an imprecise term used in mid-1950s Britain to denote a group of English writers who had little in common apart from vaguely leftish sympathies and a hatred of English provincialism and intellectual pretentiousness.

anima (*Italian*) 'soul' or 'spirit', as in *con anima*, which means that a piece should be played 'with soul' or 'with emotion'.

animato (*Italian*) 'animated'.

animo (*Italian*) 'spirit', so *con animo* indi-

cates that a piece should be performed 'with spirit'.

animoso (*Italian*) 'spirited'.

answer the second entry of the main SUBJECT (theme) of a FUGUE, played a FIFTH higher or lower than the first entry. In a *real answer,* the subject and answer are identical; in a *tonal answer,* the answer's intervals are changed.

anthem the Anglican equivalent to the Roman Catholic MOTET. An anthem is usually an elaborate musical setting of non-liturgical words sung by a church CHOIR without the congregation; SOLO parts are common and accompaniment by an ORGAN is usual.

anticipation the sounding of a NOTE (or notes) of a CHORD before the rest of the chord is played.

antinovel *see* NOVEL.

antiphon the sacred words sung in PLAINSONG by two CHOIRS, before and after a PSALM or CANTICLE in a Roman Catholic service. *Antiphonal* is an adjective applied to the musical effect achieved by two choirs (or groups of instruments) which are positioned in different parts of a hall and sing (or play) alternately, one 'answering' the other.

Antique, The remains of ancient art, in particular Greek and Roman statues, which were taken as a standard of classical order and beauty in the representation of the human form by RENAISSANCE and NEOCLASSICAL artists.

anvil a PERCUSSION INSTRUMENT consisting of steel bars that are struck with a wooden or metal mallet. Meant to sound like a blacksmith's anvil being struck with a hammer, it was used by both Verdi (in *Il Trovatore*) and Wagner (in *Das Rheingold*).

a piacere (*Italian*) 'at pleasure', meaning that the performer of a piece of music is permitted to take a certain amount of liberty, particularly with TEMPO, while playing it. *See also* AD LIBITUM.

appassionato, appassionata (*Italian*) 'impassioned' or 'with passion or feeling', hence the title *Sonata appassionata* which was given to Beethoven's Piano Sonata in F Minor (Op. 57).

applied art art that serves a useful purpose or that ornaments functional objects; often a synonym for *design*. Subjects included under this term are architecture, interior design, ceramics, furniture, graphics, etc. These are usually contrasted with the *fine arts* of painting, drawing, sculpture, printmaking, etc, and the division became more distinct at the time of the Industrial Revolution and the emergence of AESTHETICS. This division is still a matter of important debate.

appoggiando (*Italian*) 'leaning'. Applied to NOTES, this implies that they should pass very smoothly from one to the next.

appoggiatura (*Italian*) a term for a 'leaning' NOTE (*see also* APPOGGIANDO), indicated in the SCORE. (1) a *long appoggiatura* is a note of varying length that is different from the HARMONY note. (2) a *short appoggiatura* is a very short note of indefinite length, sometimes accented, sometimes not. (3) a *passing appoggiatura*, as used in the 18th century, normally occurs when the principal notes of a MELODY form a sequence of thirds, and it is played before the beat.

aquarelle the French term for watercolour painting, where a water-based paint is applied to dampened paper in thin glazes that are gradually built up into areas of varying tone.

aquatint an etching technique where a resin-coated metal plate is placed in a bath of acid that bites into the resin, producing a pitted surface. The depth of tone intensifies the longer the plate remains in the acid, and areas required to be lighter in tone are 'stopped out', using washes of varnish. The finished print resembles a watercolour wash, and the technique of overlaying separate plates of different colours can be used to build up a range of depth and colour.

arabesque (1) a florid treatment of thematic music. (2) a lyrical piece of music that employs an exaggerated and elaborate style, as used by Schumann and Debussy.

Arabian Nights Entertainments or The Thousand and One Nights a compilation of stories, the earliest of which probably originated in Persia, that were translated into Arabic in the mid-9th century and have become classics of Arab and world literature. The stories are told by Scheherazade to her husband, a king who has killed each previous bride following the consummation of the marriage. She saves her life by keeping the king in suspense, postponing the conclusion of each story until the following night.

Arcadia a region of ancient Greece which became the archetypal setting for rural bliss and innocence in the arts. Virgil's *Eclogues* in the 1st century BC established the use of Arcadia as a literary device for this purpose, but the ironic undertone in Virgil's work (Arcadia is largely barren) is usually missing from later writers' use of the myth. Virgil's dark undertone returns to Western culture in the work of several 16th- and 17th-century painters, e.g. Poussin, with reference to the phrase *Et in Arcadia Ego* ('And I [i.e. death] also in Arcadia').

archet (*French*) a BOW, such as is used to play a stringed instrument.

archi (*Italian*) 'bows', a term that refers to all stringed instruments played with a BOW.

arco (*Italian*) the singular of ARCHI. It is the usual instruction to play with the BOW after playing PIZZICATO.

ardito (*Italian*) 'bold', 'energetic'.

aria (*Italian*) a SONG or AIR. Originally the term was used for any song for one or more voices but it has come to be used exclusively for a long, SOLO song as found in ORATORIO and OPERA.

arioso (*Italian*) 'like an ARIA'. (1) a melodious and song-like RECITATIVE. (2) a short AIR in an OPERA or ORATORIO. (3) an instrumental piece that follows the style of a vocal arioso.

Armory Show the international exhibition of modern art held at the 69th Regimental Armory in New York in 1913, one of the most influential exhibitions ever shown in the US. Effectively two exhibitions in one, it represented not only a fine cross-section of contemporary American art but also a massive selection of modern European art, a total of around 1,600 works. It toured the US, arousing great controversy and excitement among the 250,000 people who paid to see it, but it served the function of restoring the life and vitality of contemporary art and critical debate in the US.

arpeggiare (*Italian*) 'to play the HARP', i.e. to play CHORDS 'spread out' as they are on the harp. *See also* ARPEGGIO.

arpeggio (*Italian*) 'HARP-wise', an indication that the NOTES of a CHORD should be played in rapid succession, as on a harp, and not simultaneously.

arrangement an adaptation of a piece of music for a medium different from that for which it was originally composed.

ars antiqua (*Latin*) the 'old art', i.e. music of the 12th and 13th centuries as opposed to **ars nova**, the new style of music that evolved in the 14th century.

Art Autre or Art Informel a name coined by art critic Michel Tapie in *Un Art Autre* (1952); he used it to describe nongeometric ABSTRACT EXPRESSIONISM.

Art Brut the work of anyone not linked to the art world either as professional or amateur, for example psychiatric patients or prisoners, etc. The term can also include graffiti and the work of young children. It refers to any work uninfluenced by the art world and its fashions.

Art Deco the decorative art of the 1920s and 1930s in Europe and North America. It was classical in style, with slender, symmetrical, geometric or rectilinear forms. Major influences were ART NOUVEAU architecture and ideas from the ARTS AND CRAFTS MOVEMENT and the BAUHAUS. The simplicity of style was easily adaptable to modern industrial production methods and contemporary materials, especially plastics. This resulted in a proliferation of utility items, jewellery and furniture in an elegant streamlined form, as well as the simplification and streamlining of interior decor and architecture.

Art Nouveau a style of decorative art popular in Europe and North America between 1890 and World War I. Primarily a design style, its main effects were seen in applied art, graphics, furniture and fabric design, and in architecture. Art Nouveau design is characterised by flowing organic forms and asymmetrical linear structures. Architectural and calligraphic forms were more austere and reserved. Its principal exponents were the Scottish architect and designer Charles Rennie Mackintosh (1868–1928) and the American designer Louis Comfort Tiffany (1848–1933).

Arts and Crafts Movement an English movement in the decorative arts towards the end of the 19th century. It was based on the ideas of the art critic John Ruskin and the architect Augustus Pugin (1812–52), with reference to the medieval guilds system, and took its name from the Arts and Crafts Exhibition Society formed in 1888. The aim was to re-establish the value of handcrafted objects at a time of increasing mass-production and industrialisation. The most important leader of the movement was William Morris.

ascription *see* ATTRIBUTION.

Ashcan School a group of American painters of urban realism (1908–1918)who declared themselves primarily American painters. They painted what they saw as American life, rejecting subject matter of academic approval. Among their influences were the works of Daumier and Goya.

assai (*Italian*) 'very', as in *allegro assai*, 'very fast'.

assemblage any sculptural type of construction using found objects, from pieces of painted wood to old shoes. *See also* COLLAGE.

assez (*French*) 'moderately', as in *assez vite*, 'moderately quick'.

atelier the French term for an artist's studio. In 19th-century France, an *atelier libre* was a studio where artists could go to paint a model. No formal tuition was provided, and a small fee was charged.

a tempo (*Italian*) 'in time', a term that indicates that a piece should revert to its normal TEMPO after a change of speed.

athematic music music that does not have any THEMES or TUNES as such; it is concerned with exploring the unconventional possibilities of sounds.

atonal music music that is not in any KEY. Atonal music is particularly associated with the works of Schoenberg, although he preferred to use the word *pantonality,* meaning a synthesis of all the keys.

attacca (*Italian*) 'attack', i.e. start the next MOVEMENT without a pause.

attribution or ascription the assigning of an unsigned picture to a painter, using similarity of style or subject as the basis.

aubade (*French*) 'morning music', as opposed to a SERENADE.

augmentation the lengthening of the time values of NOTES in melodic parts with the result that they sound more impressive and grand. The opposite of augmentation is DIMINUTION.

augmented interval the INTERVAL formed by increasing any perfect or MAJOR interval by a SEMITONE.

augmented sixth a CHORD based on the flattened SUBMEDIANT that contains the augmented sixth INTERVAL.

augmented triad a TRIAD of which the FIFTH is augmented.

a una corda (*Italian*) 'on one string' (*compare* A DUE CORDE), meaning left-hand PEDAL (of a piano), i.e. reducing the volume.

Authorised Version or King James Bible a translation of the Bible published in 1611 in the reign of James I of England. Its powerful and poetic language has made it perhaps the most influential book on writers in English from the early 17th century on. It is often said to be the greatest book ever written by a committee, but the work is based for the most part on the great translation by William Tyndale (1525). (*See* FP More, Sir Thomas.)

autograph in art, a term used to denote a painting by one artist only and not assisted by pupils or assistants.

autoharp a type of ZITHER in which CHORDS are produced by pressing down KEYS (1) that dampen some of the strings but let others vibrate freely. The instrument was invented in the late 19th century and was popular with American folk musicians.

Automatistes a Canadian group of painters formed in the 1950s whose ideas were based on the spontaneity of creativity. One of its main proponents was Paul Emile Borduas (1905–60).

avant-garde (*French*) 'vanguard', a term applied to music (or any other art) that is considered to break new ground in style, structure, or technique.

Ave Maria (*Latin*) 'Hail Mary', a prayer to the Virgin Mary used in the Roman Catholic Church. It has been set to music by numerous composers.

B (1) the seventh note of the scale of C major. (2) abbreviation for bass or for Bachelor (as in B. Mus., Bachelor of Music).

baby grand smallest size of grand PIANO.

Bach trumpet a 19th-century valved TRUMPET that was designed to make it easier to play the high-pitched parts that were originally composed by BACH and his contemporaries for a natural (unvalved) trumpet.

back the lower part of the sounding box of string instruments, connected in VIOLS to the sounding board or belly by a sound post set beneath the bridge. Its construction and material vitally affect the quality of the TONE (3) produced.

bagatelle (*French*) 'trifle', a short, light piece of music, usually for piano, e.g. Beethoven's FÜR ELISE.

bagpipes a reed instrument in which air is supplied to the PIPE or pipes from an inflated bag. Bagpipes are known to have existed for 3,000 years or more and hundreds of different types are found today. The best-known form of bagpipe is played in Scotland and consists of a *bag* that is inflated through a pipe and is held under the arm; a CHANTER (a REED pipe with finger holes) on which the MELODY is played; and several DRONE pipes, each of which is tuned to a different note. Air is rhythmically squeezed from the bag by the arm (and is then replenished with more breath) and is forced out through the chanter and drone pipes.

balalaika (*Russian*) a FOLK instrument of the GUITAR family, with a triangular body. It is of Tartar origin and usually has just three strings and a fretted FINGERBOARD. Balalaikas are made in several sizes and are often played in concert with one another.

ballabile (*Italian*) 'in a dancing style'.

ballad a narrative poem or song in brief stanzas, often with a repeated refrain and frequently featuring a dramatic incident. The songs sold by the vagabond Autolycus in Shakespeare's *As You Like It*, describing battles, public executions and the like, are typical examples of the sort of *broadside ballad* popular with the common people up to (and a bit beyond) Victorian times. In 1765, the antiquary Thomas Percy (1729–1811) published his *Reliques of Ancient English Poetry*, a collection of ancient and not-so-ancient traditional English poems, songs, and folk ballads that was to prove immensely influential. Examples of what has been termed the *literary ballad* soon began to appear. Notable examples include Coleridge's 'Rime of the Ancient Mariner' and Keats' 'La Belle Dame sans Merci'. Among the greatest examples of the form are the *Border ballads*, which stem from the violent world of the English/Scottish borders from the late Middle Ages to the 17th century. Representative examples of the Border ballads are the laments 'Sir Patrick Spens' and 'The Bonny Earl of Murray', the haunting song of fairyland 'Thomas the Rhymer', and the macabre 'Twa Corbies'. The most important collection of Border ballads is that issued by Sir Walter Scott in 1802–3, *Minstrelsy of the Scottish Borders*. Many of the ballads were written down at the dictation of the singers of the old songs themselves.

In music, a ballad is also a sentimental 'drawing-room' song of the late 19th century (sometimes referred to as a *shop ballad* to differentiate it from a broadside ballad) or a narrative song or operatic ARIA.

ballade a type of medieval French poetry, often set to music by TROUBADOURS. In music, it is a 19th-century term, coined by CHOPIN, for a long, romantic instrumental piece. Chopin wrote four outstanding ballades.

ballad opera popular OPERA composed of dialogue and SONGS with tunes borrowed from FOLK music, popular songs, and sometimes opera. They first appeared in the 18th century in England, probably the best known being *The Beggar's Opera*.

ballet a dramatic entertainment in which dancers in costume perform to a musical ACCOMPANIMENT. Mime is often used in ballet to express emotions or to tell a story. Ballet has a long history dating back to before the Middle Ages. In the 16th and 17th centuries, ballets often included singing and consequently were closely linked to OPERA. By the end of the 18th century, however, ballet had evolved more gymnastic qualities and, although it was still included as an integral part in many operas, it also kept a separate existence. In the 19th century, ballet achieved new heights of popularity in France and spread to Italy and Russia where several schools of ballet were established that

incorporated traditional dancing into their teaching. Tchaikovsky's ballet scores (e.g. *Swan Lake* and *The Sleeping Beauty*) had a massive influence on Russian ballet and greatly added to its international appeal. The Russian choreographer and entrepreneur Sergei Diaghilev encouraged young composers such as Stravinsky and Ravel to write ballet scores. At the start of the 20th century, ballet became immensely popular in England. Vaughan Williams, Bliss and Britten all composed notable pieces for ballet, and the outstanding British choreographers Sir Frederick Ashton and Sir Kenneth Macmillan helped to maintain the interest. In the USA, the choreographer George Balanchine (1904–83) had an equally powerful influence, and many American composers, such as Copland and Bernstein, wrote ballet music. Meanwhile, Prokofiev's masterpieces (e.g. *Romeo and Juliet*) maintained Russia's tradition in dancing.

band a term used to describe virtually any group of instrumentalists except a concert ORCHESTRA, for example dance band, JAZZ band, POP band, MILITARY BAND.

banjo a GUITAR-like, stringed instrument of Black American origin. It comprises a shallow metal (sometimes wood) drum with parchment stretched over the top while the bottom is (usually) left open. Banjos can have between four and nine strings, which are played by plucking either with the fingers or a PLECTRUM.

bar (1) a vertical line (bar line) drawn down one or more STAFFS of music. (2) the space between two bar lines.

barber-shop quartet a quartet of amateur male singers who perform CLOSE-HARMONY arrangements. The tradition originated in barber shops in New York in the late 19th century.

Barbizon School a group of French landscape painters in the 1840s who based their art on direct study from nature. Their initial influences included Constable as well as some of the Dutch landscape painters. Their advanced ideas represented a move away from academic conventions, and their interest in daylight effects and their bold use of colour helped prepare the way for IMPRESSIONISM.

barcarolle (*French*) a boating song with a rhythm imitating that of songs sung by gondoliers.

bard a Celtic minstrel, part of whose job it was to compose SONGS for his master. Bards traditionally held annual meetings (*Eisteddfods*) in Wales and these have been revived in recent times as competition festivals.

baritone (1) a male voice, midway between BASS and TENOR with a range of approximately two OCTAVES. (2) a BRASS INSTRUMENT of the SAXHORN family.

Baroque a cultural movement in art, music, and science in the 17th century. In terms of art history, the area of reference is slightly broader and takes in the late 16th and early 18th centuries. It specifically indicates the stage between the MANNERISM of the late High RENAISSANCE and ROCOCO, into which Baroque developed.

As a style it is characterised by movement, rhetoric and emotion, stemming from the achievements of the High Renaissance, and it represented a reaction away from Mannerist attitudes and techniques. Caravaggio was among its leading figures when it first began in Rome, and Rembrandt's work reflected Baroque trends for part of his career. Adjectivally, *baroque* can also be used to describe art from any age that displays the richness and dynamism associated with the movement.

barrel organ a mechanical ORGAN of the 18th and 19th centuries in which air was admitted into PIPES by means of pins on a hand-rotated barrel. It was restricted to playing a limited number of tunes but was nonetheless frequently used in church services. *See also* MECHANICAL INSTRUMENTS.

bass (1) the lowest adult male VOICE. (2) an abbreviation for DOUBLE BASS. (3) an addition to the instrument name to indicate the largest member of a family of instruments (except where CONTRABASS instruments are built).

bassa (*Italian*) 'low'.

bass-bar a strip of wood glued as reinforcement under the BRIDGE (1) inside the BELLY of instruments of the VIOLIN family.

bass clarinet a single-REED instrument built

an OCTAVE lower than the CLARINET, with a crook and upturned bell.

bass clef *see* CLEF.

bass drum a large PERCUSSION INSTRUMENT consisting of a cylindrical wooden hoop which is usually covered on both sides with vellum. It is common in MILITARY BANDS in which it is suspended vertically from the shoulders and beaten with two sticks.

basset horn an ALTO CLARINET.

bass flute an ALTO FLUTE with a PITCH a FOURTH lower than a 'concert' or normal flute.

basso continuo *see* FIGURED BASS.

bassoon a double-reed instrument of the 16th century, consisting of a wooden tube doubled back on itself. It has a compass from B flat below BASS CLEF to E on the fourth line of the TREBLE CLEF.

basso ostinato (*Italian*) 'obstinate bass', a GROUND BASS, i.e. a bass FIGURE that is repeated many times throughout a composition (or part of a composition) while the upper parts vary.

baton the stick used by a CONDUCTOR to give commands to performers.

batterie (*French*) (*also* **battery**) (1) a 17th- and 18th-century term for ARPEGGIO. (2) the PERCUSSION section of an ORCHESTRA.

battuta (*Italian*) *see* BEAT.

Bauhaus a German school of architecture and applied arts founded by the architect Walter Gropius at Weimar in 1919. One of its aims, as with the ARTS AND CRAFTS MOVEMENT, was to narrow the gap between fine and APPLIED ARTS; another was to focus on architecture as the environment of art. Each student took a six-month foundation course in practical craft skills. Among the first masters were the EXPRESSIONIST painters Klee and Kandinsky. A more CONSTRUCTIVIST influence came when the Bauhaus moved to Dessau in 1925. Later came a shift in emphasis from craftsmanship towards industrialised mass-production. Gropius resigned from the Bauhaus in 1928; it was moved to Berlin in 1932 and was closed by the Nazis in 1933. A number of Bauhaus masters emigrated to the US.

Bayreuth a town in Bavaria in Germany where Richard Wagner arranged for the building of a festival theatre that has subsequently become internationally famous for staging his operas. Built to resemble a Greek amphitheatre, the theatre holds 1,800 people, and the special feature of a hood surrounding the orchestra pit gives the auditorium an acoustical excellence ideal for Wagner's music.

beam the black line attached to the stem of all NOTES of less value than a QUARTER NOTE (crotchet).

beat (1) a unit of rhythmic measure in music, indicated to a CHOIR (2) or ORCHESTRA by the movement of a conductor's BATON. The number of beats in a BAR depends on the TIME-SIGNATURE. (2) a form of 20th-century POPULAR MUSIC with a steady and powerful RHYTHM.

Beat Generation a term invented by Jack Kerouac to describe a group of American writers, artists and musicians in the 1950s. Notable Beat writers included Kerouac himself, whose novel *On the Road* (1952) became the 'Beat bible', the poets Lawrence Ferlinghetti (1919–) and Allen Ginsberg, and the novelists Neal Cassady (1926–68) and William Burroughs. The Beat writers were anti-Western in their values; they dabbled in communalism, loved modern jazz, and took drugs. The term 'Beat' was said to denote (a) the weariness of struggling against materialist society, (b) jazz rhythm, which they tried to capture in their prose, (c) beautitude. The last quality is somewhat dubious.

bebop a JAZZ development of the 1940s in which complex RHYTHMS and harmonic sequences were carried out against rapidly played melodic IMPROVISATION. It is particularly associated with the jazz saxophonist, Charlie Parker.

Bebung (*German*) 'trembling', i.e. a VIBRATO effect caused by shaking a finger holding down a KEY (1) of a CLAVICHORD.

Bechstein a company of German piano manufacturers established in Berlin in 1856 by Friedrich Wilhelm Karl Bechstein (1826–1900). Branches were subsequently formed in France, England, and Russia.

bel a unit used to measure the intensity of SOUND, named after Alexander Graham Bell. *See also* DECIBEL.

bel canto (*Italian*) 'beautiful singing', a style characterised by elaborate technique,

and associated with 18th-century Italian OPERA.

bells (*orchestral*) cylindrical metal tubes (*tubular bells*) of different lengths which are suspended from a frame and struck with a wooden mallet.

belly the upper part of the body or soundbox of a stringed instrument.

ben, bene (*Italian*) 'well', as in *ben marcato*, meaning 'well marked', 'well accented'.

Benedicite (*Latin*) a CANTICLE known as the *Song of the Three Holy Children*; it is used during Lent as an alternative to the TE DEUM in the Anglican service of Morning Prayer.

Benedictus (*Latin*) (1) the second part of the SANCTUS of a Roman Catholic Mass. (2) the CANTICLE 'Benedictus Dominus Israel' or 'Blessed be the Lord God of Israel'.

berceuse (*French*) a cradle SONG.

bergamasca (*Italian*) **or bergomask** (*English*) **or bergamasque** (*French*) (1) a popular 16th- and 17th-century dance from Bergamo in Italy. (2) a 19th-century dance in quick 6/8 TIME.

Bible, The *see* AUTHORIZED VERSION.

Biedermeier a style in art and architecture in Austria and Germany between 1815 and 1848. It took its name from a fictional character of the time, Gottlieb Biedermeier, who personified the philistine artistic taste of the middle classes. Architecture associated with the style is solid and utilitarian, paintings are meticulous and unimaginative.

big band a large BAND, most commonly associated with the SWING era. Such bands were famed for the strong dance RHYTHMS they produced.

Bildungsroman (*German*) 'education novel', a novel that describes the growth of a character (usually based on the author) from youthful naivety to a well-rounded maturity. The term derives from Goethe's *Wilhelm Meister's Apprenticeship*. Two notable examples in English are Dickens' *David Copperfield* and Joyce's *Portrait of the Artist as a Young Man*.

binary form a structure, common in BAROQUE music, consisting of two related sections which were repeated. SONATA FORM evolved from it.

bis (*French*) 'twice', 'again'.

bitonality use of two keys simultaneously.

blanche (*French*) 'white', the French word for a HALF NOTE (minim).

blank verse a term sometimes used to denote any form of unrhymed verse but normally applied to unrhymed verse in iambic pentameters, i.e. a line of verse with five short-long 'feet', e.g. the actress Mrs Siddons's reputed remark: 'You brought me water, boy; I asked for beer'. The form was developed in English by the Earl of Surrey (c.1517–47) and reached its highest peak in Shakespeare's plays. Other notable works written in blank verse include Milton's *Paradise Lost*.

Blaue Reiter, Der (*German*) 'The Blue Rider', the name (from a painting by Wassily Kandinsky) of a group of German EXPRESSIONISTS formed in Munich in 1911. Although their working styles were diverse, leading members Kandinsky and Paul Klee were united by a philosophy of the creative spirit in European art. They organised two touring exhibitions in Germany (1911, 1912) and produced an *Almanac* (1912) that included major European avant-garde artists as well as tribal, folk and children's art. The idea of the *Almanac* was to unite music, art and literature in a single creative venture. It was to be the first in a series, but the group disbanded in 1914.

block chords a harmonic procedure in which the NOTES of CHORDS are moved simultaneously in 'blocks'.

Bloomsbury Group a group of artists, writers and intellectuals who lived or worked in the Bloomsbury area of London in the early decades of the 20th century and whose members included Virginia Woolf.

bluegrass a type of FOLK music originally from Kentucky, USA (*see* COUNTRY AND WESTERN).

blues a 20th-century Black American SONG or lamentation following an essentially simple form of twelve BARS to each verse. Blues music formed the basis for JAZZ; musicians favoured such instruments as the GUITAR and HARMONICA.

Bluestocking an originally disparaging term denoting members of small, mostly female groups in English 18th-century social life, who held informal discussion groups on literary and scholarly matters. The term derives from the blue stockings worn by a male member of the groups, the botanist Benjamin Stillingfleet.

bocca chiusa (*Italian*) literally 'closed mouth', i.e. humming.

body paint *see* GOUACHE.

Boehm system an improved system of KEYS (2) and levers for the FLUTE (1) which is named after its German inventor, Theobald Boehm (1794–1881). The system is also applied to other instruments, for example, the clarinet.

bolero (*Spanish*) a moderately fast Spanish dance in triple TIME. Ravel's *Bolero* (1928), a spiralling crescendo based on a repeated theme, was the music for a ballet choreographed by Nijinsky.

bones a pair of small sticks (originally bones) that are held in the hands and clicked together rhythmically.

bongos pairs of small, upright Cuban DRUMS that are often found in dance BANDS. They are played with the hands.

boogie-woogie a JAZZ and BLUES style of piano playing in which the left hand plays a persistent bass RHYTHM while the right hand plays a MELODY.

Book of Common Prayer the once official book of services for the Church of England, first published in 1549. The most loved version is that of 1662, the language of which, like that of the AUTHORIZED VERSION, has been very influential on English prose and poetry.

bop short for BEBOP.

Border ballad *see* BALLAD.

bouche fermée (*French*) *see* BOCCA CHIUSA.

bourrée (*French*) a lively French dance of the 17th century.

bouzouki a Greek stringed instrument with a long, fretted neck. Its six strings are plucked, often as an ACCOMPANIMENT to songs.

bow a wooden stick that is strung with horsehair and used to play instruments of the VIOLIN and VIOL families.

bowed harp a primitive VIOLIN dating back to at least the 12th century. It was held on the knee and played vertically.

bowing the technique of using a BOW to play an instrument.

brace the vertical line, usually with a bracket, that joins two STAFFS of music to indicate that they are played together.

branle (*French*) a French 15th-century FOLK DANCE with a swaying movement.

brass band a type of BAND that consists of BRASS INSTRUMENTS and DRUMS only. Brass bands have been popular in England since the beginning of the 19th century.

brass instruments a family of WIND IN-STRUMENTS that are made of metal but not always brass. Instruments with REEDS and those that used to be made from wood (such as the FLUTE) are excluded. A characteristic of the family is that sound is produced by the vibration of the lips, which are pressed into a funnel-shaped MOUTHPIECE. A selection of NOTES can be produced by effectively lengthening the tubing, either with a slide (as in the TROM-BONE) or with valves (as in the TRUMPET). Other brass instruments include the trombone, CORNET, BUGLE, trumpet, French HORN, TUBA, and EUPHONIUM.

bravura (*Italian*) literally 'bravery', as in a 'bravura passage', a passage that demands a VIRTUOSO display by the performer.

break (1) in JAZZ, a short improvised SOLO passage. (2) the point in a vocal or instrumental range where the REGISTER changes.

breit (*German*) 'broadly' or 'grandly', a term used to describe the manner in which a piece should be played.

breve originally the short NOTE of music (*c*.13th century), but as other notes have been introduced, it is now the longest note and is only occasionally used. Also known as a DOUBLE WHOLE NOTE; indicated by the sign ⊏.

bridge (1) a piece of wood that stands on the BELLY of stringed instruments and supports the strings. (2) a passage in a COMPOSITION (1) that links two important THEMES together.

brindisi (*Italian*) 'a toast', a drinking song in an opera during which toasts are often given.

brio (*Italian*) 'vigour', so CON BRIO means 'with vigour'.

brisé (*French*) 'broken', a term that indicates that a CHORD should be played in ARPEGGIO fashion or that music for stringed instruments should be played with short movements of the BOW.

broadside ballad *see* BALLAD.

broken octaves a term used to describe a passage of NOTES that are played alternately an OCTAVE apart; they frequently occur in piano music.

bronze a metal alloy of bronze mixed with tin and occasionally lead and zinc that has been used as a medium for sculpture since ancient times when it was cast solid using wooden models. Modern techniques use hollow casting methods of sand casting or *cire perdue* ('lost wax').

Brücke, Die (*German*) 'the bridge', a group of German artists founded in 1905 in Dresden from Nietszche's idea that a man can be seen as a bridge towards a better future. The artists saw themselves as a link with the art of the future, in a move away from REALISM and IMPRESSIONISM. They also wanted to integrate art and life, so lived together in a community. Their influences included African tribal art and the works of Van Gogh and FAUVISM. Their painting was mainly EXPRESSIONIST. They helped found the Neue SEZESSION in 1910, then split away and exhibited as a group with Der BLAUE REITER. In 1913 the group disbanded because of conflicts over aims and policies in relation to the development of CUBISM.

brushwork the 'handwriting' of a painter, i.e. the distinctive way in which he or she applies paint, either smoothly or roughly, thinly or thickly, in long strokes or short. Like handwriting, brushwork is individual to a painter.

bugle a simple BRASS INSTRUMENT with a conical tube and a cup-shaped MOUTHPIECE that was widely used for giving military signals. *See also* LAST POST.

bull roarer *see* THUNDER STICK.

burla, burlesca (*Italian*) a short and jolly piece of music.

Byzantine music music of the Christian Church of the Eastern Roman Empire, which was established in AD 330 and lasted until 1435. It influenced Western church music.

C (1) the key-note or TONIC of the SCALE of C major. (2) an abbreviation for CONTRALTO; *con* (with); *col, colla* (with the).

c.a. abbreviation for *coll' arco,* meaning 'with the BOW', as opposed to PIZZICATO (with reference to a stringed instrument).

cabaletta (*Italian*) a term for a simple ARIA with an insistent RHYTHM, or an emphatically rhythmical ending to an ARIA or DUET.

cabinet organ *see* AMERICAN ORGAN.

caccia (*Italian*) a 'hunt', as in *corno da caccia,* hunting horn. Also, a 14th-century hunting poem about country life set to music.

cachucha a Spanish solo dance in 3/4 time, resembling the BOLERO.

cacophony a discordant muddle of SOUND or DISSONANCE.

cadence literally a 'falling', a term used to describe the concluding PHRASE at the end of a section of music.

cadenza (*Italian*) literally 'cadence', but it has come to have two specific meanings: (1) an elaborate ending to an operatic ARIA. (2) a flourish at the end of a PASSAGE of SOLO music in a CONCERTO.

calando (*Italian*) 'diminishing', i.e. in both volume and speed.

calcando (*Italian*) 'pressing forward', a term used to indicate an increase in speed.

calypso a song with SYNCOPATED RHYTHMS from the West Indies, notably Trinidad; calypso LYRICS are usually witty and topical and often vehicles for political satire.

cambiata (*Italian*) an abbreviation for *nota cambiata,* CHANGING NOTE.

camera (*Italian*) literally a 'room', but in musical terms it refers to a type of music that can be performed in a place other than a church, music hall, or opera house, etc; *see* CHAMBER MUSIC.

campanelli (*Italian*) *see* GLOCKENSPIEL.

campanology bell-ringing, the study of bells.

campus novel a NOVEL with a university setting. They are invariably satirical and are equally invariably written by former or practising academics.

cancan a Parisian music-hall dance of the late 19th century in quick 2/4 time.

cancel or natural a NOTE that is neither sharpened nor flattened; indicated by the sign ♮.

cancrizans a type of music that makes sense if it is played backwards; RETROGRADE MOTION.

canon a COUNTERPOINT composition in which one part is imitated and overlapped by one or more other PARTS, e.g. a SOPRANO lead with a TENOR follow-up. In a 'strict' canon, the imitation is exact in every way.

cantabile (*Italian*) 'song-like', a term applied to instrumental pieces indicating that they should be played in a singing style.

cantata originally a piece of music of the BAROQUE period that is sung (as opposed to a SONATA, a piece that is played). It has come to be a term used to describe a vocal or CHORAL piece with an instrumental accompaniment. German cantatas were generally religious works. In many ways, the form is similar to OPERA and ORATORIO, but it tends not to be so elaborate.

canticle a HYMN that has words from the Bible, other than a PSALM.

cantor (*Latin*) a 'singer'; nowadays the term refers to the chief singer in a CHOIR or the lead singer of liturgical music in a synagogue.

cantus firmus (*Latin*) 'fixed song', i.e. a MELODY in POLYPHONIC music, often taken from PLAINSONG, with long NOTES (1) against which COUNTERPOINT tunes are sung.

canzone or canzona or canzon literally 'song', a vocal work or an instrumental piece that is modelled on music for the VOICE.

canzonet (1) a short kind of CANZONE. (2) a type of MADRIGAL or a simple SOLO SONG.

capotasto (*Italian*) the 'head of the fingerboard', i.e. the raised part or 'nut' at the top of the FINGERBOARD of a stringed instrument that defines the lengths of the strings. A moveable capotasto, comprising a wood or metal bar that can be clamped to the fingerboard, is occasionally used on fretted instruments to shorten all the strings at the same time, thus raising the PITCH.

cappella, a *see* A CAPPELLA.

capriccio (*Italian*) 'caprice', a short, lively piece.

caricature a drawing of a person in which his or her most prominent features are exaggerated or distorted in order to produce a recognisable but ridiculous portrait. The technique was pioneered in the late 16th century and flourished in the 18th and 19th centuries.

carillon (1) a set of bells, usually in a bell tower, which can be played by electrical or mechanical means to produce a tune. (2) an ORGAN STOP which produces a bell-like sound.

carol originally, any medieval English song with a refrain but now generally a song associated with Christmas.

cartoon (1) a drawing, or series of drawings, intended to convey humour, satire, or wit. Cartoons were commonly used from the 18th century onwards in newspapers and periodicals as a vehicle for social and political comment, and in comic magazines for children and adults in the 20th century. (2) a full-size preparatory drawing for a painting, mural, or fresco.

castanets a Spanish PERCUSSION INSTRUMENT comprising two shell-like pieces of wood which are clicked together by the fingers. In orchestras, they are occasionally shaken on the end of sticks.

castrato (*Italian*) an adult male singer with a SOPRANO or CONTRALTO voice produced by castration before puberty. Castrati were popular singers in the 17th and 18th centuries. The practice was abandoned in the 19th century.

catch a ROUND for three or more VOICES. The words are often humorous and frequently contain puns, e.g. *Ah, how Sophia* which, when sung, sounds like 'Our house afire'.

Cavalier Poets a loose grouping of lyric poets associated with the court or cause of Charles I during his clashes with the English Parliament and the ensuing Civil War. The most notable Cavalier poets are Herrick, Sir John Suckling (1609–41), Thomas Carew (*c*.1595–1640), and Richard Lovelace (1618–*c*.1658). The latter's witty and graceful 'To Althea' is perhaps the most loved of the Cavalier poems.

cavatina (*Italian*) a short and often slow SONG or instrumental piece.

Cave Paintings *see* ALTAMIRA; LASCAUX.

CB an abbreviation for *contrabasso* (DOUBLE BASS).

cebell a 17th-century English dance similar to the GAVOTTE.

Cecilia, St a Roman martyr of the 2nd or 3rd century and the patron saint of music. Since the 16th century music festivals to commemorate her have been annual events. Her feast day is on 22 November.

ceilidh (*Gaelic*) a gathering at which SONGS, FOLK music and dances are performed; ceilidhs are particularly associated with Scotland and Ireland.

celesta a small keyboard instrument in which HAMMERS are made to strike metal bars suspended over wooden resonators; the sound produced has an ethereal, bell-like quality. Tchaikovsky included a celesta in the 'Dance of the Sugar-Plum Fairy' in his ballet *The Nutcracker*.

cello *see* VIOLONCELLO.

cembalo (*Italian*) (1) a DULCIMER. (2) an abbreviation of *clavicembalo*, which is the Italian for HARPSICHORD.

CF abbreviation for CANTUS FIRMUS.

chaconne (*French*) a slow dance in triple time that is thought to have originated in Mexico.

chalk a soft stone, similar to a very soft limestone, used for drawing. *Crayon* is powdered chalk mixed with oil or wax.

chalumeau (*French*)) (1) a generic term for a type of REED-PIPE. (2) a term now used for the lower REGISTER of the CLARINET.

chamber music originally a term used to describe any type of music that was suitable for playing in a room of a house as opposed to a church or concert hall. However, it has come to mean music for a small number of instruments (for example, flute and piano) or group of performers (for example, STRING QUARTET, SEXTET, etc.).

chamber orchestra a small orchestra, sometimes solely of stringed instruments, for performing CHAMBER MUSIC.

change-ringing an English method of ringing a peal of church bells; the bells are rung in an established order, which then passes through a series of changes.

changing note or cambiatta a dissonant PASSING NOTE which is a third away from the preceding note, before being resolved.

chanson (*French*) a song for either a SOLO VOICE or a CHOIR. It can also mean an instrumental piece of song-like quality.

chant a general term for a type of music which is sung as part of a ritual or ceremony and used particularly for unaccompanied singing in religious services.

chanter the pipe of a BAGPIPE, on which the MELODY is played.

chanterelle (*French*) literally the 'singing one', i.e. the highest string on a bowed, stringed instrument (for example, the E string on a VIOLIN).

character piece a term used by composers for a short instrumental piece, such as may attempt to describe a specific mood. Examples are Schumann's *Fantasiestücke*, *Nachtstücke*, and *Albumblätter*.

charcoal the carbon residue from wood that has been partially burned. Charcoal will make easily erasable black marks and is used mainly to make preliminary drawings, e.g. on walls. When used on paper it has to be coated with a fixative to make the drawing permanent.

charleston a ballroom dance, similar to the FOXTROT.

chest voice the lower REGISTER (2) of VOICE (1), so called because NOTES seem to emanate from the chest. *Compare* HEAD VOICE.

chevalet (*French*) the BRIDGE of a stringed instrument.

chiaro, chiara (*Italian*) 'clear', 'distinct'.

chiaroscuro (*Italian*) literally 'light-dark', used to describe the treatment of light and shade in a painting, drawing or engraving to convey depth and shape, particularly by painters like Caravaggio or Rembrandt.

chinoiserie in the 16th and 17th centuries, trade with the Far East created a European market for Chinese art and influenced the development of a vogue for things Chinese. Pagodas and stylised scenes, plants and animals conceived to be in the Chinese style began to decorate pottery, furniture, fabrics and ornaments. These were finally mass-produced, both in Europe and the Far East, specifically for this market. A familiar product in this style is the famous Willow Pattern pottery range.

chitarrone (*Italian*) a large LUTE.

choir (1) the place, defined by special seats or 'choir stalls', in a large church or cathedral where singers are positioned. (2) a body of singers, such as a male-voice choir, church choir. (3) a section of the orchestra, e.g. 'brass choir'.

choirbook a large medieval volume that (usually) included both words and music and was designed to be read by various members of a CHOIR (2) while it was stationed on a centrally placed lectern.

choir organ the section of an ORGAN played from the lowest MANUAL and soft enough to accompany a church CHOIR (2).

choral an adjective used to describe music that involves a CHORUS.

chorale a HYMN-tune of the Lutheran Church, dating back to the 15th century.

chorale cantata a CANTATA that was written to be performed in a (Lutheran) church.

choral symphony (1) a SYMPHONY in which a CHORUS is used at some point (or, indeed, a symphony written entirely for voices). (2) the popular name of Beethoven's symphony no. 9 in D Minor, which ends with 'An die Freude' ('Ode to Joy') for chorus and soloists.

chord a combination of NOTES played simultaneously, usually not less than three.

chorus (1) a body of singers. *See* CHOIR. (2) music written for a body of singers (usually to follow an introductory piece). (3) a REFRAIN that follows a SOLO verse.

chromatic (from the Greek *chromatikos*, 'coloured') a term used to describe NOTES that do not belong to a prevailing SCALE, e.g. in C major all SHARPS and FLATS (1) are chromatic notes. The *chromatic scale* is a scale of twelve ascending or descending SEMITONES; and a *chromatic cord* is a CHORD that contains chromatic notes. *See also* TWELVE-NOTE MUSIC.

ciaccona (*Italian*) *see* CHACONNE.

cimbal, cimbalom *see* DULCIMER.

circular breathing the technique of sustaining a NOTE when playing a WIND INSTRUMENT by breathing in through the nose while sounding the note.

cittern a pear-shaped stringed instrument of the GUITAR family popular from the 16th century to the 18th century It was similar to the LUTE except that it had a flat back and wire strings, and was easier to play.

clappers virtually any kind of PERCUSSION INSTRUMENT comprising two similar pieces that can be struck together, e.g. BONES, spoons and sticks.

clarinet a single-REED WOODWIND instrument dating back to the 17th century. It has a cylindrical tube and nowadays comes in two common sizes: B flat and A. It is an instrument common to both CLASSICAL music and JAZZ.

clàrsach (*Gaelic*) a small harp of the Scottish Highlands and Ireland.

classical (1) a term used to describe a certain form of music that adheres to basic conventions and forms that are more concerned with carefully controlled expression rather than unrestrained emotion. (2) a term used to describe 'serious' music as opposed to popular music.

Classicism a style of art based on order, serenity and emotional control, referring to the classical art of the ancient Greeks and Romans. It eschews the impulsive creativity and spontaneity of Romanticism in favour of peace, harmony and strict ideals of beauty. *See also* NEOCLASSICISM.

clavecin (*French*) *see* HARPSICHORD.

claves short sticks that are held in the hand and clicked together to emphasise a BEAT (1) or RHYTHM. They originated in Cuba.

clavicembalo (*Italian*) *see* HARPSICHORD.

clavichord a keyboard instrument, dating from the 15th century, the strings of which are struck by a brass 'tangent' and can be made to sound a note of variable PITCH until the KEY (1) is released. However, the sound is soft and the keyboard is limited. The instrument fell out of favour with the introduction of the PIANO.

clavier (1) a practice keyboard that makes no sound except clicks. (2) any keyboard instrument that has strings, e.g. the CLAVICHORD, the HARPSICHORD, the PIANO.

clef a symbol positioned on a line of a STAFF that indicates the PITCH of the line and consequently all the NOTES on the staff. Three clefs are commonly used: ALTO (TENOR), TREBLE, and BASS.

Clerihew a verse form invented by Edmund Clerihew Bentley with two rhymed couplets of variable length and often encapsulating an unreliable biographical anecdote.

close harmony HARMONY in which the NOTES of the CHORDS are close together. In singing, this means that each VOICE remains fairly close to the MELODY.

coda (*Italian*) literally a 'tail', meaning a PASSAGE at the end of a piece of music which rounds it off.

col or coll' or colla or colle (*Italian*) literally 'with the', so *col basso* means 'with bass'; *colle voce*, 'with voice'.

collage a piece of art created by adhering pieces of paper, fabric, etc, on to a flat surface. The technique was popular with the CUBISTS and is a precursor of the more sculptural methods of ASSEMBLAGE.

coloratura (*Italian*) the florid ornamentation of a melodic line, especially in opera.

colour (1) in art, an effect induced in the eye by light of various wavelengths, the colour perceived depending on the specific wavelength of light reflected by an object. Most objects contain pigments that absorb certain light frequencies and reflect others, e.g. the plant pigment chlorophyll usually absorbs orange or red light and reflects green or blue, therefore the majority of plants appear to be green in colour. A white surface is one where all light frequencies are reflected and a black surface absorbs all frequencies. Artists' colours are made by combining pigments of vegetable or mineral extraction with an appropriate medium, e.g. linseed oil. (2) in music, the TONE quality of instruments and voices.

colour field painting a movement begun by abstract expressionists towards a more intellectual abstraction. Their paintings were large areas of pure, flat colour, the mood and atmosphere being created by the shape of the canvas and by sheer scale.

colourist a term in art criticism, too vague to be applied consistently, referring to an artist who places emphasis on colour over line or form, e.g. Titian and Giorgione have been called the 'Venetian Colourists'.

combination tone or resultant tone in music, a faint (third) NOTE that is heard when two notes are sounded simultaneously.

combo an abbreviation of 'combination', especially a collection of musicians who make up a JAZZ BAND.

comedy a form of drama, usually of a light and humorous kind and frequently involving misunderstandings that are resolved in a happy ending. The first major examples known, those by Aristophanes, are still among the greatest, and became known as *old comedy*. Aristophanes' plays often involved ferocious attacks on named individuals, e.g. Euripedes and Socrates. The outrage caused by his plays led to the Athenians banning the ridicule of named individuals on stage. The so-called *new* *comedy* that then developed in Greece is known to us largely through adaptations of lost Greek originals by Roman dramatists. It is this new comedy, based upon Aristotle's opinion that the business of comedy is with people of no significance (who can be safely ridiculed), that was to prevail on the stage until the advent of Chekhov, Ibsen, and Strindberg, with their downbeat comedies of middle-class life. These latter comedies may loosely be described as *tragicomedies*, although the term is normally reserved to denote those plays of the Jacobean period, such as Beaumont and Fletcher's *Philaster* (1609) and *A King and No King* (1611), and Shakespeare's 'dark comedies', e.g. *Measure for Measure* (1604), in all of which the action seems to be leading inexorably towards a tragic ending but resolves itself (more or less) happily at the end, after trials, tests, and tribulations. Other notable forms of comedy include the comedy of HUMOURS, the COMEDY OF MANNERS, SENTIMENTAL COMEDY, and COMMEDIA DELL'ARTE. *See also* MELODRAMA, *compare* TRAGEDY.

comedy of manners a form of comedy that features intrigues, invariably involving sex and/or money, among an upper region of society. The central characters are usually witty sophisticates, and there is often much mockery of characters from inferior stations who try to imitate the behaviour of their betters. The form is associated particularly with RESTORATION dramatists such as William Congreve (1670–1729), Sir George Etherege (*c*.1634–91), and Wycherley.

comic opera an OPERA that has an amusing plot, or (sometimes) an opera that includes some spoken dialogue.

commedia dell'arte a form of Italian comedy, popular from the RENAISSANCE until the 18th century, that used stock farcical characters (such as Harlequin and Columbine) and plots as a basis for improvisation. Actors wore masks representing their particular characters, and were often skilled acrobats. The form was given new life by Goldoni.

common chord a MAJOR or MINOR CHORD, usually consisting of a keynote and its third and FIFTH.

comodo (*Italian*) 'convenient', as in *tempo comodo*, at a 'convenient speed'.

compass the musical RANGE of a VOICE or instrument.

composition in art, the arrangement of elements in a drawing, painting or sculpture in proper proportion and relation to each other and to the whole. In music, (1) a work of music. (2) the putting together of sounds in a creative manner. (3) the art of writing music.

compound interval an INTERVAL that is greater than an OCTAVE.

compound time musical TIME in which each BEAT (1) in a BAR is divisible by three, for example 6/8, 9/8 and 12/8 time.

computer-generated music music that is created by feeding a formula or program into a computer that then translates the program into sounds.

con (*Italian*) 'with', so *con amore* means 'with love', i.e. lovingly, tenderly.

concert a public performance of secular music other than an OPERA or BALLET.

concert grand a large GRAND PIANO that is used in concert halls.

concertina a type of ACCORDION, hexagonal in shape, with small studs at each end that are used as keys.

concertmaster (*US*) the first violinist, or leader of an orchestra.

concerto (*plural* **concerti**) (*Italian*) (1) originally, a work for one or several voices with instrumental ACCOMPANIMENT. (2) a work for several contrasted instruments. (3) an orchestral work in several movements, containing passages for groups of SOLO instruments (*concerto grosso*). (4) a piece for a solo instrument and an accompanying orchestra.

concert overture an orchestral piece of one MOVEMENT, similar to an opera OVERTURE but written solely for performance in a concert hall. Originating in the 19th century, examples are Mendelssohn's *Hebrides* and Tchaikovsky's *Romeo and Juliet*.

concert pitch the internationally agreed PITCH, according to which A above middle C (in the middle of the TREBLE CLEF) is fixed at 440 hertz (cycles per second).

Concertstück or Konzertstück (*German*) a short CONCERTO.

concitato (*Italian*) 'agitated'.

concord a combination of sounds (such as a CHORD) that are satisfactory and sound agreeable. The opposite of DISSONANCE.

concrete art a term used to describe severely geometrical abstract art.

concrete music *see* MUSIQUE CONCRÈTE.

conducting the art of directing and controlling an ORCHESTRA or CHOIR (or operatic performance) by means of gestures. As well as indicating the speed of a piece, a conductor, who often uses a BATON to exaggerate his or her arm movements, is also responsible for interpreting the music.

conga (1) a tall, narrow DRUM that is played with the hands. (2) an entertaining dance in which the participants form a long, moving line, one behind the other.

conjunct a succession of NOTES of different PITCH.

conservatory a school that specialises in musical training. The term originates from the kind of charitable institutions for orphans, called *conservatorii* in 16th- and 17th-century Italy, where music was taught to a high standard.

consort an old spelling of the word 'concert', meaning an ENSEMBLE of instruments, e.g. a consort of VIOLS.

Constructivism in art, a movement in ABSTRACT EXPRESSIONISM concerned with forms and movement in sculpture and the aesthetics of the industrial age. It began in post-World War I Russia with the sculptors Antoine Pevsner (1886–1962), his brother Naum Gabo (1890–1979), and Vladimir Tatlin (1885–1953). Their work, which made use of modern plastics, glass and wood, was intentionally nonrepresentational. Gabo and Pevsner left Russia in 1922 and 1923 respectively and went on to exert great influence on Western art.

Constructivist theatre a form of theatre devised by Vsevolod Meyerhold (1874–1940), the Russian theatrical producer and director. Among the plays he produced at his Meyerhold Theatre were those of Mayakovsky (*see* FUTURISM). His productions abandoned traditional conventions, such as the proscenium arch, and broke plays up into episodic segments. Stage sets were determinedly Constructivist, i.e. they used technological artefacts derived from industrial processes to emphasise the kinetic, active nature of the stage. Actors were encouraged to think of themselves as 'biomechanisms' and to study circus acrobatics and the conventions of COMMEDIA DELL' ARTE. Meyerhold's ideas inevitably proved intolerable to the Soviet cultural commissars and he was executed.

continuo (*Italian*) an abbreviation of *basso continuo. See* FIGURED BASS.

contrabass (1) (adjective) describing an instrument that is an OCTAVE lower than the normal BASS of the family, e.g. contrabass TUBA. (2) (noun) a DOUBLE BASS.

contralto the lowest female VOICE, which usually has a range of about two OCTAVES.

contrapuntal relating to COUNTERPOINT.

contratenor the 14th- and 15th-century word for a VOICE with approximately the same range as a TENOR.

contredanse (*French*) a French corruption of 'country dance', i.e. a lively dance.

cor (*French*) *see* French horn *under* HORN.

cor anglais (*French*) literally 'English horn', but it is neither English nor a HORN. It is in fact an ALTO OBOE pitched a FIFTH below the standard oboe.

coranto (*Italian*) *see* COURANTE.

corda (*Italian*) a 'string', as in 'piano string'. The term *una corda* literally means 'one string', an indication to use the 'soft' PEDAL on the PIANO.

cornet (1) a BRASS INSTRUMENT with three valves that has a quality of TONE (3) lying between that of a HORN and a TRUMPET; it has great flexibility and is often used in MILITARY and JAZZ BANDS. (2) an ORGAN STOP used for playing flourishes.

cotillion a popular ballroom dance of the early 19th century.

cottage piano a small upright PIANO.

counterpoint the combination of two or more independent melodic lines that fit together to create a coherent SOUND texture. The CLASSICAL (1) conventions of HARMONY are based on counterpoint.

counter-subject a MELODY, found in a FUGUE, that is CONTRAPUNTAL to the main THEME (SUBJECT), i.e. after singing the subject, a VOICE (2) carries on to sing the counter-subject while the answer is sung.

counter-tenor the highest natural male VOICE (not to be confused with FALSETTO).

country and western a generic term for

a form of 20th-century American folk music, originating from the southeast of the USA, with Nashville, Tennessee, as its traditional home. It is usually played by small BANDS using FIDDLES, GUITARS, BANJOS, and DRUMS etc. The songs are typically of a sentimental, sometimes tragic, nature. Lively BLUEGRASS music is a form of country and western.

couplet (1) the same as DUPLET. (2) a two-note SLUR. (3) a SONG in which the same music is repeated for every STANZA.

courante (*French*) short for *danse courante* or 'running dance', a lively Baroque dance in triple time.

cow bell as used as a PERCUSSION INSTRUMENT in an orchestra, it is an ordinary square cow bell with the clapper taken out. It is played with a drumstick.

crayon *see* CHALK.

credo (*Latin*) 'I believe', the first word in the Roman Catholic Creed.

crescendo (*Italian*) 'increasing', i.e. getting gradually louder.

croche (*French*) an EIGHTH NOTE or quaver.

crook (1) a detachable section of tubing that was inserted into a BRASS or WOODWIND INSTRUMENT between the MOUTHPIECE and the body of the instrument to give it a different KEY (by increasing the length of the air column). Performers often had as many as twelve crooks, but the introduction of valved instruments in the 1850s virtually dispensed with their necessity. (2) a curved metal tube between the mouthpiece and the body of large wind instruments such as the BASSOON and BASS CLARINET.

crooning a soft, sentimental style of singing, often to DANCE MUSIC. Bing Crosby was a noted *crooner*.

cross rhythms rhythms that appear to have conflicting patterns and are performed at the same time as one another.

crotchet *see* QUARTER NOTE.

Cruelty, Theatre of a form of theatre devised by the French actor and theatre director Antonin Artaud (1896–1948) which uses non-verbal means of communication, such as pantomime, light effects, and irrational language, to project the pain and loss fostered by the modern world. His aim was to use drama to subvert the idea of art as a set of concepts separate from

real life and he has had a lasting effect on Western drama.

crumhorn *see* KRUMHORN.

Cubism an art movement started by Picasso and Braque, and influenced by AFRICAN tribal masks and carvings and by the work of Cézanne. They moved away from REALIST and IMPRESSIONIST trends towards a more intellectual representation of objects. Previously, painters had observed subjects from a fixed viewpoint, but the Cubists also wanted to represent a more cerebral understanding of their subject. The result was an explosion of multi-viewpoint images, often broken up into geometric shapes and realigned to suggest faces full on and in profile together, to explain the three-dimensional variety of an object or to imply movement.

cuckoo a short PIPE with a single finger hole; it gives two notes that imitate the sound of the bird.

cue a catchword or note on a score, used to indicate the entrance of a voice or instrument.

curtain music *see* ACT TUNE.

curtall a small BASSOON of the 16th and 17th centuries.

cycle a series or sequence of pieces of music by a single composer that have a common THEME or idea.

cymbalo *see* DULCIMER.

cymbals PERCUSSION INSTRUMENTS comprising two metal plates that are held in the hands and clashed together. They are mounted on stands for JAZZ and popular music DRUM KITS, where they are operated by pedals or struck with sticks.

czárdás a Hungarian dance with two parts (a slow section and a fast section) that alternate.

D (1) the second NOTE of the SCALE of C major. (2) abbreviation for DOMINANT, and for doctor (as in D.Mus., Doctor of Music).

da capo (*abbreviation* **DC**) (*Italian*) 'from the head', an instruction to repeat the beginning of the piece.

Dada an art movement that began in Zurich in 1915. It represented a reaction to postwar disillusion with established art. Leading figures included Jean Arp and the poet Tristan Tzara (1896–1963), and, when the movement spread to New

York, Francis Picabia (1879–1953) and Marcel Duchamp. Its aim was to reject accepted aesthetic and cultural values and to promote an irrational form of non-art or anti-art. The random juxtapositions of COLLAGE and the use of ready-made objects suited their purpose best. A notable example is Duchamp's *Fountain* (1917), which was an unadorned urinal. Dada gave way to NEUE SACHLICHKEIT around 1924 as the artists associated with the movement diversified. It led, however, to the beginnings of SURREALISM and is the source of other movements in ABSTRACT ART, such as ACTION PAINTING.

dal segno (*abbreviation* **DS**) (*Italian*) 'from the sign', i.e. go back to the point in the music marked by the relevant symbol and repeat the music that follows it.

damp the STOPPING of the vibrations of an instrument by touching it, or part of it, e.g. the strings of a HARP, the skin of a DRUM.

Dämpfer (*German*) a MUTE.

Danube School a school of German painters who developed the art of landscape painting as a genre in its own right. Its most prominent member was Albrecht Altdorfer (1480–1538).

DC *see* DA CAPO.

début (*French*) 'beginning', i.e. a first appearance.

decibel one tenth of a BEL, a unit for measuring SOUND. A decibel represents the smallest change in loudness that can be detected by the average human ear.

deciso (*Italian*) literally 'decided', i.e. with decision, or 'play firmly'.

Deconstruction *see* STRUCTURALISM.

decrescendo (*Italian*) 'decreasing', i.e. getting gradually softer.

degree a step of a SCALE; the position of each NOTE on a scale is identified by its degree.

delicatamente (*Italian*) 'delicately'.

delicato (*Italian*) 'delicate'.

demisemiquaver *see* THIRTY-SECOND NOTE.

descant (1) a soprano part, sometimes improvised, sung above a HYMN TUNE while the tune itself is sung by the rest of the congregation or CHOIR. (2) (spelt *discant* by music scholars) a general term for all forms of POLYPHONY used from the 12th century.

De Stijl *see* STIJL, DE.

deus ex machina a Latin term meaning 'god from the machine', i.e. a god introduced into the action of a play to resolve some intractable situation in the plot. The device was used commonly in both Greek and Roman drama. In Greek drama, the intervention took the form of the god being lowered onto the stage via some kind of stage mechanical apparatus. The term has come to denote any twist in a plot that resolves a problem or develops the action in a unexpected way. It became a common feature of Victorian literature and drama in the form of legacies from long-lost relatives enabling otherwise impossible marriages to take place and foiling wicked schemes.

deux temps (*French*) in 2/2 TIME. *Valse à deux temps* is a WALTZ that has only two dance steps to every three BEATS of the BAR.

development the expansion or changing in some way of parts of a THEME of music that have already been heard, e.g. by varying the RHYTHM or elaborating the PHRASE to give it new impetus.

diapason (1) the term given to a family of ORGAN STOPS that are largely responsible for the TONE of the instrument. (2) (*French*) a TUNING FORK; *diapason normal* means the same as CONCERT PITCH.

diatonic belonging to a SCALE. The diatonic NOTES of a major scale consist of five TONES (T) and two SEMITONES (S), arranged TTSTT TS. *Compare* CHROMATIC.

dièse (*French*) sharp.

Dies Irae (*Latin*) 'Day of Wrath', a part of the REQUIEM MASS, with a PLAINSONG MELODY that has often been used by ROMANTIC composers, e.g. Rachmaninov.

digital (1) one of the KEYS on the keyboard of a PIANO or ORGAN. (2) in sound recording, a method of converting audio or analogue signals into a series of pulses according to their voltage for the purposes of storage or manipulation.

diminished interval a PERFECT or MAJOR INTERVAL reduced by one SEMITONE by flattening the upper NOTE or sharpening the lower one.

diminished seventh chord a CHORD that covers a MINOR SEVENTH diminished by one SEMITONE, i.e. C-B flat diminished to C-A.

(This is in fact equivalent to a major sixth, but the term 'diminished seventh' is often used.) It is frequently employed as a means of TRANSITION into another KEY.

diminished seventh chord a MINOR TRIAD in which the FIFTH is flattened (diminished), e.g. in the KEY of C major, C-E-G flat.

diminuendo (*Italian*) 'diminishing', i.e. getting gradually quieter.

diminution the shortening of NOTE TIME-values so that a MELODY is played more quickly, usually at double speed.

diptych a pair of paintings or carvings on two panels hinged together so that they can be opened or closed.

direct a sign placed at the end of a line or page of old music that indicates the PITCH of the following NOTE or notes.

discant *see* DESCANT.

discord a CHORD or combination of NOTES that creates an unpleasant or jarring sound that needs to be resolved.

dissonance the creation of an unpleasant sound or DISCORD.

distemper an impermanent paint made by mixing colours with eggs or glue instead of oil.

divertimento (*plural* **divertimenti**) (*Italian*) an 18th-century term for a piece of music intended to be a light entertainment, i.e. a diversion. Mozart wrote many divertimenti.

divertissement (*French*) (1) a short ballet incorporated into an opera or play. (2) a short piece that includes well-known tunes taken from another source. (3) a DIVERTIMENTO.

divisé (*French*) *see* DIVISI.

divisi (*Italian*) 'divided', a term used to indicate that, where a PART is written in double NOTES, performers should not attempt to play all the notes but should divide themselves into groups to play them. It is particularly used in music for STRINGS.

division (1) a 17th-century type of VARIATION in which the long NOTES of a MELODY were split up into shorter ones. (2) an obsolete term for long vocal RUNS used by composers such as Bach and Handel.

Divisionism *see* POSTIMPRESSIONISM.

Dixieland a simple form of traditional JAZZ that originated in New Orleans at the start of the 20th century.

do (*Italian*) *see* DOH.

docudrama or drama-documentary a programme on radio or television that uses DRAMA (1) to depict real, factual events. It may use actors to portray recorded events from the recent past or combine contemporary film or recordings with dramatic reconstruction.

documentary a programme on radio or television that seeks to portray or document real events.

dodecaphonic relating to dodecaphony, the TWELVE-NOTE SYSTEM of composition.

doh the spoken name for the first NOTE of a MAJOR SCALE in TONIC SOL-FA.

dolce (*Italian*) 'sweet' or 'gentle'.

dolcissimo (*Italian*) 'very sweet'.

dolente (*Italian*) 'sorrowful'.

doloroso (*Italian*) 'sorrowfully'.

domestic tragedy a form of tragedy that appeared in the Elizabethan period and that focuses on the crises of middle-class domestic life in an unpatronising and sympathetic manner. *The London Merchant* (1731) by George Lillo (1693–1739) established the genre as a highly popular (and profitable) one. The form is closely related to SENTIMENTAL COMEDY, and was also influential on the development of MELODRAMA.

dominant (1) the fifth NOTE above the TONIC of a MAJOR or MINOR SCALE. (2) the name given to the RECITING NOTE of GREGORIAN CHANTS.

doppio (*Italian*) 'double', as in *doppio movimento*, meaning 'twice as fast'.

Dorian mode a term applied to the ascending SCALE that is played on the white keys of a PIANO beginning at D.

dot a MARK used in musical NOTATION; when it is placed after a NOTE, it makes the note half as long again; when it is placed above a note it indicates STACCATO.

dotted note *see* DOT.

double (1) a word used to describe certain instruments that are built an OCTAVE lower than normal, e.g. a double BASSOON or *contrabassoon* is built an octave lower than a standard bassoon. (2) a term used to describe a type of VARIATION found in 17th-century French instrumental music in which MELODY NOTES are embellished with ornamentation.

double bass the largest and lowest-pitched of the bowed string instruments. It used to have three strings but now it has four (sometimes five).

double counterpoint COUNTERPOINT in which the two PARTS can change places, i.e. the higher can become the lower and vice versa.

double fugue (1) a FUGUE with two SUBJECTS. In one type of double fugue both subjects are introduced at the start; in another type the second subject appears after the first and the two are eventually combined.

double whole note the longest note and is only occasionally used. Also known as a BREVE.

down beat the downward movement of a conductor's BATON or hand, which usually indicates the first BEAT of a BAR.

Doxologia Magna (*Latin*) the 'Gloria in Excelsis Deo'. *See* GLORIA.

D'Oyly Carte Company a company founded by the English impresario Richard D'Oyly-Carte (1844–1901) to perform the operas of Gilbert and Sullivan (whom he had brought together) for which he built the Savoy Theatre in London.

drama (1) a PLAY for the stage, radio or television. (2) dramatic literature as a genre.

dramatic irony a situation in which a character in a PLAY, NOVEL, etc, says or does something that has a meaning for the audience or reader, other than the obvious meaning, that he or she does not understand. Its use is common in both COMEDY and TRAGEDY.

drone (1) a PIPE that sounds a continuous NOTE of fixed PITCH as a permanent BASS. The BAGPIPES, for example, have several drone pipes. (2) a similar effect produced by stringed instruments fitted with 'drone strings'.

drum a PERCUSSION INSTRUMENT of which there are numerous types, including BASS DRUM, SIDE DRUM, TABOR, TENOR DRUM, and TIMPANI. Most drums consist of a hollow metal or wood cylinder over which is stretched a skin. Sound is produced by beating the skin with drumsticks or with the hands.

drum kit a set of DRUMS and CYMBALS arranged in such a way that they can all be played by one person sitting on a stool. They are used by JAZZ and POP drummers and can vary enormously in size.

DS *see* DAL SEGNO.

due corde (*Italian*) literally 'two strings', a term used in VIOLIN music indicating that a PASSAGE that could theoretically be played on one string should nevertheless be played on two to produce the desired effect.

duet a combination of two performers, e.g. a vocal duet, or a composition for such a pair, e.g. a piano duet.

dulcimer or cymbalo an ancient instrument that was introduced into Europe from the East in the Middle Ages. It consists of a shallow box over which strings are stretched. The instrument is placed on the knees and the strings are struck with small HAMMERS.

dulcitone a keyboard instrument containing TUNING FORKS that are struck with HAMMERS, as in a PIANO.

duplet a group of two NOTES of equal value that are played in the time normally taken by three.

duple time a form of musical TIME in which the number of BEATS in a BAR is a multiple of two, e.g. 2/4 (2 CROTCHETS) and 6/8 (6 QUAVERS in two groups of three).

dur (*German*) 'major', as in MAJOR KEY.

dynamic accents ACCENTS that correspond to the regular RHYTHM of a piece of music, as indicated by the TIME SIGNATURE.

E the third note (MEDIANT) of the SCALE of C major.

écossaise abbreviation of *danse écossaise*, i.e. 'Scottish dance', but in fact the term has little to do with Scottish dancing and merely refers to a quick dance in 2/4 TIME.

Eight, The a group of American painters, for the most part REALIST painters who campaigned vigorously on the development of progressive art away from the strictures of academic tradition. *See also* ASHCAN SCHOOL.

eighth note a NOTE that is half the length of a QUARTER NOTE (crotchet) and an eighth of a WHOLE NOTE (semibreve). Also known as a quaver. Indicated by the symbol ♪.

electronic instruments a generic term for instruments that convert electrical energy into sound, such as the SYNTHESIZER.

embouchure (1) the mouthpiece of a BRASS or WIND INSTRUMENT. (2) the correct tensioning of the lips and facial muscles when playing woodwind and brass instruments to create good TONE.

encore (*French*) 'again', the call from an English audience (the French equivalent is BIS) for more music. If the performance does continue, the additional music is also known as an 'encore'.

end pin *see* TAIL PIN.

engraving (1) a technique of cutting an image into a metal or wood plate using special tools. When ink is applied to the plate, the raised parts will print black and the engraved parts white. (2) a print produced in this way.

enharmonic intervals INTERVALS that are so small that they do not exist on keyboard instruments.

ensemble (*French*) literally 'together', a term meaning a group of players or singers, a MOVEMENT in OPERA for several singers, or the precision with which such a group performs together.

entr'acte (*French*) the music played between the acts of a play or OPERA. *See also* ACT TUNE; INTERLUDE; INTERMEZZO.

epic (1) a very long narrative poem dealing with heroic deeds and adventures on a grand scale, as Homer's *Iliad*. (2) a novel or film with some of these qualities.

episode (1) in A FUGUE, a PASSAGE that connects entries of the SUBJECT. (2) in A RONDO, a contrasting section that separates entries of the PRINCIPAL THEME.

epistolary novel a novel in the form of a series of letters written to and from the main characters, sometimes presented by the author in the anonymous role of 'editor'. The form flourished in the 18th century, an example being Samuel Richardson's *Pamela* (1741). The first draft of Jane Austen's *Sense and Sensibility* (1797–8), entitled *Elinor and Marianne*, was originally in epistolary form.

equal temperament a convenient, but technically incorrect, way of tuning a keyboard in which all SEMITONES are considered equal, e.g. F sharp and G flat are taken to be identical NOTES when theoretically they are not. Such a system makes complex MODULATIONS practicable.

escapement the mechanism in a PIANO that releases the HAMMER, allowing a string to vibrate freely after it has been struck.

espressivo (*Italian*) 'expressively'.

esquisse (*French*) a 'sketch', a title sometimes given to short instrumental pieces.

esthetics *see* AESTHETICS.

estinto (*Latin*) literally 'extinct', i.e. as soft as possible.

etching (1) a technique of making an engraving in a metal plate, using acid to bite out the image rather than tools. Tones of black or grey can be produced, depending on the extent the acid is allowed to bite. (2) a print produced in this way.

étude (*French*) a 'study' or piece of music evolved from a single PHRASE or idea. Studies are also written purely as exercises to improve technique or FINGERING.

euphonium a large BRASS INSTRUMENT, a tenor TUBA, that is mainly used in BRASS and MILITARY BANDS.

eurhythmics a system of teaching musical RHYTHM by graceful physical movements. It was invented in 1905 by the Swiss composer and teacher Émile Jaques-Dalcroze (1865–1950).

evensong *see* NUNC DIMITTIS.

Existentialism a philosophical position based on a perception of life in which man is an actor forced to make choices in an essentially meaningless universe that functions as a colossal and cruel Theatre of the ABSURD. The main writers associated with Existentialism are French, notably Sartre and Camus, and the bilingual Beckett. The roots of Existentialism are complex; one important source is NIHILISM, the influence of which is apparent in Camus' novel *The Outsider* (1942). Another important source is the Danish theologian Søren Kierkegaard, who observed that life must be lived forwards but can only be understood backwards.

exposition (1) in the SONATA FORM, the first section of a piece in which the main THEMES are introduced before they are developed. (2) in FUGUE, the initial statement of the SUBJECT by each of the PARTS.

Expressionism a term, derived from the character of some 20th-century Northern European art, that was coined in a description of an exhibition of

Fauvist and Cubist paintings at the Berlin Sezession in 1911 but quickly came to be applied to the works of Die Brücke and Der Blaue Reiter. Expressionist works represented a move away from the observational detachment of Realism and, to an extent, Impressionist trends, and were concerned with conveying the artist's feelings and emotions as aroused by his subject. Any painting technique that helped to express these feelings was considered a valid medium and included bold, free brushwork, distorted or stylised forms and vibrant, often violently clashing, colours. The term *expressionist* also refers to an expressive quality of distortion or heightened colour in art from any period or place. *See also* abstract expressionism. In music it is used to imply the expression of inner emotions.

extemporisation *see* improvisation.

F (1) the fourth note (or subdominant) of the scale of C major. (2) in abbreviations, *f* means *forte* (loud); *ff*, *fortissimo* (very loud); and *fp, forte piano* (loud and then soft).

fa in the tonic sol-fa, the fourth degree in any major scale.

fado (*Portuguese*) a type of melancholy song with a guitar accompaniment.

false relation in harmony, the occurrence of a note bearing an accidental that is immediately followed, in another part, by the same note, which does not bear an accidental, or vice versa.

falsetto (*Italian*) an adult male voice, used in the register above its normal range. It has often been used to comic effect in operas.

fancy *see* fantasia.

fandango a lively Spanish dance, thought to be South American in origin, in triple time. It is usually accompanied by guitar and castanets. Composers who have included or adapted the fandango form include Mozart in the opera *The Marriage of Figaro*, and Rimsky-Korsakov in his *Capriccio Espagnol*.

fanfare a flourish of trumpets or other instruments (e.g. the organ) that imitate the sound of trumpets.

fantasia (*Italian*) a piece in which the composer follows his imagination in free

association rather than composing within a particular conventional form. When such a piece is played, it can sound as if it is being improvised (*see* improvisation). It is also a composer's adaptation or use of another's theme, e.g. Vaughan Williams's *Fantasia on a theme by Thomas Tallis*.

Fantasie (*German*), **fantaisie** (*French*) a fantasia.

Fauvists a group of French painters, including Matisse and Derain, who painted in a particularly vivid and colourful style. The term *fauve* ('wild animal') was coined as a form of derogatory criticism of an exhibition held at the Salon d'Automne of 1905. Their use of strong, bright colours to express their response to the fierce light of the Mediterranean coast owes something to the influence of Gauguin and Van Gogh, but they were less interested in representing what they saw and more concerned to express their own feelings in the boldness and freedom of their compositions.

fauxbourdon (*French*) a 15th-century continental technique of improvising a bass part for a plainsong melody.

feminine cadence an ending in which the final chord occurs on a weak beat of the bar and not the more usual strong beat.

fermata (*Italian*) *see* pause.

ff *see* F (2).

fiddle (1) a generic term for a range of primitive stringed instruments played with a bow, as used in parts of Asia, Africa, and Eastern Europe. (2) a colloquial term for a violin, especially in relation to folk music.

fife a small flute still used in 'drum and fife' bands.

fifth an interval of five notes (the first and last notes are counted) or seven semitones, e.g. from C to G.

figurative art or representational art art that recognisably represents figures, objects or animals from real life. *Compare* abstract art.

figure a short musical phrase that is repeated in the course of a composition.

figured bass the bass part of a composition, which has numerical figures written below the notes to indicate how the harmony above should be played. It is, in effect, a type of musical shorthand in which the bass line and melody are written down while the numbers indicate which chords should be played. The system was used during the 17th and early 18th centuries.

finale (*Italian*) (1) the last movement of a work. (2) the concluding section of an opera act.

fine arts *see* APPLIED ARTS.

fingering a type of notation that indicates which fingers should be used to play a piece of music.

fino (*Italian*) 'as far as', so *fino al segno* means 'as far as the sign'.

fioritura (*Italian*) 'flowering', i.e. an embellishment.

fipple flute *see* FLAGEOLET; RECORDER.

Five, The the name given to a group of nationalistic 19th-century Russian composers who were known in Russia as *moguchaya kuchka* ('the mighty handful'). The five were Rimsky-Korsakov, Mily Alexeyevich Balakirev (1837–1910), Aleksandr Borodin (1833–87), César Antonovich Cui (1835–1918), and Mussorgsky.

flageolet a small, end-blown FLUTE with six holes, four in front and two at the back, popular in the 17th century.

flamenco a generic term for a type of Spanish song from Andalusia, usually sad and often accompanied by guitar and dancing. Flamenco guitar playing relies heavily on the strumming of powerful, dynamic rhythms.

flat (1) a note that is lowered by one SEMITONE as indicated by the flat sign (b). (2) a note (or notes) produced at too low a pitch and hence 'out of tune'.

flue pipes all ORGAN pipes that have narrow openings, or flues, into which air passes; the other pipes are REED PIPES.

Flügelhorn (*German*) a soprano brass instrument similar to a BUGLE in shape but with three PISTONS.

flute (1) the tranverse or German flute is a member of the WOODWIND family of instruments but these days it is normally made of silver or other metal. One end of the instrument is stopped and sound is produced by blowing across the mouthpiece formed around an aperture cut into the side of the instrument at the stopped end. The pitch is controlled by means of a lever system. (2) the English flute is a beaked, end-blown,

wind instrument with finger holes, now more usually called the RECORDER.

folia (*Portuguese*) 'the folly', a wild and noisy Portuguese dance.

folk dance any dance, performed by ordinary people in a pre-industrial society, that has evolved over the years and gained a traditional form. Folk dances differ widely in character, and some have symbolic significance, such as war dances, etc.

folk song properly, any song that has been preserved by oral tradition. Many composers and pop musicians have written new compositions that imitate old folk songs.

form the structure of a COMPOSITION. The basic elements of musical composition that define a given piece's form are repetition, variation, and contrast. Examples of recognised forms include FUGUE, RONDO, SONATA FORM, etc.

forte (*abbreviation* f) (*Italian*) 'loud'.

fortepiano (*Italian*) an early word for PIANOFORTE, not to be confused with FORTE PIANO.

forte piano (*abbreviation* fp) (*Italian*) 'loud then soft'.

fortissimo (*abbreviation* ff) (*Italian*) 'very loud'.

forza (*Italian*) 'force', so *con forza* means 'with force'.

forzato (*Italian*) 'forced'.

found object or objet trouvé a form of art that began with DADA and continued with SURREALISM, where an object, either natural or manufactured, is displayed as a piece of art in its own right.

fourth an INTERVAL of four notes (including the first and last) or five SEMITONES, e.g. C to F.

foxtrot a dance, originating in the USA, in duple time. It first became popular in the ballroom from about 1912. It was at the height of its popularity in the 1930s and 1940s, by which time it had acquired two variations, the quick and the slow foxtrot.

fp *see* FORTE PIANO.

free reed a type of REED found in such instruments as the ACCORDION and HARMONICA. It consists of a small metal tongue that vibrates freely in a metal slot when air is blown over it. The PITCH of the reed is determined by its thickness and length.

French horn *see* HORN.

French sixth *see* AUGMENTED SIXTH.

fresco a painting directly painted on to a wall that has previously been covered with a damp, freshly laid layer of lime plaster, the paint and plaster reacting chemically to become stable and permanent. Fresco painting worked particularly well in the warm, dry climate of Italy, where it reached its peak in the 16th century.

fret (*French*) one of a series of thin pieces of metal fitted into the wooden fingerboard of a stringed instrument to make the STOPPING of strings easier and more accurate. Each fret represents the position of a specific note.

front man the person standing at the front of the stage during a performance of JAZZ who is therefore the focus of the audience's attention. He or she is often, but not always, the leader or singer of the band.

fugue a contrapuntal composition for two or more parts (commonly called *voices*) that enter successively in imitation of each other. The first entry is called the SUBJECT and the second entry (a fifth higher or lower than the subject) is called the ANSWER. When all the voices have entered, the EXPOSITION is complete and is usually followed by an EPISODE that connects to the next series of subject entries. A COUNTERSUBJECT is a melodic accompaniment to the subject and answer, and is often in DOUBLE COUNTERPOINT. A fugue may be written for voices, instruments, or both. The form dates back to the 17th century. Possibly the greatest exponent of the fugue was Johann Sebastian Bach, and his *Art of Fugue* is the fullest statement of the form.

full close *see* CADENCE.

full organ a term used in ORGAN music to indicate that all the loud STOPS are to be used together.

funk a form of heavily syncopated, rhythmic Black dance music, originating in the United States. The adjective, often used in JAZZ terminology, is *funky.*

fuoco (*Italian*) 'fire', so *con fuoco* means 'with fire'.

furioso (*Italian*) 'furious'.

Futurism a movement of writers and artists, originating in early 20th-century Italy, that extolled the virtues of the new, dynamic machine age, which was reckoned to have rendered the aesthetic standards of the past redundant. The founding document of the movement is the poet Filipo Marinetti's (1876–1944) *Futurist Manifesto* of 1909, which, in literature, called for the destruction of traditional sentence construction and the establishment of a 'free verse in free words', owing nothing to the literary standards of the past. The English variant of Futurism is VORTICISM, which included writers such as Wyndham Lewis and Ezra Pound. The Russian variant, *Russian Futurism*, was led by the poet Vladimir Mayakovsky (1893–1930). Futurism became a spent force by the 1930s, largely because of its close association with Fascism. In art, Boccioni was among the painters in the group, whose aim was to convey a sense of movement and dynamism. The original group of painters had broken up by the end of World War I, but their work and ideas had a resounding influence on subsequent art movements.

fz abbreviation for FORZATO.

G the fifth note (or DOMINANT) of the scale of C major.

galant (*French*) 'polite', a term applied to certain graceful styles of court music, especially of the 18th century.

galanterie an 18th-century German term for a keyboard piece in the GALANT style.

galliard (*French*) a lively court dance, usually in triple time, that dates back to the 16th century.

galop a lively dance in duple time that originated in Germany and was popular in the 19th century.

gamelan a type of traditional orchestra found principally in Indonesia and Southeast Asia. Although such an orchestra includes strings and woodwind instruments, it is the array of gongs, drums, chimes, xylophones, and marimbas that produces the unique and highly complex rhythms of gamelan music.

gamut (1) the note G on the bottom line of the bass clef. (2) an alternative (now obsolete) word for the key of G. (3) the whole range of musical sounds, from lowest to highest.

gavotte an old French dance, originally of the upper Alps, in 4/4 time, which usually starts on the third beat of the bar. It was favoured by Lully in his ballets and operas and was revived in the 20th century by such composers as Prokofiev and Schoenberg.

gedämpft (*German*) 'muted'.

Generalpause (*abbreviation* **GP**) (*German*) a rest of one or more bars for all the members of an orchestra.

genre a distinctive type or category of artistic or literary composition.

genre painting a painting that has as its subject a scene from everyday life, as opposed to a historical event, mythological scene, etc.

German sixth *see* AUGMENTED SIXTH.

gigue (*French*) a lively dance or jig.

giocoso (*Italian*) 'merry'.

gioioso (*Italian*) 'joyful'.

giusto (*Italian*) 'exact', as in *tempo giusto*, which can mean either 'strict time' or 'appropriate speed'.

Glasgow Boys or Glasgow School a group of painters centred in Glasgow in the 1880s and 1890s. They represented a move away from academic strictures and were inspired by the plein air BARBIZON SCHOOL. They established an outpost of the European vogue for NATURALISM and ROMANTIC lyricism in landscape painting, and their influence extended into the 20th century.

glass harmonica at its simplest, a set of goblets that are played by rubbing a moistened finger around the rims. This idea was taken further by Benjamin Franklin, who invented a glass harmonica in which a gradated series of glass bowls is fixed to a rotating spindle and played with the fingers. Beethoven and Mozart wrote music for the instrument, which produces a high-pitched humming sound.

glee a simple, unaccompanied composition for male voices in several sections.

glissando (*Italian*) 'sliding', a rapid sliding movement up or down a scale.

Glockenspiel (*German*) **or campanelli** (*Italian*) literally 'a play of bells', an instrument, produced in a variety of sizes, comprising steel bars of different lengths that are arranged like a keyboard, each bar sounding a different note. Played with hammers, it produces sounds that have a bell-like quality.

Gloria (*Latin*) the first word of *Gloria in excelsis Deo* ('Glory to God in the highest'), the hymn used in both Roman Catholic and Anglican services. Many composers have set it to music. It is also the first word of the doxology *Gloria Patri* ('Glory be to the Father'), sung after a psalm.

gong a PERCUSSION INSTRUMENT that originated in the Far East. Gongs are made in many sizes and shapes, but an orchestral gong consists of nothing more than a large sheet of metal with a pronounced rim. Sound is produced by striking it with a hammer.

gospel song a type of popular religious song originated by African-American slaves who sang hymns to pulsating BLUES rhythms. Such songs, which are still sung fervently today in religious services, were one of the originating forces of JAZZ.

Gothic a style of architecture that lasted from the 12th to the 16th centuries in Northern Europe and Spain. Its effect on art was to produce the INTERNATIONAL GOTHIC style.

Gothic novel a type of NOVEL that was enormously popular in the late 18th century, combining elements of the supernatural, macabre or fantastic, often in wildly ROMANTIC settings. The heroes and/or heroines, whether medieval or modern, for the most part speak in a formal, stilted language curiously at odds with the appalling situations they find themselves in. Horace Walpole's *The Castle of Otranto* (1764) and *The Mysteries of Udolpho* (1794) by Ann Radcliffe (1764–1823) are among the best-known examples of the genre.

gouache or poster paint or body paint an opaque mixture of watercolour paint and white pigment.

GP an abbreviation of GENERAL PAUSE.

grace note an ornamental, extra note, usually written in small type, used to embellish a melody.

grandioso (*Italian*) 'in an imposing manner'.

grand opera a term originally used to distinguish serious OPERA, sung throughout, from opera that contained some spoken dialogue. The term is now also used to describe a lavish production.

grand orchestre (*French*) a full orchestra.

grand orgue (*French*) a great ORGAN (as opposed to a swell organ, etc).

grand piano *see* PIANOFORTE.

grand staff a STAFF created by pushing the staff with the treble clef and the staff with the bass clef closer together so that both can be located on one exaggerated staff.

grave (*Italian*) 'slow' or 'solemn'.

grazia (*Italian*) 'grace'.

grazioso (*Italian*) 'gracefully'.

great stave *see* GRAND STAFF.

Gregorian chant a term that refers to the large collection of ancient solo and chorus PLAINSONG melodies preserved by the Roman Catholic Church. They are named after Pope Gregory I (*c.* 540–604) but date from about 800.

grisaille a monochrome painting made using only shades of grey, often used as a sketch for oil paintings.

grotesque a term for a style of ornamentation that began in Roman times and reached its height with ROCOCO. It consisted of a series of figurative or floral ornaments in decorative frames that are linked by festoons.

ground bass a BASS line that is constantly repeated throughout a composition, as a foundation for variation in the upper parts.

grupetto (*Italian*) a 'little group', a general term used to describe various ORNAMENTS of one or more decorative notes.

Guarneri or Guarnerius a violin made by one of several members of a famous Italian family of violin-makers who were based in Cremona in the 17th and 18th centuries.

guitar a plucked STRING instrument that may have been introduced to Spain from North Africa. It has a flat back and usually carries six strings suspended over a fretted finger-board (12-string guitars were favoured by certain BLUES musicians). The *acoustic* (*sound-box*) *guitar* has been played by classical, FLAMENCO, and FOLK musicians for generations, but the *electric guitar* is a comparatively new development. The body may be hollow (or semi-acoustic) or solid, with pick-ups (electrically motivated resonators that respond to the vibration of the strings) mounted under the BRIDGE. The vibrations received by the pick-ups have to be electrically amplified or else they are virtually featureless. Electric guitars have a huge COMPASS.

gusto (*Italian*) 'taste', so *con gusto* means 'with taste'.

H (*German*) B natural.

habanera (*Spanish*) a dance of Cuban origin with a powerful, SYNCOPATED RHYTHM, most usually associated, however, with Spain.

Hague School a school of Dutch landscape painters, one of whose prominent leaders was Anton Mauve (1838–88) who painted small, delicately lit landscapes that show the influence of Millet.

haiku a 17-syllable sequential verse form devised by the Japanese poet Basho (1644–94).

half note formerly the shortest in time value, with half the value of a WHOLE NOTE (semibreve). Also known as a minim. Indicated by the symbol ♩.

half step a SEMITONE.

Hallé Orchestra an internationally famous orchestra founded in Manchester in 1848 by the German-born conductor and pianist Sir Charles Hallé (1819–95).

halling a lively Norwegian dance, in 2/4 TIME, in the course of which men leap high up into the air.

hammer (1) the part of the PIANO mechanism that strikes the strings. (2) a mallet for playing the DULCIMER. (3) the clapper of a BELL.

Hammond organ the brand name of an electric ORGAN first produced by the Hammond Organ Company, Chicago, in 1935. The sound it produces is electronically manufactured and attempts to reproduce the sound of the PIPE ORGAN. Its unique temperament has been exploited by JAZZ, POP and music-hall musicians the world over.

handbells bells, of various PITCH, that are held in the hands of a group of performers and rung in sequence to create a tune.

hardanger fiddle a Norwegian VIOLIN used in FOLK music. It is somewhat smaller than an ordinary violin and has four SYMPATHETIC STRINGS.

harmonica or mouth organ a small, FREE-REED instrument. Although it is a small and apparently inconsequential instrument, many BLUES and FOLK musicians have illustrated its potential by exploiting its emotive power.

harmonic minor a MINOR SCALE containing the minor sixth with the MAJOR SEVENTH, in which ascent and descent are without alteration.

harmonics the sounds that can be produced on stringed instruments by lightly touching a string at one of its harmonic nodes, i.e. at a half-length of a string, quarter-length, etc.

harmonium a small, portable REED-ORGAN developed in the 19th century. Air is pumped to the REEDS (which are controlled by STOPS and KEYS) by PEDALS worked continuously by the feet.

harmony (1) the simultaneous sounding of two or more NOTES, i.e CHORDS. A harmonious SOUND is an agreeable or pleasant sound (CONCORD); but harmonisation may also produce sounds that, to some ears at least, are unpleasant (*see* DISCORD). (2) the structure and relationship of chords.

harp an instrument, of ancient origin, consisting of strings stretched across an open frame. It is played by plucking the strings, each of which is tuned (*see* TUNING) to a separate NOTE.

harpsichord a keyboard instrument, developed in the 14th and 15th centuries in which the strings are plucked (not struck) by quills or tongues (PLECTRA). The tongues are connected to the KEYS by a simple lever mechanism. The harpsichord went out of favour in the late 18th century following the introduction of the PIANO. It has seen a revival, however, and new compositions have been written for it.

hautbois (*French*) 'high' or 'loud wood'. *See* OBOE. From the Elizabethan period to the 18th century, the English equivalent was *hautboy*.

Hawaiian guitar a style of GUITAR playing in which a steel bar is moved up and down the strings (as opposed to the more usual STOPPING of strings with the fingers) to produce a distinctive slurred sound. The guitar is usually played horizontally.

head voice the upper register of a VOICE, so called because the sound seems to vibrate in the head of the singer. *Compare* CHEST VOICE.

Heckelphone a double-REED instrument, effectively a baritone OBOE. It was used by Richard Strauss in his opera *Salomé*.

heel *see* POINT.

Heldentenor (*German*) a 'heroic tenor', i.e. a tenor with a strong voice suitable for Wagner's heroic roles.

hemiola a RHYTHM in which two BARS in triple TIME are played as though they were three bars in DUPLE TIME.

hemidemisemiquaver see SIXTY-FOURTH NOTE.

heroic tragedy a form of tragedy that became very popular during the RESTORATION. Such tragedies were usually written in bombastic rhymed couplets and featured the adventures in love and war of noble characters in exotic locations, past and present. The characteristic conflict at the heart of such plays was the clash between the equally imperious commands of love and duty.

heterophony (*Greek*) literally 'difference of sounds', i.e. two or more performers playing different versions of the same MELODY simultaneously.

hexachord a SCALE of six NOTES that was used in medieval times.

High Mass MASS that is sung throughout, as distinguished from Low Mass, which is spoken.

history painting a genre of painting that takes as its subject a scene from history, religious or mythological legend, or from great works of literature, e.g. by Dante or Shakespeare.

hocket (*French*) the breaking up of a MELODY into very short PHRASES or single NOTES, with RESTS in between them.

homophony a term applied to music in which the PARTS move 'in step' and do not have independent RHYTHMS. *Compare* POLYPHONY.

hook *see* BEAM

hootenanny a small festival of FOLK music.

horn a BRASS INSTRUMENT consisting of a conical tube coiled into a spiral and ending in a bell. The lips are pushed into a funnel-shaped MOUTHPIECE. The modern orchestral horn is called the *French horn* (because that is where it was developed) and is fitted with three (sometimes four, sometimes seven) valves that open and close various lengths of tubing so that the PITCH of the NOTES can be changed. There are two common 'horns', which are in fact WOODWIND instruments, the BASSET HORN (ALTO CLARINET) and the English horn or COR ANGLAIS (alto OBOE).

hornpipe (1) a single-REED WIND INSTRUMENT played in Celtic countries. (2) a 16th-century dance in triple TIME, originally accompanied by the hornpipe and later erroneously associated with sailors.

Hosanna (*Hebrew*) 'Save now', part of the SANCTUS in the MASS.

Hudson River School a group of American landscape painters who were active in the mid-19th century and whose work was concerned with the beauty and mysticism of nature, expressed in romantic terms on a grand and noble scale.

humoresque (*French*) **or Humoreske** (*German*) a word used by, e.g. Schumann, as the title for a short, lively piece of music.

humours, theory of (in medieval medical theory) any of the four body fluids: blood, phlegm, yellow (choleric) bile and black (melancholic) bile. It is the basis for the *comedy of humours*, notably Jonson's *Every Man in his Humour*(1598), whose characters have names and behaviour appropriate to their dominant 'humour' or personality trait. For humour in the modern sense *see* WIT.

hurdy-gurdy a medieval stringed instrument, shaped like a VIOL. A wooden wheel, coated in RESIN, is cranked at one end to make all the strings resonate. The strings are stopped by rods operated by KEYS. The hurdy-gurdy was often used to provide dance music.

hymn in the Christian Church, a poem sung to music in praise of God.

icon or ikon a religious image, usually painted on a wooden panel, regarded as sacred in the Byzantine Church and then by the Orthodox Churches of Russia and Greece. The word comes from the Greek *eikon* ('likeness'), and strict rules were devised as to the subject, generally a saint, and to the form of the painting and its use, so although icon painting flourished in the 6th century it is extremely difficult to date icons painted then or later. A reaction to what was considered idolatry took place in the 8th century, resulting in *iconoclasm*, the destruction of such images.

iconography or iconology the study and interpretation of representations in figurative art and their symbolic meanings. It is particularly important in the understanding of Christian art, especially of the medieval and RENAISSANCE periods.

idée fixe (*French*) 'fixed idea', i.e. a recurring theme.

idiophone any instrument in which SOUND is produced by the VIBRATION of the instrument itself, e.g. CYMBALS, BELLS, CASTANETS etc.

ikon *see* ICON.

Imagism a poetry movement of the early 20th century that advocated using everyday language and precise representation of the image of the subject discussed. Imagist poems were short and to the point, anti-ROMANTIC and anti-Victorian in tone, and could be on any subject under the sun. Prominent Imagists included Pound and Amy Lowell (1874–1925), whose *Tendencies in Modern American Poetry* (1917) has the best introduction to the movement.

imitation a device in COUNTERPOINT whereby a PHRASE is sung successively by different VOICES.

impasto an Italian word used to describe the thickness and textures that can be achieved with acrylic or oil paint.

imperioso (*Italian*) 'imperiously'.

impetuoso (*Italian*) 'impetuously'.

Impressionism an art movement originating in France in the 1860s, centred on a fairly diverse group of artists who held eight exhibitions together between 1874 and 1886. The main artists were Cézanne, Degas, Manet, Monet, Morisot, Pissarro, Pierre Renoir, and Sisley. The name of the movement was coined by critics from a painting by Monet in the 1874 exhibition entitled *Impression: Soleil Levant*. The Impressionists were concerned with representing day-to-day existence in an objective and realistic manner, and they rejected the ROMANTIC idea that a painting should convey strong emotions. They wanted to record the fleeting effects of light and movement, so their usual subjects were landscapes or social scenes like streets and cafés. They were on the whole much freer in their use of unusual colours and a lighter palette. Impressionism has had an enormous influence on almost every subsequent major art movement.

By analogy, Impressionism is also used to identify certain types of atmospheric music, such as the music of Debussy and Ravel.

impromptu a type of PIANO music that sounds as if it has been improvised, i.e. written in a free and easy style.

improvisation or extemporisation the art of playing or 'inventing' music that has not already been composed, i.e. spontaneous COMPOSITION. Some forms of music (especially JAZZ) often rely heavily on the ability of performers to improvise certain sections.

in alt *see* ALT.

incalzando (*Italian*) 'pressing forward', i.e. working up speed and force.

incidental music music written to accompany the action in a play or film, but the term is also commonly applied to OVERTURES and INTERLUDES.

inciso (*Italian*) 'incisive', hence an instruction that a strong RHYTHM is required.

indeciso (*Italian*) 'undecided', i.e. the pace of a piece of music can be varied according to the performer's feelings.

indeterminacy a term used by John Cage to describe music that does not follow a rigid NOTATION but leaves certain events to chance or allows performers to make their own decisions when performing it.

inflected note a NOTE with an ACCIDENTAL placed before it, i.e. it is sharpened or flattened.

inner parts the PARTS of a piece of music excluding the highest and lowest; e.g. in a work for SOPRANO, ALTO, TENOR, and BASS, the alto and tenor roles are inner parts.

In nomine (*Latin*) 'In the name of the Lord', a type of CANTUS FIRMUS used by English composers of the 16th century. It was first used by Taverner in his setting of *In nomine Domini* for one of his Masses.

instrument in music, a device on which or with which music can be played. There are five traditional categories of instrument: WOODWIND, BRASS, PERCUSSION, KEYBOARD, and STRING. However, ELECTRONIC and MECHANICAL INSTRUMENTS also exist.

instrumentation *see* ORCHESTRATION.

intaglio the cutting into a stone or other material or the etching or engraving on a metal plate of an image, the opposite of RELIEF. Intaglio printing techniques include ENGRAVING and ETCHING.

interior monologue a form of STREAM OF CONSCIOUSNESS narrative technique employed by the English novelist Dorothy Richardson (1873–1957) that anticipated Joyce's use of the technique in *Ulysses* (the device was not really new; similar effects can be found in, e.g. Dickens).

interlude a short PART of a complete composition, e.g. a piece of music performed between the acts of an opera. *See also* ACT TUNE; ENTR'ACTE; INTERMEZZO.

intermezzo (*Italian*) (1) a short piece of piano music. (2) a short comic opera performed between the acts of a serious opera, especially in the 16th and 17th centuries. *See also* ACT TUNE; ENTR'ACTE; INTERLUDE.

International Gothic a predominant style in European art covering the period between the end of the Byzantine era and the beginning of the RENAISSANCE, i.e. *c*.1375–*c*.1425. The most influential centres were Italy, France and the Netherlands. Ideas spread widely thanks to an increase in the art trade, to travelling artists, and to a certain amount of rivalry over royal commissions. International Gothic style was characterised by decorative detail and refined, flowing lines; figures were often elongated or distorted to increase an appearance of elegant charm and the use of gilts and rich colours figured strongly. Scale and perspective were more symbolic than naturalistic, although naturalism began to take hold in the later works of the period.

interpretation the way in which a performer plays a piece of composed music. No composer can possibly indicate exactly how a piece should be played and, to some degree, it is up to the performer to play it as he or she thinks fit.

interval the gap or 'sound distance', expressed numerically, between any two NOTES, i.e. the difference in PITCH between two notes. For example, the interval between C and G is called a FIFTH because G is the fifth note from C. *Perfect intervals* are intervals that remain the same in

MAJOR and MINOR KEYS (i.e. FOURTHS, fifths, OCTAVES.)

intonation a term used to describe the judgment of PITCH by a performer.

intone to sing on one NOTE. A priest may intone during a Roman Catholic or Anglican service.

introduction a section, often slow, found at the start of certain pieces of music, notably SYMPHONIES and SUITES.

Introit an ANTIPHON, usually sung in conjunction with a PSALM verse, in the Roman Catholic and Anglican LITURGIES.

invention a title used by Bach for his two-part keyboard pieces in CONTRAPUNTAL form.

inversion a term that literally means turning upside-down. It can refer to a CHORD, INTERVAL, THEME, MELODY, or COUNTERPOINT. For example, an *inverted interval* is an interval in which one NOTE changes by an OCTAVE to the other side, as it were, of the other note.

Ionian mode a MODE which, on the PIANO, uses the white NOTES from C to C.

irlandais (*French*) 'in Irish style'.

isorhythm a term used to describe a short RHYTHM pattern that is repeatedly applied to an existing MELODY which already has an distinct rhythm.

Italian sixth *see* AUGMENTED SIXTH.

italiano (*Italian*) **or italienne** (*French*) 'in Italian style'.

Jacobean tragedy in the Jacobean period, a development of REVENGE TRAGEDY. The distinction between Jacobean and revenge tragedy is a disputed one, hinging on the supposed wave of cynicism and pessimism that is alleged by some to have accompanied the accession of James VI of Scotland to the English throne. The debate is a complex one, but it is undoubtedly the case that tragedies such as Shakespeare's *Hamlet*, Middleton's *The Changeling* and Webster's *The White Devil* and *The Duchess of Malfi* display an obsession with political and sexual corruption. The language of these plays is highly sophisticated, ironic and coldly brilliant.

jam session a 20th-century slang expression for an occasion when a group of musicians join forces to improvise music (*see* IMPROVISATION). It is usually only appropriate to JAZZ, BLUES, and ROCK music.

Janissary music the music of Turkish MILITARY BANDS which influenced European composers during the 18th century. It is particularly associated with CYMBALS, DRUMS and TAMBOURINES.

jazz a term used to describe a style of music that evolved in the southern states of the USA at the turn of the 20th century. It owes a great deal to the RHYTHMS and idioms of BLUES and SPIRITUALS, but many of the favoured instruments (e.g. SAXOPHONE, TRUMPET and TROMBONE) were European in origin. Jazz traditionally relies upon a strong rhythm 'section', comprising BASS and DRUMS, which provides a springboard for other instruments. Jazz developed from being a form of music played in the back streets of New Orleans to a sophisticated art form performed by small dedicated groups as well as 'BIG BANDS' or 'jazz orchestras'. Self-expression, and therefore IMPROVISATION, has always been a crucial aspect of jazz, and this has allowed many individuals (such as Louis Armstrong and Benny Goodman) to blossom and further its cause. *See also* BEBOP.

Jazz Modern *see* ART DECO.

Jeune France ('Young France') the name adopted by a group of French composers, including Messiaen, who identified their common aims in 1936.

Jew's harp a simple instrument consisting of a small, heart-shaped metal frame to which a thin strip of hardened steel is attached. The open-ended neck of the frame is held against the teeth and the strip is twanged to produce sound, which is modified by using the cavity of the mouth as a sound-box.

jig a generic term for a lively dance. *See also* GIGUE.

jingle a short, catchy piece of music with equally catchy LYRICS, often used to enliven the commentary of radio stations broadcasting popular music.

jingles an instrument consisting of a number of small bells or rattling objects on a strap that are shaken to produce sound.

Jugendstil the German form of ART NOUVEAU.

juke box an automatic, coin-operated machine that plays records.

K when followed by a number, a reference to either a catalogue of Mozart's works compiled by an Austrian scientist, Ludwig von Köchel (1800–1877), or a catalogue of Scarlatti's works compiled by the American harpsichordist and musicologist Ralph Kirkpatrick (1911–84).

Kapellmeister (*German*) literally 'master of the chapel', i.e. director of music to a noble court or bishop.

kazoo a simple instrument consisting of a short tube with a small hole in the side that is covered with a thin membrane. When a player hums down the tube, the membrane makes a buzzing sound. It is usually considered a children's instrument although it is frequently used by FOLK and JAZZ musicians.

kettledrum *see* TIMPANI.

key (1) on a piano, harpsichord, organ, etc, one of the finger-operated levers by which the instrument is played. (2) on woodwind instruments, one of the metal, finger-operated levers that opens or closes one or more of the sound-holes. (3) a note that is considered to be the most important in a piece of music and to which all the other notes relate. Most pieces of Western music are 'written in a key', i.e. all the chords in the piece are built around a particular note, say F minor. The concept of a key is alien to certain types of music, such as Indian and Chinese.

key note *see* TONIC.

key signature the sign (or signs) placed at the beginning of a composition to define its KEY. A key signature indicates all the notes that are to be sharpened or flattened in the piece; should a piece move temporarily into another key, the relevant notes can be identified with ACCIDENTALS.

kinetic art an art form in which light or balance are used to create a work that moves or appears to move. More complicated kinetic art objects are made to move by electric motors.

King James Bible *see* AUTHORIZED VERSION.

kit a miniature violin that was particularly popular with dancing masters of the 17th and 18th centuries, who could carry one in the pocket and thereby provide music for lessons.

Klangfarbenmelodie (*German*) literally 'melody of tone colours', a term used by Schoenberg to describe a form of COMPOSITION in which the PITCH does not change; colour is achieved by adding or taking away instruments.

klavier *see* CLAVIER.

koto a Japanese zither that has 13 silk strings stretched over a long box. The strings pass over moveable bridges and are played with plectra worn on the fingers. The instrument is placed on the ground and produces a distinctive, somewhat harsh, sound.

Krumhorn or Krummhorn (*German*) **or crumhorn** a double-REED instrument, common in the 16th and early 17th centuries. The tube was curved at the lower end and the reed was enclosed in a cap into which the player blew. It was made in several sizes: treble, tenor, and bass.

Kyrie Eleison (*Greek*) 'Lord have Mercy', the formal invocation at the start of the Mass and communion service.

la or lah (1) the note A. (2) in the TONIC SOL-FA, the sixth note (or SUBMEDIANT) of the major scale.

lacrimoso (*Italian*) 'tearful'.

lai (*French*) a 13th- and 14th-century French song usually consisting of 12 irregular stanzas sung to different musical phrases.

lambeg drum a large, double-headed bass DRUM from Northern Ireland.

lament a Scottish or Irish folk tune played at a death or some disaster, usually on the bagpipes.

lamentoso (*Italian*) 'mournfully'.

lampon (*French*) a drinking song.

Lancers, the a type of QUADRILLE in which eight or 16 couples take part.

Ländler a country dance in slow 3/4 time from Austria and Bavaria, from which the WALTZ was probably derived.

langsam (*German*) 'slow'.

languido (*Italian*) 'languid'.

largamente (*Italian*) 'broadly', meaning slowly and in a dignified manner.

larghetto (*Italian*) 'slow' or 'broad', but not as slow as LARGO.

largo (*Italian*) literally 'broad', meaning slow and in a dignified manner.

Lascaux the site, in Dòrdogne, France, of some outstanding Palaeolithic cave paintings and rock engravings. Dating from *c.*15000 BC, they have survived in remarkably good condition and depict local fauna, etc, on a large scale, in a bold, direct style.

Last Post, the a bugle call of the British Army to signal the end of the day at 10 p.m. It is also played at military funerals.

lay a song or ballad.

lay clerk an adult male member of an Anglican cathedral choir.

lead (1) the announcement of a subject or theme that later appears in other parts. (2) a sign giving the cue or entry of the various parts.

leader (1) in Britain, the title of the principal first violin of an orchestra or the first violin of a string quartet or similar ensemble. (2) the leader of a section of an orchestra. (3) an alternative term for conductor.

leading motif *see* LEITMOTIF.

leading note the seventh note of the scale; it is so called because it 'leads to' the TONIC, a SEMITONE above.

ledger lines *see* LEGER LINES.

legato (*Italian*) 'smooth'.

leger lines or ledger lines short lines added above or below a STAFF to indicate the pitch of notes that are too high or low to be written on the staff itself.

leggiero (*Italian*) 'light'.

legno (*Italian*) 'wood'; *col legno* is a direction to a violinist to turn the bow over and to tap the strings with the wood.

leise (*German*) 'soft' or 'gentle'.

leitmotif or Leitmotiv (*German*) literally a 'leading theme', i.e. a recurring theme of music, commonly used in opera, that is associated with a character or idea, thus enabling the composer to tell a story in terms of music. It has been used by many composers but is particularly associated with Wagner. In the last act of *Götterdämmerung*, for example, every leitmotif associated with Siegfried is woven into the death march.

lentamente (*Italian*) 'slowly'.

lento (*Italian*) 'slow'.

LH an abbreviation for 'left hand', found in piano music.

liberamente (*Italian*) 'freely', i.e. as the performer wishes.

libretto (*Italian*) literally 'little book'. It is a term used for the text of an opera or oratorio.

licenza (*Italian*) 'license' or 'freedom'; *con alcuna licenza* means 'with some freedom'.

Lied and Lieder (*German*) 'song' and 'songs'. The term is now used for songs by the German romantic composers, e.g. Brahms, Schubert, Strauss, etc.

ligature (1) a 12th-century form of notation for a group of notes. (2) a slur indicating that a group of notes must be sung to one syllable. (3) the tie used to link two notes over a bar line. (4) the metal band used to fix the reed to the mouthpiece of a clarinet, etc.

limerick a humorous five-lined piece of light verse, with the first two lines rhyming with each other, the third and fourth lines rhyming with each other, and the fifth line rhyming with the first line. Usually there are three stressed beats in the first, second and fifth lines and two stressed beats on the third and fourth lines. Traditionally the name of a place is mentioned in the first line and may be repeated in the last line. The English humorist and painter Edward Lear (1812–88) made the form popular in the 19th century.

lira da braccio and lira da gamba Italian stringed instruments of the 15th and 16th centuries. The *lira da braccio* had seven strings and was played like a violin; the *lira da gamba* was a bass instrument played between the knees and had up to sixteen strings.

lira organizzata a type of HURDY-GURDY that included a miniature organ.

literary ballad *see* ballad.

literary criticism the formal study, discussion, and evaluation of a literary work.

liturgy a term for any official, and written down, form of religious service.

loco (*Italian*) 'place'. It is used in music to indicate that a passage is to be played at normal pitch, after a previous, contrary instruction, i.e. the music reverts to its original place on the staff.

lontano (*Italian*) 'distant'.

loure a type of BAGPIPE played in northern France, especially Normandy.

lunga pausa (*Italian*) a 'long pause'.

lusingando (*Italian*) 'flattering', i.e. in a cajoling manner.

lustig (*German*) 'merry'.

lute a plucked stringed instrument with a body resembling that of a half-pear. It is thought to have a history dating back some three thousand years and was particularly popular during the 16th and 17th centuries; it has since been revived by 20th-century instrument makers. It has a fretted fingerboard with a characteristic 'pegbox' (a string harness) bent back at an angle to the finger-board. A lute can have up to 18 strings. It was traditionally used as an instrument for accompanying dances, but many solo works have also been written for it.

Lydian mode (1) a scale used in ancient Greek music, the equivalent of the white notes on a piano from C to C. (2) from the Middle Ages onwards, the equivalent of a scale on the white notes from F to F.

lyre an instrument familiar to the ancient Greeks, Assyrians, and Hebrews. It comprised a small, hollow box from which extended two horns that supported a cross bar and anything up to 12 strings, which could be plucked or strummed. It is traditionally taken to represent a token of love (Orpheus played the lyre).

lyric a short poem, or sequence of words, for a song. The term has a particular application to 20th-century musicals and pop songs. A *lyricist* is the person who writes the words to a popular tune.

m *abbreviation for* MAIN, MANO, MANUAL.

m (me) in TONIC SOL-FA. the third note (or MEDIANT) of the major scale.

ma (*Italian*) 'but', as *andante ma non troppo*, 'slow, but not too slow'.

machete a small Portuguese guitar.

madrigal a musical setting of a secular poem for two or more voices in COUNTERPOINT, usually unaccompanied. The first madrigals date back to the 14th century, and the first publications were made in Italy about 1501. The art of madrigal spread to every part of Europe and a wealth of polyphonic vocal music was created and reached a high art before the development of instrumental music. In the 17th century madrigals were superseded by CANTATAS.

maestà the Italian word for 'majesty', used in art to denote a depiction of the Virgin and Child enthroned in majesty and surrounded by angels or saints.

maestoso (*Italian*) 'majestic' or 'dignified'.

maestro (*Italian*) literally 'master', a term used for a master musician, particularly a conductor.

maestro sostitutto (*Italian*) 'substitute conductor', an assistant conductor responsible in opera for an offstage chorus or band. Also, a RÉPÉTITEUR.

maggiore (*Italian*) 'major mode'.

magic realism a term devised in the 1920s to describe the work of a group of German painters, part of the NEUE SACHLICHKEIT, whose work exhibited a disquieting blend of surreal fantasy with matter-of-fact representationalism.

In literature, the term is often applied with particular reference to the work of certain South American novelists, notably the Peruvian novelist Mario Vargas Llosa (1936–) and the Colombian Gabriel Garcia Marquez (1928–), whose work combines deadpan description of the everyday world with (often equally deadpan) excursions into fantasy. Some European novelists have been characterised as 'magic realists', e.g. Calvino and Salman Rushdie. The techniques of magic realism have a long ancestry; Chesterton's novel *The Man Who Was Thursday* is a notable early 20th-century example, and there are clear links with the GOTHIC NOVEL.

Magnificat (*Latin*) short for *Magnificat anima mea Dominum* ('My soul magnifies the Lord'), the canticle of the Virgin Mary sung at Roman Catholic Vespers and Anglican Evensong. It is usually chanted, but many composers, such as Bach, have set it to their own music.

main (*French*) 'hand', so *main droite* means 'right hand' (particularly in piano music).

major (*Latin*) 'greater', as opposed to MINOR or 'lesser'. Major scales are those in which a major third (INTERVAL of four SEMITONES) occurs in ascending from the tonic, while the minor scales involve a minor third (three semitones). A major tone has the ratio 8 : 9 while a minor tone has the ratio 9 : 10.

malapropism the incorrect use of a word, often through confusion with a similar-sounding word, after Mrs Malaprop, a character in Sheridan's comedy *The Rivals* (1775) whose name is derived from the French *mal à propos*, 'not apposite'. Her malapropisms include 'She's as headstrong as an allegory on the banks of the Nile' and 'Illiterate him quite from your mind'.

malinconia (*Italian*) 'melancholy'.

mancando (*Italian*) 'decreasing' or 'fading away'.

mandolin or mandoline a stringed instrument, similar to the lute, but smaller, usually played with a PLECTRUM. It has four pairs of strings and is occasionally used as an orchestral instrument.

mano (*Italian*) 'hand'.

Mannerism an exaggerated and often artificial sense of style found in Italian art between *c*.1520 and 1600, i.e. between the High RENAISSANCE and BAROQUE periods. It represents a reaction against the balanced forms and perspectives of Renaissance art and is characterised by uncomfortably posed, elongated figures and contorted facial expressions. Harsh colours and unusual modes of perspective were also used to striking effect. The major artists of the period were able to create emotional responses of greater power and sophistication, and they paved the way for the development of Baroque art.

manual a keyboard on an organ or harpsichord; organs may have four manuals, named *solo*, *swell*, *great*, and *choir*.

maracas a pair of Latin-American percussion instruments made from gourds filled with seeds, pebbles or shells. Sound is made by shaking the gourds.

march a piece of music with a strict rhythm, usually 4/4 time but sometimes in 2/4, 3/4 or 6/8 time, to which soldiers can march. The pace varies with the purpose of the piece, from the extremely slow *funeral* or *dead march* to the *quickstep* (with about 108 steps a minute) and the *Sturm Marsch* or *pas de charge* with 120 steps a minute.

marcia (*Italian*) 'march', so *alla marcia*, 'in a marching style'.

mariachi (*Spanish*) a Mexican folk group of variable size; it normally includes violins and guitars.

marimba a Latin American instrument that may have originated in Africa. It is similar to a large XYLOPHONE and can be played by up to four people at the same time.

mark a sign or word used in NOTATION to indicate the time, tone, accent, or quality of a composition or the pace at which it should be performed.

martelé (*French*) *see* MARTELLATO.

martellato (*Italian*) literally 'hammered', a term used mainly in music for strings to indicate that notes should be played with short, sharp strokes of the BOW. The term is also occasionally used in guitar and piano music.

marziale (*Italian*) 'warlike'.

masque a spectacular court entertainment that was especially popular during the 17th century. It combined poetry and dancing with vocal and instrumental music to tell a simple story that invariably flattered its aristocratic audience.

Mass (*Latin* **Missa**, *Italian* **Messa**, *French* and *German* **Messe**) in musical terms, the setting to music of the Latin Ordinary of Mass (those parts of the Mass that do not vary). The five parts are the KYRIE ELEISON, GLORIA, CREDO, SANCTUS with BENEDICTUS, and AGNUS DEI.

Master of the Queen's Musick an honorary position (in Britain) awarded to a prominent musician of the time; it is his (or her) duty to compose anthems, etc, for royal occasions.

mastersinger *see* MEISTERSINGER.

Matins the name given to the first of the canonical hours of the Roman Catholic Church. The term also refers to morning prayer in the Anglican Church.

mazurka a Polish folk dance of the 17th century for up to 12 people. The music can vary in speed and is often played on bagpipes. Chopin was influenced by the music and wrote some 55 'mazurkas' for piano.

me in the TONIC SOL-FA, the third note (or MEDIANT) of the major scale.

measure (1) a unit of rhythm or notes and rests included between two bars. (2) a stately dance of the minuet or pavanne type. (3) a BAR (of music).

mechanical instruments instruments that can play complex music through the programming of their mechanism (e.g. by punched paper or pins on a spindle) when supplied with power (through foot pedals, clockwork, steam power, electricity, etc).

mediant the third note in a major or minor scale above the TONIC (lowest note), e.g. E in the scale of C major.

medium a material used in art, e.g. OIL in painting, PENCIL in drawing, or BRONZE in sculpture. The term is also used to denote a method, e.g. painting as opposed to sculpture.

Meistersinger (*German*) 'mastersinger', the title of highest rank in the song schools or guilds that flourished in German cities from the 14th century until the 19th century. Where the MINNESINGERS drew their members from the aristocracy, mastersingers were usually craftsmen or tradesmen who composed poems and music and formed themselves into powerful guilds.

melodica (*Italian*) a free-reed instrument that was developed from the HARMONICA. It is box-shaped and has a small keyboard; the player blows down a tube and plays by pressing the keys.

melodic minor scale *see* SCALE.

melodic sequence *see* SEQUENCE.

melodrama a form of drama (from the Greek for 'song' plus 'drama') that seems to have arisen in 18th-century France and that contained elements of music, spectacle, sensational incidents, and sentimentalism (*see* SENTIMENTAL COMEDY). The form reached its peak in the popular theatre of 19th-century England, when quite spectacular stage effects often accompanied the action, and villains became blacker than black in their persecution of pure heroes and heroines. *See also* DOMESTIC TRAGEDY.

melody a succession of notes, of varying pitch, that create a distinct and identifiable musical form. Melody, HARMONY, and RHYTHM are the three essential ingredients of music. The criteria of what constitutes a melody change over time.

membranophone the generic term for all instruments in which sound is produced by the vibration of a skin or membrane, e.g. DRUM, KAZOO.

meno (*Italian*) 'less', so *meno mosso* means 'slower' (less speed).

menuet (*French*) MINUET.

Messa and Messe *see* MASS.

mesto and mestoso (*Italian*) 'sad'.

metallophone an instrument that is similar to a XYLOPHONE but has metal bars (usually bronze).

metaphysical painting a rather short-lived art movement begun in Italy in 1917 by Carlo Carré (1881–1966) and de Chirico. They sought to portray the world of the subconscious by presenting real objects in incongruous juxtaposition, as in their *Metaphysical Interiors* and *Muses* series (1917). Carré soon abandoned the movement, and by the early 1920s both artists had developed other interests.

meter (1) in verse, the measured arrangement of syllables according to stress in a rhythmic pattern. (2) in music, the basic scheme of beat groupings.

metaphysical poetry a poetry movement of the 17th century, noted for intense feeling, extended metaphor, and striking, elaborate imagery, often with a mystical element. Donne is regarded as the first important metaphysical poet.

method acting a style of acting, devised by Konstantin Stanislavsky, which involves an actor immersing himself in the 'inner life' of the character he is playing, and, using the insights gained in this study, conveying to the audience the hidden reality behind the words. Stanislavsky's theories were adopted and adapted by the American director Lee Strasberg (1901–82), whose method style of acting achieved world fame (or notoriety) through pupils such as James Dean and Marlon Brando.

metronome an instrument that produces regular beats and can therefore be used to indicate the pace at which a piece of music should be played. The first clockwork metronome was invented in 1816 and had a metal rod that swung backwards and forwards on a stand. The speed of ticking could be altered by sliding a weight up or down the rod. Electronic metronomes are also manufactured today.

mezzo (*Italian*) literally 'half', so *mezzo-soprano* means a voice between soprano and contralto.

mezzo forte (*abbreviation* **mf**) (*Italian*) 'moderately loud'.

mezzo piano (*abbreviation* **mp**) (*Italian*), meaning 'half-soft'.

mezzo voce (*abbreviation* **mv**) (*Italian*), 'half voice', i.e. softly.

microtones INTERVALS that are smaller than a SEMITONE (half step) in length, e.g. the QUARTER TONE.

middle C the note C that occupies the first LEDGER LINE below the treble staff, the first ledger line above the bass staff, and is indicated by the C clef.

military band a band in the armed forces that plays military music, usually for marching. There are many different types of military band, and the number of players varies. Most bands comprise a mixture of brass, woodwind, and percussion instruments.

minim *see* HALF NOTE.

Minnesingers the poet-musicians of Germany in the 12th and 13th centuries, who were of noble birth, like the TROUBADOURS of France, and who produced *Minnelieder*, or love songs. Wagner's *Tannhäuser* is a minnesinger. They were succeeded by the MEISTERSINGERS.

minor (*Latin*) 'less' or 'smaller'. Minor intervals contain one SEMITONE less than MAJOR. The minor third is characteristic of scales in the minor mode.

minstrel a professional entertainer or musician of medieval times. Such people were often employed by a royal court or aristocratic family.

minuet a French rural dance in 3/4 time that was popular during the 17th and 18th centuries. It was incorporated into classical sonatas and symphonies as a regular movement.

miracle play *see* MYSTERY PLAY.

mirliton (*French*) any wind instrument in which a thin membrane is made to vibrate and make a noise when the player blows, hums or sings into it. It is now known as the KAZOO.

mirror music any piece of music that sounds the same when played backwards.

Miserere (*Latin*) short for *Miserere mei Deus* ('Have mercy upon me, O God'), the first line of the 51st Psalm. It has been set to music by several composers, including Verdi.

Missa (*Latin*) 'Mass', so *Missa brevis* means 'short Mass'; *Missa cantata* means 'sung Mass'; *Missa pro defunctis* is Mass for the dead, or Requiem; and *Missa solemnis* is solemn or high Mass.

misterioso (*Italian*) 'mysteriously'.

misura (*Italian*) 'measure', equivalent to a BAR.

Mixolydian mode (1) the set of notes, in ancient Greek music, that are the equivalent of the white notes on a piano from B to B. (2) in church music of the Middle Ages onwards, the equivalent of the white notes on a piano from G to G.

mixture an organ STOP that brings into play a number of pipes that produce HARMONICS above the pitch corresponding to the actual key that is played.

mobile a moving sculpture devised by the American sculptor Alexander Calder (1898–1976).

moderato (*Italian*) 'moderate' (of speed).

modes the various sets of notes or SCALES that were used by musicians until the concept of the KEY was accepted (*c*.1650). Modes, originally used by the ancient Greeks and adapted by medieval composers for church music, were based on what are now the white notes of the piano.

modulation the gradual changing of key during the course of a part of a COMPOSITION by means of a series of harmonic progressions. Modulation is *diatonic* when it is accomplished by the use of chords from relative keys; *chromatic* when by means of non-relative keys; *enharmonic* when effected by the alteration of notation; *final*, or *complete*, when a new tonality is established; and *partial*, or *passing*, when the change of key is only transient.

moll (*German*) 'minor' (as opposed to 'major', DUR).

molto (*Italian*) 'very', so *allegro molto* means 'very fast'.

monochrome a drawing or painting executed in one colour only. *See also* GRISAILLE.

monodrama a dramatic work for a single performer.

monody a type of accompanied solo song that was developed during the late 16th and early 17th centuries. It contained dramatic and expressive embellishments and devices, and consequently had an influence on OPERA.

monothematic a piece of music that is developed from a single musical idea.

monotone declamation of words on a single tone.

montage an art technique similar to COLLAGE, where the images used are photographic.

morbido (*Italian*) 'soft' or 'gentle'.

morceau (*French*) a 'piece' (of music).

mordent a musical ornament where one note rapidly alternates with another one degree below it; it is indicated by a sign over the note.

morendo (*Italian*) 'dying', i.e. decreasing in volume.

moresca (*Italian*) a sword dance dating from the 15th and 16th centuries, which represents battles between the Moors and the Christians. It was the origin of the English MORRIS DANCE. It has been included in OPERAS, often to a marching rhythm.

morisco (*Italian*) 'in Moorish style'.

morris dance a style of English dance, the music for which is provided by pipe and tabor. It was originally a costume dance, the characters often being those from the Robin Hood ballads. Of Moorish or Spanish origin, the dance later became associated with many tunes, some in 4/4, others in 3/4 time.

mosso (*Italian*) 'moved', so *piu mosso* means 'more moved', i.e. quicker, and *meno mosso* 'less speed'.

motet a musical setting of sacred words for solo voices or choir, with or without accompaniment. The first motets were composed in the 13th century.

motif or motive a small group of notes that create a melody or rhythm, e.g. the first four notes of Beethoven's 5th symphony.

motion the upward or downward progress of a melody. It is said to be *conjunct* when the degrees of the scale succeed each other; *disjunct* where the melody proceeds in skips; *contrary* where two parts move in opposite directions; *oblique* when one part moves while the other remains stationary; and *similar*, or *direct*, when the parts move in the same direction.

moto (*Italian*) 'motion', so *con moto* means 'with motion' or 'quickly'.

motto theme a short theme that recurs during the course of a composition,

and in this way, it dominates the piece.

mouth organ *see* HARMONICA.

movement a self-contained section of a larger instrumental composition, such as a symphony or sonata.

mp *see* MEZZO PIANO.

muffled drum a DRUM with a piece of cloth or towelling draped over the vibrating surfaces. It produces a sombre tone when struck and is usually associated with funeral music.

musette (*French*) (1) a type of small BAGPIPE popular at the French court in the 17th and 18th centuries. (2) an air in 2/4, 3/4 or 6/8 time that imitates the drone of the bagpipe. (3) a dance tune suitable for a bagpipe. (4) an organ reed stop.

musica (*Italian*) 'music'.

musica ficta or cantus fictus (*Latin*) 'feigned music' or 'feigned song', a term for ACCIDENTALS used in MODE music.

musical a type of play or film in which music plays an important part and the actors occasionally sing, e.g. *West Side Story*.

musical box a clockwork MECHANICAL INSTRUMENT in which a DRUM studded with small pins plays a tune by plucking the teeth of a metal comb.

musical comedy a term used between 1890 and 1930 to describe a humorous play with light music and singing in it.

music drama a term first used to describe the operas of Wagner, where the action and music are completely interlocked, with, for example, no pauses for applause after arias or repetition within a piece.

musicology the scientific study of music.

musique concrète a term coined by the French composer Pierre Schaffer in 1948 to describe a type of music in which taped sounds are distorted or manipulated by the composer. The term ELECTRONIC MUSIC is now more generally used.

muta (*Italian*) 'change', a musical direction: (1) that the key be changed in horn or drum music; (2) that the MUTE be used.

mutation stops organ STOPS that produce sound, usually a HARMONIC, which is different from the normal or octave pitch corresponding to the key that is depressed.

mute any device used to soften or reduce the normal volume or alter the tone of an instrument. With bowed instruments, a small clamp is slotted on to the BRIDGE; in brass instruments a hand or bung is pushed into the bell; in the piano the soft (left) PEDAL is pressed; and with DRUMS, cloths are placed over the skins or sponge-headed drumsticks are used.

mv abbreviation for *mezzo voce*.

mystery play or miracle play a form of dramatic entertainment based on sacred subjects and given under church auspices which was used before the development of either OPERA or ORATORIO.

Nabis a group of painters working in France in the 1890s. Influenced by Gauguin and oriental art, they worked in flat areas of strong colour, avoiding direct representation in favour of a symbolic approach.

Nachdruck (*German*) 'ACCENT' or 'emphasis'.

Nachschlag (*German*) 'after beat', a grace or ORNAMENT, like a short APPOGGIATURA, but occurring at the end instead of at the beginning of a NOTE.

Nachspiel (*German*) a POSTLUDE.

Nachtmusik (*German*) 'night music', i.e. music that is suitable for performing in the evening or that is suggestive of night.

naive art works by untrained artists whose style is noted for its innocence and simplicity. Scenes are often depicted literally, with little attention to formal perspective and with an intuitive rather than studied use of pictorial space, composition and colour. Naive painters work independently of contemporary trends or movements in art.

naker the medieval English name for a small KETTLEDRUM (often with snares, *see* SIDE DRUM) of Arabic origin, from which TIMPANI developed. Nakers were always used in pairs.

national anthem a SONG or HYMN that is formally adopted by a country and sung or played at official occasions.

nationalism a late 19th-century and early 20th-century music movement in which a number of composers set out to write work which would express their national identity, often by reference to FOLK music and by evocation of landscape. It was in part a reaction to the dominance of German music.

natural *see* CANCEL.

Naturalism a term deriving from the late-19th French literary movement of the same name, denoting fiction characterised by close observation and documentation of everyday life, with a strong emphasis on the influence of the material world on individual behaviour. Naturalistic NOVELS therefore tended to adopt a very deterministic approach to life and fiction, and most practitioners of the form would have described themselves as socialists or social Darwinists. The influence of the school on anglophone writers was patchy; however, there are strong elements of naturalism in the work of Arnold Bennett.

natural key KEY of C major.

Nazarenes an art movement based on the Brotherhood of St Luke formed in Vienna in 1809. It involved painters of German and Austrian origin, who worked mainly in Italy. Inspired by the medieval guild system, they worked cooperatively with a common goal of reviving Christian art. Influences included German medieval art and Italian RENAISSANCE painting.

neck the narrow projecting part of a stringed instrument that supports the FINGERBOARD; at the end of the neck lies the PEG-BOX.

nel battere (*Italian*) on the BEAT or down stroke (DOWN-BEAT).

Neoclassicism a term denoting any movement in the arts emphasising the virtues of imitating the style and precepts of the great classical writers and artists (Neoclassicist principles in literature derive mostly from the writings of Aristotle—principally the *Poetics*—and some observations by the Roman poets, Virgil and Horace). The hallmarks of Neoclassicism are traditionally defined as balance, moderation, attention to formal rules—such as the dramatic *Unities*, in which time and space are strictly ordered around a sequential plot with a beginning, middle, and end—avoidance of emotional display and distrust of enthusiasm, and the assumption that human nature has changed little since CLASSICAL times. It is frequently contrasted with ROMANTICISM, and its strongest period in art and architecture is contemporary with the peak period of Romanticism, the late 18th and early 19th centuries.

In literature, Neoclassicism is generally held to have begun with Petrarch in the mid-14th century. The greatest Neoclassical English poets are Dryden and Pope; the greatest Neoclassical English critic is sometimes said to be Dr Johnson, but his espousal of Neoclassical virtues was heavily qualified, particularly in response to French criticism of Shakespeare as virtually a 'literary savage'.

In art and architecture, Neoclassicism was the dominant style in Europe in the late 18th and early 19th centuries. It followed on from, and was essentially a reaction against, BAROQUE and ROCOCO styles. Classical forms were employed to express the reasoned enlightenment of the age, and Neoclassical painters adhered to the Classical principles of order, symmetry and calm, at the same time feeling free to embrace Romantic themes.

In music, Neoclassicism was a 20th-century movement that reacted against the overtly Romantic forms of the late 19th century. Composers who adhered to the philosophy (especially Stravinsky, Hindemith, Poulenc and Prokofiev) attempted to create new works with the balance and restraint found in the work of 18th-century composers, especially J. S. Bach.

Neoimpressionism *see* POINTILLISM.

Neoplatonism a synthesis of Platonic and mystical concepts that originated in the Greek-speaking Mediterranean world of the 3rd century. Plotinus (*c.*205–*c.*270) was the main figure behind the synthesis. His ideas, such as the notion of a world soul and the perception of the poet as an inspired prophet who sees the real world behind the shadowy illusions of the material world, have been influential on many English writers, notably Shelley.

neume a sign used in musical NOTATION from the 7th to 14th centuries before the invention of the STAFF. It indicated PITCH.

Neue Sachlichkeit (*German*) 'new objectivity', the title of an exhibition of postwar figurative art that then came to represent any art concerned with objective representation of real life, such works being the opposition to EXPRESSIONIST subjectivity.

new comedy *see* COMEDY.

Nibelungenlied an anonymous medieval German epic recounting the hero Siegfried's capture of a hoard of gold belonging to a race of dwarfs (the Nibelungs). The epic forms the basis for Wagner's great opera cycle, *The Ring of the Nibelungs*, and was influential on Tolkien's *Lord of the Rings*.

niente (*Italian*) 'nothing', used in *quasi niente*, 'almost nothing', indicating a very soft tone.

Nihilism a philosophical movement originating in mid-19th century Russia that rejected all established authority and values. The revolutionary Bazarov in Turgenev's *Fathers and Sons* is the first significant fictional portrait of a nihilist. Much of Dostoevsky's work, e.g. *The Possessed*, is concerned with exposing the essential shallowness and banality of nihilism.

ninth an INTERVAL of nine NOTES in which both the first and last notes are counted.

No *see* Noh.

Nobel prize any of the annual awards endowed by the Swedish chemist Alfred Nobel (1833–96) for significant contributions in the fields of chemistry, physics, literature, medicine or physiology, and peace, with economics added later. Winners of the Nobel prize for literature include Kipling (1907), Yeats (1923), Shaw (1925), T. S. Eliot (1948), Pasternak (1958), Beckett (1969), Golding (1983) and Walcott (1992). More recent names include Harold Pinter (2005), J. M. Coetzee (2003) and V. S. Naipaul (2001).

nobile and nobilmente (*Italian*) 'noble' and 'nobly'.

nocturne literally a 'night piece', i.e. a piece of music, often meditative in character and suggesting the quietness of night. The form was invented by John Field and later perfected by Chopin.

Noh or No a form of highly stylised drama originating in 14th-century Japan. The typical Noh play is short, slow-paced, draws heavily on classical Japanese symbolism and usually involves song, dance, mime and intricately detailed costume.

noire (*French*) literally 'black', a QUARTER NOTE or crotchet.

nomenclature *see* NOTATION.

nonet (1) a group of nine instruments. (2) a piece of music for such a group.

normal pitch standard PITCH.

nota (*Latin, Italian*) 'NOTE', so *nota bianca*

means 'white note' or HALF-NOTE (minim); *nota buona* is an accented note; *nota cambita* or *cambiata* is a CHANGING NOTE; *nota caratteristica* is a LEADING NOTE; *nota cattiva* is an unaccented note.

notation or nomenclature the symbols used in written music to indicate the PITCH and RHYTHM of NOTES, the combination and duration of TONES, as well as the graces and shades of expression without which music can become mechanical.

note (1) a SOUND that has a defined PITCH and duration. (2) a symbol for such a sound. (3) the KEY of a PIANO or other keyboard instrument.

note row *see* TWELVE-NOTE MUSIC.

novel a sustained fictional prose narrative. Although most of the essential characteristics of the form can be found in ancient texts, such as the Greek romances of the 3rd century, and in the works of writers of the Roman world, the novel as the term is generally understood, with complex characterisation and multilayered strands of plot and character development, is essentially a creation of 18th-century writers in English, e.g. Defoe, Richardson, and Fielding.

In the early years of the 19th century, the dual tradition of the novel—adventure in the great world outside and exploration of personality—reached striking new levels in the novels of Sir Walter Scott and Jane Austen respectively. In the course of the 19th century, writers throughout Europe and America, e.g. Dickens, Stendhal, George Eliot, Tolstoy, Dostoyevsky, Balzac, Melville and Henry James, developed the novel into a highly sophisticated vehicle for exploring human consciousness. The 20th century saw many adaptations of the traditional novel, from the use of the STREAM OF CONSCIOUSNESS technique by Joyce and Woolf to the MAGIC REALISM of South American writers to the so-called *antinovels* of writers such as the French novelist Alain Robbe-Grillet (1922–).

novella a short version of the NOVEL; a tale usually leading up to some point, and often, in early versions of the form, of a satirical or scabrous nature.

nuance a subtle change of speed, TONE, etc.

number (1) an integral portion of a musical composition, particularly in opera where it can mean an ARIA, etc. (2) one of the works on a program.

Nunc Dimittis (*Latin*) the Song of Simeon, 'Lord, now lettest Thou Thy servant depart in peace', which is sung at both Roman Catholic and Anglican evening services. It has been set to music by numerous composers.

nursery rhyme a (usually traditional) short verse or song for children. Many nursery rhymes, e.g. 'Ring a Ring a Roses' (which refers to the Great Plague), have their roots in ancient and occasionally unsavoury events.

nut (1) the part of the BOW of a stringed instrument that holds the horsehair and that incorporates a screw that tightens the tension of the hairs. (2) the hardwood ridge at the PEG-BOX end of a stringed instrument's fingerboard that raises the strings above the level of the fingerboard.

o when placed over a NOTE in a musical SCORE for strings, indicates that the note must be played on an open string or as a harmonic.

ob abbreviation for OBOE and OBBLIGATO.

obbligato (*Italian*) 'obligatory', a term that refers to a PART that cannot be dispensed with in a performance (some parts can be optional). However, some 19th-century composers used the word to mean the exact opposite, i.e. a part that was optional.

ober (*German*) 'over', 'upper', as OBER-WERK.

objet trouvé *see* FOUND OBJECT.

oblique motion two parallel MELODY lines or PARTS: one moves up or down the SCALE while the other stays on a consistent NOTE.

oboe a WOODWIND instrument with a conical bore and a double REED. Its history dates back to ancient Egyptian times. SHAWMS evolved from these Egyptian predecessors and became known as HAUTBOIS instruments in the 17th and 18th centuries. The modern oboe (the word is a corruption of 'hautbois') dates from the 18th century. The established variations of the instrument are the oboe (TREBLE), the COR ANGLAIS (ALTO) or the BASSOON (tenor), and the double bassoon (BASS).

ocarina a small, egg-shaped WIND INSTRU-MENT, often made of clay, that is played in a way similar to a RECORDER. It was invented in the mid-19th century and is still made, mainly as a toy.

octave an INTERVAL of eight NOTES, inclusive of the top and bottom notes, e.g. C to C.

octet (1) a group of eight instruments or VOICES. (2) a piece for such a group.

octobass a huge kind of three-stringed DOUBLE BASS, some four meters in height, which incorporated hand- and pedal-operated levers for STOPPING the immensely thick strings. It was invented by J.B. Vuillaume in Paris in 1849 but proved impractical.

oeuvre (*French*) a 'work' (OPUS).

offertory an ANTIPHON sung (or music played on the ORGAN) while the priest prepares the bread and wine at a communion service.

ohne (*German*) 'without', hence *ohne worte*, 'without words'.

oil paint a paint made by mixing colour pigments with oil (generally linseed oil) to produce a slow-drying, malleable sticky substance. Oil paint has been the dominant medium in European art since the 15th century because of the range of effects that can be produced.

old comedy *see* comedy.

Ondes Martenot or Ondes Musicales an ELECTRONIC musical instrument patented in 1922. It was used by Messiaen.

Op, op abbreviation for OPUS.

Op Art or Optical Art an ABSTRACT ART that uses precise, hard-edged patterns in strong colours that dazzle the viewer and make the image appear to move.

open harmony *see* HARMONY.

open note (1) in stringed instruments, an OPEN STRING. (2) in BRASS or WOODWIND instruments, a NOTE produced without using VALVES, CROOKS, or KEYS.

open string any string on an instrument that is allowed to vibrate along its entire length without being stopped (*see* STOPPING).

Oper (*German*) 'opera'.

opera a dramatic work in which all, or most of, the text is sung to orchestral ACCOMPANI-MENT. It is a formidable musical form and has a history dating back to Italy in the 16th century. This Italian form of opera

reached its culmination in the operas of MONTEVERDI, in particular his *Orfeo*, but thereafter developed into a rigidly prescribed form of art. The growth of the science of HARMONY and the development of the modern ORCHESTRA led to a revolt against Italian opera, headed by Gluck, Mozart and, later, by Weber in Germany. Wagner gave a new impetus to operatic composition. His approach assumed that music that detracted from interest in the progress of the drama was bad music and that the purpose of music, architecture, lighting, costume and acting was to enforce the dramatic interest of the text. Opera demands a LIBRETTO, an orchestra, singers, an ample stage, and, only too often, considerable funds to produce. It also requires some suspension of disbelief, for opera is the convention of unreality, but in that unreality lies its ability to work magic.

opéra-bouffe (*French*)**or opera buffa** (*Italian*) similar to OPÉRA COMIQUE but with the dialogue sung throughout and spoken only occasionally in *opera buffa* modelled on the French style.

opéra comique (*French*) literally 'a comic OPERA' but in fact an opera consisting of dramatic pieces with music and dancing and instrumental ACCOMPANIMENT, often along tragic rather than comic lines. Like the German SINGSPIEL, all or nearly all of the dialogue is spoken.

opera seria (*Italian*) 'serious OPERA', as usually applied to work of the 17th and 18th centuries.

operetta a short OPERA or, more usually, a term taken to mean an opera with some spoken dialogue and a romantic plot with a happy ending.

Optical Art *see* OP ART.

opus (*Latin*, *plural* **opera**) 'work', a term used by composers (or their cataloguers) to indicate the chronological order of their works. It is usually abbreviated to Op and is followed by the catalogued number of the work.

oratorio the musical setting of a religious or epic LIBRETTO for soloists, CHORUS and ORCHESTRA, performed without the theatrical effects of stage and costumes, etc. Oratorio had its beginnings in the MYSTERY PLAYS of the Middle Ages. At first they were performed in MADRIGAL style and became popular throughout Italy. From Italy, where it was soon overshadowed by OPERA, the oratorio spread to the rest of Europe. The church CANTATAS of J. S. Bach and his PASSIONS can be regarded as its highest expression in northern Germany. In England it was Handel's recourse when opera was no longer profitable or was forbidden. His *Messiah* and Haydn's *Creation* and *The Seasons* were the culmination of the form, but later composers also wrote oratorios, e.g. Mendelssohn's *Elijah* and Elgar's *Dream of Gerontius*.

orchestra a group of instruments and their players. The word comes from Greek and means 'dancing place'. This was a space in front of the stage in which a raised platform was built for the accommodation of the CHORUS. The early composers of OPERA applied the name to the place allotted to their musicians, and it is now used to designate the place, the musicians, or the instruments. Orchestras have grown over the centuries in response to larger auditoriums. A standard, modern orchestra contains four families of instruments: STRINGS, WOODWIND, BRASS, and PERCUSSION. The exact number of players within each section can vary, and extra instruments can be called for by a particular SCORE.

orchestration the art of writing and arranging music for an ORCHESTRA.

organ a keyboard wind instrument, played with the hands and feet, in which pressurised air is forced through PIPES to sound NOTES. PITCH is determined by the length of the pipe. There are essentially two types of pipe: FLUE PIPES, which are blown like a WHISTLE, and REED PIPES in which air is blown over vibrating strips of metal. Flue pipes can be 'stopped' (blocked off at one end) to produce a sound an OCTAVE lower than when open. There are a number of keyboards on an organ, one of which is operated by the feet (PEDAL board). Those operated by the hands are called MANUALS, and there are four common categories: the solo (used for playing SOLO MELODIES), the swell (on which notes can be made to sound louder or softer, *see also* SWELL ORGAN), the great (the manual that opens up all the most powerful pipes), and the

choir (which operates the softer sounding pipes, *see also* CHOIR ORGAN). In addition there are a number of 'STOPS' (buttons or levers) that can alter the pitch or TONE of specific pipes.

The organ dates back to before the time of Christ and has gone through many stages of evolution. ELECTRONIC organs (*see* HAMMOND ORGAN) have been invented and these tend to produce sounds rather different from those in which pumped air is actually used.

organum (1) (*Latin*) 'ORGAN'. (2) measured music, as opposed to unmeasured PLAINSONG, an early form of POLYPHONY.

ornaments and graces embellishments to the NOTES of a MELODY, indicated by symbols or small notes. They were used frequently in the 17th and 18th centuries.

Orpheus the legendary poet and musician of Greek mythology whose name has been adopted by numerous musical societies, etc, and has also been used as the title of several collections of vocal music. The story of Orpheus and his search in the underworld for his wife Eurydice has been the subject of many musical forms.

Orphism or Orphic Cubism a brief but influential art movement developed out of Cubist principles. Their aim was to move away from the objectivity of CUBISM towards a more lyrical and colourful art. The artists were influenced in part by Italian FUTURISM, and typical works use juxtaposed forms and strong colours. The movement had a deep influence on some of the German EXPRESSIONISTS and on SYNCHROMISM.

oscillator an ELECTRONIC INSTRUMENT that converts electrical energy into audible sound.

ossia (*Italian*) 'or', 'otherwise', 'else', used to indicate an alternative PASSAGE of music.

ostinato (*Italian*) 'obstinate'; a short PHRASE or other pattern that is repeated over and over again during the course of a composition.

ottava (*Italian*) OCTAVE.

overblow to increase the wind pressure in a WOODWIND instrument to force an upper PARTIAL note instead of its fundamental note, thus producing a harmonic.

overtones *see* HARMONICS.

overture a piece of music that introduces an OPERA, ORATORIO, BALLET, or other major work. Overtures may be built out of the principal THEMES of the work that is to follow or may be quite independent of them. Beethoven composed no fewer than four overtures to his only opera, *Fidelio*, and Verdi's *Otello* and other operas have no overture whatever. Overtures are nearly always in the SONATA FORM, being, in fact, similar to the first MOVEMENT of a SYMPHONY on a somewhat larger scale. The CONCERT OVERTURE is often an independent piece, written for performance in a concert hall.

p (1) abbreviation for PIANO (*Italian*), meaning 'soft'. (2) abbreviation for 'PEDAL' (ORGAN).

pan *see* STEEL DRUM.

pandora a plucked stringed instrument of the CITTERN family. It was particularly popular in England during the 16th century.

panpipes a set of graduated PIPES, stopped at the lower end, that are bound together by thongs. Each pipe makes a single NOTE, and sound is produced by blowing across the open end. They are popular in South America and parts of Eastern Europe.

pantomime a combination of dancing and gesticulation by which a drama may be represented without words although accompanied by music. In Britain, the term is now applied to a musical show with dialogue, traditionally based on a fairy tale and performed at Christmas time.

pantonality *see* ATONAL.

parameter a 20th-century term used to describe aspects of SOUND that can be varied but nevertheless impose a limit. It is particularly applied to ELECTRONIC MUSIC with regard to volume, etc.

part (1) a VOICE or instrument in a group of performers. (2) a piece of music for it.

parte (*Italian*) 'PART', so *colla parte* means 'with the part'.

part-song a composition for unaccompanied VOICES in which the highest part usually sings the MELODY while the lower parts sing accompanying HARMONIES.

passacaglia (*Italian*) a type of slow and stately dance originating in Spain, for which keyboard music was written in the 17th century. It has come to mean a work in which such a THEME recurs again and again.

passage a FIGURE or PHRASE of music; a RUN.

passage work a piece of music that provides an opportunity for VIRTUOSO playing.

passamezzo (*Italian*) 'half-step', a quick Italian dance in DUPLE TIME that became popular throughout Europe in the late 16th century.

passepied (*French*) a French dance in triple TIME, like a quick MINUET, that is thought to have originated in Brittany. It was incorporated into French ballets of the mid-17th century.

passing note a NOTE that is dissonant with the prevailing HARMONY but that is nevertheless useful in making the TRANSITION from one CHORD or KEY to another.

Passion music the setting to music of the story of Christ's Passion (the story of the Crucifixion taken from the Gospels). The first dramatic representation of the Passion is said to have been made in the 4th century by St Gregory Nazianzen (329–389), Bishop of Antioch. It was sung throughout. From the 13th century, the Passion was changed to PLAINSONG melodies by priests in churches during Holy Week. The most celebrated of later Passions are those of J. S. Bach, the *St John Passion* and the *St Matthew Passion*.

pastel a paint medium of powdered colour mixed with gum arabic to form a hard stick. When applied to paper, the colour adheres to the surface.

pasticchio (*Italian*) literally 'pie', a dramatic entertainment that contains a selection of pieces from various composers' works.

pastoral any piece of literature celebrating the country way of life. The first pastoral poems of any significance are those of Theocritus (*c*.310–*c*.250 BC), a Greek poet whose work established the standard frame of the form: shepherds and shepherdesses singing to one another of their loves in a world of peace and plenty. Death, however, is occasionally present in the form of a shepherd lamenting the death of a friend (Shakespeare's 'Dead shepherd' couplet from *As You Like It* is a later example of this convention being used as a tribute to Marlowe). Theocritus' form was used by Virgil in his *Eclogues*, so establishing a tradition that lasted for centuries. Later practitioners of the form include Petrarch, Milton and Shelley.

pastorale (1) a vocal or instrumental MOVEMENT or composition in COMPOUND triple TIME that suggests a rural subject; it usually has long BASS notes that imitate the sounds of the BAGPIPE drone. (2) a stage entertainment based on a PASTORAL.

patter song a kind of comic SONG that has a string of tongue-twisting syllables and is usually sung quickly to minimal ACCOMPANIMENT.

Pauken (*German*) KETTLEDRUMS.

pausa (*Italian*) 'REST'.

pause a symbol over a NOTE or REST (U) to indicate that this should be held for longer than its written value.

pavan or pavane a stately court dance, normally in slow DUPLE TIME, that was occasionally incorporated into instrumental music in the 16th century.

pavillon (*French*) literally a 'tent', so, with reference to the shape, the bell of a BRASS INSTRUMENT.

peal a set of church bells or, as a verb, to ring a set of church bells.

ped abbreviation for PEDAL.

pedal the part of an instrument's mechanism that is operated by the feet, such as on a PIANO, ORGAN, or HARP. The *forte*, or loud, pedal on a piano by raising the dampers enriches the TONE. The *piano*, or soft, pedal enables the player to strike only one or two strings or to reduce the volume of tone. Harp pedals sharpen, flatten, or neutralise one NOTE throughout the COMPASS.

Organ pedals produce notes of the lower register independently of the MANUAL or alter the arrangement of the registers.

peg-box the part of a stringed instrument that houses the pegs that anchor and tune the strings.

pencil a mixture of graphite and clay in stick form and covered by a hard casing. The greater the clay element, the harder is the pencil. Graphite replaced lead as the principal component in the 16th century.

Until the end of the 18th century, the word 'pencil' also denoted a fine brush.

penny whistle *see* TIN WHISTLE.

pentatonic scale a SCALE composed of five notes in an octave. It is found in various types of folk music from Scottish to Chinese.

per (*Italian*) 'by' or 'for'.

percussion (1) the actual striking of a DISCORD after it has been prepared and before its RESOLUTION. (2) the mechanism by which the tongue of a REED is struck with a HAMMER as air is admitted from the wind chest, thus ensuring immediate 'speaking'.

percussion instrument an instrument that produces TONE when struck, such as the PIANO or XYLOPHONE, but more especially one of the family of instruments that produce SOUND when struck or shaken, e.g. MARACAS, DRUMS, TRIANGLE.

perdendosi (*Italian*) 'losing itself', i.e. dying away both in volume of TONE and in speed.

perfect interval *see* INTERVAL.

period a complete musical sentence (*see* PHRASE).

perpetuum mobile (*Latin*) 'perpetually in motion', i.e. a short piece of music with a repetitive NOTE pattern that is played quickly and without any PAUSES.

perspective in art, the representation of a three-dimensional view in a two-dimensional space by establishing a vanishing point in the distance at which parallel lines converge, the objects or figures in the distance being smaller and closer together than objects or figures nearer the viewer. It is demonstrated in the works of Giotto, and its rules were formulated by the Italian writer, architect, sculptor and painter Leon Battista Alberti (1404–72) in *De Pictura* (1435), but by the 20th century these were being abandoned.

pesante (*Italian*) 'heavy', 'ponderous', or 'solid'.

PF abbreviation for PIANOFORTE, PIANO FORTE, and PIÙ *forte*.

Phantasie (*German*) *see* FANTASIA.

philharmonic (*Greek*) literally 'music loving', an adjective used in the titles of many orchestras, societies, etc.

phrase a short melodic section of a

composition, of no fixed length, although it is often four BARS long.

piacere (*Italian*) 'pleasure', so *a piacere* means 'at (the performer's) pleasure'.

piacevole (*Italian*) 'pleasantly'.

piangevole (*Italian*) 'sadly'.

pianissimo (*abbreviation* **pp, PP**) (*Italian*) 'very quiet'.

piano (1) (*abbreviation* **p**) (*Italian*) 'soft'. (2) the common abbreviated form of PIANOFORTE.

piano accordion *see* ACCORDION.

piano à queue (*French*) a grand PIANO.

piano carré (*French*) a square PIANO.

pianoforte or piano a keyboard instrument that was invented by Bartolomeo Cristofori in Florence in 1709, and for which important works were being written by the end of the 18th century. Most modern instruments usually have 88 KEYS and a COMPASS of $7^1/_3$ OCTAVES, although it is possible to find larger versions. The keys operate HAMMERS that strike STRINGS at the back of the instrument. These strings can run vertically (*upright piano*) or horizontally (*grand piano*). Most pianos have one string for the very lowest NOTES, two parallel strings for the middle REGISTER notes, and three strings for the highest notes. Normally, when a NOTE is played, a damper (*see* DAMP) deadens the strings when the key returns to its normal position, but a sustaining (right) PEDAL suspends the action of the dampers and allows the note to continue sounding. The soft (left) pedal mutes the sound produced, either by moving the hammers closer to the strings so that their action is diminished, or by moving the hammers sideways so that only one or two strings are struck. On some pianos, a third, SOSTENUTO pedal, allows selected notes to continue sounding while others are dampened.

pianola *see* PLAYER PIANO.

pibroch (*Gaelic*) a type of Scottish BAGPIPE music with the form of THEME and VARIATIONS.

picaresque novel a type of NOVEL in which the hero (very rarely, the heroine—Defoe's Molly Flanders is the best-known example in English) undergoes an episodic series of adventures. The term derives from the Spanish *picaro*, a 'rogue' or 'trickster'.

Many examples appear in 16th-century Spanish literature, when the genre first established itself, but picaresque novels have been appearing since the very earliest days of the novel. The first major English example is Thomas Nashe's lurid *The Unfortunate Traveller*, which appeared in the 1590s. Several great novels of the 18th and 19th centuries, e.g. Smollett's *Roderick Random*, Fielding's *Tom Jones* and Dickens' *Pickwick Papers*, have picaresque elements but inhabit an entirely different emotional and moral world from that of the earlier examples of the genre.

piccolo a small FLUTE with a PITCH an OCTAVE higher than a concert flute. It is used in orchestras and MILITARY BANDS.

pick a common expression for plucking the strings on a GUITAR.

pietà (*Italian*) 'pity', a term used in art to denote a painting or sculpture of the body of the dead Christ being supported by the Virgin, often with other mourning figures.

pipe a hollow cylinder in which vibrating air produces SOUND. On many instruments, the effective length of the pipe can be altered to produce a range of NOTES by means of holes that are opened or closed by the fingers.

pipe organ an American term for a real ORGAN, as opposed to an AMERICAN ORGAN.

pistons the VALVES on BRASS instruments that allow players to sound different NOTES.

pitch the height or depth of a SOUND, which determines its position on a SCALE.

più (*Italian*) 'more', so *più* ALLEGRO means 'faster', and *più* FORTE 'more loudly'.

pizz. an abbreviation of PIZZICATO.

pizzicato (*Italian*) 'plucked' (with specific reference to using the fingers to pluck the STRINGS on a bowed instrument).

plainsong the collection of ancient MELODIES to which parts of Roman Catholic services have been sung for centuries. The best-known is GREGORIAN CHANT. Plainsong is usually unaccompanied and sung in UNISON. It is also in free RHYTHM, i.e. it does not have BARS but follows the prose rhythm of the PSALM or prayer.

Platonism the theory of forms devised by Plato in which objects as we perceive them are distinguished from the idea of the objects, a theory that has had a strong influence on many writers, e.g. Donne, Wordsworth, and, most of all, Shelley (*see also* NEOPLATONISM). Plato's speculations are contained in dialogue form in several works, e.g. the *Symposium* and *Phaedo*, and in *The Republic* (an examination of the principles of good government).

player piano or pianola a mechanical PIANO operated pneumatically by a perforated roll of paper.

plectrum (*plural* **plectra**) a small piece of horn, plastic or wood that is used to pluck the STRINGS of a GUITAR, MANDOLIN, ZITHER, etc.

plein air (*French*) 'open air', used of paintings that have been produced out of doors and not in a studio. Plein air painting was particularly popular with the BARBIZON SCHOOL and became a central tenet of IMPRESSIONISM.

poco (*Italian*) 'little' or 'slightly', so *poco* DIMINUENDO means 'getting slightly softer' and *poco a poco* means 'little by little'.

poem an arrangement of words, especially in METER, often rhymed, in a style more imaginative than ordinary speech.

poet laureate a poet appointed to a court or other formal institution. In the UK until 1999 the post was held for life. The poet laureate is expected, although not forced, to write a poem to commemorate important events. Ben Jonson held the post unofficially, being succeeded by Sir William Davenant (1606–68). The first official poet laureate was Dryden, who was also the first to lose the post before his death, in the upheaval surrounding the 'Glorious Revolution'. Dryden's successor in 1689 was Thomas Shadwell (*c*.1642–92). Nahum Tate (1652–1715) held the office from 1692, and Nicholas Rowe (1674–1718) from 1715. Laurence Eusden (1688–1730) succeeded in 1718, more for political reasons than for poetic ones (he is better known for being mentioned in Pope's *Dunciad* for his drinking habits than for any skill as a poet). His successor in 1730, the actor and dramatist Colley Cibber (1671–1757), also became a target of the *The Dunciad*, Pope personifying him as 'Dullness' in the final

edition. The appointment in 1757 of the dramatist William Whitehead (1715–85) also attracted satirical comment. Thomas Warton (1728–90) held the post from 1785, and Henry James Pye (1745–1813) from 1790. The reputation of the post was revived a little with the appointment of Southey in 1813 and greatly with those of Wordsworth (1843–50) and Tennyson (1850–92), but suffered a setback with the appointment of Alfred Austin (1835–1913) in 1896. The 20th-century holders of the post were Robert Bridges (1844–1930) from 1913, Masefield (1930–67), Day-Lewis (1968–72), Betjeman (1972–84) and Ted Hughes (1984–98). Andrew Motion (1950–), for the first time, was appointed in 1999 for a fixed term of ten years.

poi (*Italian*) 'then', SO SCHERZO DA CAPO, *poi la* CODA means 'repeat the scherzo, then play the coda'.

point the tip of a BOW, the opposite end from the part that is held (the *heel*).

point d'orgue (*French*) 'ORGAN point'. It can indicate, a harmonic PEDAL (a NOTE sustained under changing HARMONIES); the sign for a PAUSE; or a CADENZA in a CONCERTO.

pointillism a scientific and logical development of IMPRESSIONISM pioneered by the pointillist painters, notably Seurat and Pissarro. The brokenly applied brushwork of Monet and Renoir was extended and refined to a system of dots of pure colour, applied according to scientific principles with the intention of creating an image of greater purity and luminosity.

In music, the term was borrowed to describe a style in which NOTES seem to be isolated as 'dots' rather than as sequential parts of a MELODY. It is applied to the works of certain 20th-century composers, such as Webern.

polacca (*Italian*) *see* POLONAISE.

polka a ROUND DANCE in quick 2/4 TIME from Czechoslovakia. It became popular throughout Europe in the mid-19th century.

polonaise (*French*) **or polacca** (*Italian*) a stately ballroom dance of Polish origin in moderately fast 3/4 TIME. It was used by Chopin in sixteen strongly patriotic piano pieces.

polyphony (*Greek*) literally 'many sounds', i.e. a type of music in which two or more PARTS have independent melodic lines arranged in COUNTERPOINT. The blending of several distinct MELODIES is what is aimed for rather than the construction of a single melody with harmonised ACCOMPANIMENT.

polyptych a painting, usually an ALTARPIECE, consisting of two or more paintings within a decorative frame. *See also* DIPTYCH; TRIPTYCH.

polytonality the use of two or more KEYS at the same time.

ponticello (*Italian*) 'BRIDGE' (of a stringed instrument).

Pop Art a realistic art style that uses techniques and subjects from commercial art, comic strips, posters, etc. Notable exponents include Lichtenstein, the Swedish artist Claes Oldenburg (1929–); and the American Robert Rauschenberg (1925–).

pop music short for 'popular' music, i.e. 20th-century music specifically composed to have instant appeal to young people. There are many types of pop music, with influences ranging from JAZZ and FOLK to ROCK and REGGAE.

portamento (*Italian*) literally 'carrying', an effect used in singing or on bowed instruments in which sound is smoothly 'carried' or slid from one NOTE to the next without a break.

portraiture the art of painting, drawing, or sculpting the likeness of someone, either the face, the figure to the waist, or the whole person. Portraits vary from the idealised or romanticised to the realistic.

position a term used in the playing of stringed instruments for where the left hand should be placed so that the fingers can play different sets of NOTES; e.g. first position has the hand near the end of the strings, second position is slightly further along the fingerboard.

poster paint *see* GOUACHE.

posthorn a simple (valveless) BRASS instrument similar to a BUGLE but usually coiled in a circular form.

Postimpressionism a blanket term used to describe the works of artists in the late 19th century who rejected IMPRESSIONISM. It was not a movement in itself, and most of the artists it refers to worked in widely divergent and independent styles, e.g. Braque, Picasso, Cézanne, Gauguin, Van Gogh, and Matisse. The name was coined by the English art critic Roger Fry (1866–1934), an enthusiastic supporter of modern art, who organised the first London exhibition of Postimpressionist painters in 1912.

postlude the closing section of a composition.

Poststructuralism *see* STRUCTURALISM.

pot-pourri (*French*) a medley of well-known tunes played at a concert.

pp, PP an abbreviation for PIANISSIMO, 'very soft'; **ppp** means 'even softer'.

precentor the official in charge of music, or the leader of the singing, at a cathedral, monastery, etc. *See also* CANTOR.

precipitato, precipitoso (*Italian*) 'precipitately', hence also 'impetuously'.

prelude an introductory piece of music, or a self-contained PIANO piece in one MOVEMENT.

Pre-Raphaelite Brotherhood a movement that was founded in 1848 by Holman Hunt, Millais, and Rossetti, who wanted to raise standards in British art. They drew their imagery from medieval legends and literature in an attempt to provide an escape from industrial materialism. They sought to recreate the innocence of Italian painting before Raphael, and were influenced by the works of the NAZARENES. They had a large following, partly because of the support of the critic John Ruskin, which included William Morris. The movement broke up in 1853.

presto (*Italian*) 'lively'; *prestissimo* indicates the fastest speed of which a performer is capable.

prima donna (*Italian*) the 'first lady', the most important female singer in an opera.

primary colours the colours red, blue and yellow, which in painting cannot be produced by mixing other colours. Primary colours are mixed to make *secondary colours*: orange (red and yellow), purple (red and blue) and green (blue and yellow).

primo (*Italian*) 'first', as the first or top PART of a PIANO DUET (the lower part being termed *secondo*, 'second').

principal (1) the LEADER of a section of an orchestra (e.g. principal HORN). (2) a singer who regularly takes leading parts in an OPERA company but not the main ones (e.g. a principal TENOR).

principal subject the first SUBJECT in a SONATA FORM or a RONDO.

Prix de Rome (*French*) an annual prize that was awarded by the French government to artists of various disciplines who had been sent to study in Rome for four years. Berlioz, Bizet, and Debussy were all winners, but Ravel failed after many attempts. It was first awarded in 1803 and was discontinued in 1968.

programme music music that attempts to tell a story or evoke an image. The term was first used by Liszt to describe his SYMPHONIC POEMS. Beethoven made occasional incursions into the realm of programme music, notably in his symphony no. 6 in F (1808), the *Pastoral Symphony*, each of the five movements of which has an evocative title.

progression MOTION from NOTE to note or from CHORD to chord.

Promenade Concerts an annual season of concerts given in London's Royal Albert Hall. The 'Proms' were instituted in 1895 and were conducted until 1944 by Sir Henry Wood. Cheap tickets are available for standing-room; people do not, however, walk about. Several cities around the world have similar concert seasons.

psalm a poem (song) from the Old Testament's Book of Psalms. Attributed to King David, psalms were inherited by the Christian churches from the earlier service of the Jews. The word is from Greek and means 'to pluck a string', hence HARP song.

psalmody the singing of PSALMS to music or the musical setting of a psalm.

psalter a book of PSALMS and psalm tunes.

psaltery a medieval stringed instrument, similar to the DULCIMER except that the STRINGS are plucked and not struck. It is usually trapezium-shaped and is generally played horizontally.

pulse *see* BEAT.

Pult (*German*) 'desk', i.e. the music stand that two orchestral players share.

punta (*Italian*) 'POINT', so *a punta d'arco*

means 'at the point of the BOW', indicating that only the tip of the bow should be used to play the strings.

quadrille a French dance, very fashionable in the early 19th century, comprising five sections in alternating 6/8 and 2/4 time.

quadruple counterpoint four-PART COUNTERPOINT so constructed that all the parts may be transposed.

quadruplet a group of four NOTES of equal value played in the time of three.

quadruple time or common time the TIME of four QUARTER NOTES (crotchets) in a BAR, indicated by the time signature 4/4 or C.

quarter note a NOTE with a quarter of the time value of a WHOLE NOTE (semibreve). Also known as a crotchet. Indicated by the symbol ♩.

quarter tone half of a SEMITONE, which is the smallest INTERVAL traditionally used in Western music.

quartet (1) a group of four performers. (2) a composition for four SOLO instruments or for four VOICES.

quasi (*Italian*) literally 'as if' or 'nearly', so *quasi niente* means 'almost nothing', or as softly as possible.

quattrocento an Italian term that refers to 15th-century Italian art, often used descriptively of the early RENAISSANCE period.

quaver *see* EIGHTH NOTE.

quickstep a MARCH in quick TIME, which also developed into the modern ballroom dance.

quintet (1) a group of five performers. (2) a composition for five SOLO instruments or for five VOICES.

quintuple time five BEATS, usually QUARTER NOTES (crotchets), in a BAR, i.e. 5/4 TIME.

quodlibet (*Latin*) 'what you will', a term used to describe a collection of tunes that are cleverly woven together to create an amusing entertainment.

R an abbreviation for RIPIENO or for 'right'.

racket or rackett or ranket a WOODWIND instrument with a double REED used between the late 16th and early 18th centuries. It came in four sizes (SOPRANO, TENOR, BASS, double bass) and created a distinctive buzzing sound.

rag a piece of RAGTIME music, notably as developed by Joplin.

raga a type of Indian SCALE or a type of MELODY based on such a scale. Each raga is associated with a mood and with particular times of the day and year.

ragtime a style of syncopated (*see* SYNCOPATION) popular dance music, dating from the late 19th century, which was adopted by many composers, e.g. Debussy with *Cakewalk* and Stravinsky with *Ragtime*. The combination of ragtime and BLUES led to the development of JAZZ. Scott Joplin was a famous ragtime composer.

rallentando (*Italian*) 'slowing down'.

ranket *see* RACKET.

rap a term for an influential type of POP MUSIC of the late 20th century, which has a pulsating RHYTHM and in which LYRICS for SONGS are usually spoken to the BEAT and not sung.

rattle a type of PERCUSSION INSTRUMENT that traditionally consists of a hollowed-out gourd filled with seeds that rattle when shaken. An alternative type is a contraption in which a strip of wood held in a frame strikes against a cog-wheel as the frame is twirled round. It is occasionally required as a percussion instrument in orchestras.

re or ray in the TONIC SOL-FA, the second NOTE of the MAJOR SCALE.

Realism in literature, a true and faithful representation of reality in fiction. Once defined, discussion of the term usually breaks down into personal prejudices of various kinds. The process of distinguishing the term from NATURALISM is particularly fraught; any artist must select from the chaos of life in order to create, and in the process of choosing must impose some personal vision on the world, and in the process either convince the reader that the world portrayed is a real one, or fail. In the last analysis, there is only good writing and bad writing. Balzac is regarded as the founding father of literary realism.

In art, Realism is taken to be, in general, the objective representation of scenes. The term is used particularly of the 19th-century French painters, e.g. Daumier and Courbet, who broke away from CLASSICISM and ROMANTICISM.

reality show a television programme which focuses on ordinary people rather than actors, often in unusual or bizarre situations that have been engineered by the programme makers.

rebec or rebeck a small instrument with a pear-shaped body and, usually, three strings that were played with a BOW. It developed from the Arabian *rebab* and was used in Europe from the 16th century.

recapitulation *see* SONATA FORM.

recit. an abbreviation of RECITANDO or RECITATIVE.

recital a public concert given by just one or two people, e.g. a singer with PIANO ACCOMPANIMENT.

recitando (*Italian*) 'reciting', i.e. speaking rather than singing.

recitative a way of singing (usually on a fixed NOTE) in which the RHYTHM and lilt are taken from the words, and there is no tune as such. It is commonly used in OPERA and ORATORIO.

reciting note in PLAINSONG, the NOTE on which the first few words of each verse of a PSALM are sung.

recorder a straight, end-blown FLUTE, as opposed to a side-blown (concert) flute. Notes can be played by opening or closing eight holes in the instrument with the fingers. Recorders come in CONSORTS (families): DESCANT, TREBLE, TENOR, and BASS.

reed the small part found in many blown instruments that vibrates when air is blown across it and actually creates the sound. It is usually made of cane or metal. In single-reed instruments (e.g. CLARINET, SAXOPHONE), the reed vibrates against the instrument itself; in double-reed instruments (e.g. COR ANGLAIS, BASSOON), two reeds vibrate against each other; in free-reed instruments (e.g. HARMONIUM, CONCERTINA), a metal reed vibrates freely within a slot.

reed organ the generic term for a number of instruments that have no PIPES and use FREE REEDS to produce their NOTES. Examples are the ACCORDION and the HARMONIUM.

reed pipe an ORGAN pipe with a metal REED in the mouthpiece that vibrates when air is passed over it.

reel a Celtic dance, usually in quick 4/4 TIME and in regular four-BAR PHRASES.

refrain the CHORUS of a BALLAD.

regal a portable REED ORGAN of the 16th and 17th centuries.

reggae a type of Jamaican POP MUSIC with a heavy and pronounced RHYTHM and strongly accented UPBEAT. Its best-known exponent was Bob Marley.

register (1) a set of ORGAN PIPES that are controlled by a single STOP. (2) a part of a singer's vocal COMPASS, e.g. CHEST register, HEAD register, etc. The term is also applied to certain instruments.

related keys *see* MODULATION.

relative major and relative minor terms used to describe the connection between a MAJOR KEY and a MINOR KEY that share the same KEY SIGNATURE, e.g. A minor is the relative key of C major.

relief a sculptural form that is not freestanding. The three-dimensional shape is either carved, e.g. in stone, wood, ivory, etc, or built up, as in metal, etc. Relief sculpture can be *low relief* (*basso relievo* or *bas-relief*), where the depth of the pattern is less than half; *medium relief* (*mezzo relievo*), where the depth is roughly half; or *high relief* (*alto relievo*), where practically all the medium has been removed. The extremely low-relief technique of *stiacciato*, 'drawing in marble', was devised by Donatello.

Renaissance in literature, the revival of the arts that occurred in Europe in the 14th–16th centuries, as a result of the rediscovery of the writing of the great classical writers, notably the works of Plato and Aristotle. In the case of the latter, the 'rediscovery' occurred in terms of reinterpretation; instead of taking the texts of Aristotle as literal, unchallengeable authority, as medieval scholars had tended to do, the new thinkers, such as Francis Bacon (the father of modern scientific method) approached written authority with a new, sceptical eye. The Renaissance period in England is usually given as 1500–1660, i.e. from the visit of Erasmus in 1599 to the RESTORATION.

In art, the early Renaissance was established in Italy with the works of Giotto, in a spectacular move away from Gothic conventions and ideals. The sculptors Pisano and Donatello emulated Greek and Roman sculpture in an expression of the new humanist and aesthetic values

of the 'age of reason'. The movement reached a peak between 1500 and 1520 with the works of Leonardo da Vinci, Michelangelo, and Raphael. The Northern Renaissance took place as ideas spread to Germany, the Netherlands, and the rest of Europe during the early 16th century.

repeat two or four DOTS in the spaces of the STAFF that indicate that the PASSAGE so marked is to be played through twice.

répétiteur (*French*) a person hired to teach musicians or singers their PARTS, particularly in OPERA.

replica (*Italian*) 'repeat', so *senza replica* means 'without repetition'.

representational art *see* FIGURATIVE ART.

reprise a musical repetition; it is often found in musical comedies when songs heard in one act are repeated in another.

reredos *see* ALTARPIECE.

Requiem a MASS for the dead in the Roman Catholic Church, so called because of the opening words at the beginning of the IN-TROIT, *Requiem aeternam dona eis, Domine* ('Grant them eternal rest, O Lord'). It is sung annually in commemoration of the dead on All Souls' Day and may also be sung at the funeral and on the anniversary of the death of an individual. Besides the Introit, the other chief divisions are the KYRIE; the Gradual, *Requiem aeternam*, and tract, *Absolve Domine*; the *Sequence*, DIES IRAE; the *Offertorium, Domine Jesu Christi* ('Lord Jesus'); the SANCTUS; the BENEDICTUS; the AGNUS DEI, the *Communion, Lux aeterna* ('Light eternal'); and sometimes the *Responsorium, Libera me* ('Deliver me'); and the *Lectio, Taedet animam meam*. Notable settings of the Requiem have been composed by Palestrina, Mozart, Brahms, Beethoven, and Verdi.

resolution a term for a process in HARMONY by which a piece moves from DISCORD to CONCORD.

resonance the intensification and prolongation of a SOUND or a musical NOTE produced by sympathetic VIBRATION.

responses the PLAINSONG replies of a CHOIR or congregation to SOLO CHANTS sung by a priest.

rest a sign employed in NOTATION indicating silence.

Restoration (1) the re-establishment of the British monarchy in 1660, following the return to England of Charles II in that year. (2) the period of Charles II's reign (1660–85). The characteristics of Restoration literature are wit, salaciousness, and religious and philosophical questioning.

Restoration comedy *see* COMEDY OF MANNERS.

resultant tone *see* COMBINATION TONE.

retable *see* ALTARPIECE.

retardation a SUSPENSION in which a DISCORD is resolved upwards by one step rather than downwards.

retrograde motion a term for music that is played backwards.

revenge tragedy a form of tragedy that appeared in the late Elizabethan period, heavily influenced by the bloodthirsty language and plots of Seneca's plays in which revenge, often for the death of a son or father, is the prime motive. Thomas Kyd's *The Spanish Tragedy* (1588–9) is the earliest example, Shakespeare's *Hamlet* (1602) the greatest. *See also* JACOBEAN TRAGEDY.

reveille (pronounced 'revally') a BUGLE call used by the army to awaken soldiers.

rf, rfz abbreviations for RINFORZANDO.

RH abbreviation for 'right hand'.

rhapsody the title commonly given by 19th- and 20th-century composers to an instrumental composition in one continuous movement. Rhapsodies are often based on FOLK tunes and are nationalistic or heroic in tone.

rhythm the regular recurrence of beat, accent, or silence in the flow of sound, especially of words and music. In music NOTATION, rhythm is determined by the way in which NOTES are grouped together into BARS, the number and type of BEATS in a bar (as governed by the TIME SIGNATURE) and the type of emphasis (ACCENT) that is given to the beats. Along with MELODY and HARMONY, it is one of the essential characteristics of music.

rhythm and blues a type of POP MUSIC that combines elements of BLUES and JAZZ. It developed in the USA and was widely accepted by white audiences and pop musicians. ROCK 'N' ROLL evolved from rhythm and blues.

rhythm-names *see* TIME-NAMES.

rhythm section the name given to the PERCUSSION and DOUBLE BASS section of a JAZZ band; it provides the all-important BEAT.

ribs the sides uniting the back and belly of an instrument of the VIOLIN family.

rigaudon or rigadoon a jaunty dance from southern France that has two or four BEATS to the BAR. It was used in French ballets and operas, and it became popular in England in the late 17th century.

rigoroso (*Italian*) 'rigorously', i.e. in exact TIME.

rinforzando (*abbreviations* **rf, rfz**) (*Italian*) literally 'reinforcing', i.e. a sudden strong ACCENT on a NOTE or CHORD.

ripieno (*abbreviation* **R**) (*Italian*) literally 'full', a term used to describe PASSAGES that are to be played by the whole BAROQUE orchestra rather than only a soloist.

risoluto (*Italian*) 'resolute' or 'in a resolute manner'.

ritardando (*abbreviation* **rit.**) (*Italian*) 'becoming gradually slower'.

ritenuto (*Italian*) 'held back' (in TEMPO), i.e. slower.

ritmo or ritmico (*Italian*) 'RHYTHM', 'rhythmic'.

ritornello (*Italian*) literally a 'small repetition'. (1) a short PASSAGE for the whole orchestra in a BAROQUE ARIA or CONCERTO during which the soloist is silent. (2) a short instrumental piece played between scenes in early OPERA.

rock a type of POP MUSIC that evolved from ROCK 'N' ROLL in the USA during the 1960s. It mixes COUNTRY AND WESTERN with RHYTHM AND BLUES and is usually played loudly on electric instruments.

rock 'n' roll a type of POP MUSIC, with a strong, catchy RHYTHM, that evolved in the USA during the 1950s and is often associated with 'jiving' (fast dancing that requires nimble footwork). Elvis Presley was one of its greatest early exponents.

Rocky Mountain School an American school of painters who painted landscapes of this formidable countryside in the middle of the 19th century. Its principal member was Albert Bierstadt (1830–1902), a German-born American landscape painter.

Rococo a style in art following on from

BAROQUE and even more exaggerated in terms of embellishments and mannered flourishes. It became established around the beginning of the 18th century and spread throughout Europe, lasting up until the advent of NEOCLASSICISM in the 1760s. The main exponents of the style were Fragonard and Watteau in France and, to a lesser extent, Tiepolo in Italy and Hogarth in England. It continued in some areas to the end of the century, particularly in church decoration.

Music from the same period is sometimes similarly termed.

roll a TRILL on PERCUSSION INSTRUMENTS produced by sounding NOTES so rapidly that they overlap and appear to produce a continuous sound.

romance a love SONG or composition of a romantic character.

Romanticism a term denoting any movement in the arts that emphasises feeling and content as opposed to form and order. The Romantic movement can be roughly dated from the late 18th century to the early 19th century, although the contrast between the need to express emotion and the desirability of following artistic rules dates back as far as the great Athenian dramatists. Other distinctive features of the Romantic movement are: the supremacy of individual over collective judgment; a 'progressive' faith in the reformability and essential goodness of humanity; the supremacy of 'natural' and 'organic' virtues over society's artificial construction. The extent and meaning of Romanticism in 18th-century English literature is still a matter of debate. It is true that elements of what we call Romanticism can be found in poets such as Cowper and even in Dr Johnson's writings, but the first great works of Romantic literature are Blake's works of the 1790s and Wordsworth and Coleridge's *Lyrical Ballads* (1798). Other prominent Romantic poets are Byron, Shelley, Keats, Heine, and Scott. *Compare* NEOCLASSICISM.

In art, the movement dates from the late 18th until the mid-19th century. It was a reaction to the balanced harmony and order of Classicism, and identified with the Romantic writers of the age. In response to increasing industrialisation, Romantic painters viewed nature from a nostalgic point of view, imbuing landscapes with powerful emotions, often in a melancholic or melodramatic way. Notable Romantic artists include Fuseli, Goya, Delacroix, Géricault, Constable, Turner and the visionary Blake.

In music, Romanticism lasted from *c*.1820 to *c*.1920. During this phase music tended to be more poetic, subjective, and individualistic than previously. Lyricism, drama, and often nationalistic feeling were characteristic of Romantic music.

Rome, Prix de *see* PRIX DE ROME.

ronde (*French*) literally 'round'; as a noun, a WHOLE NOTE (semibreve).

rondo a form of instrumental music that incorporates a recurring THEME, either in an independent piece or more usually as part of a MOVEMENT. It usually starts with a lively tune (the 'SUBJECT') that is repeated at intervals throughout the movement. Intervening sections are called EPISODES; these may or may not be in different keys from the subject. Rondo forms often occur in the final movements of SYMPHONIES, SONATAS and CONCERTOS.

root the lowest ('fundamental' or 'generating') NOTE of a CHORD. Hence, for example, the chord C-E-G has a root of C

rosin a hard resin that is applied to the hair of BOWS used to play VIOLINS, etc. It causes increased friction between the hairs of the bow and the strings.

round a short CANON in which each PART enters at equal INTERVALS and in UNISON.

round dance a dance in which partners start opposite each other and subsequently form a ring.

roundelay (1) a poem with certain lines repeated at intervals. (2) the tune to which such a poem was sung.

rubato (*Italian*) literally 'robbed', i.e. the taking of TIME from one NOTE or PASSAGE and passing it on to another note or passage.

rumba a sexually suggestive and fast Afro-Cuban dance in syncopated (*see* SYNCOPATION) 2/4 TIME.

run a SCALE or succession of NOTES rapidly played, or, if vocal, sung to one syllable.

Russian Futurism *see* FUTURISM.

S abbreviation for SEGNO, SENZA, SINISTRA, SOLO, SORDINO, SUBITO.

sackbut an instrument of the 15th century, probably originating in Spain. It is similar to the TROMBONE, but smaller.

sacra conversazione (*Italian*) 'holy conversation', in art denoting a painting in one panel of the Virgin and Child with saints.

St Cecilia *see* CECILIA, ST.

Saite (*German*) a 'string'.

salon (*French*) 'room', now also denoting an art exhibition. In the 19th century, the Salon was the annual exhibition of the ACADÉMIE FRANÇAISE, whose powerful and conventional jury increasingly refused to show the work of innovative artists. In 1863 Napoleon III ordered that there be an exhibition of artists' work rejected by the Salon, the Salon des Refusés.

saltando (*Italian*) literally 'leaping', i.e. an instruction to the string player to bounce the BOW lightly off the string.

saltarello a festive Italian FOLK dance in 3/4 or 6/8 TIME.

samba a Brazilian carnival dance in 2/4 TIME but with syncopated (*see* SYNCOPATION) rhythms.

samisen *see* SHAMISEN.

sämtlich (*German*) 'complete', as in *sämtliche Werke*, the 'complete works'.

Sanctus (*Latin*) 'Holy, holy, holy', a part of the Ordinary of MASS in the Roman Catholic Church. It has been set to music by many composers.

sarabande (*French*) a slow dance in 3/2 or 3/4 TIME, which came to Italy from Spain.

Satz (*German*) a 'MOVEMENT' or 'piece of music'.

sautille (*French*) a SALTANDO.

Savoy Operas a name for the light operas written by Gilbert and Sullivan that were first performed at the Savoy Theatre in London by the D'OYLY CARTE COMPANY.

saxhorn a family of BUGLE-like BRASS instruments patented by the Belgian instrument-maker Adolphe Sax (1814–94) in 1845. They were innovative in that they had VALVES, as opposed to the KEYS normally associated with the bugle family.

saxophone a family of instruments patented by Adolphe Sax (*see* SAXHORN) in 1846 which, although made of brass, actually belong to the WOODWIND group because

they are REED instruments. Saxophones come in many different sizes (e.g. SOPRANO, TENOR) and are commonly used in JAZZ bands as well as orchestras.

scala (*Italian*) 'staircase', from which the Teatro alla SCALA gets its name, but in music a RUN or SCALE.

Scala, La or **Teatro alla Scala** the premier opera house in Milan, and indeed Italy, which was opened in 1778.

scale an ordered sequence of NOTES that ascend or descend in PITCH. The most frequently used scales in Western music are the MAJOR and MINOR scales, which use whole notes (TONES) and half notes (SEMITONES) as steps of progression.

scat singing a type of singing used in JAZZ in which nonsense SOUNDS rather than words are sung.

scena (*Italian*) 'scene', a division of an act marked by a change of scenery. In OPERA, a solo movement of dramatic purpose, generally an extended aria.

scherzando, scherzoso (*Italian*) 'playful', or 'lively', as of a phrase or movement.

scherzetto (*Italian*) a short SCHERZO.

scherzo (*Italian*) 'joke', i.e. a cheerful, quick piece of music, either vocal or instrumental. The third MOVEMENT (of four) in many SYMPHONIES, SONATAS, etc, often takes the form of a scherzo.

schnell (*German*) 'quick'.

school in art, a group of artists who hold similar principles and work in a similar style. In art history, it also denotes that a painting has been executed by a pupil or assistant. In music, the characteristics of certain composers, whose style made a school.

Schottische (*German*) 'Scottish'; a ROUND DANCE, similar to the POLKA, popular in the 19th century. It is not in fact Scottish, but is so called because it is what those on the Continent thought a Scottish dance should be like.

Schrammel quartet a Viennese ENSEMBLE usually comprising two VIOLINS, a GUITAR and an ACCORDION, or the music composed for such an ensemble. It takes its name from Joseph Schrammel (1858–93), who wrote WALTZES for such a group.

scordatura (*Italian*) 'mistuning', i.e. the TUNING of stringed instruments to abnormal NOTES so as to produce special effects.

score music written down in such a way that it indicates all the PARTS for all the performers, i.e. the whole COMPOSITION. A *full* or *orchestral score* is one with separate STAFFS for each part. A *piano score* is one in which all the instrumental parts are represented on two staffs. A *vocal score* is a piano score with two additional staffs for the vocal parts. A *short close* or *compressed score* has more than one part to the staff.

scoring the writing of a SCORE.

Scotch snap the name for a RHYTHM that leaps from a short NOTE to a longer note. It is found in many Scottish FOLK tunes.

scraper a PERCUSSION INSTRUMENT in which SOUND is produced by scraping a stick over a series of notches cut into a piece of wood or bone.

scroll the decorative end of the PEG-BOX of a VIOLIN (or other stringed instrument) that may be carved into a curl resembling a scroll or an animal head.

sec (*French*), **secco** (*Italian*) 'unornamented', 'plain'.

secondary colours *see* PRIMARY COLORS.

Section d'Or (*French*) 'golden section') a group of painters in France who associated between 1912 and 1914 and whose aim was to hold group exhibitions and encourage debate of their aesthetic ideals. They admired the work of Cézanne and drew inspiration from FUTURISM. Painters involved with the group included Marcel Duchamp, and Fernand Léger.

segno (*abbreviation* S) (*Italian*) 'sign', used in NOTATION to mark a repeat, usually as *al segno*.

segue (*Italian*) 'follows', i.e. a direction to start playing the following MOVEMENT without a break.

seguidilla a Spanish dance in 3/8 or 3/4 TIME in the style of the BOLERO but much faster.

semibreve *see* WHOLE NOTE.

semidemisemiquaver an alternative name for a hemidemisemiquaver or SIXTY-FOURTH NOTE.

Semiotics *see* STRUCTURALISM.

semiquaver *see* SIXTEENTH NOTE.

semitone 'half a TONE', the smallest INTERVAL regularly used in modern Western music. Also known as a half step or half tone.

semplice (*Italian*) 'unornamented', 'in a simple manner'.

sempre (*Italian*) 'throughout', 'continually'; as *sempre* FORTE, 'loud throughout'.

sentimental comedy a form of English COMEDY that arose in the early 18th century, focusing on the problems of middle-class characters. The plays always end happily and feature strongly contrasting good and bad characters and high emotional peaks. The form was developed by Steele in a conscious reaction to the excesses of Restoration comedy (see COMEDY OF MANNERS). Examples include Steele's *The Tender Husband* (1705) and, notably, *The Conscious Lovers* (1722). The form led on to MELODRAMA (*see also* DOMESTIC TRAGEDY).

senza (*abbreviation* S) (*Italian*) 'without', so *senza* SORDINO means 'without MUTE' (in music for strings).

septet (1) a group of seven performers. (2) a piece of music written for such a group.

septuplet a group of seven NOTES of equal time-value to be played in the time of four or six.

sequence (1) the repetition of a short PASSAGE of music in a different PITCH. (2) a form of HYMN in Latin used in the Roman Catholic Mass, such as DIES IRAE and STABAT MATER.

serenade (1) a love SONG, traditionally sung in the evening and usually accompanied by a GUITAR or MANDOLIN. (2) a DIVERTIMENTO performed during an evening entertainment.

serenata (*Italian*) an 18th-century form of secular CANTATA or a short OPERA composed for a patron.

serialism a method of composition developed by Schoenberg in which all SEMITONES are treated as equal, i.e. tonal values are eliminated. *See also* TWELVE-NOTE MUSIC.

serpent an obsolete BASS WOODWIND instrument with several curves in it (hence its name). It was used during the 16th century in church orchestras and MILITARY BANDS.

seventh an INTERVAL in which two NOTES are seven steps apart (including the first and last), e.g. F to E.

sevillana a Spanish FOLK DANCE originally from the city of Seville. It is similar to the SEGUIDILLA.

sextet (1) a group of six performers. (2) a piece of music written for such a group.

sextolet or sextuplet a group of six notes to be performed in the time of four notes.

Sezession (*German*) 'secession', adopted as a name in the 1890s by groups of painters in Austria and Germany when they broke away from official academies to work and exhibit in contemporary styles, e.g. IMPRESSIONISM. In Germany, the first German Sezession was in Munich in 1892, followed by the Berlin Sezession of 1899, which in turn in 1910 repudiated Die BRÜCKE, which resulted in the latter forming the *Neue Sezession*. In Austria, the Vienna Sezession was organised by Klimt in 1897.

sf or sfz abbreviation for SFORZANDO.

sforzando (*Italian*) 'forcing', i.e. a strong ACCENT placed on a NOTE or CHORD.

sfumato a subtle modelling of light and shade between figures and background, deployed by Leonardo da Vinci. It represented a remarkable departure from the RENAISSANCE art stress on strong lighting and outline.

shake an alternative term for TRILL.

shamisen or samisen a Japanese long-necked LUTE with three strings. It has no FRETS and is plucked with a PLECTRUM.

shanai a double REED instrument from India, similar to a SHAWM.

shanty a SONG, with a pronounced RHYTHM, that was sung by sailors to help them coordinate their actions in the days of sailing ships. Shanties usually follow a format in which SOLO verses are followed by a CHORUS.

sharp the sign that raises the PITCH of the line or space on which it stands on a STAFF by a semitone; indicated by the sign #.

shawm or shawn a double-REED WOODWIND instrument that dates from the 13th century. It was developed from Middle Eastern instruments and produced a coarse, shrill sound. It was a forerunner of the OBOE.

sheng a sophisticated Chinese HARMONICA, dating back some 3,000 years.

shift a change of position of the hands when playing on a string instrument.

shofar or shophar an ancient Jewish WIND INSTRUMENT made from a ram's horn, which is still used in synagogues.

shop ballad *see* BALLAD.

siciliano a slow dance from Sicily in 6/8 or 12/8 TIME, with a characteristic lilting RHYTHM.

side drum or snare drum a cylindrically shaped DRUM that is the smallest usually used in an orchestra. Snares, made of gut or sprung metal, are stretched across the bottom parchment and vibrate against it when the upper membrane of parchment is struck; this gives the drum its characteristic rattling sound. The snares can be released so that a more hollow sound is produced.

signature *see* KEY SIGNATURE; TIME SIGNATURE.

signature tune a few BARS of catchy music that are associated with a performer or broadcast show.

similar motion the simultaneous PROGRESSION of two or more PARTS in the same direction.

simple interval any INTERVAL that is an octave or less. *Compare* COMPOUND INTERVAL.

simple time *see* COMPOUND TIME.

sine tone an electronically produced NOTE that is entirely 'pure'.

sinfonia (*Italian*) 'SYMPHONY', i.e. an instrumental piece. It is also a term used for a small ORCHESTRA.

sinfonietta a short SYMPHONY or a symphony for a small ORCHESTRA.

singing the act of producing musical TONE by means of the VOICE.

single chant *see* ANGLICAN CHANT.

Singspiel (*German*) literally 'sing-play', i.e. a comic opera in German with spoken dialogue replacing the sung RECITATIVE.

sinistra, sinistro (*abbreviation* S) (*Italian*) 'left', as in MANO *sinistra*, 'left hand'.

sistrum an ancient type of RATTLE in which loose wooden or metal discs are suspended on metal bars strung across a frame.

sitar a type of Indian LUTE that is believed to have originated in Persia. It has movable metal FRETS and three to seven 'MELODY' strings. Below these strings lie twelve or so SYMPATHETIC STRINGS that create a droning sound. The sitar is plucked with a long wire PLECTRUM. It has a distinctive 'twangy' sound and is usually played in consort with the TABLA. Ravi Shankar is perhaps the world's best player of the sitar.

Six, Les (*French*) 'The Six', the name given in 1920 to six young French composers by the poet and music critic Henri Collet who, with another of their champions, the poet Jean Cocteau, was passionately anti-Wagner. The six were Georges Auric (1899–1983), Louis Durey (1888–1979), Honegger, Milhaud, Poulenc, and Germaine Tailleferre (1892–1983). Subsequently a number of other composers also became members of the group, but it ceased to have an effective function after 1925.

sixteenth note a NOTE with half the time-value of an EIGHTH NOTE (a quaver) and a sixteenth of the time-value of a WHOLE NOTE (semibreve). Also known as a semiquaver. Indicated by the symbol ♪.

sixty-fourth note i.e. a note with a value of a quarter of a SIXTEENTH NOTE (semiquaver) or $\frac{1}{64}$th of a WHOLE NOTE (semibreve). Also known as the hemidemisemiquaver. Indicated by the symbol Δ.

sketch in art, a preliminary drawing made by an artist to establish points of composition, scale, etc. In music, a short PIANO or instrumental piece.

skiffle a type of POP MUSIC played in England during the 1950s. Skiffle BANDS relied on American idioms (e.g. BLUES) and attempted to become 'authentic' by incorporating home-made instruments (such as tea-chest 'basses') into their outfits.

slancio, con (*Italian*) 'with impetus'.

sleigh bells small metal bells with steel balls inside that are mounted together in groups to produce a richly textured jingling sound. Traditionally hung on sleighs, they are occasionally used in orchestras for special effects.

slide (1) a passing from one to note to another without an INTERVAL. (2) a mechanism on the TRUMPET and TROMBONE that lengthens the tube to allow a new series of harmonics.

slide trombone *see* TROMBONE.

slide trumpet an early form of TRUMPET that had a SLIDE similar to that used in the TROMBONE. It became obsolete when the VALVE trumpet was invented.

slur a curved line that is placed over or under a group of NOTES to indicate that they are to be played, or sung, smoothly, i.e.

with one stroke of the BOW (VIOLIN music) or in one breath (singing).

smorzando (*Italian*) 'fading' or 'dying away', i.e. the music is to become softer and slower.

snare drum *see* SIDE DRUM.

soave (*Italian*) 'soft' or 'gentle'.

soca music a type of powerful, rhythmic dance music from the English-speaking islands of the Caribbean. It evolved from soul (hence *so*) and calypso (*ca*).

socialist realism the name given to official art in the former Soviet Union, which was intended to glorify the achievements of the Communist Party.

social realism a form of REALISM, in which an artist's political viewpoint (usually on the left) affects the content of his or her work.

soft pedal *see* PIANO.

soh in the TONIC SOL-FA, the fifth NOTE (or DOMINANT) of the MAJOR SCALE.

solemnis (*Latin*) 'solemn', as in MISSA *Solemnis,* 'Solemn Mass'.

solenne (*Italian*) 'solemn'.

solennelle (*French*) 'solemn'.

sol-fa *see* TONIC SOL-FA.

solfeggio (*Italian*) a type of singing exercise in which the names of the NOTES are sung. *See* TONIC SOL-FA.

solo (*abbreviation* S) (*Italian*) 'alone', i.e. a piece to be performed by one person, with or without ACCOMPANIMENT.

solo organ a manual on an ORGAN with strong, distinctive STOPS, used for individual effect.

sonata originally a term for any instrumental piece to distinguish it from a sung piece or CANTATA. During the 17th century, however, two distinct forms of sonata arose: the *sonata da* CAMERA (chamber sonata), in which dance movements were played by two or three stringed instruments with a keyboard ACCOMPANIMENT, and the *sonata da chiesa* (church sonata), which was similar but more serious. In the 18th century the sonata came to be a piece in several contrasting movements for keyboard only or for keyboard and one SOLO instrument.

sonata form a method of arranging and constructing music that is commonly used (since *c.*1750) for SYMPHONIES, SONATAS,

CONCERTOS, etc. There are three sections to sonata form: the EXPOSITION (in which the SUBJECT or subjects are introduced), the DEVELOPMENT (in which the subject(s) are expanded and developed), and the recapitulation (in which the exposition, usually modified in some way, is repeated).

sonata-rondo form a type of RONDO, popular with such composers as BEETHOVEN, which is a combination of rondo and SONATA FORM.

sonatina a short SONATA.

song (1) a musical setting of poetry or prose. (2) a poem that can be sung. (3) a name used to designate the second SUBJECT of a SONATA.

song cycle a set of SONGS that have a common THEME or have words by a single poet. Schubert, Schumann and Mahler wrote notable song cycles.

sopra (*Italian*) 'above', so *come sopra* means 'as above'.

soprano the highest PITCH of human VOICE, with a range of about two OCTAVES above approximately middle C. The term is also applied to some instruments, such as soprano SAXOPHONE (the highest pitched saxophone). *See also* MEZZO.

sordino (*abbreviation* **S**) (*Italian*) 'MUTE'.

sospirando (*Italian*) 'sighing'.

sospiro (*Italian*) literally 'sigh', in music meaning a QUARTER NOTE (crotchet) rest

sostenuto (*Italian*) 'sustained'.

sotto (*Italian*) 'below', as in *sotto voce,* which literally means 'under the VOICE' or whispered.

soul music a type of emotionally charged music developed by African-American musicians in America. 'Soul', as it is usually called, derives from BLUES and GOSPEL music with the addition of ROCK RHYTHMS.

sound a term in ACOUSTICS for TONES resulting from regular VIBRATIONS, as opposed to noise.

sound hole the opening in the BELLY of a stringed instrument, e.g. the f-shaped holes in a violin or the round hole in a guitar.

soundpost a piece of wood connecting the BELLY of a stringed instrument (such as a VIOLIN) to the back. It helps to distribute VIBRATIONS through the body of the instrument.

sousaphone a giant TUBA that encircles the player's body and was designed for his band by the American bandmaster and composer John Philip Sousa (1854–1932) who formed a successful MILITARY-style BAND that toured the world giving concerts.

Spanish guitar the classic GUITAR with a narrow waist, six strings and a central SOUND HOLE.

special effects a non-specific term used of any extraordinary noises or SOUNDS that may be required of an orchestra, or part of an orchestra, to satisfy the demands of a composer, such as COW BELLS, etc.

species a discipline used in teaching strict COUNTERPOINT, developed by Johann Fux (1660–1741), who listed five rhythmic patterns ('species') in which one VOICE PART could be combined with another.

spinet a type of small HARPSICHORD.

spirito (*Italian*) 'spirit', so *con spirito* means 'with spirit'.

spiritual a type of religious FOLK SONG or HYMN that was developed by black (and white) Americans in the 18th and 19th centuries. Spirituals are characterised by strong SYNCOPATION and simple MELODIES. They were superseded by GOSPEL music.

Sprechgesang (*German*) literally 'speech-song', i.e. a type of singing that is half speech. It was used by Schoenberg in his song cycle *Pierrot Lunaire*.

Stabat Mater (*Latin*) 'The Mother stood', the initial words of a hymn describing the sorrows of the Virgin at the Crucifixion. It was set to music, other than its original PLAINSONG, by Palestrina; later settings include those by Haydn, Schubert and Rossini.

stabile a non-moving MOBILE, as devised by Alexander Calder.

staccato (*Italian*) 'detached', i.e. NOTES should be shortened and played with brief INTERVALS between them.

staff a set of horizontal lines (usually five) on which music is written. Each line, and the gaps between them, represent a different PITCH.

stave *see* STAFF.

steel drum a PERCUSSION INSTRUMENT (*pan*) made by West Indian musicians (particularly from Trinidad) out of discarded oil drums. Each DRUM can be tuned to play a range of notes by beating and heat-treating different sections of the 'head', i.e. the top of the drum.

Steinway a firm of piano manufacturers founded by Henry Steinway (originally Heinrich Steinweg) (1797–1871) in New York in 1853. A London branch opened in 1875.

stem the line attached to the head of all notes smaller than a WHOLE NOTE (semibreve).

stesso (*Italian*) 'same', so *lo stesso* TEMPO means 'the same speed'.

stiacciato *see* relief.

Stijl, De a group of Dutch artists, founded to spread theories on ABSTRACT ART, principally through the *De Stijl* magazine, which was published 1917–28. The group rejected the representational in art, believing that art's object was to convey harmony and order, achieved by the use of straight lines and geometrical shapes in primary colours or black and white. Their ideas had great influence, particularly on BAUHAUS, on architecture, and on commercial art.

still life a genre of painting depicting inanimate objects such as fruit, flowers, etc, begun by Dutch artists seeking secular commissions after the Reformation and the loss of Church patronage. Within the genre, the *vanitas* still life contains objects symbolic of the transience of life, e.g. skulls, hourglasses, etc, while others contain religious symbols, such as bread and wine. In the 18th century, new life was given to the form by the French painter Jean-Baptiste Chardin (1699–1779) and in the 19th century Cézanne's use of it in his experiments with structure influenced the CUBISTS.

stomp a BLUES composition in which the BEAT is literally stamped on the floor.

stop a handle or knob on an ORGAN that admits or prevents air from reaching certain PIPES and that can therefore be used to modify the potential output of the MANUALS and PEDALS.

stopping on stringed instruments, the placing of fingers on a string to shorten its effective length and raise its PITCH.

Stradivari or Stradivarius a violin made by Antonio Stradivari (1644–1737), an Italian violin-maker whose instruments are unsurpassed for the quality of their sound.

strathspey *see* REEL.

stream of consciousness a term coined by William James in his *The Varieties of Religious Experience* (1902) that has been adapted by literary critics to denote a fluxive method of narration in which characters voice their feelings with no 'obtrusive' authorial comment and with no orthodox dialogue or decription. The term has particular reference to the work of Joyce and Woolf.

Streichquartett (*German*) a 'STRING QUARTET'.

strepitoso (*Italian*) 'boisterously'.

stretto 'close together', i.e. a quickening of TEMPO.

stride (piano) a JAZZ piano technique characterised by the use of single bass notes on the first and third beats, and chords on the second and fourth.

string a vibrating cord for the production of tone, in the piano of drawn cast steel wire, in instruments of the violin family of catgut or spun silk, and in the guitar of catgut or wire.

stringendo (*Italian*) 'tightening', i.e. increasing tension, often with accelerated TEMPO.

string quartet (1) a group of four performers who use stringed instruments (two VIOLINS, VIOLA, and CELLO). (2) a piece of music written for such a group.

strings a general term for the stringed instruments of the VIOLIN family.

Stroh violin a VIOLIN made of metal (invented by Charles Stroh in 1901) that incorporates a TRUMPET bell and does not have a normal violin body.

Structuralism in literary criticism, a critical approach to literature in which the text being studied is viewed as a 'cultural product' that cannot be 'read' in isolation and in which the text is held to absorb its meaning from the interconnected web of linguistic codes and symbols of which it is but a part. The process of studying the codes, etc., and their relation to each other, is called *Semiotics*. To illustrate: a Structuralist approach to the novels of Fenimore Cooper would, for example, include recognition of the linguistic and cultural conventions underlying the author's use of language, with particular reference to the significance of both the 'Noble Savage' myth in Western culture and the emerging frontier myth in American culture. The heroic persona of the Deerslayer, and his portrayal as a transient figure between the mythic world of primitive America and the swelling wave of modern civilisation, results in a creative tension ripe for hours of happy exploration and parallel.

Figures associated with the development of Structuralist theory are the Canadian critic Marshall McLuhan, whose studies of mass culture and communication include *The Gutenberg Galaxy* (1962) and *The Medium is the Message* (1967), the linguist Ferdinand de Saussure, the French anthropologist Claude Lévi-Strauss (1908–), the critic Roland Barthes, and the psychoanalyst Jacques Lacan (1901–81). Structuralism is thus an approach drawing on a wide range of disciplines, with some critics, e.g. followers of Lacan, focusing on the play between unconscious and conscious concepts, while others, e.g. followers of Saussure, will focus on the linguistic relativism that emerges between the *signifier* (the spoken word) and the *signified* (the mind's concept of the word). *Deconstruction*, a concept developed by the French philosopher Jacques Derrida (1930–2004), is a term for the process or 'strategy' of examining the elements (signs) of language in isolation from other elements, thus exposing the contradictions inherent within language. It is also called *Poststructuralism*.

The psychologist Jean Piaget usefully defines structure as composed of wholeness, transformation and self-regulation. Thus, Homer's *Iliad*, for example, (a) is a work with a unity of structure conforming to the conventions of EPIC poetic form; (b) includes recognisable 'types' of characters who appear in other such works, e.g. warriors, who may also behave in ways outside the expected form, as when the young Achilles hides himself amongst women dressed as a girl; (c) can alter its meaning according to external factors; e.g. the reader's understanding of the characters' behaviour can vary at different times

as fresh experiences alter the reader's perception.

Stück (*German*) 'piece'.

study in art, a drawing or painting of a detail for use in a larger finished work.

In music, a piece written to demonstrate technique in playing a musical instrument or using the voice.

subdominant the fourth NOTE of the MAJOR or MINOR SCALE.

subito (*abbreviation* **S**) (*Italian*) 'suddenly', as in PIANO *subito,* 'suddenly soft'.

subject a musical THEME on which a composition (or part of a composition) is constructed, e.g. the first and second SUBJECTS in the EXPOSITION in SONATA FORM; the subject in a FUGUE; also the leading VOICE (first PART) of a fugue.

submediant the sixth NOTE of the MAJOR or MINOR SCALE.

subsidiary theme any THEME that is less important than the main theme(s) of a composition.

suite a collection of short pieces that combine to form an effective overall composition; the BAROQUE suite was a set of (stylised) dances.

sul, sull' (*Italian*) 'on' or 'over', so *sul ponticello* means 'over the BRIDGE' (in VIOLIN bowing).

Suprematism a Russian art movement based on principles of nonobjectivity. It was begun by the painter Kasimir Malevich (1878–1935) in 1913 and evolved on a parallel with CONSTRUCTIVISM. *White on White* by Malevich is typical of the work of the movement. The influence of Suprematism spread through the BAUHAUS to Europe and the US.

Surrealism an avant-garde art movement of the 1920s and 1930s in France, which grew out of DADA and was inspired by the dream theories of Freud and by the literature and poetry of Rimbaud and Baudelaire. Surrealism took from Dadaism a love for the juxtaposition of incongruous images, the purpose of which in the Surrealist view was to express the workings of the unconscious mind. The term 'Surrealism' had been coined by the poet Apollinaire, but the movement really got going with the publication by the poet André Breton (1896–1966) of his first *Surrealist Manifesto* in 1924. According to Breton (influenced by Freud), the 'higher reality' could only be achieved in art by freeing the mind from the lower world of superficial rationality.

In art, its influences include the works of de Chirico. There were two main trends: *automatism*, or *free association*, was explored in the works of Miró, Ernst, and others, who sought deliberately to avoid conscious control by using techniques of spontaneity to express the subconscious. The world of dreams was the source of inspiration for the incongruously juxtaposed, often bizarre, but precisely painted imagery of Dali, and Magritte.

suspension a device used in HARMONY, in which a NOTE sounded in one CHORD is sustained while a subsequent chord is played (or sung), producing a DISSONANCE that is then resolved.

sustaining pedal *see* PIANO.

swell organ a MANUAL on an ORGAN. The notes played on this manual can become louder and softer by the opening and closing of the shutters on the *swell box*, which encloses the PIPES.

swing a type of American POPULAR MUSIC of the 1935–45 era; it was played by BIG BANDS and had an insistent RHYTHM. Glenn Miller and his ENSEMBLE were influential in its development.

Symbolism in literature, a French poetry movement of the late-19th century that rejected the dictates of both REALISM and NATURALISM by seeking to express a state of mind by a process of suggestion rather than by attempting to portray 'objective reality'. As Mallarmé put it, 'not the thing, but the effect produced'. Other prominent poets associated with Symbolism include Verlaine and Rimbaud. The movement has strong links with the world of Impressionist composers, e.g. Debussy. Poets outside the French-speaking world influenced by Symbolism include T. S. Eliot, Pound, Rilke and, notably, Yeats, whose epigram 'Three Movements' serves as an epitaph both for the movement and for his own involvement with it. Several important plays of the late 19th century, e.g. Chekhov's *The Seagull* (1895) and Ibsen's *The Master Builder* (1896), also display the influence of Symbolism.

In art, also in late 19th-century France, Symbolism represented a response to the intrinsically visual work of the Impressionists and fell into two distinct trends: some painters were inspired by the images of Symbolist literature, while others, including Gauguin, Van Gogh, and the NABIS, explored the symbolic use of colour and line to express emotion.

sympathetic strings strings on certain instruments, such as the SITAR, that are not actually plucked or bowed but are set in sympathetic VIBRATION and produce a NOTE without being touched when the same note is played on a 'melody' string.

symphonic poem or tone poem an orchestral composition, a form of PROGRAMME MUSIC, usually in one MOVEMENT, that attempts to interpret or describe an emotion, idea, or story. The term was coined by Liszt.

symphony in essence, a prolonged or extended SONATA for an ORCHESTRA. Most symphonies have four MOVEMENTS (sections) that, although interrelated, tend to have recognised forms, e.g. a quick first movement, a slow second movement, a MINUET third movement, and a vibrant fourth movement (FINALE).

Synchronism an art movement originating in the USA in 1913 the members of which were concerned with the balanced arrangement of pure colour, or 'colours together'. The movement influenced a number of American painters.

syncopation an alteration to the normal arrangement of accented BEATS in a BAR. This is usually done by placing ACCENTS on beats or parts of a beat that do not normally carry an accent.

synthesiser an ELECTRONIC instrument, operated by a keyboard and switches, that can generate and modify an extensive range of SOUND.

tabla a pair of Indian DRUMS, beaten with the hands, that are often used to accompany the SITAR in classical Indian music.

table an alternative name for the upper surface, or BELLY, of instruments of the VIOLIN family.

tabor an early type of SIDE DRUM.

tace (*Italian*) 'silent'.

Tafelmusik (*German*) 'table music', i.e.

music sung during a banquet as an entertainment.

tail the line attached to the head of a HALF-NOTE (minim) or a smaller NOTE.

tail piece the piece of wood at the base of a VIOLIN to which the strings are attached.

tail pin the metal rod at the bottom of a CELLO or DOUBLE BASS that can be pulled out to adjust the height of the instrument above the floor.

Takt (*German*) 'TIME', so *im Takt* means 'in time'.

talon (*French*) the 'nut' or heel of a BOW.

tambourin (1) a lively 18th-century piece in the style of a FOLK DANCE from Provence, usually in 2/4 TIME. (2) a narrow DRUM, played along with a PIPE, as the ACCOMPANIMENT to dancing.

tambourine a small, shallow DRUM with a single skin fastened over a circular frame. Small metal CYMBALS (jingles) are slotted into the frame and rattle when the instrument is shaken or beaten with the hand.

tampon a drumstick that has a head at each end, held in the middle to produce a DRUM ROLL.

tango a Latin-American dance in moderately slow 2/4 TIME, originating from Argentina. It makes use of syncopated RHYTHMS (*see* SYNCOPATION) and became popular in Europe in the 1920s.

tanto (*Italian*) 'so much', as in ALLEGRO *non tanto*, meaning 'quick, but not too quick'.

Tanz (*German*) 'dance'.

tap dance a dance in which the feet are used to tap out a RHYTHM. Tap dancing was made popular by performances in films by Fred Astaire during the 1930s. Special shoes with steel plates at the toe and heel are usually worn.

tarantella a very fast, wild FOLK DANCE from southern Italy in 6/8 TIME and gradually increasing in speed. Chopin used the form in a concert piece.

tasto (*Italian*) the keyboard of a PIANO or the fingerboard of a stringed instrument.

tattoo originally a night DRUM beat calling soldiers to their quarters, now a military display.

Te Deum laudamus (*Latin*) 'We Praise Thee, O God', a Christian HYMN sung at MATINS. Numerous composers (e.g. Purcell, Handel, Verdi) have set it to music.

tempera a paint medium made by mixing colour pigments with egg. It was much used until the 15th century and the development of oil paint.

temperament the way in which INTERVALS between NOTES have been 'tempered', or slightly altered, in Western music so that the slight discrepancy in seven OCTAVES is distributed evenly over the range. In EQUAL TEMPERAMENT an octave is divided into twelve SEMITONES, which means that, for example, D SHARP is also E FLAT: this is a compromise, for strictly there is a marginal difference between D sharp and E flat.

tempo (*Italian*) 'TIME'; the time taken by a composition, therefore the speed at which it is performed, hence the pace of the BEAT. *A tempo* means 'in time'. It can also mean a movement of a SONATA or SYMPHONY, e.g. *il secondo tempo*, 'the second MOVEMENT'.

ten. (*Italian*) an abbreviation for TENUTO.

tenor (1) the highest adult male VOICE with a range an OCTAVE to either side of middle C. (2) as a prefix to the name of an instrument, it indicates the size between an ALTO member of the family and a BASS, e.g. tenor SAXOPHONE. (3) the RECITING NOTE in PSALM singing. (4) an obsolete term for a VIOLA (tenor VIOLIN).

tenor drum a DRUM, often used in MILITARY BANDS, between a SIDE DRUM and BASS DRUM in size and PITCH, and without snares.

tenor violin a VIOLONCELLO.

tenuto (*abbreviation* **ten.**) (*Italian*) 'held'; a term indicating that a NOTE should be held for its full value or in some cases even longer.

ternary form a term applied to a piece of music divided into three self-contained parts, with the first and third sections bearing strong similarities.

ternary time *see* TRIPLE TIME.

terzett, terzetto (*Italian*) *see* TRIO.

tessitura (*Italian*) 'texture'; a term that indicates whether the majority of NOTES in a piece are high up or low down in the range of a VOICE (or instrument).

tetrachord a group of four NOTES.

theme the MELODY, or other musical material, that forms the basis of a work or a MOVEMENT and that may be varied or developed. It may return in one form or another throughout a composition.

thirty-second note a note having $1/32$ the duration of a whole note. Also known as a demisemiquaver. Indicated by the symbol ♪.

thorough bass *see* FIGURED BASS.

thunder stick or bull roarer or whizzer an instrument consisting of a flat piece of wood fastened to a piece of string. When the piece of wood is whirled around the head, it creates a roaring sound.

tie a curved line that joins two NOTES of the same PITCH together, indicating that they should be played as one long note.

timbre (*French*) the quality of TONE or the characteristic SOUND of an instrument.

time the rhythmic pattern (number of BEATS in a BAR) of a piece of music, as indicated by the TIME SIGNATURE. DUPLE TIME has two beats in a bar, *triple time* has three beats in a bar, and so on.

time-names or rhythm-names a French method of teaching TIME and RHYTHM in which beats are given names, such as 'ta', 'ta-te', etc.

time signature a sign placed at the beginning of a piece of music that indicates the number and value of BEATS in a BAR. A time signature usually consists of two numbers, one placed above the other. The lower number defines the unit of measurement in relation to the WHOLE NOTE (semibreve); the top figure indicates the number of those units in a bar; e.g. 3/4 indicates that there are three QUARTER NOTES (crotchets) in a bar.

timpani or kettledrums the main orchestral PERCUSSION INSTRUMENTS, consisting of bowl-shaped shells over which the membrane is stretched. The shell is supported on a frame at the base of which, in 'pedal timpani', is the foot PEDAL that can alter the PITCH of the drum as it is played. The drum can also be tuned (*see* TUNING) by screws, which alter the tension of the membrane.

Tin Pan Alley the nickname given to West 28th Street in New York, where the popular-song publishing business used to be situated. It consequently became a slang expression for the POPULAR MUSIC industry.

tin whistle or penny whistle a metal whistle-FLUTE, similar to a RECORDER but with six finger holes. It produces high-pitched sounds and is commonly used to play FOLK music.

toccata (*Italian*) 'touched', a type of music for a keyboard instrument that is intended to show off a player's 'touch' or ability.

tonality the use of a KEY in a composition.

tondo (*plural* **tondi**) the Italian word for 'round', used in art to denote a circular picture or sculpture.

tone (1) an INTERVAL comprising two SEMITONES, e.g. the interval between C and D. (2) (US) a musical NOTE. (3) the quality of SOUND, e.g. good TONE, SHARP tone, etc. (4) in PLAINSONG, a MELODY.

tone poem *see* SYMPHONIC POEM.

tonguing in the playing of a WIND INSTRUMENT, the interruption of the flow of breath by the tongue so that detached NOTES are played or the first note of a PHRASE is distinguished.

tonic the first NOTE of a MAJOR or MINOR SCALE.

tonic sol-fa a system of NOTATION and sight-singing used in training in which NOTES are sung to syllables. The notes of the major scale are: DOH, RE, ME, FAH, SOH, LA, TE, DOH (doh is always the TONIC, whatever the KEY). The system was pioneered in England by John Curwen (1816–80) in the mid-19th century.

tosto (*Italian*) 'rapid', as in PIÙ *tosto*, 'quicker'.

trad jazz literally 'traditional JAZZ', a term referring to the type of comparatively simple jazz, with a strong MELODY, as played in New Orleans, which preceded the development of BEBOP.

tragedy a form of drama in which a hero or heroine comes to a bad end. The cause of the protagonist's failure can be either a personal flaw or a circumstance beyond his or her control, or both. The earliest tragedies known, those by Aeschylus, Sophocles, and Euripides, are still among the greatest. The first critical study of the form is in Aristotle's *Poetics*, where Aristotle defines tragedy as an imitation (*mimesis*) of a serious, complete action on a grand scale, 'grand' meaning a momentous action involving highly placed characters in society. The protagonist will make an 'error of judgment' (*hamartia*, which has often been rendered, a bit misleadingly, as 'tragic flaw') but the protagonist's main fault is as often the result of having to undertake a certain action at a certain time, as in any character defect; thus, in Sophocles' *Antigone*, the heroine is in the position of having to choose between divine and human law. The protagonist is usually a good person, but not perfect, and progresses from happiness to misery. Another important concept in the *Poetics* is that of *catharsis*, the 'purging' (or purification, cleansing) of the emotions of pity and fear aroused in the spectators by the play.

The great tradition of the Greek tragedians was filtered through the plays of Seneca to the dramatists of the Renaissance, although Renaissance tragedies, such as those of Shakespeare, differ significantly from those of the past. The interplay in Shakespeare's tragedies between the heroic and the ironic or comic commonplace worlds, e.g. the banter between the rustic clown and Cleopatra at the end of *Antony and Cleopatra*, is profoundly foreign to the world of the *Poetics*, just as the pagan and fate-haunted world of the Greeks was ultimately alien to Renaissance dramatists brought up in the Christian tradition.

Several 20th-century dramatists, e.g. Arthur Miller and O'Neill, have tried to adapt the form of Athenian tragedy to the modern stage. The most that can be said for these is that they may result in effects similar to those of the originals. The fact that such dramas invariably have as subtext the notion that this state of affairs is reformable, and the equally invariable ironic presentation of the protagonists as 'losers of history' rather than as victims of forces as permanent as they are merciless, puts such plays as Miller's *Death of a Salesman* at a further remove from the Athenian drama than, say, Shakespeare's *King Lear*, with its bleak vision of a fallen world in which tyranny is an ever present threat. *See also* DOMESTIC TRAGEDY, HEROIC TRAGEDY, JACOBEAN TRAGEDY, REVENGE TRAGEDY.

tragicomedy *see* COMEDY.

tranquillo (*Italian*) 'calm'.

transcription *see* ARRANGEMENT.

transition (1) see MODULATION. (2) a PASSAGE linking two sections of a piece, which often involves a change of key.

transposing instruments instruments that sound NOTES different from those actually written down, e.g. a piece of music in E flat for the B flat CLARINET would actually be written in F.

transposition the changing of the PITCH of a composition. Singers sometimes ask accompanists to transpose a SONG higher or lower so that it is better suited to their voice range.

treble (1) the highest part in harmonised music; soprano. (2) a term describing the highest pitch or range; a voice, singer, or instrument (3) the highest pitched peal of a bell.

treble clef G CLEF on the second line of the STAFF, used for TREBLE VOICES and instruments of medium or high PITCH, e.g. VIOLINS, FLUTES, OBOES, CLARINETS, HORNS and TRUMPETS.

trecento the Italian term for the 14th century.

tremolando (*Italian*) 'trembling'.

tremolo (*Italian*) the rapid repetition of a single NOTE, or the rapid alternation between two or more notes.

triad a CHORD of three NOTES that includes a third and a FIFTH.

triangle a PERCUSSION INSTRUMENT comprising a thin steel bar bent into a triangle but with one corner left unjoined. It is normally struck with a thin metal bar.

trill or shake an ORNAMENT in which a NOTE is rapidly alternated with the note above. It is used in both vocal and instrumental pieces.

trio (1) a group of three performers. (2) a piece of music written for such a group. (3) the middle section of a MINUET, as found in SONATAS, SYMPHONIES, etc. It was originally a section scored for three PARTS.

triplet a group of three NOTES played in the time of two notes.

triple time *see* TIME.

triptych a painting, usually an altarpiece, consisting of three hinged parts, the outer two (or wings) folding over the larger middle section. *See also* DIPTYCH; POLYPTYCH.

tritone an INTERVAL consisting of three WHOLE TONES.

tromba marina a long, stringed instrument of the 15th century. It consisted of a long, tapered box with one string, mounted on top, which was played with a BOW; inside the box were some twenty SYMPATHETIC STRINGS.

trombone a BRASS instrument that has changed little for 500 years. The body of the instrument has a cylindrical bore with a bell at one end and a MOUTHPIECE at the other. A U-shaped SLIDE is used for lengthening or shortening the tubing and therefore for sounding different NOTES. TENOR and BASS trombones are often used in orchestras.

trope (*Latin*) an addition of music or words to traditional PLAINSONG LITURGY.

troppo (*Italian*) 'too much', as in ALLEGRO *non troppo*, meaning 'fast but not too fast'.

troubadour a poet-musician of the early Middle Ages who originally came from the South of France and sang in the Provençal language.

trumpet a BRASS instrument that has a cylindrical bore with a funnel-shaped MOUTHPIECE at one end and a bell (flared opening) at the other. The modern trumpet has three valves (operated by PISTONS) that bring into play extra lengths of tubing and are therefore used to change the pitch of the instrument. Trumpets are used in orchestras, JAZZ BANDS, and MILITARY BANDS. 'Trumpet' is also a generic term used to describe any number of very different types of instrument that are found all over the world.

tuba a large BRASS instrument with a wide conical bore, a large cup-shaped MOUTHPIECE and a large bell that faces upwards. It can have between three and five valves and comes in three common sizes: TENOR (EUPHONIUM), BASS, and double bass. Tubas are found in orchestras and military bands.

tubular bells *see* BELLS.

tune a MELODY or AIR.

tuning the adjusting of the PITCH of an instrument so that it corresponds to an agreed note; e.g. an orchestra will usually have all its instruments tuned to the note of A.

tuning fork a two-pronged steel device that,

when tapped, will sound a single, 'pure' note. It was invented by John Shore in 1711 and is used to tune instruments, etc.

tutti (*Italian*) 'all'; in orchestral music, a *tutti* passage is one to be played by the whole orchestra.

twelve-note music or twelve-tone system a method of composition formulated and advanced by Schoenberg. In the system, the twelve CHROMATIC NOTES of an OCTAVE can only be used in specific orders, called *note rows*; no note can be repeated twice within a note row, and the rows must be used complete. In all, there are forty-eight ways in which a note row can be arranged (using INVERSION, RETROGRADE MOTION, and inverted retrograde motion), and it is with note rows that compositions are constructed.

ukelele a small, four-stringed GUITAR that was developed in Hawaii during the 19th century. It was a popular music-hall instrument during the 1920s.

unison the sounding of the same NOTE or its OCTAVE by two or more VOICES or instruments.

Unities *see* NEOCLASSICISM.

up beat the upward movement of a conductor's BATON or hand, indicating the unstressed (usually the last) BEAT in a BAR.

upright *see* PIANO.

Urtext (*German*) 'original text'.

Utopian novel a form of NOVEL developed from *Utopia* (1516), a fantasy of a supposedly ideally organised state written by Sir Thomas More. The work spawned a host of imitations throughout the centuries but the impact of 20th-century totalitarianism has lessened enthusiasm for the form. Aldous Huxley's *Island* (1962) is a modern example of a Utopian novel; the same author's *Brave New World* (1932) is an example of its opposite, a 'dystopia' or 'bad place'.

Utrecht School a movement in Dutch art begun by Gerrit van Honthorst (1590–1656), Hendrick Terbrugghen (1588–1629), and Dirck van Baburen (*c*.1595–1624), who were in Rome between 1610 and 1620 and were strongly influenced by Caravaggio, whose style they took back to the Netherlands, thus influencing in turn such northern masters as Vermeer and Rembrandt.

V an abbreviation for VIOLIN, VOCE, VOLTA.

VA an abbreviation of VIOLA.

valse (*French*) *see* WALTZ.

valve a device attached to horns, trumpets, and other brass instruments to lengthen or reduce the extend of tubing, hence lowering or raising the pitch respectively, to complete the scale.

vamp to improvise an ACCOMPANIMENT.

variation the modification or DEVELOPMENT of a THEME.

vaudeville (*French*) originally a type of popular satirical SONG sung by Parisian street musicians. In the 18th century these songs (with new words) were incorporated into plays, and the word came to mean the last song in an opera in which each character sang a verse. In the 19th century stage performances with songs and dances were called 'vaudevilles', and in the US the terms used to describe music-hall shows.

veloce (*Italian*) 'fast'.

Venite (*Latin*) the first word of PSALM 95, '*Venite, exultemus Domino*' ('O come let us sing unto the Lord'), which is sung as a prelude to psalms at Anglican MATINS.

verismo (*Italian*) 'realism'; the term is used to describe a type of opera that was concerned with representing contemporary life of ordinary people in an honest and realistic way, e.g. *Cavalleria Rusticana* by Mascagni.

verse (1) a line of poetry or a stanza of a poem. (2) a composition in METER, especially of a light nature. (3) a short section of a chapter in the Bible.

versification (1) the art of making verses. (2) the METER or verses of a poem.

Vespers the seventh of the Canonical Hours (services of the day) in the Roman Catholic Church. Many composers have written musical settings for the service.

vibraphone or vibes an American instrument, similar to the GLOCKENSPIEL, that consists of a series of metal bars that are struck with mallets. Underneath the bars hang tubular resonators, containing small discs that can be made to spin by means of an electric motor. When the NOTES are sustained the spinning discs give the sound a pulsating quality.

vibration a term in ACOUSTICS for the wave-like MOTION by which a TONE is produced.

Sound vibrations are mechanical; radio vibrations are electromagnetic and inaudible.

vibrato (*Italian*) literally 'shaking', i.e. a small but rapid variation in the PITCH of a NOTE.

vierhändig (*German*) 'four-handed', i.e. a piano duet.

villanella (*Italian*) literally a 'rustic SONG', a popular PART-SONG of the 17th century.

Vingt, Les a group of 20 Belgian painters who exhibited together in Brussels for ten years from 1884. Their exhibitions also included works by innovative French painters, e.g. Seurat, Gauguin and Cézanne.

viol a family of stringed instruments played with a BOW that were widely used in the 16th and 17th centuries. The instruments came in several sizes and designs, but they all usually had six strings and FRETS. Although they were similar in appearance to members of the VIOLIN family, they were constructed differently and gave a much softer sound.

viola (*abbreviation* VA) originally a general term for a bowed stringed instrument. However, it is now the name of the ALTO member of the VIOLIN family. It has four strings.

viola da braccio (*Italian*) literally an 'arm VIOL', a generic term for any stringed instrument played on the arm. It came to mean a VIOLIN or VIOLA.

viola da gamba (*Italian*) literally a 'leg VIOL', a term originally used of those members of the viol family played vertically between the legs or on the lap, but it came to be used exclusively for the BASS viol.

viola d'amore (*Italian*) literally a 'love VIOL', i.e. a tenor VIOL with seven strings (instead of six) and seven or fourteen SYMPATHETIC STRINGS, so called because it had a particularly sweet TONE.

violin (*abbreviation* **V**) a stringed instrument played with a BOW that was introduced in the 16th century. It was developed independently of the VIOL from the medieval FIDDLE. It has no FRETS and just four strings. The violin family includes the violin itself (TREBLE), VIOLA (ALTO), and VIOLONCELLO or 'cello' (TENOR). The DOUBLE BASS developed from the double BASS VIOL, but it is now included in the violin family.

violoncello or cello the tenor of the VIOLIN family, dating from the 16th century. It is held vertically between the legs of the seated player, and the TAIL PIN rests on the ground. It has four strings, which are played with a BOW.

virginal a keyboard instrument dating from the 16th century in which the strings are plucked by quills. It was similar to the HARPSICHORD except that it had an oblong body with strings running parallel to the keyboard. The word has also been used to describe any member of the harpsichord family.

virtuoso (*plural* **virtuosi**) (*Italian*) a skilled performer on the VIOLIN or some other instrument. The word was formerly synonymous with 'amateur'.

vivace (*Italian*) 'lively'.

vivamente (*Italian*) 'in a lively way'.

vivo (*Italian*) 'lively'.

vocalisation control of the VOICE and vocal sounds, and the method of producing and phrasing NOTES with the voice.

vocal score *see* SCORE.

voce (*abbreviation* **V**) (*Italian*) 'VOICE', as in *voce di petto*, 'CHEST VOICE'.

voice (1) the SOUND produced by human beings by the rush of air over the vocal chords, which are made to vibrate. There are three categories of adult male voice (BASS, BARITONE, and TENOR); three female categories (CONTRALTO, MEZZO-SOPRANO, and SOPRANO); and two boy categories (TREBLE and ALTO). (2) Parts in contrapuntal (*see* COUNTERPOINT) compositions are traditionally termed 'voices'. *See also* FUGUE.

volta (*abbreviation* **V**) (*Italian*) 'time'.

volti subito (*Italian*) 'turn over quickly' (of a page).

voluntary (1) an improvised piece of instrumental music (16th century). (2) an ORGAN SOLO (sometimes improvised) played before and after an Anglican service.

Vorticism a short-lived English Cubist art movement devised by Wyndham Lewis, who also edited the two issues of its magazine, *Blast* (1914, 1915). *See* FUTURISM.

waltz a dance in triple TIME. Waltzes evolved in Germany and Austria during the late-18th century and became particularly popular in Vienna.

watercolour a paint medium of colour pigments mixed with water-soluble gum arabic. When moistened, a watercolour paint produces a transparent colour that is applied to paper, usually white, the paper showing through the paint.

wedding march a tune played at the start or end of a wedding service. The two most famous wedding marches are Mendelssohn's 'Wedding March', from his incidental music to *A Midsummer Night's Dream*, and Wagner's 'Bridal Chorus' (better known as 'Here Comes the Bride') from the opera *Lohengrin*.

whistle (1) a toy FLUTE. (2) the making of a musical sound with the lips and breath without using the vocal cords, the hollow of the mouth forming a RESONANCE BOX. Whistling PITCH is an OCTAVE higher than is generally supposed.

whizzer *see* THUNDER STICK.

whole note the NOTE with the longest time-value normally used in modern Western NOTATION. Also known as a semibreve, a 'half of a BREVE'. Indicated by the symbol ○.

whole-tone scale a SCALE in which all the INTERVALS are whole-tones, i.e. two SEMITONES.

wind instrument a musical INSTRUMENT the SOUND of which is produced by the breath of the player or by means of bellows.

wit 'What oft was thought but ne'er so well expressed' (Pope, *An Essay on Criticism*). The term has had many meanings and shades of meanings through the years and can denote either the thing itself or a notable practitioner of it. The main shifts of meaning to bear in mind are: (a) Elizabethan usage, meaning intelligence or wisdom; (b) early 17th-century usage, meaning ingenious thought, 'fancy' and original figures of speech, as in Donne's verse and METAPHYSICAL POETRY; (c) the period relevant to Pope's definition, roughly from the mid-17th century to the last half of the 18th, which is discussed below; (d) 19th-century to modern times usage, meaning an amusing, perhaps surprising observation, usually involving paradox. Wit as defined by Pope must be distinguished from what we now regard as humour: wit can be malicious, humour is benevolent. Swift is witty, Addison and Steele, who set the pattern for the future, are both witty and humorous. Wits tended to congregate in groups of like-minded intellectuals sharing similar political, social, and religious views. By the late half of the 18th century, the term largely ceased to be used to describe intellectual groups, implying as it did either heartless frivolity or political faction. Intellectual groupings became looser, although certainly no less formidable: a literary gathering in 1780 London, for example, could include figures as diverse as Sheridan, Dr Johnson, Burke, and Edward Gibbon, all of whom could be described as sharp-witted heavyweight thinkers and controversialists, although not 'wits' in the previous sense of the term.

woodwind a term for a group of blown instruments that were traditionally made of wood (some of which are now made of metal, e.g. FLUTES, OBOES, CLARINETS, and BASSOONS, etc).

xylophone a PERCUSSION INSTRUMENT made up of hardwood bars arranged like a keyboard on a frame. It is played by striking the bars with mallets. Xylophones used in orchestras have steel resonators suspended beneath each bar.

zarzuela a type of Spanish COMIC OPERA that has a satirical theme and includes dialogue. It usually comprises just one act.

zither the generic term for a range of stringed instruments. The European zither consists of a flat box that is strung with a variety of different kinds of string (up to 40). The player uses a PLECTRUM to play melodies on one set of strings while the fingers on the other hand pluck a series of open strings to form a drone accompaniment.

Famous People

Achebe, Chinua (1930–) Nigerian novelist and poet whose work focuses on Ibo society and the legacy of colonialism. He won the Nobel prize for literature in 1989.

Acheson, Dean Gooderham (1893–1971) American lawyer and statesman who was responsible for formulating and developing several important strands of American foreign policy, notably the MARSHALL Plan and the establishment of NATO.

Adams, Ansel Easton (1902–84) American photographer, noted for his detailed, deep-focus studies of American landscape.

Adams, John (1735–1826) Federalist politician and second president of the US (1797–1801).

Adams, John Quincy (1767–1848) Democratic Republican politician and sixth president of the US (1825–29).

Addison, Joseph (1672–1719) English essayist and poet. With his friend Richard STEELE he founded the influential magazine *The Spectator* in 1711.

Adenauer, Konrad (1876–1967) German statesman who was imprisoned twice by the Nazi regime (1934, 1944). As chancellor of West Germany (1949–63) he had a major role in world politics.

Adler, Alfred (1870–1937) Austrian psychiatrist. He was an associate of FREUD, whose emphasis on sexuality he rejected, founding a school of psychoanalysis based on the individual's quest to overcome feelings of inadequacy (the 'inferiority complex').

Aeschylus (524–456 BC) Greek dramatist regarded as the founder of Greek tragedy (*see* AML tragedy). Seven of his plays survive, including *Prometheus Bound* and the *Oresteia* trilogy.

Agassi, Andre Kirk (1970–) American tennis player who won many top events during the 1990s and the early years of the 21st century. Popular for his breathtaking agility on court and his quixotic temperament, he is married to Stefi Graf.

Akihito *see* HIROHITO.

Akram, Wasim (1966–) Pakistani cricketer renowned for his abilities as a fast-bowler

and rated by many as the best of all time. He was at the peak of his career during the 1980s to early1990s and retired from the game in 2003.

Albee, Edward (1928–) American dramatist. His plays include *Who's Afraid of Virginia Woolf* (1962) and *A Delicate Balance* (1966).

Alberti, Leon Battista *see* AML perspective.

Alexander VI, Pope *see* BORGIA, RODRIGO.

Alexander the Great (356–323 BC) Macedonian king. The pupil of ARISTOTLE, he inherited the kingdom of Macedon from his father **Philip II** (382–336 BC). He conquered Greece in 336, Egypt in 331 and the Persian Empire by 328. He extended his conquests to the east and defeated an Indian army in 326. He died in Babylon and was buried in the city he founded, Alexandria.

Ali, Muhammad [Cassius Clay] (1942–) American boxer and world heavyweight champion (1964–67, 1974–78, 1978).

Allen, Woody [Allen Stewart Konigsberg] (1935–) American film director, actor and writer noted for his satirical films about the neuroses of New York intellectuals.

Allende [Gossens], Salvador (1908–73) Chilean politician. Elected president in 1970, the first freely elected Marxist president in Latin America, he was overthrown and killed in a coup that brought PINOCHET to power.

Altdorfer, Albrecht *see* AML Danube School

Amin [Dada], Idi (1925–2003) Ugandan dictator. He ruled Uganda from 1971 to 1979 (appointing himself president for life in 1976), but was overthrown.

Amis, Sir Kingsley (1922–95) English novelist and poet whose first novel, *Lucky Jim* (1954), a satire on academic life, is a comic masterpiece. His later novels are darker in tone. He was the father of **Martin Amis** (1949–), who is also a novelist.

Amundsen, Roald (1872–1928) Norwegian explorer and navigator, leader of the first expedition to reach the South Pole in 1911.

Andersen, Hans Christian (1805–75) Danish writer, best known now for his fairy tales, e.g. 'The Emperor's New Clothes'.

Anderson, Carl David *see* HESS, VICTOR FRANCIS.

Andropov, Yuri Vladimirovich (1914–84) Soviet statesman. Former head of the KGB and president of the USSR (1983–84).

Angelou, Maya (1928–) American dramatist, poet and short-story writer. She is one of the leading African-American writers of the 20th century.

Antony, Mark [Marcus Antonius] (*c*.83–30 BC) Roman soldier who fought with Julius CAESAR in the Gallic wars and after Caesar's assassination defeated Brutus and Cassius at the battle of Philippi (42). He deserted his wife for the Egyptian queen, **Cleopatra** (69–30 BC), their forces being defeated by AUGUSTUS at Actium. He and Cleopatra committed suicide.

Anwar, Saeed (1968–) Pakistani cricketer, known for his bursts of electrifying skill as a batsman. He achieved the record for the highest number of runs in one-day cricket—a record that still remains unbeaten. He retired from the fame in 2003.

Apollinaire, Guillaume [Apollinaris Kostrowitzky] (1880–1918) French art critic and writer who had great influence among avant-garde artists and poets at the beginning of the 20th century.

Aquinas, Thomas *see* THOMAS AQUINAS.

Aquino, [Maria] Corazon (1933–) Filipino politician. She was elected President of the Philippines in 1986, following the assassination of her husband, Benigno Aquino, the most prominent opponent of MARCOS. Aquino's administration survived three military coups.

Arafat, Yasser (1929–2004) Palestinian leader, who helped found the anti-Israeli guerrilla force *Al Fatah* and became chairman of the Palestine Liberation Organisation in 1968. In 1993 he signed the Israeli-Palestinian Peace Accord with Israeli Prime Minister YITZHAK RABIN, which conferred Palestinian autonomy in certain of the long-disputed occupied territories.

Aragon, Louis (1897–1982) French poet, essayist and novelist. He was one of the founders of both Dadaism and Surrealism (*see* AML).

Arden, John (1930–) English dramatist regarded as one of the leading left-wing playwrights of his generation.

Ardiles, Osvaldo [Ossie] Cesar (1952–) Argentinian football player and a member of the successful national team who won the World Cup in 1978. He played for Tottenham Hotspur during the 1980s but took famous leave of absence during the Falklands war, when Britain and Argentina fought over the sovereignty of the islands. He became manager of Tottenham during the 1990s and has lately been coach to Beiter Jerusalem (until October 2006).

Aristophanes (*c*.448–380 BC) Greek comic dramatist, 11 of whose comedies survive. The objects of his satire ranged from politicians to his fellow dramatists (EURIPIDES being one), and his plays are a valuable record of the intellectual debates of the day. The most popular of his plays now is *Lysistrata*.

Aristotle (384–322 BC) Greek philosopher. He taught at PLATO's Academy for 20 years and was tutor to ALEXANDER THE GREAT. He formed his own school (the Lyceum) in Athens in 335. His works, including *Nicomachean Ethics*, *Poetics* and *Politics*, were re-introduced to the Western world in the Middle Ages via Arabian scholarship and had a profound influence on almost every field of intellectual inquiry until the Renaissance. *See also* AML tragedy.

Armstrong, [Daniel] Louis 'Satchmo' (1900–71) American jazz trumpeter, singer and leader of many popular jazz bands. He had a genius for improvisation and became one of the best-loved entertainers of the 20th century. He also appeared in several films, including *High Society* (1956).

Armstrong, Neil Alden (1930–) American astronaut. He commanded the Apollo 11 moon-landing mission in 1969, in which he became the first man to walk on the moon.

Arp, Jean or Hans (1887–1966) German-born French sculptor and painter. A founder of Dadaism (*see* AML), his work was abstract in form.

Artaud, Antonin *see* AML Cruelty, Theatre of

Arthur (*fl.* 6th century AD) a possibly mythical Celtic warrior-king of post-Roman

Britain who may have organised resistance against the Saxon invaders.

Arthur, Chester A (1829–86) American Republican politician and the 21st president of the US. Served from 1881–1885.

Ashcroft, Dame Peggy (1907–91) English actress. One of the most popular stage and film actresses of her generation, she won an Oscar for her role in *A Passage to India* (1984).

Ashe, Arthur (1943–93) American tennis player. The first African American tennis player to win the US Open (1968), the Australian Open (1970) and the Wimbledon men's singles competition (1975).

Ashton, Sir Frederick William Mallandaine (1906–88) Ecuadorian-born British choreographer and co-founder of the Royal Ballet. His ballets include *A Month in the Country* (1976).

Asquith, Herbert Henry, 1st Earl of Oxford and Asquith (1852–1928) British statesman. He was leader of the Liberal Party (1908–26) and prime minister (1908–16).

Astaire, Fred [Frederick Austerlitz] (1899–1987) American dancer, singer and actor. His partnership with **Ginger Rogers [Virginia McMath]** (1911–95) resulted in a series of classic song-and-dance films, e.g. *Top Hat* (1935).

Astor, Nancy Witcher Langhorne, Viscountess Astor (1879–1964) American-born British politician. Elected to parliament as a Conservative MP, she became the first woman to take her seat in Parliament.

Atatürk, Kemal [Mustafa Kemal Atatürk] (1881–1938) Turkish general and statesman, regarded as the creator of the modern Turkish state.

Attenborough, Sir Richard Samuel (1923–) English film director, producer and actor. He was created a life peer in 1993. His brother **Sir David Frederick** (1926–) is a naturalist and broadcaster.

Attlee, Clement Richard, 1st Earl Attlee (1883–1967) British statesman. Leader of the Labour Party (1939–55) and prime minister (1945–51), his 1945 administration introduced widespread nationalisation and a programme of social security reforms.

Auden, W[ystan] H[ugh] (1907–73) English-born American poet. The leading left-wing poet of his generation, he later drifted away from Marxism towards a Christian and socially conservative position.

Augustine, Saint [Augustine of Hippo] (354–430) Latin Church Father. Born in what is now Tunisia, his father was a pagan and he was brought up a Christian by his mother. Reacting against the licentious life he led in Carthage, he converted to Manichaeanism for a while before returning to the Church. He was Bishop of Hippo (396–430) and wrote a spiritual autobiography, *Confessions*, and *City of God*, a major work of Christian apologetics.

Augustine, Saint (d. 604) Italian monk. He was sent to Britain in 597 by Pope GREGORY I to convert the Anglo-Saxons to Christianity and impose the authority of Rome on the Celtic Church. He became the first Archbishop of Canterbury in 601.

Augustus [Gaius Octavianus] (63 BC–14 AD) Roman emperor. After adoption by his uncle, Julius CAESAR, in 44 he took the name Gaius Julius Caesar Octavianus. He became the first emperor of Rome in 31 after defeating Mark ANTONY.

Aurelius, Marcus (121–80) Roman emperor and philosopher. Renowned for his nobility and learning, he spent much of his reign in war against the incoming 'barbarians' in the eastern part of the Empire.

Auric, Georges *see* AML Six, Les.

Austen, Jane (1775–1817) English novelist. Her six novels, *Sense and Sensibility* (1811), *Pride and Prejudice* (1813), *Mansfield Park* (1814), *Emma* (1816), *Northanger Abbey* and *Persuasion* (1818) are set in the society in which she lived, the well-bred essentially rural middle class of Regency England. She is renowned for her masterly dialogue, finely tuned satire and moral sense. *See also* AML epistolary novel.

Austin, Alfred *see* AML poet laureate.

Ayckbourn, Alan (1939–) English dramatist noted for satirical comedies including *The Norman Conquests* (1974).

Ayer, Sir A[lfred] J[ules] (1910–89) English philosopher, whose work is based on 'logical positivism' and the rejection of metaphysics and has been highly influential on British 'common-sense' philosophy.

Baade, Wilhelm Heinrich Walter (1893–1960) German-born American astronomer who made a valuable contribution to the understanding of gallactic and stellar evolution.

Baader, Andreas *see* MEINHOFF, ULRIKE.

Babbage, Charles (1792–1871) English mathematician. His primitive 'calculating machines' are regarded as the precursors of the modern computer.

Baburen, Dirck van *see* AML Utrecht School.

Bacall, Lauren *see* BOGART, HUMPHREY.

Bach, Johann Sebastian (1685–1750) German composer. His works include some of the greatest music in several forms, e.g. his six cello suites, choral masterpieces such as the *St Matthew Passion*, and works for harpsichord, clavichord and the organ, such as *The Well-Tempered Clavier* and *The Art of Fugue.* Four of his sons were also composers: **Wilhelm Friedemann Bach** (1710–84), **Karl Philipp Emanuel Bach** (1714–88), **Johann Christoph Friedrich Bach** (1732–95) and **Johann [John] Christian Bach** (1735–82), who became a court musician in London, where he was known as 'the English Bach' and influenced MOZART.

Bacon, Francis (1561–1626) English philosopher and statesman. He served both Elizabeth I and her successor, James VI and I, in various offices until his conviction and disgrace for bribery in 1621. His writings on philosophy and the need for rational scientific method are landmarks in the history of human thought.

Bacon, Francis (1909–92) Irish-born British painter. His works feature twisted and contorted human shapes, often in weird landscapes or spaces, reflecting a personal view of repulsion at the human condition.

Baez, Joan (1941–) American folksinger, renowned for her 'protest songs' on civil rights and the Vietnam war in the 1960s.

Bailey, David (1938–) British photographer who came to prominence in the 1960s and is famous for his images of that period.

Baird, John Logie (1888–1946) Scottish engineer who invented a mechanically scanned system of television in the mid-1920s.

Baker, Dame Janet Abbott (1933–) English mezzosoprano who became one of Britain's most popular opera singers in the 1960s and had parts created for her by composers such as BRITTEN.

Balakirev, Mily Alexeyevich *see* AML Five, The.

Balanchine, George *see* AML ballet.

Baldwin, James Arthur (1924–87) American novelist, dramatist and essayist. His novels include *Go Tell it on the Mountain* (1953).

Ballesteros, Seve (1957–) Spanish golfer who has won three Open titles, his most successful years being the 1980s. His 'swashbuckling' style has inspired many young golfers and a whole army of fans. He remains a popular figure to this day.

Balzac, Honoré de (1799–1860) French novelist. His many novels and short stories describe the lives of French men and women of every class and include *La Comédie humaine* ('the Human Comedy').

Bancroft, Anne *see* BROOKS, MEL.

Banda, Hastings Kamuzu (1905–97) Malawi statesman, first president of Nyasaland from 1963 and president of Malawi (formerly Nyasaland) (1966–1994).

Banks, Gordon (1937–) English football player and goal keeper and a member of football's elite Hall of Fame. Banks was a member of the English team that won the World Cup in 1966 and he also played for Chesterfield, Leicester and Stoke City.He was awarded an OBE in 1970.

Banks, Sir Joseph (1743–1820) English botanist and explorer. He sailed with COOK on his 1768–71 voyage round the world as a representative of the Royal Society and discovered many species of animals and plants.

Bannister, Sir Roger (1929–) British athlete and doctor who became the first man to run a mile in less than four minutes in May 1954, when he recorded a time of three minutes 59.4 seconds at Oxford.

Banting, Sir Frederick Grant (1891–1941) Canadian physician whose research into diabetes with the American physiologist **Charles Herbert Best** (1899–1978) resulted in the isolation of the hormone insulin in a form for treating diabetes.

Barak, Ehud *see* RABIN, YITZHAK.

Barber, Samuel (1910–81) American composer who worked with recognisably

19th-century harmonies and forms. His works include the popular *Adagio for Strings* (1936).

Bardeen, John (1908–91) American physicist and electrical engineer. He won two Nobel prizes, the first in 1956 for research that led to the invention of the transistor, the second in 1972 for research into the theory of superconductivity.

Barenboim, Daniel (1942–) Argentine-born Israeli concert pianist and conductor. He married the cellist Jacqueline DU PRÉ in 1967.

Barrie, Sir J[ames] M[atthew] (1860–1937) Scottish dramatist and novelist, remembered principally for *Peter Pan* (1904).

Barth, Karl (1886–1968) Swiss Protestant theologian whose theology was based on an orthodox 'theocentric' conception of divine grace. He was a committed and courageous opponent of Nazism.

Barthes, Roland (1915–80) French literary and cultural critic. His works include *Elements of Sociology*. *See* AML Structuralism.

Bartók, Béla (1881–1945) Hungarian composer and pianist. He was a noted collector of folk songs, upon which many of his works are based. His works include the ballet *The Miraculous Mandarin*, string quartets and *Concerto for Orchestra*.

Basho *see* AML haiku.

Basie, Count [William] (1904–84) American jazz composer and bandleader. He was a jazz pianist of great ability and his big band featured singers such as Ella FITZGERALD and Frank SINATRA.

Bates, H[erbert] E[rnest] (1905–74) English novelist and short-story writer. His works include the comic novel *The Darling Buds of May* (1958) featuring the Larkins, an unruly farming family.

Baudelaire, Charles (1821–67) French poet noted for his fascination with the macabre and alleged Satanism. He became a leading Symbolist poet (*see* AML Symbolism) and his works include *Les Fleurs du mal*. *See also* AML Surrealism.

Beadle, George Wells *see* TATUM, EDWARD LAWRIE.

Beaumont, Sir Francis *see* FLETCHER, JOHN.

Beauvoir, Simone de (1908–86) French novelist and essayist whose works explore the female predicament from the standpoint of Existential feminism, e.g. *The Second Sex* (1949). She had a long-term relationship with Jean-Paul SARTRE.

Beaverbrook, Max [William Maxwell Aitken], 1st Baron Beaverbrook (1879–1964) Canadian-born British newspaper proprietor and Conservative politician. In World War I he served as minister of information (1918) and in World War II as minister of aircraft production (1940–41).

Bechet, Sidney (1897–1959) American jazz saxophonist and clarinettist. He never learned to read music but became one of the greatest soprano saxophone virtuosos.

Bechstein, Wilhelm Karl *see* AML Bechstein.

Becket, Thomas à (1118–70) English saint. Of Norman descent, he became Chancellor of England in 1155 and Archbishop of Canterbury in 1162. Relations between Becket and Henry II deteriorated because of the former's strong allegiance to Church rather than king, and Becket was murdered by four of the king's knights. Becket was canonised in 1173.

Becker, Boris (1967–) German tennis player noted for his power and agility on court. He was the youngest male winner at Wimbledon when he took the trophy in 1985 at the age of 17. He successfully defended the title the following year and he remains an influential figure in the sport to this day.

Beckett, Samuel (1906–89) Irish dramatist and novelist. His works, generally bleak and Existentialist in philosophy, include the play *Waiting for Godot* (1952) and the short novel *Malone Dies* (1951). *See also* AML Existentialism.

Beckham, David (1975–) English and international football star and captain of the national team from 2000 to 2006. He is a member of the elite 'FIFA 100' roll of honour. He played for Manchester United from 1992 to 2005, then joined Real Madrid and lately the American side, L A Galaxy. An international celebrity off the pitch, Beckham is married to the former Spice Girl, Victoria [Posh]

Adams. For many years he has acted as a goodwill ambassador for UNICEF and has been honoured in his home country with an OBE.

Becquerel, Antoine Henri *see* CURIE, MARIE.

Bede, the Venerable, Saint (*c*.673–735) Anglo-Saxon monk and historian. Prodigiously learned, he settled for life in the monastery at Jarrow in 682.

Beerbohm, Sir [Henry] Max[imilian] (1872–1956) English parodist, caricaturist and essayist. His only novel is *Zuleika Dobson* (1912).

Beethoven, Ludwig van (1770–1827) German composer. Regarded as the greatest Romantic composer, he became famous in the 1790s as a brilliant pianist with a special gift for improvisation. His works include a violin concerto, nine symphonies, piano sonatas, string quartets, masses and one of the greatest operas, *Fidelio* (1805).

Begin, Menachem (1913–92) Polish-born Israeli statesman. He was commander of the Irgun militant Zionist group (1943–48) and prime minister of Israel (1977–84). He and SADAT were awarded the Nobel peace prize in 1978 after Egypt and Israel signed a peace treaty.

Behan, Brendan (1923–64) Irish dramatist and poet. He was an Irish Republican Army supporter from an early age, and two of his works were directly based on his imprisonment for IRA activity, *The Quare Fellow* (1954) and *Borstal Boy* (1958).

Beiderbecke, [Leon] Bix (1903–31) American jazz cornettist, pianist and composer who is regarded as one of the few White jazz musicians to have had any significant influence on the development of jazz.

Bekenbaur, Franz Anton (1945–) German football player, coach and manager, who goes by the nickname 'the Emperor' (der Kaiser). He is recognised as one of the most brilliant footballers of modern times and he is a member of football's National Hall of Fame and remains a leading figure in international football.

Bell, Alexander Graham (1847–1922) Scottish-born American inventor and scientist. He succeeded in producing a device for transmitting the voice in 1875 and patented the telephone the following year.

He founded the Bell Telephone Company in 1877 and patented the gramophone in 1887.

Bellini, Giovanni (*c*.1430–1516) Italian painter. The most prominent of a family of noted artists, including his father **Jacopo** (*c*.1400–*c*.1470) and his brother **Gentile** (*c*.1429–*c*.1507).

Belloc, Hilaire (1870–1953) French-born English poet, essayist and historian noted for his prolific output of all kinds of books.

Bellow, Saul (1915–2005) Canadian-born American novelist, widely regarded as one of the greatest 20th-century writers. His novels include *Dangling Man* (1944), *Humboldt's Gift* (1975) and *More Die of Heartbreak* (1987). He was awarded the Nobel prize for literature in 1976.

Ben Bella, [Mohammed] Ahmed (1918–) Algerian statesman. A leading figure of his country's independence movement in the late 1940s and 1950s, he became prime minister in 1962 shortly after independence. He was deposed in 1965 following a military coup and was imprisoned until 1980.

Ben-Gurion, David [David Gruen] (1886–1973) Polish-born Israeli statesman. He settled in Palestine in 1906, where he was active in the socialist wing of the Zionist movement. He was the first prime minister of Israel (1948–53) and was prime minister again (1955–63).

Bentham, Jeremy (1748–1832) English philosopher. He is famous for his proposition that the prime aim of political and philosophical inquiry should be the 'greatest happiness of the greatest number', expounded in his *Introduction to the Principles of Morals and Legislation* (1789).

Bentine, Michael *see* MILLIGAN, SPIKE.

Bentley, Edmund Clerihew (1875–1956) English journalist, noted for his classic detective novel, *Trent's Last Case* (1913) and his invention of the clerihew (*see* AML clerihew).

Berenson, Bernard (1865–1959) Lithuanian-born American art critic. He was highly influential in the early development of art history.

Berg, Alban (1885–1935) Austrian composer. He studied under SCHOENBERG and his works include songs, chamber works and the operas *Wozzeck* and *Lulu*.

Bergman, Ingmar (1918–2007) Swedish film and stage director. His films, which include *The Seventh Seal* (1956), *Wild Strawberries* (1957) and *Cries and Whispers* (1972), are claustrophobic psychological studies that have been very influential. *Fanny and Alexander* (1982) won an Oscar for Best Foreign Language Movie.

Bergman, Ingrid (1915–82) Swedish actress regarded as one of the most talented and beautiful actresses of her generation. Her films include *Casablanca* (1942).

Bergson, Henri Louis (1859–1941) French philosopher whose writings expound his theory of a 'vital spirit' moving in the world, bridging the apparent chasm between metaphysics and science. He was awarded the Nobel prize for literature in 1927.

Beria, Lavrenti Pavlovich (1899–1953) Georgian-born Soviet politician. He rose to power in the 1930s under STALIN and became head of the secret police (1938–53). He was tried for treason and executed.

Berio, Luciano (1925–) Italian composer whose works are based on a system of serialism and often feature electronic components.

Berkeley, Busby [William Busby Enos] (1895–1976) American film director, noted especially for his elaborate, often Surreal, dance choreography.

Berlin, Irving [Israel Baline] (1888–1989) Russian-born American songwriter. He began his career as a street singer and eventually wrote around a thousand songs, many of which featured in highly successful shows and in several film musicals.

Berlin, Sir Isaiah (1909–97) Latvian-born British philosopher and historian. His works focus on the history of ideas, with particular reference to historical determinism.

Berlioz, Hector (1803–69) French composer. Regarded as a founder of modern orchestral techniques, his works include *Symphonie Fantastique* and the opera *The Trojans*.

Bernstein, Leonard (1918–90) American composer and conductor. He was musical director of the New York Philharmonic (1958–70) and a tireless populariser of classical music. His works include chamber and choral music and several very popular musicals, e.g. *West Side Story* (1957).

Bertolucci, Bernardo (1940–) Italian film director. His films, which include *The Conformist* and *The Last Emperor*, are among the most influential in modern cinema.

Best, Charles Herbert *see* BANTING, SIR FREDERICK.

Best, George (1946–2005) Northern Irish football player. One of the world's finest and most entertaining wingers, his career slowly folded in a haze of alcohol abuse.

Betjeman, Sir John (1906–84) English poet and essayist whose work was popular with critics and public alike. He was appointed poet laureate in 1972 and also wrote widely on architecture.

Bevan, Aneurin (1897–1960) Welsh statesman. He was Labour MP for Ebbw Vale for 30 years (1929–60) and one of the main spokespeople for the radical socialist opposition during World War II. As minister of health under Clement ATTLEE (1945–51), he oversaw the formation of the welfare state (*see* BEVERIDGE).

Beveridge, William Henry, 1st Baron Beveridge (1879–1963) Indian-born English economist. His 'Beveridge Report', the *Report on Social Insurance and Allied Services* (1942), became the basis for the welfare state introduced by ATTLEE's administration.

Bevin, Ernest (1881–1951) English trade unionist and statesman. He helped found the Transport and General Workers Union (1922) and was minister of labour (1940–45) in the coalition war government and Labour's foreign secretary (1945–51).

Bhutto, Zulfikar Ali (1928–79) Pakistani statesman. He was the first civilian president of Pakistan (1971–73) then prime minister (1973–77). He was deposed in a coup and executed. His daughter, **Benazir Bhutto** (1953–2008), was prime minister of Pakistan (1988–90), was re-elected in 1993 before being defeated in the 1997 Pakistani election . She fell victim to an apparent suicide attack during an election rally in 2008.

Bierstadt, Albert *see* AML Rocky Mountain School.

Biko, Steve [Stephen Bantu Biko] (1947–77)

South African Black radical leader who helped found the Black People's Convention in order to build confidence in South African Blacks that they could defeat apartheid. His death in police custody while awaiting trial was universally regarded as murder.

Birtwistle, Sir Harrison (1934–) English composer regarded as a leading postwar composer. His works include *Gawain and the Green Knight* (1991).

Bismarck, Prince Otto von (1815–98) German statesman who was prime minister of Prussia (1862–90) and defeated first Austria during the 'Seven Weeks' War' (1866) and then France (1870–71). He became the first chancellor of united Germany and was dubbed the 'Iron Chancellor'.

Bizet, Georges (1838–75) French composer who is best known for his operas, e.g. *The Pearl Fishers*, *Carmen*, but who also wrote a symphony, several songs and suites.

Blair, Tony [Anthony] (1953–) English Labour statesman. He became a member of the Shadow Cabinet in 1984 and leader of the Labour Party in 1994. In 1997, he led the Labour Party to its first election victory since 1974, with the largest majority ever held by the party. Blair became the youngest prime minister of the 20th century and, under his leadership, Labour won a second term in office for the first time in 2001.He relinquished the premiership in 2007 and was replaced by Gordon BROWN.

Blake, William (1757–1827) English Romantic poet and artist. His main poetic and artistic theme was innocence crippled by cynical experience.

Blankers-Koen, Fanny (1918–) Dutch sportswoman hailed as the greatest-ever female track and field athlete. At the 1948 London Olympics, she became the only woman in history to win 4 gold medals.

Blériot, Louis (1872–1936) French aviator and aeronautical engineer. A pioneer in aircraft design, he made the first flight across the English Channel in one of his monoplanes in 1909.

Bliss, Sir Arthur (1891–1975) English composer whose works include a choral symphony, ballets and film music. He was Master of the Queen's Music (1953–75).

Blum, Léon (1872–1950) French statesman, the first socialist and Jewish prime minister of France (1936–37, 1938, 1946–47).

Blunt, Anthony Frederick (1907–83) English art historian who was appointed Surveyor of the Queen's Pictures in 1945, a post he held until 1972. He was knighted in 1956 but was stripped of his knighthood in 1979 following the public revelation that he had been a Soviet spy.

Blyton, Enid Mary (1897–1968) English children's writer whose most well-known books have featured such characters as Noddy and Big Ears and, for older children, *The Famous Five*.

Boas, Franz (1858–1942) German-born American anthropologist whose emphasis on linguistic structure and scientific methodology has been very influential on anthropology.

Boccioni, Umberto (1882–1916) Italian painter and sculptor who became the leading Futurist artist of the early 20th century and one of the movement's principal theorists (*see* AML Futurism).

Boehm, Theobald *see* AML Boehm system.

Bogarde, Sir Dirk [Derek Jules Gaspard Ulric Niven van den Bogaerde] (1920–99) English actor and author whose films include *Death in Venice* (1970).

Bogart, Humphrey De Forest (1899–1957) American actor. He formed one of the best-known screen partnerships with his (fourth) wife **Lauren Bacall [Betty Joan Perske]** (1924–).

Bohr, Niels Henrik David (1885–1962) Danish physicist and first to apply quantum theory to explain the stability of the nuclear model of the atom. He was awarded the 1922 Nobel prize for physics.

Bolivar, Simon (1783–1830) Venezuelan-born revolutionary. He overthrew Spanish rule in Venezuela, Ecuador, Colombia and Peru. Upper Peru was renamed Bolivia in his honour.

Bond, Edward (1934–) English dramatist and screenwriter. His work was often controversial and public debate over his play *Saved* (1965) led to the abolition of stage censorship in Britain.

Bonhoeffer, Dietrich (1906–45) German Lutheran pastor and theologian who was active in the anti-Nazi Resistance during World War II and was hanged by the Gestapo in 1945. His writings are among the key spiritual works of the 20th century.

Bonnard, Pierre (1867–1947) French painter and lithographer. His work is notable for being intensely colourful.

Booth, William (1829–1912) English religious leader who established a Christian mission in London's East End in the 1860s and founded the Salvation Army in 1878.

Borduas, Paul Emile *see* AML Automatistes.

Borg, Bjorn (1956–) Swedish tennis player who won five consecutive Wimbledon championship titles (1976–80).

Borges, Jorge Luis (1899–1986) Argentinian short-story writer, poet and critic who had a remarkable gift for creating short fictions with a beguiling metaphysical content.

Borgia, Cesare (1476–1507) Italian soldier and politician. The son of **Rodrigo Borgia** (1431–1503), he became a cardinal in 1493 after his father became pope (as Alexander VI) in 1492. He tried to bring Italian affairs under his control in an atmosphere of intrigue, war and assassination, and was the model for MACHIAVELLI's *Prince*. His sister **Lucrezia** (1480–1519) was a patron of the arts and acquired a reputation for conspiracy.

Borodin, Aleksandr *see* AML Five, the.

Bosch, Hieronymous [Jerome van Aeken or Aken] (*c*.1450–1516) Dutch painter, known for his fantastic and often grotesque allegorical paintings that use imagery drawn from folk tales and religious symbolism.

Bose, Sir Jagadis Chandra (1858–1937) Indian physicist and plant physiologist. He invented the crescograph, a device that automatically records plant movements.

Bose, Subhas Chandra (1897–1945) Indian nationalist leader and president of the Indian National Congress (1938–39). In collaboration with the Japanese during World War II, he organised the Indian National Army to combat British rule in India.

Boswell, James *see* JOHNSON, SAMUEL.

Botha, Louis (1862–1919) South African general and statesman. As general of the Transvaal army, he led the Boer forces against the British in the Boer War. He

supported the Allies during World War I and became first prime minister of South Africa (1910–19).

Botha, P[ieter] W[illem] (1916–2006) South African politician. As prime minister (1978–84) and then president (1984–89), he introduced limited reforms of apartheid.

Botham, Ian (1955–) English cricketer who gained both fame and notoriety during the 1980s and became internationally recognised as a brilliant player when on form. He continued in the international game until 1992 and was honoured that year with an OBE. He is now a television cricket commentator.

Botticelli, Sandro (1444–1510) Florentine painter, best known for his graceful and serene religious works.

Boulez, Pierre (1925–) French composer and conductor who developed a composition style based on total serialism and electronic instruments.

Boycott, Geoffrey (1940–) English and Yorkshire cricketer from the mid-1960s to the early 1980s, known for his strong defensive play. He was the first cricketer to bat on all five days of a test match (in 1977 at Trent Bridge, playing against Australia) and he achieved two great centuries during that year. He became a commentator after his retirement from the game and remains a well-known personality in English cricket.

Brabham, Sir Jack (1926–) Australian Formula One racing driver and founder of the Brabham team, 'Black Jack' was known for his reserve and shunning of the limelight in what is generally regarded as a glamorous sport. Winner of many races, he was knighted in 1985.

Bradbury, Malcolm *see* AML campus novel.

Bradman, [Sir] Don[ald George] (1908–2001) Australian cricketer. A brilliant batsman, he scored 117 centuries during the 1930s and 1940s. He was Australian captain (1936–48).

Brahms, Johannes (1833–97) German composer. He regarded himself as firmly in the Classical (as opposed to Romantic) tradition. His works include the great choral *German Requiem* (1869), four symphonies and chamber music.

Branagh, Kenneth (1961–) Irish-born British actor and director. He founded the Renaissance Theatre Company in 1986 and appeared regularly in films with the actress Emma Thompson to whom he was married from 1990–96.

Brando, Marlon (1924–2004) American actor. His many celebrated screen performances, in e.g. *On the Waterfront* (1954) for which he won an Oscar, display the highly influential 'method' acting style.

Brandt, Willy [Herbert Ernst Karl Frahm] (1913–92) German statesman. He was active in the German Resistance during World War II and became mayor of Berlin (1957–66) and chancellor of West Germany (1969–74). He was awarded the Nobel peace prize in 1971.

Branson, Sir Richard (1950–) British entrepreneur and businessman and founder of the iconic Virgin empire, including airline, train and recorded music companies.

Braque, Georges (1882–1963) French painter. The term Cubism was coined in 1909 to describe his works. He also pioneered the use of collage in modern painting.

Brattain, Walter *see* SHOCKLEY, WILLIAM.

Braudel, Fernand (1902–85) French historian. His influential works focused on socio-economic trends and the changing relationship between man and the environment rather than on politics or military events.

Brecht, Bertolt (1898–1956) German dramatist who devised the theatre of alienation which he used in *The Threepenny Opera* (1928), for which WEILL wrote the music and developed in plays such as *Galileo* (1938) and *Mother Courage* (1941). He settled in the US during Nazi rule in Germany, returning to East Berlin in 1949 where he founded the Berliner Ensemble Theatre.

Breughel *see* BRUEGHEL.

Brezhnev, Leonid Ilyich (1906–82) Soviet statesman. He helped organise KHRUSHCHEV's downfall in 1964 and became general secretary of the Communist Party (1977–82) and Soviet president (1977–82). The period of his rule is now described as the 'period of stagnation' in the USSR.

Bridges, Robert *see* AML poet laureate.

Britten, [Edward] Benjamin, 1st Baron Britten (1913–76) English composer and pianist. His works include the operas *Peter Grimes* (1945) and *A Midsummer Night's Dream* (1960), chamber music, orchestral works and song cycles. His works are noted for their romantic lyricism. He was created a peer in 1976.

Brontë, Anne (1820–49), **Charlotte** (1816–55) and **Emily** (1818–48) English novelists and poets. Charlotte's *Jane Eyre*, based on her experiences as a teacher and governess, was published in 1847, and Anne's *Agnes Grey* and Emily's *Wuthering Heights* followed in 1848. Anne's *Tenant of Wildfell Hall* was published in 1848, in which year Emily died of consumption. Charlotte wrote two more novels, *Shirley* (1849) and *Villette* (1853).

Brook, Peter Stephen Paul (1925–) English stage and film director based in Paris. He is regarded as one of the finest experimental directors of the modern era.

Brooke, Rupert Chawner (1887–1915) English poet. His World War I poems were very popular with the public for their idealised vision of the nobility of war.

Brooks, Mel [Melvin Kaminsky] (1926–) American comedian, film writer and director, best known for his fast-moving, irreverent comic films, such as *Blazing Saddles*. His wife is the actress **Anne Bancroft [Anna Maria Italiano]** (1931–2005) who is probably best-known for her role as Mrs Robinson in *The Graduate*.

Brown, George Mackay (1921–96) Scottish writer and poet, much of whose work was set in his native Orkney.

Brown, James Gordon (1951–) British politician and chancellor of the exchequer from 1997 until 2007 when he replaced Tony Blair as leader of the Labour Party and prime minister.

Browning, Robert (1812–89) English poet renowned for his innovative experiments in form and narrative skill. His wife, **Elizabeth Barrett Browning** (1806–61), whom he married in 1846, was also a major poet.

Brubeck, Dave (1920–) American jazz composer and pianist. He studied musical composition with SCHOENBERG and MILHAUD, forming his 'Dave Brubeck Quartet' in 1951.

Bruce, Lenny (1925–66) American comedian who developed an influential style often scabrous comedy that frequently brought him into conflict with the authorities.

Bruegel or Brueghel, Pieter (the Elder) (*c*. 1525–69) Flemish painter who painted peasant scenes and allegories. He is best known for his magnificent landscape painting *The Hunters in the Snow* (1565). His sons **Jan Brueghel** (1568–1625) and **Pieter Brueghel (the Younger)** (*c*. 1564–1637) were also painters.

Brunel, Isambard Kingdom (1806–59) English engineer. He designed steamships and in the late 1820s planned and designed the Clifton Suspension Bridge. His father, **Sir Marc Isambard Brunel** (1769–1849), was a French engineer who designed a tunnel under the Thames in London.

Buber, Martin (1878–1965) Austrian-born Jewish theologian and Existentialist philosopher. His philosophy, which centres on the relationship between man and God, has had a large impact on both Jewish and Christian theology.

Buchan, John, 1st Baron Tweedsmuir (1875–1940) Scottish novelist, statesman and historian. He wrote several best-selling novels, was created a peer in 1935 and was governor-general of Canada (1935–40).

Buchanan, James (1791–1868) American Democrat politician and the 15th president of the USA (1857–1861).

Buchman, Frank Nathan Daniel (1878–1961) American evangelist who founded the Oxford Group and the longer-lived Moral Rearmament, which were intended to provide ideological alternatives to capitalism and communism.

Buddha, 'The Enlightened' [Prince Gautama Siddartha] (*c*.563–*c*.483) the founder of Buddhism. At the age of around 30 he left his princely luxuries behind for a life of self-deprivation and is said to have achieved enlightenment when sitting beneath a tree near Buddh Gaya in Bihar.

Bunche, Ralph Johnson (1904–71) American diplomat and UN official. The grandson of a slave, he became the first Black American to be awarded the Nobel peace prize, in 1950, for his attempt at reconciling Israel and the Arab states (1948–49).

Bunyan, John (1628–88) English author. Writer of several devotional works, the most famous being the remarkable allegory *Pilgrim's Progress* (1678–84).

Buñuel, Luis (1900–83) Spanish-born film director. His early films were made in collaboration with Salvador DALI. He is regarded as a master of Surrealist cinema.

Burgess, Anthony [John Anthony Burgess Wilson] (1917–93) English novelist, critic and composer. His novels include the controversial futuristic fantasy of juvenile crime *A Clockwork Orange* (1962, filmed by KUBRICK in 1971).

Burgess, Guy (1911–63) English diplomat and spy. Recruited by Soviet Intelligence in the 1930s, he worked for MI5 during World War II and served with PHILBY at the British Embassy in Washington DC after the war. With his fellow agent, **Donald Maclean** (1913–83), he fled to the USSR in 1951.

Burke, Edmund (1729–97) Anglo-Irish statesman and philosopher. He entered parliament for the Whig Party in 1765 and was soon established as the dominant political thinker of the day.

Burnet, Sir Frank Macfarlane *see* MEDAWAR, SIR PETER BRIAN.

Burns, Robert (1759–96) Scottish poet, renowned as both a lyric poet and a satirist. The son of a farmer, his identification with folk tradition and his rebellious lifestyle also contribute to the unwavering popularity of his work in Scotland.

Burroughs, William S[eward] (1914–97) American novelist. His luridly obscene fiction features the squalid, nightmarish underworld of drug addiction, as in *The Naked Lunch* (1959).

Burton, Richard [Richard Jenkins] (1925–84) Welsh actor, regarded as one of the most talented actors of his generation. He formed a screen partnership with Elizabeth TAYLOR, to whom he was married twice (1964–70, 1975–76).

Busby, Sir Matt[hew] (1909–94) Scottish football player and manager of Manchester United (1946–69). Many members of his highly regarded team of 1958 died in a plane crash at Munich in the same year.

His rebuilt team of 'Busby Babes' became the first English team to win the European Cup (1968).

Bush, George Herbert Walker (1924–) American Republican politician and 41st president of the USA (1989–93). He served in the US Navy (1942–45), became US ambassador to the UN (1971–73), special envoy to China (1974–75) and CIA director (1976). He served under Ronald REAGAN as vice-president (1980–88).

Bush, George Walker (1946–) American Republican politician and 43rd president of the USA (2001–2007). Eldest son of 41st president of the US, George H. W. BUSH.

Buthelezi, Chief Gatsha (1928–) South African Zulu chief and politician. He helped found the paramilitary organisation Inkatha.

Byron, Lord George Gordon, 6th Baron Byron of Rochdale (1788–1824) English poet. His works include the long satirical poem *Don Juan* (1819–21).

Cadbury, George (1839–1922) English businessman, social reformer and philanthropist. With his brother **Michael Cadbury** (1835–99) he established the model village of Bournville, near Birmingham, for the Cadbury work force.

Caesar, [Gaius] Julius (100–44 BC) Roman soldier and historian. He negotiated and formed the 'First Triumvirate' with the politician **Marcus Licinius Crassus** (*c*. 114–53 BC) and the statesman and general **Pompey [Gnaeus Pompeius Magnus]** (106–48 BC) in 60, after which he fought in Gaul for nine years and invaded Britain in 55 and 54. Appointed dictator by the Senate in 49, he defeated Pompey at Pharsalia in 48 and was himself assassinated by a largely aristocratic group of conspirators.

Cage, John (1912–92) American composer. His experimental music, e.g. *four minutes 33 seconds* (1952), in which the performers remain silent, has been derided and admired in equal proportions.

Cagney, James (1899–1986) American film actor, originally a dancer but best remembered for his many portrayals of gangsters, e.g. in *The Public Enemy* (1931) and *Angels with Dirty Faces* (1938).

Calder, Alexander *see* AML mobile; stabile.

Caligula [Gaius Caesar Augustus Germanicus] (12–41) Roman emperor (37–41) who became tyrannical and was assassinated by a conspiracy and succeeded by his uncle, CLAUDIUS.

Callaghan, [Leonard] James, Baron Callaghan of Cardiff (1912–2005) British Labour statesman and prime minister (1976–79). After a vote of no confidence in his premiership in the House of Commons, he called a general election that Labour lost.

Callas, Maria (1923–77) American-born Greek operatic soprano renowned both for her voice and acting skills which made her one of the most revered opera singers of her time.

Calvin, John (1509–64) French religious reformer who had to flee from France to Switzerland, where he published his *Institutes of the Christian Religion* (1536), a summation of his Protestant faith and the founding text of Calvinism. He settled in Geneva and established the first Presbyterian government.

Calvino, Italo (1923–85) Cuban-Italian novelist, essayist and critic. His early novels belonged in the Italian realist tradition, while his later, highly complex explorations of fantasy and myth have been compared to Latin American 'magic realism'.

Campbell, Sir Malcolm (1885–1948) English racing driver. He was awarded a knighthood in 1931, the year he set a land speed record of 246 mph, for his achievements in setting land and water speed records. His son, **Donald [Malcolm] Campbell,** (1921–67) held the water speed record, at a speed of 276 mph, but he died on Lake Coniston while trying to break it.

Campbell, Mrs Patrick [Beatrice Stella Tanner] (1865–1940) English actress. She was regarded as one of the finest (and wittiest) actresses of her generation.

Campbell-Bannerman, Sir Henry (1836–1908) British statesman. He was Liberal prime minister (1905–08) and played a major part in healing rifts in the Liberal Party after the Boer War.

Camus, Albert (1913–60) French novelist, essayist and dramatist, and a leading

Existentialist writer (*see* AML Existentialism). He was awarded the Nobel prize for literature in 1957. His major works include the novel *The Outsider* and *The Rebel*, a study of 20th-century totalitarianism.

Canaletto, Giovanni Antonio Canal (1697–1768) Venetian painter. An unrivalled architectural painter with an excellent sense of composition, his work includes many views of Venice.

Capa, Robert [André Friedmann] (1913–54) Hungarian photographer who became one of the best-known war photographers of the century. He was killed by a mine in Vietnam.

Capek, Karel (1890–1938) Czech dramatist, novelist and essayist. With his brother **Josef Capek** (1887–1945), he wrote *The Insect Play* (1921), a prophetic satire on totalitarianism.

Capote, Truman (1924–84) American novelist and socialite. His varied works include light romances, e.g. *Breakfast at Tiffany's* (1958), as well as realist explorations of murder.

Capra, Frank (1897–1991) Italian-born American film director. His comedies, usually portraying an ultimately successful struggle by a decent, everyday American against the flawed political system, were enormously popular in the 1930s.

Caravaggio, Michelangelo Merisi da (1573–1610) Italian painter. Noted for his bold, expressive use of chiaroscuro, his religious paintings caused controversy by using ordinary people as the models for his Biblical characters.

Carew, Thomas *see* AML Cavalier Poets.

Carlyle, Thomas (1795–1881) Scottish historian and essayist. Hailed by many of his contemporaries as a great social critic and philosopher, he frequently attacked the materialism of the Industrial Age. His works include *The French Revolution*.

Carnap, Rudolf (1891–1970) German-born American philosopher. He attempted to develop a formal language that would remove ambiguity from scientific language.

Carné, Marcel (1906–1996) French film director. His films include the highly acclaimed theatrical epic *Les Enfants du Paradis* (1944), filmed during the German occupation of France.

Carnegie, Andrew (1835–1919) Scottish-born American industrialist and philanthropist who believed that personal wealth should be used for the benefit of all members of society.

Carré, Carlo *see* AML metaphysical painting.

Carreras, José [Maria] (1946–) Spanish lyric tenor, one of the finest tenors (with DOMINGO, PAVAROTTI) of the late 20th century.

Carroll, Lewis (pseud. of Charles Lutwidge Dodgson) (1832–98) English author, clergyman and mathematician. His most famous works are the two remarkable 'Alice' books, *Alice's Adventures in Wonderland* and *Through the Looking Glass*.

Carter, Jimmy [James] Earl (1924–) American Democratic statesman and 39th president of the US (1977–81). He was governor of Georgia (1974–77) and defeated Gerald FORD in the 1976 presidential campaign. He made significant attempts at linking overseas trade with human rights issues.

Cartier-Bresson, Henri (1908–2004) French photographer and film director. His documentary black-and-white photographs were taken without prior composition and an uncropped frame.

Caruso, Enrico (1873–1921) Italian tenor. Born in Naples, he sang most of the great tenor roles in Italian and French opera and is regarded as perhaps the most outstanding operatic tenor of all time. He was one of the first great singers to make recordings.

Casals, Pablo (1876–1973) Spanish cellist, pianist and composer. His recordings of BACH's cello suites and of the DVORÁK cello concerto are particularly highly regarded.

Casement, Sir Roger David (1864–1916) British consular official and Irish nationalist. While working for the British colonial service, he exposed the repression of the people of the Congo by its Belgian rulers in 1904. Knighted in 1911, he adopted Irish nationalism shortly afterwards and was hanged for treason.

Cassady, Neal *see* AML Beat Generation.

Castro [Ruz], Fidel (1927–) Cuban statesman, prime minister (1959–76), and president for 49 years (1976–2008). He led a coup in 1959 and shortly afterwards announced his conversion to communism.

Catherine II 'the Great' (1729–96) Russian empress. She became empress on the death of her husband, **Peter III** (1728–62), who was murdered by one of her lovers. She consolidated and expanded the Russian Empire.

Cavell, Edith Louisa (1865–1915) English nurse. She treated both German and Allied casualties in Brussels during the German occupation and was executed by the German authorities, who accused her of helping British soldiers to escape to Holland.

Caxton, William (*c*.1422–91) English printer and translator. His *Recuyell of the Historyes of Troy* (printed at Bruges, 1475) is the first book to be printed in English.

Ceausescu, Nicolae (1918–89) Romanian dictator. Secretary general of the Romanian Communist Party from 1969 and president of Romania from 1974, his regime was overthrown by dissident Communists in 1989, and he and his wife were executed.

Cecil, William, 1st Baron Burghley (1520–98) English statesman who served, with skill and dexterity, both HENRY VIII and MARY I (converting to Roman Catholicism under Mary) and one of the prime architects of ELIZABETH I's succession.

Cervantes [Saavedra], Miguel de (1547–1616) Spanish novelist, dramatist and poet. His most famous work was the satirical masterpiece *Don Quixote de la Mancha*.

Cézanne, Paul (1839–1906) French painter whose works include landscapes and still lifes. He was very influential on succeeding generations of painters, notably the Cubists.

Chadwick, Sir James (1891–1974) English physicist. He discovered the neutron in 1932 and was awarded the Nobel prize for physics in 1935.

Chagall, Marc (1887–1985) Russian-born French painter. His vividly coloured work features unusual compositions drawing on symbolism from Russian and Jewish folk art.

Chain, Sir Ernst Boris (1906–79) German-born British biochemist. He prepared penicillin for clinical use and with FLOREY and Alexander FLEMING, shared the 1945 Nobel prize for physiology or medicine.

Chamberlain, [Arthur] Neville (1869–1940) British statesman and Conservative prime minister (1937–40). He pursued a policy of appeasement towards the totalitarian powers of Germany, Italy and Japan in the 1930s.

Chandler, Raymond Thornton (1888–1959) American novelist and screenwriter. His detective novels, e.g. *Farewell, My Lovely* (1940), are classics of the genre.

Chanel, Coco [Gabrielle Bonheur Chanel] (1883–1971) French couturière and perfumer who originated the .thin, low-waist style for women's clothes.

Chaplin, Charlie [Sir Charles Spencer] (1889–1977) English comedian and film director. His gentleman-tramp character with a beguiling shuffle, bowler hat and cane, a familiar figure in many films including *City Lights* (1931), became perhaps the most famous comic creation of the 20th century.

Chardin, Jean-Baptiste *see* AML genre painting; still life.

Charlemagne (*c*.742–814) king of the Franks and Holy Roman emperor. In 771 he became sole ruler of the Frankish kingdom and spent the early part of his reign conquering (and converting to Christianity) neighbouring kingdoms. He led an army into Spain to fight the Moors in 778. In 800 he was crowned emperor after crushing a Roman revolt against the Pope.

Charles, Prince [Charles Philip Arthur George, Prince of Wales] (1948–) heir apparent to ELIZABETH II of the United Kingdom. He married Lady DIANA Spencer (1961–97) in 1981, and they had two children, William and Harry [Henry]. They were divorced in 1996. He married Camilla Parker Bowles in 2005.

Charles, Ray [Ray Charles Robinson] (1930–) American singer, pianist and songwriter. Originally a blues/jazz singer, he became very popular pop singer.

Charlton, Bobby [Robert] (1937–) English football player who was capped over 100 times for England. His brother **Jack Charlton** (1935–), also an England player, became the manager of the Irish international team and led them to the World Cup finals in 1990 and 1994.

Chatham, William Pitt, 1st Earl of *see* PITT, WILLIAM.

Chaucer, Geoffrey (*c*.1340–70) English poet. His great narrative skill is displayed at its finest in *The Canterbury Tales* (*c*.1387), a masterpiece of wit and humour in which various pilgrims tell each other stories.

Chekhov, Anton Pavlovich (1860–1904) Russian dramatist and short-story writer. A physician, he became one of the greatest writers of his age. His works, notable for their wit and dramatic power, include the plays *Uncle Vanya* and *Three Sisters*, and the short story 'The Lady with the Little Dog'.

Cherenkov, Pavel Alekseievich (1904–90) Soviet physicist. In the mid-1930s he discovered the form of radiation known as Cherenkhov radiation and was awarded the 1958 Nobel prize for physics.

Cherubini, Luigi (1760–1842) Italian composer who settled in Paris. He wrote operas, e.g. *Médée*, and other works and was much admired by BEETHOVEN, whose opera, *Fidelio*, followed the story of *Médée* closely in its study of feminine psychology and stress on democratic values.

Chesterton, G[ilbert] K[eith] (1874–1936) English essayist, novelist, critic and poet. With his friend BELLOC, he became known as a gifted disputant for what they saw as the glory of old, rural Roman Catholic England.

Chiang Ch'ing or Jiang Qing (1913–91) Chinese Communist politician and actress. She married MAO as his third wife in 1939 and was the main force behind the savage purges of the Cultural Revolution in the late 1960s. After Mao's death, her power waned, and she was arrested in 1976 with three confederates (the 'Gang of Four') and charged with murder and subversion. She was sentenced to death in 1981, the sentence later being suspended.

Chiang Kai-shek or Jiang Jie Shi (1887–1975) Chinese general and statesman. He was president of China (1928–38, 1943–49), then, after losing the civil war to MAO TSE-TUNG and his forces, fled the mainland to establish the nationalist republic of China in Formosa of which he was president (1950–57).

Chirico, Giorgio de (1888–1978) Greek-born Italian painter whose dreamlike pictures of open, deserted squares were hailed by the Surrealists as precursors of their own works in the early 1920s.

Chomsky, [Avram] Noam (1928–) American linguist, philosopher and political activist. His innovative work in linguistics is based on the principles that humans are born with an innate capacity for learning grammatical structures. He was a notable opponent of the Vietnam war.

Chopin, Frédéric [François] (1810–49) Polish pianist and composer. His emotional, melancholy works, often regarded as quintessentially Polish in mood, include over 50 mazurkas, two piano concertos and 25 preludes.

Chou En-Lai or Zhou En Lai (1898–1976) Chinese Communist statesman. He was foreign minister (1949–58) and prime minister (1949–76) of the People's Republic of China and was regarded as a moderate during the chaos of China's Cultural Revolution in the late 1960s.

Christie, [Dame] Agatha Clarissa Mary (1890–1976) English detective story writer whose ingeniously plotted novels, e.g. *The Murder of Roger Ackroyd*, established her as one of the great writers in the genre.

Churchill, Sir Winston Leonard Spencer (1874–1965) British Conservative statesman and writer. After an adventurous early life that included escape from imprisonment during the Boer War, he held several posts under both Liberal and Conservative governments. He opposed CHAMBERLAIN's policy of appeasement in the 1930s and served as prime minister (1940–45) during World War II. His works include *History of the English-Speaking Peoples*. He was awarded the Nobel prize for literature (1953).

Cibber, Colley *see* AML poet laureate.

Clapton, Eric (1945–) English guitarist. Recognised as one of the most influential rock guitarists, he played with the Yardbirds (1963–65) and Cream (1966–68).

Clark, Jim [James] (1936–68) Scottish racing driver who was World Champion in 1963 and 1965 and winner of 25 Grand

Prix events. He was killed in a crash in West Germany.

Claudius (10 BC–54) Roman emperor who extended the Empire, initiated the conquest of Britain in 43 and extended Roman citizenship. His fourth wife (and niece), Agrippina, was the mother of his successor NERO.

Cleese [Cheese], John Marwood (1939–) English comedy actor and writer. He was one of the main talents involved in the highly influential TV comedy series, *Monty Python's Flying Circus* (1969–74).

Clemenceau, Georges [Eugène Benjamin] (1841–1929) French statesman. A leading left-winger, he was an outspoken critic of the French government's war policy in the early days of World War I. He was prime minister (1906–19, 1917–20) and his forceful negotiation of the Versailles Treaty is believed to have led directly to World War II.

Cleopatra *see* ANTONY, MARK.

Cleveland, Grover (1837–1908) American Democrat politician and the 22nd president of the USA (1885–89). He served as 24th president (1893–97).

Clinton, Bill [William] Jefferson Davis (1946–) American politician and 42nd president of the USA (1993–2001). A lawyer, he became Arkansas attorney general (1974–79), then state governor (1979–81, 1983–92). before defeating George BUSH in the 1992 presidential election. *See also* GORE.

Clive, Kitty *see* GARRICK, DAVID.

Clive, Sir Robert, 1st Baron Clive of Plassey (1725–74) English general and administrator in India. He worked for the East India Company (1743–46) before joining the Indian army. He was an MP in England (1760–62) and governor of Bengal (1764–67).

Cockcroft, Sir John Douglas (1897–1967) English nuclear physicist. With the Irish physicist **Sir Ernest [Thomas Sinton] Walton** (1903–95), he produced the first laboratory splitting of an atomic nucleus, for which they shared the 1951 Nobel prize for physics.

Cockerell, Sir Christopher Sydney (1910–99) English engineer. He invented the hovercraft, the prototype of which

first crossed the English Channel in 1959.

Cocteau, Jean (1889–1963) French film director, novelist, dramatist, poet and critic. His experimental, Surreal films, including *Orphée* and *La Belle et la bête*, were highly influential on modern filmmakers. The best known of his novels is *Les Enfants Terribles*.

Coleridge, Samuel Taylor (1772–1834) English poet and critic. With WORDSWORTH he published *Lyrical Ballads* in 1798, a landmark in English poetry in its rejection of a special 'poetic' language and advocacy of clear everyday language.

Colette, Sidonie Gabrielle (1873–1954) French novelist. Her novels, e.g. *Chéri* and *Gigi*, are often erotic and display a strong sympathy for animals and the natural world.

Collins, Michael (1890–1922) Irish Republican politician. A Sinn Fein leader, he negotiated the 1922 peace treaty with Britain that resulted in the establishment of the Irish Free State. He was killed in an ambush during the civil war that followed.

Coltrane, John William (1926–67) American jazz saxophonist. A virtuoso on the tenor and soprano saxophones, he became an influential and popular jazz musician.

Columba, Saint (521–97) Irish missionary. He fled to the Western Isles of Scotland to proselytise for Christianity and established a monastic settlement on the island of Iona.

Columbus, Christopher (1451–1506) Italian navigator. Under the patronage of Spain, he led an expedition to seek a western route to the Far East. He discovered the New World in 1492, making landfall in the West Indies and made two subsequent voyages in 1493 and in 1498, when he reached South America.

Comaneci, Nadia Elena (1961–) Romanian gymnastics star and winner of a total of 5 Olympic gold medals. The first gymnast to achieve a perfect score of 10 points, she is now a naturalised American citizen, married to fellow gymnast **Bart Conner**.

Compton, Arthur Holly (1892–1962) American physicist. He was a prominent researcher into X-rays, gamma rays and nuclear energy, and discovered the

Compton effect. He was awarded the 1927 Nobel prize for physics.

Compton-Burnett, Dame Ivy (1892–1969) English novelist. Her novels were mostly in dialogue and featured the traumas of upper-middle-class Edwardian family life.

Compton-Burnett, Thomas (1489–1556) English prelate. Appointed Archbishop of Canterbury in 1533 (while secretly married), he pronounced the annulment of the marriage of HENRY VIII to Catherine of Aragon in 1533. A moderate Protestant reformer, he was executed by MARY I.

Compton-Burnett, William (1731–1800) English poet. He was best known in his own day as an engaging satirist and nature poet, but his darker religious poems are now seen as of more lasting importance.

Compton, Dennis (1918–97) English cricketer of the postwar years, known for his audacity as a batsman.After retiring from the game he became a commentator and sports journalist, remaining a popular figure until the time of his death.

Congreve, Sir William *see* AML comedy of manners.

Connery, Sean Thomas (1930–) Scottish film actor. One of the most charismatic of his generation, he initially achieved worldwide fame as Ian FLEMING's character James Bond.

Connors, Jimmy (1952–) American tennis player. He achieved great success in the mid-1970s to early 1980s, winning the US Open championships on five occasions and Wimbledon twice.

Conrad, Joseph [Josef Teodor Konrad Korzeniowski] (1857–1924) Polish-born English writer. His work includes the short story 'Heart of Darkness'.

Constable, John (1776–1837) English painter. Drawing inspiration from nature, he produced works such as *View on the Stour* and along with TURNER is considered to be among the most important of English landscape painters.

Constantine I (*c*.274–337) Roman emperor. He became the first Christian emperor in 312, when, before a battle, he reportedly saw a cross in the sky inscribed 'In this sign conquer'. Christianity became the Empire's official religion in 324.

Cook, (Captain) James (1728–79) English

explorer who charted and claimed the east coast of Australia for Britain and discovered New Caledonia. On his third and last voyage to the Pacific (1776–79), he was killed by islanders in Hawaii.

Coolidge, Calvin (1872–1933) American Republican politician and the 30th president of the US. Served for two terms from 1923–1925 and 1925–1929.

Cooper, Gary [Frank James Cooper] (1901–61) American film actor who specialised as the quiet, courageous hero in many Westerns and adventure films, e.g. *High Noon* (1952).

Cooper, James Fenimore (1789–1851) American novelist. His adventure novels, such as *The Last of the Mohicans*, established the enduring 'frontier myth' of America.

Copernicus, Nicolas (1473–1543) Polish astronomer. His great work *De Revolutionibus* (1543) sets out his theory that the earth and planets revolve around the sun.

Copland, Aaron (1900–1990) American composer, pianist and conductor. His works include the ballet score *Rodeo*.

Coppola, Francis Ford (1939–) American film director and screenwriter. His most successful films include the modern classics *The Godfather* and *Apocalypse Now*.

Corday, Charlotte *see* MARAT, JEAN PAUL.

Corman, Roger (1926–) American film director and producer. Known primarily as a creator of cheap B-movies he also fostered the careers of many directors and actors, including COPPOLA, DE NIRO and SCORSESE.

Cosgrave, W[illiam] T[homas] (1880–1965) Irish nationalist politician. He became first president of the Irish Free State (1922–32). His son **Liam Cosgrave** (1920–) became Fine Gael prime minister of the Republic of Ireland (1973–77).

Courbet, Gustave (1819–77) French painter. Considered to be the founder of Realism, his work was frequently condemned as 'socialistic' because he scorned the established Classical outlook.

Cousteau, Jacques Yves (1910–97) French oceanographer. He invented the aqualung (1943) and developed techniques of underwater cinematography that were influential in raising awareness of the world's oceans.

Coward, Sir Noel Pierce (1899–1973) English dramatist, actor and composer. His witty, sophisticated comedies and amusing songs were regarded as mildly shocking in their day and include *Private Lives* and *Blithe Spirit*.

Crassus *see* CAESAR, JULIUS.

Crawford, Joan [Lucille Le Sueur] (1908–77) American film actress. She was one of the first leading women in Hollywood although many of her films were formulaic melodramas, such as *Mildred Pierce* (1945).

Crick, Francis Harry Compton (1916–2004) English molecular biologist. With James Dewey WATSON, he discovered the structure of DNA and shared the 1962 Nobel prize for physiology or medicine with Watson and Maurice WILKINS.

Crippen, Hawley Harvey (1862–1910) American doctor who poisoned his wife in London in 1910. His dramatic capture on board ship involved the first use of radio for police purposes.

Cripps, Sir [Richard] Stafford (1889–1952) British Labour statesman. A leading left-winger, as chancellor of the exchequer (1947–50) he introduced a programme of high taxation and wage restraint to deal with Britain's economic problems.

Cromwell, Oliver (1599–1658) English soldier and statesman. A Puritan country squire and MP, he was a noted critic of CHARLES I during the 1628–29 Parliament. He led Parliament's New Model Army to victory at Naseby (1645) during the Civil War and crushed Welsh and Scottish rebellions before signing Charles I's death warrant (1649). He was nominated 'Lord Protector' of the Commonwealth in 1653.

Cromwell, Thomas (*c*.1485–1540) English statesman. Of humble origin, he rose to power through the patronage of Cardinal WOLSEY and became HENRY VIII's chief adviser. He fostered the passing of Reformation legislation, established the king's legal status as head of the Church in England and oversaw the dissolution of the monasteries.

Cronin, A(rchibald) J(oseph) (1896–1981) Scottish novelist, dramatist and physician.

The successful television series, *Dr Finlay's Casebook* was adapted from his work.

Cronin, James Watson (1931–) American physicist. With **Val Logsdon Fitch** (1923–) he demonstrated the non-conservation of parity and charge conjugation in particle reactions. In 1980 Cronin and Fitch shared the Nobel prize for physics for their work.

Cronkite, Walter Leland Jnr (1916–) American journalist and broadcaster. He was anchorman for CBS Evening News (1962–81) and won a reputation for impartiality, honesty and straightforwardness.

Crosby, Bing [Harry Lillis Crosby] (1904–77) American singer and actor. His relaxed, jazz-influenced style of 'crooning' made him one of the most popular and imitated singers of the century. He appeared in over 60 films and formed a notable comedy partnership with Bob HOPE in the '*Road to . . .*' series.

Cruijff, Hendrik Johannes (1947–) Dutch football player, manager and coach known as 'Pythagoras in boots' for his deadly, mathematical accuracy and also for a move that became known as the 'Cruijff turn'. Three-times winner of the European Footballer of the Year award, he remains a Dutch national hero and highly influential figure in the sport.

Cui, César Antonovich *see* AML Five, The.

Cummings, E[dward] E[stlin] (1894–1962) American poet, novelist and artist. His experimental free verse and distinctive use of typography influenced many other poets.

Curie, Marie (1867–1934) Polish-born French chemist. With her husband, **Pierre Curie** (1859–1906), also a chemist, and the physicist **Antoine Henri Becquerel** (1852–1908), she was awarded the 1903 Nobel prize for physics for work on radioactivity, the first woman to win a Nobel prize. She subsequently became the first person to win two Nobel prizes when her discovery of radium and polonium led to her being awarded the 1911 Nobel prize for chemistry.

Curwen, John *see* AML tonic sol-fa.

Cyrano de Bergerac, Savinien (1619–1655) French soldier, poet and dramatist. He was most famous in the popular imagination for having an enormous nose and for having (reputedly) fought around a thousand duels. His works include several satires, and his life was dramatised by ROSTAND in a verse drama.

Dahl, Roald (1916–90) English author (of Norwegian parentage) known primarily for his entertaining children's stories, e.g. *Charlie and the Chocolate Factory*, *Mathilda*, and collections of humorous poems. Stories for adults include the collection *Kiss, Kiss*.

Daladier, Edouard (1884–1970) French socialist statesman. He was prime minister (1933, 1934, 1938–40) and signed the Munich Pact of 1938. He denounced the Vichy government in 1943 and was imprisoned.

Dalai Lama [Tenzin Gyatso] (1935–) Tibetan spiritual and temporal leader. He became the 14th Dalai Lama in 1940 and fled Tibet in 1959 following the Chinese invasion of his country. He was awarded the 1989 Nobel peace prize in recognition of his commitment to the non-violent liberation of his homeland.

Dalcroze, Emile Jaques *see* AML eurhythmics.

Dale, Sir Henry Hallett (1875–1968) English physiologist. He and **Otto Lowei** (1873–1961) were awarded the 1936 Nobel prize for physiology or medicine for their work on the chemical basis of nerve impulse transmission.

Dali, Salvador (1904–89) Spanish Surrealist painter. His finely executed paintings, or 'dream photographs', did much to popularise the Surrealist movement. He also collaborated with the film director Luis BUÑUEL on the films *Un Chien Andalou* and *L'Age d'or*. Dali was a memorably eccentric individual, often given to paranoia and acts of exhibitionism.

D'Annunzio, Gabriele (1863–1938) Italian poet, novelist, dramatist and political adventurer. He seized the city of Fiume in 1919, which he ruled until 1920, and later became a supporter of MUSSOLINI.

Dante Alighieri (1265–1321) Italian poet. Expelled from Florence in 1309 for political reasons, he spent 20 years in wandering exile during which he wrote his masterpiece, the *Divine Comedy*. His literary influence was enormous and resulted in Tuscan becoming the language of literary Italy.

Danton, Georges Jacques (1759-94) French revolutionary. After the fall of the monarchy in 1792, he became minister of justice and voted for the death of LOUIS XVI. His efforts to moderate the Terror failed and he himself was executed.

Darwin, Charles Robert (1809–82) English naturalist. The grandson of the physician and poet **Erasmus Darwin** (1731–1802), he sailed as a naturalist to South America and the Pacific (1831–36) where his studies among the animal and plant life of the area formed the basis for his revolutionary theory of evolution by natural selection.

Daumier, Honoré (1808–79) French cartoonist, painter and sculptor. A most proficient satirist, his caricatures of the French king resulted in a term in jail.

David, Jacques-Louis (1748–1825) French painter. The leading artist of the French Revolution, he was imprisoned after the death of ROBESPIERRE but survived to become painter to NAPOLEON.

Davies, Sir Peter Maxwell (1934–) English composer. With BIRTWISTLE, he founded the Pierrot Players (later the Fires of London). Since 1970 he has been based in Orkney.

Davis, Bette [Ruth Elizabeth Davis] (1908–89) American actress, whose electrifying and commanding screen presence made her a highly rated film actress. Her films include *All About Eve* (1950).

Davis, Sir Colin Rex (1927–) English conductor. Noted particularly for his interpretations of BERLIOZ, he was conductor of the BBC Symphony Orchestra (1967–71).

Davis, Jefferson (1808–89) American president of the Confederate states and Secretary of War (1853–1857). He published *The Rise and Fall of the Confederate Government* in 1881.

Davis, Miles Dewey (1926–91) American jazz trumpeter, composer and bandleader. The leading exponent of the influential 'cool jazz' school.

Davisson, Clinton Joseph *see* THOMSON, SIR GEORGE PAGET.

Davy, Sir Humphry (1778–1829) English chemist. An ingenious experimenter, he discovered many new metals, e.g. sodium and potassium, and invented the 'Davy lamp' for miners in 1815.

Dawes, Charles G[ates] (1865–1951) American banker. He devised the Dawes Plan of 1924 for German reparation payments after World War I. He was US vice-president (1925–29) and was awarded the 1925 Nobel peace prize.

Day, Doris [Doris Kappelhoff] (1924–) American film actress, famous for her light-hearted, girl-next-door image.

Dayan, Moshe (1915–81) Israeli general and statesman. He commanded the Israeli forces during the Sinai invasion (1956) and was minister of defence during the Six Day War of 1967. He played an important part in the talks leading to the Israel-Egypt peace treaty of 1979.

Day Lewis, Cecil (1904–72) Irish-born English poet. In the 1930s he was regarded as part of the 'AUDEN generation' of left-wing poets. He became poet laureate in 1968.

Dean, Christopher *see* TORVILL, JAYNE.

Dean, James Byron (1931–55) American film actor. He became a cult figure in the 1950s for his portrayal of troubled, disaffected adolescence, e.g. in *East of Eden* and *Rebel Without a Cause* (both 1955). He died in a car crash.

Debussy, [Achille] Claude (1862–1918) French composer. Regarded as the founder of Impressionism in music, he had a strong influences on modern music. His works include orchestral pieces, e.g. *La Mer*, and the opera *Pelléas et Mélisande*.

Defoe, Daniel (1600–1731) English novelist and pamphleteer. His works include two remarkable novels, *Robinson Crusoe* (1719) and *Moll Flanders* (1722), although he was better known in his lifetime as a skilled and prolific propagandist.

Degas, [Hilaire Germain] Edgar (1834–1917) French painter and sculptor, especially noted for his paintings and pastel drawings of racehorses and ballet dancers. He met Monet in the 1860s, after which he began exhibiting with the Impressionists.

de Gaulle, Charles André Joseph Marie (1890–1970) French general, statesman and first president (1958–69) of the Fifth Republic. He granted independence to France's colonies in Africa (1959–60),

oversaw increased economic prosperity, fostered France's independent nuclear deterrent policy and strongly opposed the UK's entry into the Common Market.

de Klerk, F[rederik] W[illem] (1936–) South African statesman who succeeded P. W. BOTHA as leader of the ruling National Party and president (1989). He continued the policy of dismantling apartheid, in 1990 legalising the African National Congress and organising Nelson MANDELA's release from prison. He presided over South Africa's first free elections in 1994 and was defeated by Mandela with whom he shared the 1993 Nobel peace prize.

Delacroix, Eugène (1798–1863) French painter. His early work, while Romantic in subject matter, owes much to Classical composition. He studied CONSTABLE's work and in turn influenced other artists.

de la Mare, Walter John (1873–1956) English poet and novelist. Much of his work was written for children and the loss of childhood innocence is a major theme in his work.

Delaunay, Robert (1885–1941) French painter who founded Orphism and influenced many others, e.g. KLEE.

Delius, Frederick (1862–1934) English composer. Unconnected to any traditional school, he is noted for his six operas, including *A Village Romeo and Juliet* (1901), in addition to his great orchestral pieces.

de Mille, Cecil B[lount] (1881–1959) American film producer and director. With GOLDWYN, he is credited with creating the mass movie industry of Hollywood. His films were extravagant epics that achieved enormous success throughout the world, e.g. *The Ten Commandments*.

Dempsey, Jack [William Harrison] (1895–1983) American boxer. An ex-miner who became one of the most popular boxers of his day, he was world heavyweight champion (1919–26). Known as the 'Manassa Mauler', he retired from fighting to become a boxing referee and a restaurateur.

Deng Xiaoping or Teng Hsiao-p'ing (1904–97) Chinese Communist statesman. He took part in the 'long march' of 1934–5 and was elected to the central committee of the Communist Party in 1949, becoming

General Secretary in 1956. Denounced in the Cultural Revolution of the late 1960s as a 'capitalist roader', he re-emerged as a powerful figure in the late 1970s. At the time of his death he held no major office but was still regarded as the dominant political power in the country.

De Niro, Robert (1943–) American actor, who is regarded as one of the finest modern screen actors, with a remarkable facility for submerging himself in a wide variety of roles. His films include *The Godfather II* (1974), for which he won an Oscar, *Taxi Driver* (1976) and *Midnight Run*.

Depardieu, Gerard (1948–) French actor. Established in the 1970s as a leading man in French films, his strong performances and independent character have made him popular worldwide, notably in *Danton* (1982), *Cyrano de Bergerac* and *Green Card*.

Derain, André (1880–1954) French painter. He was one of the leading Fauvist painters (*see* AML Fauvists).

Desai, Morarji Ranchhodji (1896–1995) Indian statesman. He held several posts under NEHRU, founded the Janata Party in opposition to Indira GANDHI's Congress Party, which he defeated in the 1977 general election, and was prime minister of India (1977–79).

Descartes, René (1596-1650) French philosopher and mathematician. He proposed a dualistic philosophy, his most famous dictum being '*Cogito ergo sum*', 'I think, therefore I am'.

De Sica, Vittorio (1902–74) Italian film director and actor. His early films, e.g. *Bicycle Thieves* (1948), are regarded as among the finest Italian neo-realist films for their insight into the lives of the poor.

Dev, Kapil (1959–) Indian cricketer and one of that nation's great fast bowlers and all-rounders. He was voted India's Cricketer of the Century in 2002.

De Valera, Eamon (1882–1975) American-born Irish statesman. He was sentenced to death by the British government for his part in the 1916 Easter Rising but was reprieved after US intervention. He was president of Sinn Féin (1917–26), prime minister (1932–48, 1951–54, 1957–59) and president (1959–73).

De Vries, Hugo [Marie] (1848–1935) Dutch botanist and geneticist. He rediscovered the genetic principles first put forward by MENDEL and developed the theory of evolution through the mutation of genes.

Diaghilev, Sergei Pavlovich (1872–1929) Russian ballet impresario. Founder of the Ballet Russe de Diaghilev in 1911, he became a very influential ballet impresario, drawing on the talents of composers such as STRAVINSKY and artists such as PICASSO.

Diana, Princess of Wales (1961–97) formerly Lady Diana Frances Spencer. She married CHARLES, Prince of Wales, heir to the British throne, in 1981, and they had two sons, William and Harry [Henry]. They divorced in 1996 but her support for charities and international causes ensured that she retained her popularity. In August 1997 she and film producer **Dodi Fayed** were killed in a Paris car crash.

Dickens, Charles John Huffam (1812–70) English novelist. His prolific output included plays, pamphlets and lectures as well as novels and short stories. Immensely popular in both the USA and UK, he continues to be one of the most widely read writers in the English language. His novels include *David Copperfield* (1849–50), *Bleak House* (1852–53) and *Great Expectations* (1860–61).

Dickinson, Emily (1830–86) American poet. Although only seven of her 2000 poems were printed in her lifetime she became recognised as a uniquely gifted poet following the wider publication of her work in the 1890s.

Diderot, Denis (1713–84) French philosopher. With others, he edited the great *Encyclopédie*, 17 volumes of which appeared under Diderot's overall direction between 1751 and 1772.

Dietrich, Marlene [Maria Magdelene von Losch] (1902–92) German-born American singer and film actress, notable for her sexual presence and husky, alluring voice.

Dimaggio, Joe [Joseph] (1914–99) iconic American baseball player. Nicknamed 'Joltin Joe', he rose to prominence playing for the New York Yankees in 1936 and quickly became a star. He was a three-times winner of the American League's Most Valuable Player accolade, and briefly married to Marilyn MONROE (1954).

Dior, Christian (1905–57) French couturier who created the 'New Look' of the late 1940s, with a narrow waist and full pleated skirt, which was very popular in the austerity of postwar Europe.

Dirac, Paul Adrien Maurice (1902–84) English physicist. He devised a complete mathematical formulation of EINSTEIN's theory of relativity and predicted the existence of antimatter. In 1933 he shared the Nobel prize for physics with SCHRÖDINGER.

Disney, Walt[er] Elias (1901–66) American cartoonist and film producer. His cartoon films of the 1930s and 40s achieved high critical and popular acclaim, Mickey Mouse and Donald Duck being two of his famous creations. He built Disneyland amusement park in California (1955) and planned Disney World in Florida (1971).

Disraeli, Benjamin, 1st Earl of Beaconsfield (1804–81) British statesman and novelist. He became a Tory member of parliament in 1837 and prime minister (1868, 1874–80).

Dobzhansky, Theodosius (1900–75) Russian-born American geneticist. His seminal studies of genetic variation linked DARWIN's evolutionary theory with MENDEL's heredity laws.

Doenitz, Karl *see* DÖNITZ, KARL.

Dolci, Danilo (1924–97) Italian social reformer. Described as the 'GANDHI of Italy', he built schools and community centres in poverty-stricken Sicily.

Dollfus, Engelbert (1892–1934) Austrian statesman. A devout Roman Catholic, he became leader of the Christian Socialist Party and was elected chancellor (1932–34). He opposed the German Anschluss and was assassinated by Austrian Nazis.

Domingo, Placido (1941–) Spanish tenor who studied in Mexico City. He is regarded as one of the finest modern operatic tenors for his sophisticated vocal technique and considerable acting ability.

Dominic, Saint (*c*.1170–1221) Spanish monk. Noted for his asceticism, he founded the Dominican Order of monks and helped the forces of the Inquisition

in their barbarous treatment of the Albigensians in Southern France. He was canonised in 1234.

Donatello [Donato di Niccolò di Betto Bardi] (*c*.1386–1466) Florentine sculptor. One of the leading sculptors of the early Renaissance, his most famous work is the huge bronze statue of *David* (1430s).

Dönitz or Doenitz, Karl (1891–1980) German admiral. He was commander of the German navy (1943–45). As head of the Nazi state following HITLER's suicide, he surrendered unconditionally to the Allies and was sentenced at Nuremberg to ten years' imprisonment for war crimes.

Donne, John (1573–1631) English poet and divine. He became Dean of St Paul's in 1621 and was regarded as one of the greatest preachers of his day. His poetry is among the finest metaphysical verse.

Doré, Gustave (1832–83) French sculptor, painter and illustrator. Trained as a caricaturist, he became well known for his book illustrations and realistic drawings of London slums.

Dostoyevsky, Fyodor Mikhailovich (1821–81) Russian novelist. His novels, e.g. *Crime and Punishment* (1866), are profound explorations of sin and redemption through suffering. With TOLSTOY he has had a great influence on modern literature.

Douglas-Home, Sir Alec, Baron Home of the Hirsel (1903–95) Scottish Conservative politician. He renounced his title of 14th Earl of Home in 1963 to contest (and win) the seat of Kinross after succeeding Harold MACMILLAN as prime minister.

Doyle, Sir Arthur Conan (1859–1930) Scottish novelist, short-story writer and physician. His most famous creation is the amateur detective Sherlock Holmes.

D'Oyly Carte, Richard *see* AML D'Oyly Carte company.

Drake, Sir Francis (*c*.1540–96) English sailor who circumnavigated the world (1577–80) and was one of the leading lights in the victory over the Spanish Armada (1588).

Dreyfus, Alfred (1859–1935) French army officer. Imprisoned in 1894 on Devil's Island on a false charge of espionage, the 'Dreyfus affair' scandalised much of

Europe for the anti-semitism of the prosecution case. ZOLA's pamphlet *J'accuse* (1898) was written in his defence, and Dreyfus was released in 1906.

Dryden, John (1631–1700) English poet, dramatist and critic. An important literary figure of his time, he was also a highly significant contributor to the religious and political controversies of the day. His works include the social comedy *Marriage à la Mode* (1672) and the verse tragedy *All for Love* (1678). He became poet laureate in 1668 but lost the post in 1688 (*see* AML poet laureate).

Dubcek, Alexander (1921–92) Czech statesman. As first secretary of the Communist Party (1968–69), he introduced political reforms that ended with the Russian invasion of 1968. Following Czechoslovakian independence, he was appointed chairman of the federal assembly (1989).

Dubuffet, Jean (1901–85) French painter. He devised the concept of 'Art Brut' (see AML Art Brut) in reaction against 'museum art', and made paintings assembled from bits of rubbish, broken glass, etc.

Duchamp, Marcel (1887–1968) French-born American painter and sculptor. One of the early pioneers of Dada (*see* AML Dada), he introduced the concept of the 'found object'.

Dulles, John Foster (1888–1959) American Republican statesman and lawyer. He was secretary of state (1953–59) under EISENHOWER and developed the confrontational foreign policy of 'brinkmanship' in the Cold War against the USSR.

Dumas, Alexandre [Dumas père] (1802–70) French novelist and dramatist whose entertaining romantic novels, e.g. *The Three Musketeers* (1844–45), achieved instant and lasting popularity. His illegitimate son, also called **Alexandre Dumas [Dumas fils]** (1824–95) also wrote novels and plays, e.g. *La Dame aux Camélias* (1852).

Du Maurier, Dame Daphne (1907–89) English novelist and short-story writer. Several of her works have been made into successful films, e.g. the novel *Rebecca* (1938), and the short story 'Don't Look Now'.

Duncan, Isadora (1878–1927) American dancer and choreographer. She developed a free, interpretative style of dancing that was influential on the development of modern dance (e.g. on DIAGHILEV). She died in a terrible accident when the scarf she was wearing became caught in the rear wheel of the car in which she was travelling.

du Pré, Jacqueline (1945–87) English cellist. She became recognised as one of the world's finest cellists in the 1960s and married Daniel BARENBOIM in 1967, with whom she frequently performed. Her performing career came to an end in 1973 after she developed multiple sclerosis. She pursued an active teaching career until her death.

Dürer, Albrecht (1471–1528) German engraver and painter. A leading figure of the Northern Renaissance, his work is outstanding in its attention to detail and its emotional content. His albums of engravings were highly influential on other artists.

Durey, Louis *see* AML Six, Les.

Durrell, Lawrence George (1912–90) English poet, novelist and travel writer. His masterpiece is a series of sexual and linguistically elaborate novels comprising the *Alexandria Quartet* (1957–60). His naturalist brother **Gerald Durrell** (1925–95) also wrote many books including *My Family and Other Animals* which documented his earliest animal adventures and the antics of the Durrell family on Corfu.

Dvořák, Antonin (1841–1904) Czech composer. Strongly influenced by Slavonic folk music, his work was widely praised and he was made a director of the New York Conservatory in 1891. His most famous work is *Symphony No. 9 from the New World*.

Dyck, Sir Anthony van (1599–1641) Flemish painter. Renowned for his unique and influential style of portraiture, investing his sitters with character and refinement of detail, he became court painter to CHARLES I in 1632.

Dylan, Bob [Robert Allen Zimmerman] (1941–) American folk/rock singer and songwriter. He became the most prominent 'protest' folksinger in the 1960s and his lyrics are very highly regarded by some critics. *See also* BAEZ.

Earhart, Amelia (1898–1937) American aviator. She was the first woman to make a solo flight across the Atlantic (1932). She disappeared on a flight across the Pacific while attempting a round-the-world flight.

Eastman, George (1854–1932) American inventor of photographic equipment and philanthropist. His invention of the Kodak roll-movie camera revolutionised the photographic industry, as did his development of colour photography in the late 1920s.

Eco, Umberto (1932–) Italian semiologist. A leading literary critic, he is also highly regarded as a writer of fiction. His best-known work is the medieval philosophical whodunit, *The Name of the Rose* (1981).

Eddy, Mary Baker (1821–1910) American religious leader. A faith healer, she devised a system of healing based on the Bible, which she called 'Christian Science', and founded the Church of Christ, Scientist, in Boston (1879).

Eden, Sir [Robert] Anthony, 1st Earl of Avon (1897–1977) British Conservative statesman. He served several terms as foreign minister and was prime minister (1955–57). He resigned following the Suez Crisis, when British and French occupation of Egypt after NASSER'S nationalisation of the Suez Canal received worldwide condemnation.

Edison, Thomas Alva (1847–1931) American inventor. One of the most prolific and successful inventors of all time, he patented over a thousand inventions, including the gramophone, the incandescent electric light bulb and the microphone.

Edward VIII [later The Prince Edward, Duke of Windsor] (1894–1972) English monarch, (1936). Highly popular with the British public for his apparent concern at the lot of the unemployed, he abdicated to marry the American divorcée, **Wallis Simpson** (1896–1986), after BALDWIN had made plain his opposition to the notion of Mrs Simpson becoming queen. He married her in 1937, after which they lived in exile, the Duke becoming governor of the Bahamas during World War II. After the war he was never given another official appointment and spent the remainder of his life in retirement

Edward, Prince *see* ELIZABETH II.

Ehrlich, Paul (1854–1915) German bac-

teriologist. He did significant research into immunology and chemotherapy, and developed a cure for syphilis (1910). He was awarded the 1908 Nobel prize for physiology or medicine.

Eichmann, [Karl] Adolf (1906–62) Austrian Nazi leader and war criminal. He oversaw the 'Final Solution' (deportation of Jews to death camps) and escaped to Argentina at the end of World War II but was captured and tried for crimes against humanity by the Israelis in 1960 and executed.

Eijkman, Christiaan (1858–1930) Dutch physician who discovered that beriberi is caused by nutritional deficiency. His research led to the discovery of vitamins. He shared the 1929 Nobel prize for physiology or medicine with Sir Frederick HOPKINS.

Einstein, Albert (1879–1955) German-born physicist and mathematician. His formulations of the special theory of relativity (1906) and general theory of relativity (1916), and research into quantum theory, mark him as one of the greatest of all thinkers. He was awarded the 1921 Nobel prize for physics. He was forced to flee Nazi Germany in 1933 and became a US citizen in 1940.

Eisenhower, Dwight D[avid] (1890–1969) American general and Republican statesman, known as 'Ike'. He became supreme commander of the Allied forces in 1943 and 34th president of the US (1953–60).

Eisenstein, Sergei Mikhailovich (1898–1948) Soviet film director. He became one of the most influential directors of all time with films such as *Battleship Potemkin* (1925), in which he deployed his theory of film montage.

Elgar, Sir Edward William (1857–1934) English composer. A master of many styles, he became recognised as the leading British composer with works such as the *Enigma Variations*, the oratorio *The Dream of Gerontius* and his famous *Cello Concerto*.

El Greco [Domenikos Theotocopolous] (1541–1614) Cretan-born Spanish painter, sculptor and architect. He studied in Italy before settling in Toledo where he worked in an spiritually evocative style, using a palette of cold blues and greys at a time when the vogue was for warmer colours. His works include *The Burial of Count Orgaz*.

Eliot, George [Mary Ann Evans] (1819–80) English novelist. Her novels, e.g. *The Mill on the Floss* (1860) and *Middlemarch* (1871–72) deal with the problems of ethical choice in the rapidly changing rural environment of 19th-century England. She lived, unmarried, with her partner, the English writer **George Henry Lewes** (1817–78).

Eliot, T[homas] S[tearns] (1888–1965) American-born English poet and critic. His early poetry, e.g. *The Waste Land* (1922), is concerned with the breakdown of civilised values in the postwar Jazz Era. He also wrote verse dramas and critical works.

Elizabeth II (1926–) queen of the United Kingdom (1952–). Daughter of GEORGE VI, she married Prince PHILIP in 1947 and has four children: Prince CHARLES, **Princess Anne** (1950–), **Prince Andrew** (1960–) and **Prince Edward** (1964–).

Ellington, Duke [Edward Kennedy Ellington] (1899–1974) American jazz composer, pianist and band-leader. Regarded as a fine jazz composer, his many works include 'Mood Indigo' and 'Sophisticated Lady'.

Elton, Charles Sutherland (1900–91) English ecologist. His field studies of animal communities in their environments raised awareness of the ability of animals to adapt to changing habitats.

Emerson, Ralph Waldo (1803–82) American essayist, philosopher and poet who developed a philosophy of 'transcendentalism', based upon the authenticity of the individual conscience against both church and state.

Engels, Friedrich *see* MARX, KARL.

Epicurus (341–271 BC) Greek philosopher. He founded the Epicurean school of philosophy, which teaches that the highest good and proper study of mankind is pleasure and that this can be attained through a life of simplicity and moderation.

Erasmus, Desiderius (*c*.1466–1536) Dutch humanist. One of the leading scholars of the Renaissance, he was a strong advocate of tolerance in an intolerant age. His works

include *Praise of Folly*, written partly in tribute to his friend Thomas MORE.

Ernst, Max (1891–1976) German-born French painter. He was a leading member of both the Dada and Surrealist movements (see AML Dada; Surrealism) and pioneered the use of collage and photomontage.

Etherege, Sir George *see* AML comedy of manners.

Euripides (480–406 BC) Greek dramatist. He was the youngest of the three great Greek tragedians, the others being AESCHYLUS and SOPHOCLES. Nineteen of his plays are extant, the most notable including *Medea* and *The Trojan Women*. *See also* AML tragedy.

Eusden, Laurence *see* AML poet laureate.

Evans, Sir Arthur John (1851–1941) English archaeologist. His excavations of the palace of Knossos in Crete resulted in the rediscovery of Minoan civilisation.

Evans, Dame Edith (1888–1976) English actress notable for her command of a wide variety of roles. She created the role of Lady Utterwood in SHAW's *Heartbreak House* and gave a definitive performance as Lady Bracknell in WILDE's *The Importance of Being Earnest*.

Evert, Chrissie [Christine] (1954–) American tennnis player, known for her skill and accuracy on the baseline and her ability to stay cool under pressure. She dominated the women's game for almost 10 years from the mid-1970s, winning every major title including three Wimbledon championships (1974, 1976, 1981).

Eysenck, Hans Jürgen (1916–97) German-born British psychologist. He was a notable critic of FREUD's theory of psychoanalysis and holder of controversial views on the role of genetic factors in determining intelligence.

Fairbanks, Douglas, Senior [Douglas Elton Ullman] (1883–1939) American film actor and producer, who became a leading star of silent films. His son, **Douglas Fairbanks Junior** (1909–2000), was also an actor. His first wife was Joan CRAWFORD.

Faldo, Nick (1957–) British golfer. He has won six major titles, three of them Open championships. He reached the peak of his career in the early 1990s.

Fangio, John Manuel (1911–95) Argentinian Formula One racing driver, considered by many to be the greatest of all time. He was World Champion five times and after his retirement in 1957, his championship record remained unbeaten for 46 years.

Faraday, Michael (1791–1867) English chemist and physicist. He was an assistant to DAVY and discovered electromagnetic induction and investigated electrolysis.

Farouk, King *see* NASSER, GAMAL ABDEL.

Farquhar, George (1678–1707) Irish dramatist. His lightly satirical plays, e.g. *The Beaux' Stratagem* (1707), mark an important transitional stage between the bawdy world of Restoration comedy and the more decorous 18th-century stage.

Fassbinder, Rainer Werner (1946–82) German film director. His films, e.g. *The Bitter Tears of Petra Von Kant* (1975), are noted for their social comment, particularly on postwar Germany.

Faulkner, William Harrison (1897–1962) American novelist. A master of the modern novel, his best-known work, *The Sound and the Fury* (1929), deals with social tensions in the Old South. He was awarded the 1949 Nobel prize for literature.

Fawcett, Dame Millicent, [neé Garrett] (1847–1929) English feminist. She became first president of the National Union of Women Suffrage Societies (1897–1919) and opposed the more militant tactics of Emmeline PANKHURST.

Fellini, Federico (1920–93) Italian film director. The best known of his highly individual films is *La Dolce Vita* (1960), a cynical portrayal of Roman high society.

Ferlinghetti, Lawrence *see* AML Beat Generation.

Fermat, Pierre de (1601–65) French mathematician. The founder of number theory, he initiated, with PASCAL, the study of probability theory.

Fermi, Enrico (1901–54) Italian-born American physicist. Awarded the Nobel prize for physics in 1938 for his work on radioactive substances and nuclear bombardment, he fled to the USA. He built the first nuclear reactor at Chicago in 1942.

Ferrier, Kathleen (1912–53) English contralto. A highly regarded singer whose short career ended with her death from cancer, she created the title role in BRITTEN's *Rape of Lucretia* and sang regularly with WALTER.

Feydeau, Georges (1862–1921) French dramatist, noted for his bedroom farces, e.g. *Hotel Paradise*.

Feynman, Richard (1918–88) American physicist. He shared the 1965 Nobel prize for physics for his work in quantum electrodynamics.

Field, John (1782–1837) Irish composer and pianist who settled in Russia (1804–32) then in London. He is noted for his 19 *Nocturnes* and was an influence on CHOPIN.

Fielding, Henry (1707–54) English novelist and dramatist. His greatest work, *Tom Jones* (1749), surveys the whole of English society with masterly insight and compassion. He also wrote important tracts on social problems and worked tirelessly against legal corruption. *See also* AML picaresque novel.

Fields, W. C. [William Claude Dukenfield] (1880–1946) American comedian, noted for his hard drinking, red nose, gravel voice and antipathy to children and animals.

Fillmore, Millard (1800–1874) American Whig politician and the 13th president of the USA (1850–1853).

Fischer, Bobby [Robert] James (1943–2008) American chess player. A grandmaster at 15 he became the first US player to win the world championship (1972) when he won against SPASSKY.

Fittipaldi, Emerson (1946–) Brazilian Formula One racing driver, who became the youngest ever World Champion in 1972 at the age of 25, driving a Lotus.

Fitzgerald, Ella (1918–1996) American jazz singer whose highly praised vocal range, rhythmic subtlety and clarity of tone made her a very popular singer of her day.

Fitzgerald, F[rancis] Scott [Key] (1896–1940) American novelist and short-story writer. His works are moralistic fables set in the high society of the Jazz Age in the 1920s and include *The Great Gatsby* and *Tender is the Night*.

Flagstad, Kirsten (1895–1962) Norwegian soprano, noted for her roles in Wagner's operas. She is regarded as one of the finest Wagnerian singers of all time.

Flaherty, Robert Joseph (1884–1951) American documentary film director. His films, e.g. *Nanook of the North* (1921), set high standards for all documentary film makers.

Flaubert, Gustave (1821–80) French novelist. His masterpiece is his first published novel, *Madame Bovary* (1857), a study of self-deception, adultery and suicide in rural France. He is noted for his meticulously impersonal and objective narrative.

Fleming, Sir Alexander (1881–1955) Scottish bacteriologist. He discovered the antibacterial qualities of the enzyme lysozyme, the substance he dubbed 'penicillin'. He shared the 1945 Nobel prize for physiology or medicine with CHAIN and FLOREY.

Fleming, Ian Lancaster (1908–64) English novelist. His series of novels featuring the British secret agent James Bond, e.g. *Goldfinger*, were enormous successes and have all been filmed.

Fletcher, John (1579–1625) English dramatist. A popular dramatist of his day, he frequently collaborated with others, most notably with **Sir Francis Beaumont** (1584–1616).

Florey, Howard Walter, Baron (1898–1968) Australian pathologist. He shared the 1945 Nobel prize for physiology or medicine with Sir Alexander FLEMING and CHAIN for their work on penicillin.

Flynn, Errol [Leslie Thomas Flynn] (1909–59) Australian-born American film actor. His starring roles in the swashbuckling tradition, e.g. *Captain Blood* (1935), earned him considerable popularity.

Foch, Ferdinand (1851–1929) French general and marshal of France (1918). Given command of the Allied forces in March 1918, he led the Allies to victory following the arrival of US troops in July 1918.

Fokine, Michel (1880–1942) Russian-born American ballet dancer and choreographer. With DIAGHILEV in Paris he created a new style of ballet in which all the elements—dance, music, costume and *mise en scène*—formed a coherent whole.

Fonda, Henry James (1905–82) American film actor, often seen as the epitome of 'decent' America, a man determined to set injustices right. His daughter, **Jane Seymour Fonda** (1937–), also won recognition as an actress, although her outspoken opposition to the Vietnam war was heavily criticised.

Fonteyn, Dame Margot [Margaret Hookham] (1919–91) English ballerina. Regarded as one of the finest classical ballerinas of her time, she partnered NUREYEV at the age of 43.

Foot, Michael Mackintosh (1913–) British Labour politician. A leading left-winger and pacifist, he was secretary of state for employment (1974–76), leader of the House of Commons (1976–79) and leader of the Labour Party (1980–83).

Ford, Ford Madox [Ford Hermann Hueffer] (1873–1939) English novelist, poet and critic. Writer of over 80 novels, e.g. *The Good Soldier* (1915), he also founded the *Transatlantic Review* in 1924 and gave generous encouragement to many writers.

Ford, Gerald R[udolph] (1913–2006) American Republican statesman and 38th president of the US (1974–77). He replaced AGNEW as NIXON's vice-president in 1973, becoming president after Nixon's resignation.

Ford, Henry (1863–1947) American car designer and manufacturer. His Model T Ford (1908) was very successful and its production line manufacture became a role model for much of industry.

Ford, John (1586–*c*.1639) English dramatist notable for such revenge tragedies as *'Tis Pity She's a Whore* (1633).

Ford, John [Sean Aloysius O'Fearna] (1895–1973) American film director, regarded as a great director for his epic and poetic vision of history, particularly that of the American West in e.g. *Stagecoach* (1939) and *The Searchers* (1956).

Forster, E[dward] M[organ] (1879–1970) English novelist and critic. His novels, e.g. *Howards End* (1910), are mainly concerned with moral and ethical choices, and the relationships of educated middle-class people.

Fox, Charles James (1749–1806) English Whig statesman. A formidable orator, he was a vigorous opponent of the slave trade.

Fox, George (1624–91) English religious leader. He founded the Society of Friends (known popularly as 'Quakers') in 1647.

Fragonard, Jean-Honoré (1732–1806) French painter. One of the greatest exponents of Rococo art, his early works were historical scenes on a grand scale, but he is known for his smaller, picturesquely pretty canvases.

Francesca, Piero della *see* PIERO DELLA FRANCESCA.

Francis of Assisi, Saint [Giovanni Bernardone] (1181–1226) Italian monk. He abandoned a military career to care for the poor and founded a 'brotherhood' of friars in 1210, and, in 1212, an order for women, the Poor Clares. He preached poverty, chastity and obedience to the Church, and received the stigmata in 1224. He was canonised in 1228.

Franck, César Auguste (1822–90) Belgian-born French composer. His best works were written late in life, e.g. his string quartet, and received public acclaim only after his death.

Franck, James (1882–1964) German-born American physicist. With the German physicist **Gustav Ludwig Hertz** (1887–1975), he shared the 1925 Nobel prize for physics for work on the quantum theory, notably the effects of bombarding atoms with electrons.

Franco, Francisco (1892–1975) Spanish general and dictator. He led the right-wing rebellion against the Spanish Republican government during the Spanish Civil War (1936–39). He became leader of the Fascist Falange Party in 1937 and ruled Spain from 1939 until his death.

Frank, Anne (1929–45) German-born Dutch Jewish girl. Her journal describing her family's experiences while hiding from the Nazis is one of the most moving accounts of the terrible suffering of the Jewish people during World War II.

Franklin, Benjamin (1706–90) American statesman and scientist. He helped draft the American Declaration of Independence and played an active role in American political life for most of his long life. He also invented the lightning conductor.

Franklin, Rosalind Elsie (1920–58) British chemist. Her X-ray crystallography research into DNA contributed to the discovery of its structure by James WATSON and CRICK.

Frazer, Sir James George (1854–1941) Scottish scholar and anthropologist. His study of religious customs and myth influenced FREUD and many 20th-century writers.

Frazier, Joe (1944–) American boxer who held the world heavyweight boxing title from 1968–73, becoming the first man to beat MUHAMMED ALI in a professional boxing match in the process.

Frege, [Friedrich Ludwig] Gottlob (1848–1925) German mathematician and philosopher. He is regarded as having laid the foundations for both modern mathematical logic and the philosophy of language.

French, Sir John Denton Pinkstone, 1st Earl of Ypres (1852–1925) English field marshal. He commanded the British Expeditionary Force in France (1914–15) and became Lord Lieutenant of Ireland (1918–21) during the Anglo-Irish War.

Freud, Lucian (1922–) German-born British painter. A grandson of Sigmund FREUD, he is renowned for his nudes and portraits, often painted from odd angles in a realist style.

Freud, Sigmund (1856–1939) Austrian psychiatrist who founded psychoanalysis. His writings have been enormously influential. His main tenet is that neuroses and dreams are repressed manifestations of sexual desire. His stress on the importance of sex was rejected by ADLER and JUNG. His daughter, **Anna Freud** (1895–1982), pioneered child psychology in the UK.

Friedman, Milton (1912–2006) American economist. His controversial monetarist theory, stressing the need for minimal government intervention, became the dominant economic theory of the 1980s. He was awarded the 1976 Nobel prize for economics.

Friedrich, Casper David (1774–1840) German Romantic painter. His work was highly controversial in its treatment of landscape.

Frisch, Otto Robert (1904–79) Austrian-born British nuclear physicist. He and his aunt, Lise MEITNER, discovered nuclear fission, and their work led directly to the invention of the atom bomb.

Frisch, Ragnar *see* TINBERGEN, JAN.

Frost, Robert Lee (1874–1963) American poet. His quiet, lyrical poems, e.g. 'Stopping by Woods on a Snowy Evening', have been admired for their use of symbolism.

Fry, C[harles] B[urgess] (1872–1956) English sportsman, regarded as one of the greatest all-round sportsmen ever, representing England in athletics, cricket and football.

Fry, Christopher (1907–2005) English dramatist, whose verse dramas, e.g. *The Lady's Not for Burning* (1949), were popular with both critics and public.

Fry, Elizabeth (1780–1845) English prison reformer. A Quaker and preacher, she campaigned for prison reform and founded hostels for the homeless.

Fry, Roger *see* AML Postimpressionism.

Fuchs, Klaus Emil Julius (1911–88) German-born British physicist. He began work on British atom-bomb research in 1941 and was jailed in 1950 for 14 years for passing details to the Soviet Union.

Fuchs, Sir Vivian Ernest (1908–99) English explorer and scientist. He led the Commonwealth Trans-Antarctic Expedition (1955–58), which made the first overland crossing of Antarctica.

Fugard, Athol (1932–) South African dramatist, whose plays, e.g. *Boesman and Lena* (1968), explore the tragedy of racial tension caused by apartheid in South Africa.

Fuller, [Richard] Buckminster (1895–1983) American architect and engineer. He invented the 'geodesic dome', a lightweight framework consisting of a set of polygons in the shape of a shell.

Furtwängler, Wilhelm (1886–1954) German conductor. He became one of the most popular conductors in Europe, particularly for his highly charged interpretations of WAGNER's music.

Fuseli, Henry [Johann Heinrich Füssli] (1741–1825) Swiss-born British painter. His paintings are mannered and Romantic with a sense of the grotesque and macabre.

Fux, Johann *see* AML species.

Gable, [William] Clark (1901–60) American film actor. His rugged good looks, sardonic wit and easy-going charm made him one of the most popular film stars of his day. His films include *Gone with the Wind* (1939).

Gabo, Naum *see* AML Constructivism.

Gabor, Dennis (1900–1979) Hungarian-born British engineer. He was awarded the 1971 Nobel prize for physics for his invention (in 1947) of the hologram.

Gaddafi or Qaddafi, Moammar al (1942–) Libyan statesman and military dictator. He took power in a coup in 1969 and became president in 1977. Regarded almost universally as an unpredictable and often dangerous leader, Gaddafi has openly supported terrorist groups around the world.

Gagarin, Yuri Alekseevich (1934–68) Soviet cosmonaut who became, in 1961, the first man in space, when his *Vostok I* satellite circled the earth. He died in a plane crash.

Gainsborough, Thomas (1727–88) English portrait painter whose keen interest in landscape painting pervades most of his work, his sitters often being portrayed out of doors. He developed a light, rapid painting style based on a delicate palette.

Gaitskell, Hugh Todd Naylor (1906–63) British Labour politician. Introduced, as chancellor of the exchequer (1950–51), National Health Service charges. He was Labour Party leader (1955–63).

Galbraith, John Kenneth (1908–2006) Canadian-born American economist and diplomat notably critical of the wastefulness of capitalist society. His works include *The Affluent Society* (1958).

Galilei, Galileo (1564–1642) Italian astronomer, mathematician and natural philosopher. An innovative thinker and experimenter, he showed that falling bodies of differing weight descend at the same rate. He also perfected the refracting telescope and became convinced of the truth of COPERNICUS's theory that the earth revolved around the sun. He was unable to prove it and was forced to retract his support publicly.

Gallup, George Horace (1901–84) American statistician. He developed the opinion poll into a sophisticated device, the 'Gallup Poll', for testing public opinion.

Galsworthy, John (1867–1933) English novelist and dramatist. His plays, e.g. *Strife* (1909), attacked social injustice. His novels include the Forsyte saga trilogy (1909–29).

He was awarded the 1932 Nobel prize for literature.

Galton, Sir Francis (1822–1911) English scientist. A cousin of DARWIN, he travelled widely in Africa and made significant contributions to meteorology and heredity. He also developed the science of fingerprinting.

Gama, Vasco da (c.1469–1525) Portuguese navigator. He discovered the route to India round the Cape of Good Hope (1497–99) and became Portuguese viceroy in India in 1524.

Gandhi, Indira (1917–84) Indian stateswoman and prime minister. The daughter of NEHRU, she became prime minister (1966–77). Her second term of office (1980–84) saw much ethnic strife and she was assassinated by her Sikh bodyguards. Her son **Rajiv** (1944–91) became prime minister in 1984 and was killed in a suicide bomb attack.

Gandhi, Mahatma [Mohandas Karamchand Gandhi] (1869–1948) Indian nationalist statesman and spiritual leader ('Mahatma' means 'Great Soul'). A passionate advocate of non-violent resistance, his long campaign against British rule in India, using tactics of civil disobedience through passive resistance and hunger strikes, had great influence on world public opinion. He also struggled for reconciliation between Hindus and Moslems, and championed the cause of the Hindu Harijan caste of 'untouchables'. He was assassinated by a Hindu extremist in the wake of India's independence and partition.

Ganguly, Sourav (1972–) Indian cricketer and the country's most successful captain of a test match series during the early years of the 21st century.

Garbo, Greta [Greta Lovisa Gustafson] (1905–90) Swedish-born American film actress noted for her austere, remote beauty. Her films include *Queen Christina* (1933).

Garfield, James (1831–81) American Republican politician and 20th president of the US (1881). He was shot by a disappointed office-seeker, Charles Guiteau, on 2 July 1881 and died on 19 September.

Garibaldi, Giuseppe (1807–82) Italian patriot. Forced into exile in 1834, he returned during the year of revolutions, 1848, and took part in the defence of Rome against the French, and in 1860 with a force a thousand strong, he took Naples and Sicily for the newly united Italy. He is regarded as the most significant figure in the struggle for Italian independence.

Garland, Judy [Frances Gumm] (1922–69) American film actress and singer. She became one of the most loved child stars of the cinema in *The Wizard of Oz* (1939) and later starred in such films as *Easter Parade* (1948) and *A Star is Born* (1954).

Garrick, David (1717–79) English actor. A pupil of Samuel JOHNSON at Lichfield, he soon made his mark as an actor. At home with tragedy, comedy or farce, he dominated the English stage for many years and was actor-manager of Drury Lane Theatre 1747–76.

Gaskell, Mrs Elizabeth [Elizabeth Cleghorn Stevenson] (1810–65) English novelist. Her novels, e.g. *North and South* (1855), are often concerned with the injustices of the 'two-nation' society of 19th-century England, although her most popular novel is *Cranford* (1853), a gentle study of life in a small village.

Gates, Bill [William Henry] (1955–) American entrepreneur and wealthy chairman of the Microsoft computer empire. He is co-founder with his wife, Melinda, of the Bill and Melinda Gates Foundation which provides funding to organisations to improve health and reduce poverty in the developing world.

Gauguin, Paul (1848–1903) French painter. One of the greatest exponents of Postimpressionism (*see* AML Postimpressionism), his interest in primitive art led to him settling in the South Pacific islands, where he painted some of his most important masterpieces.

Gay, John (1685–1732) English dramatist and poet. His masterpiece is *The Beggars' Opera* (1728), the ballad opera on which BRECHT based his *Threepenny Opera*.

Gell-Mann, Murray (1929–) American physicist. He introduced the quark hypothesis into physics and was awarded the 1969 Nobel prize for physics for his research into particle physics.

Genet, Jean (1910–86) French dramatist

and novelist. His works are often based on his experiences in the criminal underworld where he spent much of his life.

Genghis Khan [Temujin] (*c*.1162–1227) Mongol leader who united the Mongol tribes and conquered China, establishing an empire that stretched from the Black Sea to the Pacific.

Géricault, Théodore (1791–1824) French Romantic painter. The realism and Baroque dynamism of his work had a huge influence on many painters.

Gershwin, George (1898–1937) American composer and pianist. He and his brother, the lyricist **Ira Gershwin** (1896–1983), created many popular musicals now considered masterpieces of American music.

Getty, Jean Paul (1892–1976) American industrialist and art collector, renowned for his miserliness and acquisition of works of art. His son, **John Paul Getty** (1932–2003), donated over £140 million to the cause of British culture including some £50 million to the National Gallery.

Ghirlandaio, Domenico (1449–94) Florentine painter who ran a workshop with his brothers **Benedetto** (1458–97) and **Davide** (1452–1525) where he produced frescos and altarpieces for churches in Florence.

Giacometti, Alberto (1901–66) Swiss sculptor and painter. He became a Surrealist in 1930 and was influenced by SARTRE's Existentialism.

Gibbon, Edward (1737–94) English historian. His masterpiece is his *History of the Decline and Fall of the Roman Empire* (1776–88), a work that remains a great historical study.

Gielgud, Sir [Arthur] John (1904–2000) English stage and film actor and producer. Regarded as one of the leading Shakespearian actors of his time, he also appeared in several films, e.g. *Providence* (1977).

Gierek, Edward (1913–2001) Polish Communist statesman. He became leader of the Polish United Workers Party following GOMULKA's resignation in 1971. He presided over increasing industrial unrest and the rise of the union Solidarity.

Gilbert, Sir W[illiam] S[chwenck] (1836–1911) English dramatist and librettist. His collaboration with the composer **Sir**

Arthur Sullivan (1842–1900) resulted in the 13 popular 'Savoy Operas', e.g. *The Mikado* (1885) and *The Gondoliers* (1889), all of which have retained their popularity.

Gill, [Arthur] Eric Rowton (1882–1940) English sculptor, engraver, typographer and writer. His work has been influential in several areas of art and design.

Gillespie, Dizzy [John Birks Gillespie] (1917–93) American jazz trumpeter and bandleader, renowned as a virtuoso.

Ginsberg, Allen (1926–97) American poet, regarded as the leading poet of the Beat Generation (*see* AML Beat Generation), who had much influence on the hippy culture of the 1960s.

Giorgione [Giorgio da Castelfranco] (*c*.1477–1510) Venetian painter. Little of his work survives, although he was very influential, the importance of his work lying in his treatment of landscape, imbuing it with strong atmosphere and moods.

Giotto di Bondone (1267–1337) Florentine painter and architect who developed spatial perspective and fully rounded figures in a departure from the flat, decorative imagery of the Byzantine era.

Giscard d'Estaing, Valéry (1926–) French statesman. He served as minister of finance under DE GAULLE (1962–66) and POMPIDOU (1969–74) and was elected president (1974–81) following the latter's death.

Gladstone, William Ewart (1809–98) British statesman. He became the leader of the Liberals in 1867 and was subsequently prime minister four times (1868–74, 1880–85, 1886, 1892–94).

Glashow, Sheldon *see* WEINBERG, STEVEN.

Glass, Philip (1937–) American composer. One of the leading avant-garde composers of the 1970s, he is noted for his deep interest in Eastern harmonies and use of repeated motifs.

Glennie, Evelyn (1965–) Scottish virtuoso percussionist who has overcome profound deafness to achieve popular international success.

Gluck, Christoph Wilibald von (1714–87) German composer. He is especially noted for his operas, e.g. *Orfeo and Eurydice*.

Godard, Jean-Luc (1930–) French film director who is regarded as one of the most influential New Wave French directors of the 1950s with such films as *Breathless* and *Week-End*.

Gödel, Kurt (1906–78) Austrian-born American logician and mathematician. 'Gödel's incompleteness theorem' shows the existence of undecidable elements in arithmetic systems.

Godwin, William (1756–1836) English novelist and philosopher. He had a strong influence on many radicals, including SHELLEY, who married his daughter Mary.

Goebbels, [Paul] Joseph (1897–1945) German Nazi politician who was head of the Nazi Party propaganda section in 1929 and minister of enlightenment and propaganda (1933–45). He committed suicide after shooting his wife and children.

Goering, Hermann *see* GÖRING, HERMANN.

Goethe, Johann Wolfgang von (1749–1832) German poet, dramatist, novelist, philosopher, scientist and statesman. He was one of the most learned and influential figures of his time. His masterpiece is the verse drama *Faust* (1808, 1832).

Gogh, Vincent Van (1853–90) Dutch painter who studied theology before taking up painting in 1880. His art was unacademic in its realistic subject matter and bold, expressionistic style, e.g. *The Potato Eaters*, but he was later influenced by the colours of DEGAS and GAUGUIN. He spent the last two years of his life in southern France, partly in an asylum, a period of intense creativity arising out of personal anguish, e.g. *The Cornfield*, painted at the scene where he shot himself.

Gogol, Nikolai Vasilievich (1809–52) Russian short-story writer, dramatist and novelist. His two greatest works are the play *The Government Inspector* (1836) and the novel *Dead Souls* (1842).

Golding, William Gerald (1911–93) English novelist. His first novel *The Lord of the Flies* (1954) established him as a major modern novelist. He was awarded the Nobel prize for literature in 1983.

Goldoni, Carlo (1707–93) Italian dramatist. Around 150 of his 250 plays are comedies, frequently featuring satirical attacks on the aristocracy and set in his native Venice.

Goldsmith, Oliver (1728–1774) Irish poet and essayist who settled in London in 1756.

One of the leading poets of his day, he did not receive acclaim until late in life. His two greatest works are the novel *The Vicar of Wakefield* (1766) and his hugely successful play *She Stoops to Conquer* (1773).

Goldwyn, Samuel [Samuel Goldfish] (1882–1974) Polish-born American film producer. One of the founders of the Hollywood movie business, forming Metro-Goldwyn-Mayer with Louis B. MAYER in 1924, he was famous for his (mainly apocryphal) 'Goldwynisms', e.g. 'Include me out'.

Goodman, Benny [Benjamin David] (1909–86) American jazz clarinettist and bandleader. Known as the 'King of Swing', he was one of the first White jazz bandleaders to hire Black players.

Gorbachev, Mikhail Sergeevich (1931–) Soviet Communist statesman. He became general secretary of the Soviet Communist Party in 1985 and soon began instituting far-reaching social and political reforms. He became 'executive president' in 1990, facing strong opposition from radicals such as YELTSIN and from hard-line Communists. His powers were insufficient to withstand the break-up of the USSR, and he resigned in December 1991.

Gore, Al[bert] (1948–) American politician. A former investigative reporter, tobacco and livestock farmer, and developer, he became vice-president of the USA (1993–2001). He ran unsuccessfully as Democrat candidate for the presidency against Republican GEORGE W. BUSH in 2000 although the race was controversially close. Known also for raising the profile of human-induced global warming and climate change through his promotion of the 2006 film *An Inconvenient Truth*.

Göring or Goering, Hermann Wilhelm (1893–1946) German Nazi politician and military leader. He served HITLER as Prussian prime minister, minister of the interior and air minister (1933–45), organising the rebuilding of the Luftwaffe.

Gorki or Gorky, Maxim [Aleksey Maximovich Peshkov] (1868–1936) Russian novelist, dramatist and short-story writer. A firm communist, he helped formulate the doctrine of socialist realism in the USSR in the 1930s.

Gorky, Arshile [Vosdanig Manoog Adoian] (1905–48) Armenian-born American painter. Originally a Surrealist, he developed an abstract approach that was influential on action painters.

Goya y Lucientes, Francisco de (1746–1828) Spanish painter and printmaker. His strong, free-flowing technique and powerful pictorial style are demonstrated in early portraits of the royal family, to whom he was court painter, and in later works inspired by the behaviour of the French army in the invasion of Spain.

Grace, W[illiam] G[ilbert] (1848–1915) English cricketer and physician, one of the first English cricketers to become a national institution. He was also noted for his cunning gamesmanship.

Graf, Steffi (1969–) German tennis player from 1987 until her retiral in 1999. Known for her power and accuracy, especially on the baseline. She won the 'Grand Slam' of all four major titles in 1988 (Wimbledon and the US, Australian and French Opens). She is married to Andre AGASSI.

Graham, Billy [William Franklin Graham] (1918–) American evangelist. His evangelical crusades go all over the world.

Graham, Martha (1893–1991) American dancer and choreographer who is regarded as one of the founders of modern dance.

Grahame, Kenneth (1859–1932) Scottish author. His masterpiece, *The Wind in the Willows* (1908), is a children's classic.

Grainger, Percy Aldridge (1882–1961) Australian-born American pianist and composer. He was a notable enthusiast of folk songs, on which many of his works are based.

Grant, Cary [Archibald Alexander Leach] (1904–86) English-born American film actor and one of Hollywood's leading stars in light comedy roles and thrillers.

Grant, Ulysses S[impson] (1822–85) American soldier and 18th US President (1869–77). He was commander of the Union forces in the Civil War. He established universal suffrage for all citizens, regardless of colour.

Grappelli, Stéphane (1908–97) French jazz violinist. A founder of the Quintette de Hot Club de France, which became the leading European jazz group, he is regarded as the finest jazz violinist ever.

Grass, Günter Wilhelm (1927–) German novelist, dramatist and poet. His works include the novel *Die Blechtrommel* (*The Tin Drum*, 1959), a grimly comic satire on the collapse of the Third Reich as seen through the eyes of a boy.

Graves, Robert Ranke (1895–1985) English poet, novelist and critic. His works include his classic autobiographical account of World War I soldiering, *Goodbye to All That* (1929), poems and historical novels.

Gray, Thomas (1716–71) English poet. His best-known poem, 'Elegy Written in a Country Churchyard' (1751), is one of the most-quoted poems in the English language.

Greene, [Henry] Graham (1904–91) English novelist. Regarded as one of the great modern novelists, he converted to Roman Catholicism in 1926 and his religious beliefs play an important part in his work, e.g. *The Heart of the Matter* (1948).

Greer, Germaine (1939–) Australian feminist, writer and broadcaster who is best known for her controversial work *The Female Eunuch* (1970).

Gregory, Pope *see* AML Gregorian chant.

Gregory Nazianen, Saint *see* AML Passion music.

Grieg, Edvard Hagerup (1843–1907) Norwegian composer of Scottish descent. Strongly influenced by Norwegian folk music, his works include music for IBSEN's *Peer Gynt*.

Grierson, John (1898–1972) Scottish documentary film director and producer, described as the 'father of British documentary'.

Griffith, Arthur (1871–1922) Irish nationalist leader and first president of the Irish Free State. He founded Sinn Féin in 1905 and (with Michael COLLINS) signed the Anglo-Irish Treaty of 1921.

Griffith, D[avid] W[ark] (1875–1948) American film director and producer. In 1919 he founded United Artists with CHAPLIN, PICKFORD and FAIRBANKS.

Gris, Juan [José Victoriano Gonzàlez] (1887–1927) Spanish painter. He settled in Paris in 1906, where he became an associate of PICASSO and BRAQUE, and one of the leading Cubist painters.

Gromyko, Andrei Andreyevich (1909–89) Soviet statesman and diplomat. He was Soviet foreign minister (1957–1985) and a Politburo member (1973–89) and adapted effortlessly to each stage of relations with the West, from the Cold War through 1970s' detente to the GORBACHEV era.

Gropius, Walter (1883–1969) German-born architect. He is regarded as one of the most innovative and influential architects of the 20th century.

Grunewald, Matthias (c.1460–1528) German painter noted for his use of perspective, Gothic imagery, strong colour and an expressionistic style of distortion.

Guevara, Che [Ernesto Guevara de la Serna] (1928–67) Argentinian-born Communist revolutionary. He joined Fidel CASTRO's forces in the Cuban revolution (1956–59). He subsequently led a guerrilla group in Bolivia, where he was killed by government troops.

Guinness, Sir Alec (1914–2000) English stage and film actor. Regarded as one of the most versatile stage actors of his generation, he became a household name through his films, e.g. *Kind Hearts and Coronets* (1949) and *Star Wars* (1977).

Gulbenkian, Calouste Sarkis (1869–1955) Turkish Armenian-born British financier, industrialist, diplomat and philanthropist. He endowed the Gulbenkian Foundation for the arts and sciences. His son, **Nubar Sarkis Gulbenkian** (1896–1972), was an Iranian diplomat and a philanthropist.

Guthrie, Sir [William] Tyrone (1900–71) English actor and theatrical producer.

Guthrie, Woody [Woodrow Wilson Guthrie] (1912–67) American folksinger and writer. His songs, which attack racial bigotry and the economic exploitation of the poor and immigrants, were a strong influence on 1960s' 'protest' singers.

Hadlee, Sir Richard John (1951–) New Zealand cricketer and one of the greatest fast bowlers and all-rounders in the game. The first player to achieve 400 test wickets, he is now chairman of the board of selectors for the New Zealand cricket team.

Hadrian [Publius Aelius Hadrianus] (76–138) Roman soldier and emperor. He spent much of his reign travelling through the empire, the boundaries of which he

was concerned to make firm. He built Hadrian's Wall in the north of England.

Hahn, Otto (1879–1968) German physical chemist. Awarded the 1944 Nobel prize for chemistry, he undertook significant research with MEITNER and others which led to the discovery of nuclear fission.

Haig, Douglas, 1st Earl (1861–1928) British field marshal. In World War I he was appointed commander in chief of the British forces on the western front (1915–18). The terrible losses of soldiers under his command led to fierce criticism of his tactics. He founded the British Legion.

Haile Selassie [Ras Tafari Makonnen] (1892–1975) emperor of Ethiopia (1930–36, 1941–74). He lived in Britain during the occupation of his country by Italy (1936–41). In the early 1960s he helped establish the Organisation of African Unity. He is worshipped as a god by the Rastafarian cult.

Haitink, Bernard Johann Herman (1929–) Dutch conductor, renowned particularly as an interpreter of the music of MAHLER.

Hall, Sir Peter Reginald Frederick (1930–) English stage director and theatre manager. He was director of the Royal Shakespeare Company (1960–68), assistant director and then director of the National Theatre (1973–88), and artistic director of the Old Vic.

Hall, Wes [Wesley] (1937–) West Indian fast bowler and a cricketer who was hugely popular with devotees of the game during the 1960s. He is currently president of his country cricket board.

Hallé, Sir Charles *see* AML Hallé Orchestra.

Halley, Edmund (1656–1742) English astronomer and mathematician. In 1583, he calculated the orbit of the comet now named after him and correctly predicted its return in following years.

Hals, Frans (c.1581–1666) Dutch painter. Noted for his lively and innovative group portraiture that moved away from formal trends. His most famous work is *The Laughing Cavalier*.

Hamilton, Alexander (1757–1804) American statesman. He founded the Federalist Party (1787) and, as first secretary of the Treasury (1789–95), the US federal bank.

Hammarskjöld, Dag [Hjalmar Agne Carl] (1905–61) Swedish secretary general of the United Nations (1953–61). His period of office was a turbulent one, and he died in a plane crash during the Congo crisis. He was posthumously awarded the 1961 Nobel peace prize.

Hammerstein II, Oscar (1895–1960) American songwriter and librettist, best known for his musicals written with Richard RODGERS, e.g. *Oklahoma!*, *South Pacific* and *The Sound of Music*.

Hammett, [Samuel] Dashiell (1894–1961) American novelist. He wrote realistic crime novels based on his own experiences as a Pinkerton detective including *The Maltese Falcon* (1930) and *The Thin Man* (1932).

Hancock, Tony [Anthony John] (1924–68) English comedian. His popular BBC radio and TV series *Hancock's Half Hour* established his well-known comic persona of the belligerent misfit. He committed suicide.

Handel, George Frederick [Georg Friedrich Händel] (1685–1759) German-born English composer. He wrote over 40 operas, e.g. *Semele*, and many concertos and oratorios, e.g. *The Messiah*, as well as chamber and orchestral music, e.g. *Water Music*.

Hannibal, (247–182 BC) Carthaginian general. During the Second Punic War with Rome, he invaded Italy and crossed the Alps in 218. For 15 years he campaigned in Italy but was finally defeated in 204 BC.

Hardie, [James] Keir (1856–1915) Scottish Labour politician. He was the first leader of the parliamentary Labour Party (1906–07). A committed pacifist, he withdrew from politics following the failure of parties of the Left in Europe to oppose World War I.

Harding, Warren G. (1865–1923) American Republican politician and the 29th president of the US. Served from 1921–23.

Hardy, Oliver *see* LAUREL, STAN.

Hardy, Thomas (1840–1928) English novelist, short-story writer and poet. As well known for his influential novels, e.g. *Far from the Madding Crowd* (1874), as for his poetry, he is now ranked, with T. S. ELIOT and YEATS, as one of the three great modern poets in English.

Harlow, Jean [Harlean Carpentier] (1911–37) American film actress who became one of the screen's main sex symbols of the 1930s, with her tough, wise-cracking, 'platinum blonde' image.

Harris, Sir Arthur Travers (1892–1984) English air force officer, nicknamed 'Bomber Harris' for his advocacy of heavy bombing raids on German cities during World War II. The policy lasted from 1942 to the fire-bombing of Dresden in 1944.

Harrison, Benjamin (1833–1901) American Republican politician and the 23rd president of the US (1889–93).

Harrison, George (1943–2002) English singer-songwriter. He played lead guitar for the Beatles (1962–70) and also had a succesful solo career.

Harrison, William Henry (1773–1841) American Whig politician and 9th president of the US (1841).

Hart, Lorenz Milton (1895–1943) American lyricist who is best known for his collaborations with the composer Richard RODGERS, e.g. *The Boys from Syracuse* and *Pal Joey*.

Hasek, Jaroslav (1883–1923) Czech novelist and short-story writer. His masterpiece, *The Good Soldier Svejk* (1925), is based on his own experiences in the Austro-Hungarian army.

Hastings, Warren (1732–1818) British administrator in India, the first governor-general of Bengal (1773–85). He established the East India Company as one of the most powerful forces in India.

Haughey, Charles James (1925–2006) Irish Fianna Fáil politician. He was prime minister of the Republic of Ireland (1979–81, 1982, 1988–92) but was forced to resign after several scandals.

Havel, Vàclav (1936–) Czech dramatist and statesman. His plays satirised the brutality and corruption of Czech communism and he was imprisoned for several years after the Soviet invasion of 1968. He was elected his country's president in 1989 but resigned in 1992. From 1993 to 2003 he was president of the Czech Republic.

Hawke, Robert James Lee (1929–) Australian trades unionist and Labour statesman. He was prime minister (1983–91).

Hawking, Stephen William (1942–) English physicist. Widely regarded as perhaps the greatest physicist since EINSTEIN, his research into the theory of black holes has been highly acclaimed. He has suffered from a rare crippling nervous disease since the early 1960s and is confined to a wheelchair.

Hawks, Howard (1896–1977) American film director and producer. His films include several classics starring BOGART and **Lauren Bacall**, e.g. *The Big Sleep* (1946), John WAYNE and Marilyn MONROE.

Hawthorne, Nathaniel (1804–64) American novelist and short-story writer. New England Puritanism profoundly shaped his life and work, as in his masterpiece, *The Scarlet Letter* (1850).

Haydn, [Franz] Joseph (1732–1809) Austrian composer. An innovative composer, he established the form of both the symphony and the string quartet. His works include over 100 symphonies, 84 string quartets and the oratorio *The Creation*.

Hayek, Friedrich August von (1899–1992) Austrian-born British economist. A supporter of free-market policies and against government economic management, he shared the 1974 Nobel prize for economics with MYRDAL.

Hayes, Rutherford B. (1822–93) American Republican politician and the 19th president of the US. Served from 1877–81.

Hazlitt, William (1778–1830) English essayist and critic who remains one of the most important literary critics, especially for his essays on his contemporaries.

Healey, Denis Winston (1917–) English Labour politician. Chancellor of the exchequer (1974–79) and deputy leader of his party (1980–83), he was widely regarded as one of the most impressive of modern British politicians.

Heaney, Seamus Justin (1939–) Irish poet and critic regarded by many as the finest Irish poet since YEATS. In 1995 he was awarded the Nobel prize for literature.

Hearst, William Randolph (1863–1951) American newspaper publisher and politician. In the late 1920s he owned more than 25 daily newspapers and built a spectacular castle at San Simeon in California. He was congressman for New York (1903–07). Orson WELLES' film, *Citizen Kane*, is a thinly disguised account of his life.

Heath, Sir Edward Richard George (1916–2005) British Conservative statesman and prime minister (1970–74). A fervent pro-European, he negotiated Britain's entry into the Common Market in 1973.

Hegel, Georg Wilhelm Friedrich (1770–1831) German philosopher. His highly influential works, which describe how the Absolute is being reached by man's evolving powers of consciousness, influenced Karl MARX.

Heidegger, Martin (1889–1976) German philosopher. He is usually described as an Existentialist, despite his disclaimer of the label, and his concepts, such as 'angst', had a great influence on Existentialists such as SARTRE.

Heifetz, Jascha (1901–87) Lithuanian-born American violinist. His flamboyant and expressive interpretation of music from BACH to WALTON has been widely acclaimed.

Heine, Heinrich (1797–1856) German poet and critic. His masterpiece is his *Book of Songs* (1827), which includes some of the finest lyric poems ever written.

Heisenberg, Werner Karl (1901–76) German theoretical physicist. He was awarded the 1932 Nobel prize for physics for his work on quantum theory.

Heller, Joseph (1923–2001) American novelist. His most popular novel, *Catch–22* (1961), is a grim, Surrealist satire on military life and logic.

Hemingway, Ernest [Millar] (1899–1961) American novelist and short-story writer whose laconic narrative style made a big impression on his contemporaries. Major novels include *A Farewell to Arms* (1929) and *For Whom the Bell Tolls* (1940). He was awarded the Nobel prize for literature in 1954. He committed suicide.

Hendrix, Jimi [James Marshall Hendrix] (1942–70) American rock guitarist, singer and songwriter. With his trio, the Jimi Hendrix Experience, he became perhaps the most influential of all rock guitarists. He died of alcohol and drug abuse.

Henson, Jim [James Maury Henson] (1936–90) American puppeteer and film producer who created the engaging cast of 'muppets', including Kermit the Frog and Miss Piggy.

Henze, Hans Werner (1926–) German

composer. His works, which often reflect his enthusiasm for left-wing causes, include the opera *Elegy for Young Lovers* with a libretto by AUDEN.

Hepburn, Katharine (1909–2003) American film and stage actress noted for her wit and versatility. She had a long personal and acting relationship with Spencer TRACY. Her films include *The African Queen* (1951) and *Guess Who's Coming to Dinner* (1967).

Hepworth, Dame [Jocelyn] Barbara (1903–75) English sculptor. She became one of Britain's leading abstract sculptors in the 1930s, noted for her strong, often monumental carving.

Herbert, George (1593–1633) English Anglican priest and poet. His poems are among the greatest devotional poems in the language and are characteristic of metaphysical poetry in their subtle, paradoxical exploration of spiritual themes.

Herrick, Robert (1591–1674) English Anglican priest and poet.

Hertz, Gustav Ludwig *see* FRANCK, JAMES.

Hertzog, James Barry Munnik (1866–1942) South African statesman. He founded the Nationalist Party (1913) and advocated non-cooperation with Britain during World War I. He became prime minister (1924–39) and founded the Afrikaner Party in 1941.

Herzog, Werner (1942–) German film director. Bizarre enterprises are a notable feature of his films.

Heseltine, Michael *see* THATCHER, MARGARET.

Hess, Dame Myra (1890–1965) English pianist. She was also a much acclaimed concert pianist and an influential teacher.

Hess, [Walter Richard] Rudolf (1894–1987) German Nazi politician. He was deputy leader of the Nazi Party (1934–41). On the eve of Hitler's invasion of Russia, he flew to Scotland, apparently in the hope of negotiating peace terms with Britain. He spent the rest of his life imprisoned.

Hess, Victor Francis (1883–1964) Austrian-born American physicist. He shared the 1936 Nobel prize for physics with the American physicist **Carl David Anderson** (1905–91) for his research into cosmic rays.

Hesse, Hermann (1877–1962) German-born Swiss novelist, short-story writer and poet awarded the Nobel prize for literature in 1946. His fiction reflects his fascination with oriental mysticism, spiritual alienation and worldly detachment.

Heston, Charlton [John Charlton Carter] (1923–2008) American film and stage actor, renowned principally for his physique, noble profile and commanding presence in religious epics.

Heyerdahl, Thor (1914–2002) Norwegian anthropologist. His practical demonstration of his theory that South Americans emigrated to Polynesia on rafts of balsa wood (later discredited) caught the public imagination and he subsequently launched similar expeditions.

Hicham, El Gouerrouj (1974–) Moroccan track-and-field athlete and World Record holder in the 1500m, 2000m and mile events. Now retired he serves as a goodwill ambassador for UNICEF and has received the Cordon de Commandeur (2004) in his native country.

Hillary, Sir Edmund Percival (1919–2008) New Zealand explorer and mountaineer. Along with the Tibetan sherpa **Tenzing Norgay** (1914–86), he made the first ascent of Mount Everest in 1953. His other exploits include an overland trek to the South Pole in 1958.

Himmler, Heinrich (1900–45) German Nazi leader chosen by HITLER to head the SS in 1929. By 1936 he was in command of the German police structure. Through his secret police, the Gestapo, he organised repression first in Germany then in occupied Europe, and oversaw the construction of the Nazi concentration and death camp system and the genocide of the Jews.

Hindemith, Paul (1895–1963) German composer and violist. The Nazis banned his works for their 'impropriety', and he settled in the US in 1939. Highly prolific, he wrote operas, symphonies, song cycles, ballet and chamber music.

Hindenburg, Paul von Beneckendorff und von (1847–1934) German field marshal and statesman. He shared command of the German forces in World War I (1916–18) and became president of Germany (1925–34). He defeated HITLER in the presidential election of 1932 but was persuaded to appoint Hitler chancellor in 1933.

Hines, Earl Kenneth 'Fatha' (1903–83) American jazz pianist, bandleader and songwriter. He was one of the most influential jazz pianists of the 1930s and 1940s.

Hirohito (1901–89) Japanese emperor (1926–89). A direct descendant of Japan's first emperor, Jimmu, he ruled Japan as a divinity until her defeat in 1945 by Allied forces. After this he became a constitutional monarch, known primarily for his marine biology research. He was succeeded by his son **Akihito** (1933–).

Hitchcock, Sir Alfred (1899–1980) English film director, known as the 'Master of Suspense'. His suspenseful thrillers, e.g. *The Thirty-Nine Steps* (1935) and *Psycho* (1960), have long been regarded as masterpieces. Hitchcock also appeared in all his films in a crowd scene or in a minute cameo role.

Hitler, Adolf (1889–1945) Austrian-born German dictator. He co-founded the National Socialist Workers' Party in 1919 and was jailed for nine months following his part in the failed Munich coup of 1923, during which time he wrote *Mein Kampf* ('My Struggle'), an anti-Semitic 'testament' of his belief in the superiority of the Aryan race. He was appointed chancellor by HINDENBURG in 1933 and consolidated his brutal regime through HIMMLER'S Gestapo. He allied himself temporarily with STALIN in 1939, in which year he invaded Poland, beginning World War II. He invaded Russia in 1941 but his troops suffered great losses at Stalingrad in 1943, forcing them to retreat. As the Allies began to win the war, Hitler faced opposition from within Germany. Having survived an assassination attempt in 1944, he committed suicide in Berlin in the final days of the war. Hitler's war resulted in some 40 million dead.

Ho Chi Minh [Nguyen That Tan] (1890–1969) Vietnamese statesman. A Marxist nationalist, he led the Viet Minh forces, with US help, against the occupying Japanese during World War II and became president of Vietnam (1945–54), during which time he led his forces to victory against

French colonial rule. He became president of North Vietnam (1954–69) after the country's partition at the 1954 Geneva conference.

Hockney, David (1937–) English painter and etcher. Associated with the Pop Art movement in his early work, he is now regarded as one of the world's leading representational painters.

Hodgkin, Sir Alan Lloyd (1914–98) English physiologist. With **Sir Andrew Fielding Huxley** (1917–) and Sir John Carew ECCLES, he shared the 1963 Nobel prize for physiology or medicine for research into nerve impulses.

Hodgkin, Dorothy [Dorothy Mary Crowfoot] (1910–94) English chemist. She was awarded the 1964 Nobel prize for chemistry for her work on the molecular structures of penicillin, insulin and vitamin B_{12}.

Hofstadter, Robert *see* MOSSBAUER, RUDOLF LUDWIG.

Hogan, Ben (1912–1997) American golfer, considered by many to be one of the greatest players of all time. He won four US Open titles, one British Open, two USPGA championships and two US Masters.

Hogarth, William (1697–1764) English artist. Trained as an engraver in the Rococo tradition, by 1720 he had established his own illustration business. He then began his series of 'conversation pieces' and was executing some fine portraits. He also produced a remarkable series of paintings following a sequential narrative, the best known of which is *Marriage à la Mode*.

Holbein, Hans (the Younger) (c.1479–1543) German painter. He painted mainly portraits and religious paintings, the most memorable of the latter being *The Death of Christ* (1521).

Holiday, Billie 'Lady Day' [Eleanora] (1915–59) American jazz singer. She became one of the most influential jazz singers of her time, with her sad, elegiac and subtle interpretations of popular songs.

Holly, Buddy [Charles Hardin Holley] (1936–59) American rock singer, songwriter and guitarist. He was one of the first rock singers to use the back-up of lead, rhythm and bass guitars, with drums. He died in a plane crash.

Holst, Gustav Theodore (1874–1934) English composer of Swedish descent. Much of his music was inspired by the English landscape and Thomas HARDY. His best-known composition is *The Planets* (1917).

Homer (*c*.800 BC) Greek poet, author of the two great epic poems *The Iliad*, the story of the Greek war against Troy, and *The Odyssey*, which describes the adventures of the Greek hero Odysseus (known to the Romans as Ulysses) on his voyage home from the war. The characters and events of the poems have had a profound influence upon Western literature.

Honecker, Erich (1912–94) East German Communist politician. Appointed head of state in 1976, he fell from power in 1989 and was charged in 1990 with treason and corruption following the unification of East and West Germany.

Honegger, Arthur (1892–1955) French composer. One of the group of Parisian composers, 'Les Six', his works include ballet music, symphonies and film scores.

Honthorst, Gerrit van *see* AML Utrecht School.

Hoover, Herbert Clark (1874–1964) American Republican statesman and 31st president (1929–33). He was widely perceived as failing to cope with the crisis of the Great Depression.

Hoover, J[ohn] Edgar (1895–1972) American public servant and founder of the Federal Bureau of Investigation (1924–1972). He made the FBI into a highly effective federal crime-fighting force in the 1930s but also used his organisation's considerable powers against anyone perceived as 'radical' in politics.

Hope, Bob [Leslie Townes Hope] (1903–2003) English-born American comedian and film actor, known for his snappy wisecracks.

Hopkins, Sir Philip Anthony (1937–) Welsh actor who has gained international fame from films such as *The Silence of the Lambs* and *The Remains of the Day*.

Hopkins, Sir Frederick Gowland (1861–1947) English biochemist. He shared the 1929 Nobel prize for physiology or medicine with EIJKMAN for his discovery of 'accessory food factors', which came to be called vitamins.

Hopkins, Gerard Manley (1844–89) English Jesuit priest and poet. A convert, he frequently expressed in his poems the keen conflict he felt between his desire to serve God as both priest and poet. None of his work was published in his lifetime.

Hopkins, Johns (1795–1873) American businessman, who amassed a large fortune. He gave $4,500,000 to found a free hospital and $3,000,000 to found the Johns Hopkins University.

Hopper, Edward (1882–1967) American artist regarded as the foremost realist American painter. His paintings have a still, introspective and often mysterious quality.

Horace [Quintus Horatius Flaccus] (65–8 BC) Roman poet and satirist. He looked to the literature of Greece for inspiration, but his sardonic, realistic and tightly controlled language is wholly Roman.

Houdini, Harry [Eric Weiss] (1874–1926) Hungarian-born American magician and escapologist. He was famous for seemingly being able to escape from any kind of bond or container. He was a campaigner against fraudulent mediums and was president of the Society of American Magicians.

Housman, A[lfred] E[dward] (1859–1936) English poet and scholar. A distinguished Classical scholar, he published *A Shropshire Lad* (1896). Other volumes of poetry were published posthumously.

Howe, Sir Geoffrey *see* MAJOR, JOHN.

Hoyle, Sir Fred (1915–2001) English astronomer, mathematician, broadcaster and writer. He became the main proponent of the theory of the universe which holds that the universe is basically unchanging (as opposed to the big-bang theory).

Hubble, Edwin Powell (1889–1953) American astronomer. His discovery of galactic 'red shift' and other research established the theory of the expanding universe.

Hughes, Howard Robard (1905–76) American industrialist, aviator and film producer. He greatly extended his inherited oil wealth and made several epic flights, including a record round-the-world trip. He became increasingly eccentric and went into seclusion in 1966.

Hughes, Ted [Edward James Hughes] (1930–98) English poet, noted for his violent poetic imagery drawn from the natural world. He was married (1956–63) to Sylvia PLATH. He was poet laureate (1984–98).

Hugo, Victor (1802–85) French novelist, dramatist and poet. His socially challenging dramas established Hugo as the leader of the French literary Romantics. His novels include *The Hunchback of Notre Dame* (1831) and *Les Misérables* (1862).

Hume, David (1711–76) Scottish philosopher, economist and historian. An empiricist and sceptic, his works include *A Treatise of Human Nature* (1739–40).

Hunt, James (1947–93) British Formula One racing driver with a larger than life playboy personality. He won the World Championship in 1976 and on his retiral became a commentator for the BBC. He died of a heart attack at the age of 45.

Hunt, Leigh *see* KEATS, JOHN.

Hunt, William Holman (1827–1910) English painter. A founder of the Pre-Raphaelite movement, he sought inspiration from nature and natural composition.

Hussein, Ibn Talal (1935–99) king of Jordan. He lost the West Bank of his country to Israel after the Six Day War of 1967 and trod an uneasy diplomatic line between friendship with the West and his efforts on behalf of the Palestinians.

Hussein, Saddam (1937–2006) Iraqi dictator. He became president of Iraq in 1979 and established a reputation for ruthlessness in the suppression of his opponents. After his invasion of Kuwait in 1990, UN forces forced his withdrawal in the Gulf War of 1991. He was deposed during the American-led invasion of Iraq in 2003. Put on trial by the new Iraqi government, he was sentence to death and hanged in 2006.

Huston, John [Marcellus] (1906–87) American film director. His films include several classics, e.g. *The Maltese Falcon* (1941) from a story by HAMMET. His last film, *The Dead* (1987), from a short story by JOYCE, starred his daughter, the actress **Anjelica Huston** (1952–).

Hutton, Len [Sir Leonard] (1916–1990) English cricketer hailed as one of the greatest batsmen of all time. He was England's first professional captain (1952) but ill health forced his retirement in 1956.

Huxley, Aldous Leonard (1894–1963) English novelist, short-story writer and essayist and brother of Julian HUXLEY. His early work depicted the brittle world of 1920s' English intellectual life, but his masterpiece is *Brave New World* (1932), a chilling fable of a totalitarian state (*see also* AML Utopian novel).

Huxley, Sir Andrew Fielding *see* HODGKIN, SIR ALAN.

Huxley, Sir Julian Sorell (1887–1975) English biologist and brother of Aldous HUXLEY. He became one of Britain's best-known scientists and humanists and was the first director-general of UNESCO (1946–48).

Huxley, Thomas Henry (1825–95) English biologist and grandfather of Aldous, Julian and Andrew HUXLEY. The most prominent scientific defender of DARWIN's theory of evolution, he gradually lost his belief in a deity and coined the term 'agnostic'.

Ibn Saud, Abdul Aziz (1880–1953) king of Saudi Arabia. He became the first king of Saudi Arabia (1932–53) and negotiated terms with American oil companies after the discovery of oil in his country (1938).

Ibsen, Henrik (1828–1906) Norwegian dramatist. His early verse dramas, e.g. *Peer Gynt* (1867), plays of social realism, e.g. *Ghosts* (1881), and later symbolic plays, e.g. *The Master Builder* (1896), were all hugely influential on later dramatists.

Ignatius Loyola, Saint (1491–1556) Spanish saint. A former soldier who was severely wounded in action, he had a spiritual conversion and founded the Society of Jesus (the Jesuits) in 1534.

Ingres, Jean Auguste Dominique (1780–1867) French painter. One of the greatest exponents of Neoclassical art, his excellent draftsmanship influenced DEGAS, MATISSE and PICASSO.

Ionesco, Eugène (1912–94) Romanian-born French dramatist. His plays, regarded as masterpieces of the Theatre of the Absurd, include *The Bald Prima Donna* and *The Lesson*.

Irving, Washington (1783–1859) American essayist and historian. His best-known stories are 'Rip Van Winkle' and 'The Legend of Sleepy Hollow'. He wrote a biography of WASHINGTON.

Isherwood, Christopher William Bradshaw (1904–86) English-born American novelist and dramatist. His best-known works are set in pre-World War II Berlin. One of his short stories was the inspiration for the musical (and later film) *Cabaret*.

Ives, Charles Edward (1874–1954) American composer. His works are frequently experimental but based firmly within the American tradition.

Jackson, Andrew (1767–1845) American Democrat politician and 7th president of the US. Served two terms, from 1829–33 and 1833–37.

Jackson, Glenda (1936–) English actress. Highly regarded on film and stage, she became a Labour MP in 1992.

Jackson, Jesse (1941–) American Democrat politician. A Baptist minister and one of Martin Luther KING's aides, he campaigned twice for the Democratic presidential nomination.

Jackson, Michael (1958–) American pop singer. The youngest of five brothers who as children formed the Jackson Five, he became a solo performer in the late 1970s. His album *Thriller* (1982) sold 35 million copies. In recent years he has become a more controversial figure. He released a new album called *Thriller 25* in 2008.

Jackson, Peter (1961–) New Zealand film director famous for his production of the very successful *Lord of the Rings* film trilogy (based on TOLKIEN's novels).

Jagger, Mick [Michael Philip] (1943–) English singer and songwriter and lead singer with the Rolling Stones rock group, the original members of which, with Jagger, were the guitarist and co-writer with Jagger of many of their songs, **Keith Richard** (1943–), bass guitarist **Bill Wyman** (1936–), drummer **Charlie Watts** (1941–) and guitarist **Brian Jones** (1944–69).

James, Henry (1843–1916) American-born British novelist, short-story writer and critic, and brother of William JAMES. Much of his work is concerned with the contrast between American innocence and the older, wiser European culture, e.g. *Daisy Miller* (1879).

James, William (1842–1910) American philosopher, psychologist and brother of Henry JAMES. His works include *The Varieties of Religious Experience*, in which he coined the term 'stream of consciousness'.

Janácek, Leos (1854–1928) Czech composer. His works, heavily influenced by Czech folk music and culture, include the operas *The Cunning Little Vixen* and *The House of the Dead*, and two highly regarded string quartets.

Jefferson, Thomas (1743–1826) American statesman. He was the main creator of the Declaration of Independence in 1776 and became secretary of state (1790–93) under WASHINGTON. He was the 3rd president of the United States (1801–09).

Jenner, Edward (1749–1823) English physician. He investigated the traditional belief that catching cowpox gave protection against smallpox and discovered that vaccination was efficacious in preventing smallpox.

Jesus Christ (*c.*6 BC–*c.*30 AD) founder of Christianity. The New Testament records that he was born in Bethlehem, the son of Joseph and Mary, and Christians have traditionally believed that he is the Son of God. The Book of Acts describes how the Christian gospel was spread through the Mediterranean world by his disciples, notably **Paul** and **Peter**, the latter being recognised as the founder of the Roman Catholic church.

Jiang Jie Shi *see* CHIANG KAI-SHEK.

Jiang Qing *see* CHIANG CH'ING.

Jinnah, Mohammed Ali (1876–1948) Pakistani statesman. An early member of the Indian Muslim League, he became convinced of the need for Indian partition into Hindu and Muslim states and was the first governor-general of Pakistan (1947–48).

Joan of Arc (*c.*1412–31) French patriot. From a peasant family, at 13 she had a vision urging her to free France from the invading English. She helped raise the siege of Orléans in 1429 and brought Charles VII to Rheims to be crowned king of France. Captured by the English in 1430, she was condemned for witchcraft and burned at the stake. She was canonised in 1920.

John, Augustus [Edwin] (1878–1961) Welsh painter and a superb draftsman and portraitist. His sister, **Gwen John** (1876–1939), was also a painter of renown.

John Paul II [Karel Jozef Wojtyla] (1920–2005) Polish pope (1978–2005). He was the first Polish pope and first non-Italian pope for over 450 years. The early years of his reign were marked by his opposition to communism and later in his primacy he spoke out against war, fascism, communism, dictatorship, materialism, abortion, contraception, relativism, and unrestrained capitalism. He also travelled extensively, visiting over 100 countries.

Johns, Jasper (1930–) American painter, sculptor and printmaker. His work, especially his use of everyday images such as the stars and stripes, was very influential on later Pop artists.

Johnson, Andrew (1801–1875) American Democrat politician and the 17th president (1865–1869).

Johnson, Amy (1903–41) English aviator. She was the first woman to fly solo from England to Australia (1930). Her other records include a solo flight from London to Cape Town (1936). She was presumed drowned after baling out over the Thames Estuary while serving as a transport pilot in World War II.

Johnson, Lyndon B[aines] (1908–73) American Democrat statesman. Following John F. KENNEDY's assassination in 1963, he became the 36th president (1963–69).

Johnson, Dr Samuel (1709–84) English critic, lexicographer and poet. His works include the *Dictionary of the English Language* (1755) and an important edition of SHAKESPEARE. In 1763 he met **James Boswell** (1740–95) with whom he toured the Western Isles. Boswell's biography of Johnson is considered to be the finest in the language.

Jones, Brian *see* JAGGER, MICK.

Jonson, Benjamin (1572–1637) English dramatist. His plays include *Bartholomew Fair* (1614), *Volpone* (1616) and *The Alchemist* (1616). He became the first poet laureate in 1616.

Joplin, Scott (1868–1917) American pianist and composer. His ragtime compositions, e.g. *Maple Leaf Rag*, were enormously popular in the USA, selling over a million copies of sheet music.

Joyce, James Augustine Aloysius (1882–1941) Irish novelist and short-story writer. His works include the short-story collection *Dubliners* (1914) and two great novels, *Portrait of the Artist as a Young Man* (1914–15) and *Ulysses* (1922), the latter being one of the key novels of the 20th century.

Joyce, William (1906–46) American-born British traitor (of Anglo-Irish descent). Dubbed 'Lord Haw-Haw' by the British public, he broadcast rabid Nazi propaganda to Britain during World War II and was executed for treason in 1946.

Juan Carlos (1938–) king of Spain from 1975. Nominated by FRANCO in 1969 as his successor, Juan Carlos carefully steered his country towards democracy after Franco's death in 1975.

Jung, Carl Gustav (1875–1961) Swiss psychiatrist. He began his career as a follower of Freud, but split with him after challenging his concentration on sex. His theory of the 'collective unconscious', and his use of the term 'archetype' to denote an image or symbol drawn from this store, have been highly influential.

Kafka, Franz (1883–1924) Czech-born German novelist and short-story writer. His novels, *The Trial* (1925) and *The Castle* (1926), and several of his short stories, notably 'Metamorphosis' (1915), are established classics of 20th-century literature.

Kahn, Oliver (1969–) German goalkeeper for his national team from 1995 to 2006, known for his safe pair of hands and skill in deflecting and capturing difficult balls.

Kandinsky, Wassily (1866–1944) Russian-born French painter. He co-founded (with KLEE and MARC) the *Blaue Reiter* group in 1912 and is regarded as the first major abstract artist (*see* AML Blaue Reiter).

Kant, Immanuel (1724–1804) German philosopher. His works include *The Critique of Pure Reason* (1781) and *The Critique of Practical Reason* (1788).

Karajan, Herbert von (1908–89) Austrian conductor. His recordings, notably of BEETHOVEN's symphonies, are held by some critics to be definitive.

Karloff, Boris [William Henry Pratt] (1887–1969) English-born film star of the 1920s who became best known for his roles in horror films, especially as the monster in *Frankenstein* (1931) and as Imhotep in *The Mummy* (1932).

Kauffmann, Angelica (1741–1807) Swiss painter. Influenced by Neoclassicism, she settled in London in 1776. She was a founder of the Royal Academy.

Kaunda, Kenneth David (1924–) Zambian politician. He was the first president of Zambia (1964–91) after his country became independent.

Keaton, Buster [Joseph Francis Keaton] (1895–1966) American film comedian and director. Widely regarded as one of the all-time great comedians of the cinema, with his 'deadpan' expression and remarkable acrobatic skill, his silent comedy films include *The Navigator* (1924) and *The General* (1926).

Keats, John (1795–1821) English poet. Savagely criticised early in his career, Keats went on to write some of the greatest works of English Romantic literature.

Keller, Helen Adams (1880–1968) American writer. She became deaf and blind when 19 months old and was taught to read and write by the partially sighted Anne Sullivan.

Kelly, Gene [Eugene Curran Kelly] (1912–96) American dancer, choreographer and film director, who was noted for his athleticism and witty dancing style. His films include *Singin' in the Rain* (1952).

Kelly, Grace [Patricia] (1929–82) American film actress. She married **Prince Rainier III** (1923–2005) of Monaco in 1956 and gave up her career. They had three children: Caroline, Albert and Stephanie. Princess Grace died in a car crash.

Kennedy, John Fitzgerald (1917–63) American Democrat politician who became 35th president (1961–63). He was the first Roman Catholic and the youngest man elected to the presidency. His period of office, cut short by his assassination in Dallas, was subsequently seen by many as a period of hope and social reform. His brother **Robert (Bobby) Francis Kennedy** (1925–68), who became attorney general (1961–64) and senator for New York (1965–68) and furthered civil rights legislation, was also assassinated. Another brother, **Edward (Ted) Moore Kennedy** (1932–), has served as a US senator since

1962. JFK's son, **John Kennedy Junior** (1960–99), died in a plane accident.

Kennedy, Nigel (1956–) English violinist known in the world of classical music for his recordings of Vivaldi. He has helped to raise the profile of classical music among younger people.

Kenyatta, Jomo (*c.* 1893–1978) Kenyan politician. He was jailed for six years (1952–58) for his leadership of the Mau-Mau rebellion. He became prime minister of Kenya on independence in 1963 and president (1964–78).

Kerenski, Alexsandr Feodorovich (1881–1970) Russian revolutionary leader. A member of the Social Democratic Party's liberal wing, he became prime minister of the Russian provisional government of 1917 but was deposed by LENIN's Bolsheviks.

Kern, Jerome David (1885–1945) American composer and songwriter. A highly prolific writer of music and songs, he influenced the American musical tradition. His best-known work is the musical *Show Boat* (1927).

Kerouac, Jack [Jean-Louis Lebris de Kérouac] (1922–69) American novelist and poet who was a much imitated central figure of the Beat Generation (*see* AML Beat Generation).

Keynes, John Maynard, 1st Baron (1883–1946) English economist. He argued that unemployment was curable through macroeconomic management of monetary and fiscal policies and advocated the creation of employment through government schemes.

Khan, Imran (1952–) Pakistani cricketer viewed by many as the best of all time. Renowned as a fast-bowler, he dominated world cricket during the 1980s. He has taken up a new career in the political arena of Pakistan.

Khomeini, Ayatollah Ruholla (1900–89) Iranian religious leader who established a theocratic dictatorship that crushed all dissent and declared his intention of 'exporting' the Shiite revolution to other Islamic countries. He aroused Western anger by proclaiming a death sentence against Salman RUSHDIE in 1989.

Khrushchev, Nikita Sergeyevich (1894–1971) Soviet politician. He was first secretary of the Communist Party (1953–64) and prime minister (1958–64). His standing in the USSR was somewhat compromised after the Cuban Missile Crisis of 1962, when his climbdown against JOHN F. KENNEDY prevented a war with the USA. He was deposed in 1964 in the Kremlin coup that brought BREZHNEV to power.

Kierkegaard, Søren Aabye (1813–55) Danish theologian and philosopher and the founder of Existentialism (*see* AML Existentialism), he rejected the spiritual authority of organised religion and emphasised the centrality of individual choice.

Killy, Jean-Claude (1943–) French downhill ski champion. One of the fastest and most daring of competitors, especially during the years 1966 to 1968, he gained three gold medals at the 1968 Winter Olympics as well as many other wins.

Kim Il Sung (1912–94) North Korean marshal and Communist politician. He became prime minister (1948–72) and president (1972–94) of the Democratic People's Republic of Korea (popularly known as North Korea), establishing a Stalinist dictatorship based on a personality cult of himself as the 'great leader'. His son, **Kim Jong Il** (1942–), succeeded him as president.

King, Billie Jean (1943–) American tennis player. Regarded as one of the finest women players ever, she won 20 Wimbledon titles between 1965 and 1980.

King, Martin Luther, Junior (1929–68) American civil rights leader and Baptist minister. Influenced by GANDHI's policy of nonviolent resistance, he organised opposition to segregationist policies in the southern USA. Awarded the 1964 Nobel peace prize, he was assassinated in 1968.

Kinnock, Neil Gordon (1942–) Welsh Labour politician. Leader of the Labour Party in 1983 in succession to Michael FOOT and leader of the Opposition (1983–1992), he was a European Commissioner from 1995 to 2004, and has been head of the British Council since 2004.

Kipling, [Joseph] Rudyard (1865–1936) Indian-born English short-story writer, poet and novelist. Although best known for his stories for children, e.g. *The Jungle Book* (1894), he was also a caustic

observer of Anglo-Indian society and critical of many aspects of colonialism in his writing.

Kirkpatrick, Ralph *see* AML K.

Kissinger, Henry Alfred (1923–) German-born American statesman. He shared the 1973 Nobel peace prize with the North Vietnamese negotiator **Le Duc Tho** (1911–90) for the treaty ending US involvement in Vietnam. As secretary of state (1973–76) he fostered détente with the Soviet Union and China, and helped negotiate peace between Israel and Egypt in 1973.

Kitchener, [Horatio] Herbert, 1st Earl Kitchener of Khartoum (1850–1916) Anglo-Irish field marshal. Commander in chief of the British forces during the Boer War of 1901–02 and of the British forces in India (1902–09), he was appointed secretary for war in 1914 and had mobilised Britain's largest yet army by the time of his death by drowning (when his ship hit a mine).

Klee, Paul (1879–1940) Swiss painter and etcher who developed a style of mainly abstract work characterised by doodle-like drawings. He was a member of the *Blaue Reiter* group (*see* AML Blaue Reiter).

Klemperer, Otto (1885–1973) German-born conductor. A great interpreter of both classical and contemporary works, he became director of the Los Angeles Symphony Orchestra in 1936 and director of the Budapest Opera (1947–50).

Klimt, Gustav (1862–1918) Austrian painter. An excellent draftsman, his early works were influenced by Impressionism, Symbolism and Art Nouveau. A founder of the Vienna Sezession, he had a great influence on younger artists.

Knox, John (*c.*1513–1572) Scottish Protestant reformer. He was noted for his antagonistic relationship with Mary Queen of Scots and for his single-minded determination in the pursuit of religious reformation.

Köchel, Ludwig von *see* AML K.

Kodály, Zoltán (1882–1967) Hungarian composer. His works include the comic opera *Hary Janos*.

Kohl, Helmut (1930–) German Christian Democrat statesman. He became chancellor of West Germany (1982–90) and the first chancellor of a united Germany (1990–98).

Kokoschka, Oskar (1886–1980) Austrian-born painter and dramatist. A leading Expressionist painter, noted particularly for his landscapes and portraits, he fled to Britain in 1938.

Korda, Sir Alexander (Sandor Kellner) (1893–1956) Hungarian-born British film-maker. His films as a director include *The Private Life of Henry VIII* (1933) and as a producer *The Third Man* (1949).

Korbut, Olga Valentinova (1955–) Belarussian gymnast who won a total of four gold and two silver medals for the USSR in the 1972 and 1976 Olympics. She captured the heart of people throughout the world with her dazzling performances and charming personality. She is now a naturalised American citizen.

Kreisler, Fritz (1875–1962) Austrian-born American violinist and composer. ELGAR's violin concerto was dedicated to him, and he became one of the most popular violinists of his day.

Kubrick, Stanley (1928–99) American film director and producer. His films include the anti-war classic *Paths of Glory* (1957), the black nuclear war comedy *Dr Strangelove* (1963), the innovative science fiction classic *2001: A Space Odyssey* (1968) and the still highly controversial *A Clockwork Orange* (1971). His last film was *Eyes Wide Shut* (1999).

Kundera, Milan (1929–) Czech novelist. His masterpiece is *The Unbearable Lightness of Being* (1984), a love story set against the background of repression following the 1967 Russian invasion of Czechoslovakia.

Kurosawa, Akira (1910–98) Japanese film director. His films include the samurai classic *The Seven Samurai* (1954) and samurai versions of *Macbeth*, titled *Throne of Blood* (1957), and *King Lear*, titled *Ran* (1985). He was happiest with the epic form and had a 'family' of actors he used regularly.

Kyd, Thomas (1558–94) English dramatist. His most important work is his revenge tragedy *The Spanish Tragedy* (1592), which served as a model for SHAKESPEARE's *Titus Andronicus*.

Lacan, Jacques *see* AML Structuralism.

Laing, R[onald] D[avid] (1927–89) Scottish psychiatrist. He became a counterculture guru in the 1960s for his revolutionary ideas about mental disorders.

Laker, Jim [James Charles] (1922–1986) English cricketer, renowned for his skill as a bowler. His unique, crowning achievement was taking 19 wickets from Australia for 90 runs in a test match in 1956.

Lamarck, Jean [Baptiste Pierre Antoine de Monet] Chevalier de (1744–1829) French naturalist. His theory of the evolution of species through the acquisition of inherited characteristics prepared the ground for DARWIN's theory of evolution.

Lamb, Charles (1775–1834) English essayist and critic. A friend of HAZLITT, WORDSWORTH and COLERIDGE, his writings display the charm his friends describe.

Landseer, Sir Edwin Henry (1802–73) English painter. Highly regarded for his animal studies, his notable works include *The Monarch of the Glen* (1850) and the lions modelled for Trafalgar Square in London in 1867.

Lansbury, George (1859–1940) English Labour politician. Noted for his support for women's suffrage and pacifism, he became leader of his party (1931–35) when MAC-DONALD joined the National Government. His daughter, **Angela Lansbury** (1925–) became a popular film and TV actress.

Larkin, Philip Arthur (1922–85) English poet. Known for his dark, sardonic lyricism, he is regarded as one of the greatest of modern English poets.

Lasdun, Sir Denys Louis (1914–2001) English architect. Influenced by LE CORBUSIER, his buildings include the University of East Anglia and the National Theatre in London.

Lasker, Emanuel (1868–1941) German chess player. His reign as world champion (1894–1921), is still a record.

Lauda, Niki [Nikolas Andreas Lauda] (1949–) Austrian racing driver. World champion in 1975, 1977 and 1984, he suffered dreadful injuries in the 1976 German Grand Prix but returned to winning form in 1977 and 1978. He retired in 1985 having won his final race for the McLaren team.

Lauder, Sir Harry [Hugh MacLennan] (1870–1950) Scottish music-hall comedian and singer, who made an international career out of his Scottish comedy routines and songs.

Laughton, Charles (1899–1962) English-born American stage and film actor, renowned for his larger-than-life performances in many memorable films, e.g. *The Private Life of Henry VIII* (1933).

Laurel, Stan [Arthur Stanley Jefferson] (1890–1965), English-born American comedian, and **Oliver Hardy** (1892–1957) American comedian. Laurel began his career on the English music-hall stage (understudying CHAPLIN at one point), and Hardy performed with a minstrel troupe before going into films. They formed their Laurel (thin, vacant and bemused one) and Hardy (fat, blustering one) partnership in 1929 and made some very funny films, e.g. *Another Fine Mess* (1930).

Laval, Pierre (1883–1945) French statesman. Prime minister (1931–32, 1935–36, 1942–44), he sided openly during the occupation with the Germans and was executed for treason in 1945 by the victorious Free French.

Laver, Rod [Rodney] (1958–) Australian tennis player renowned for his powerful serve. He won the Grand Slam in 1962 and 1969 thereby earning his place in sporting history.

Lavoisier, Antoine Laurent (1743–94) French chemist. Regarded as the founder of modern chemistry, he discovered oxygen and established its role in combustion and respiration.

Lawrence, D[avid] H[erbert] (1885–1930) English novelist, poet and short-story writer. His novels caused much controversy for their frank treatment of sex. *Lady Chatterley's Lover* (1928), was not published in its unexpurgated form until 1960.

Lawrence, Gertrude [Gertrud Alexandra Dagmar Lawrence-Klasen] (1898–1952) English actress, noted for her professional relationship with Noel COWARD, many of whose plays had parts written for her.

Lawrence, T[homas] E[dward] (1888–1935) Welsh-born Anglo-Irish soldier and author, known as 'Lawrence of Arabia'. In World War I he helped the Arab revolt against the Turks and was instrumental in the conquest of Palestine (1918).

Lawson, Nigel *see* MAJOR, JOHN.

Leach, Bernard Howell (1887–1979) English potter. The most prominent of British studio potters, he became widely recognized as a master in his field. He revolutionised the production of pottery by creating reasonably priced, attractively designed studio pottery.

Leadbelly [Huddie Ledbetter] (1888–1949) American blues singer. Discovered in a Louisiana prison in 1933, he later recorded several songs that soon became recognised as blues/folk classics, e.g. 'Rock Island Line' and 'Goodnight, Irene'.

Leakey, Louis Seymour Bazett (1903–72) Kenyan-born British archaeologist and anthropologist, and **Mary Douglas Leakey** (1913–96) English archaeologist. Married in 1936, the Leakeys made several important discoveries about humanity's origins in East Africa. Their son, **Richard Erskine Frere Leakey** (1944–), is a paleontologist and conservationist.

Lean, Sir David (1908–91) English film director whose films include many classics, e.g. *Brief Encounter* (1946), *Great Expectations* (1946) and *Dr Zhivago* (1965).

Lear, Edward *see* AML limerick.

Le Carré, John [David John Moore Cornwell] (1931–) English novelist. His popular earlier novels are sombre antiromantic narratives of Cold War espionage, e.g. *The Spy Who Came in from the Cold* (1963) and *Smiley's People* (1980).

Le Corbusier [Charles Edouard Jeanneret] (1887–1965) Swiss-born French architect and town planner. One of the most influential (praised and reviled) architects and planners of the 20th century, his work is characterised by use of reinforced concrete and modular, standardised units of construction (based upon the proportions of the human figure), with the house famously defined as a 'machine for living in'.

Lederberg, Joshua (1925–2008) American geneticist. He shared the 1958 Nobel prize for physiology or medicine (with George Beadle and Edward TATUM) for his bacterial research.

Le Duc Tho *see* KISSINGER, HENRY.

Lee Kuan Yew (1923–) Singaporean politician. He became Singapore's first prime minister (1965–90), establishing a strict regime noted for its economic achievements and authoritarianism.

Lehár, Franz (1870–1948) Hungarian composer and conductor, noted for his operettas, e.g. *The Merry Widow*.

Leigh, Vivien [Vivien Mary Hartley] (1913–67) Indian-born English stage and film actress. She became an international star with *Gone With the Wind* (1939) in which she co-starred with Clark GABLE.

Lenin, Vladimir Ilyich [Vladimir Ilyich Ulyanov] (1870–1924) Russian revolutionary leader and Marxist philosopher. He was instigator of the Bolshevik October Revolution that overthrew KERENSKI's government and leader of the Bolsheviks in the Civil War (1918–21). The failure of his economic policy after the war led to the institution of the New Economic Policy of 1921, which fostered limited private enterprise. He was a brilliant demagogue and an influential philosopher.

Lennon, John Winston (1940–80) English guitarist, singer and songwriter. With Paul McCARTNEY, George HARRISON and Ringo STARR, he formed the Beatles, the most popular rock group ever. The band's success was based on the Lennon/McCartney songwriting partnership. He married the artist **Yoko Ono** (1933–) and pursued a solo career after the Beatles split in 1969. He was assassinated in New York.

Leonardo da Vinci (1452–1519) Florentine painter, draftsman, engineer, musician and thinker. His greatest paintings include *The Last Supper* (1489) and his portrait of *Mona Lisa* (1504). His later years were devoted to scientific studies, and his work in mechanics, aeronautics, physiology and anatomy displays an understanding far beyond his times.

Le Pen, Jean-Marie (1928–) French politician. He founded the National Front in 1972, a right-wing party with anti-immigrant policies.

Lessing, Doris [May] (1919–) Iranian-born English novelist and short-story writer. Her breakthrough work, written in 1962, was *The Golden Notebook*. In 2007, Lessing won the Nobel prize for literature.

Lévi-Strauss, Claude *see* AML Structuralism.

Lewes, George Henry *see* ELIOT, GEORGE.

Lewis, Carl [Frederick Carlton] (1961–) American track-and-field athlete. By the time he retired in 1997 he had amassed a total of nine Olympic gold medals: four gold medals in 1984 , two gold and one silver in 1988, two gold in 1992 and another gold in 1996.

Lewis, C[live] S[taples] (1898–1963) English novelist and critic. His works include studies of medieval literature, e.g. *The Allegory of Love* (1936), works of Christian apologetics, e.g. *The Problem of Pain* (1940), and science fiction novels, e.g. *Out of the Silent Planet* (1938). He is best remembered for his enchanting Narnia stories for children, e.g. *The Lion, the Witch and the Wardrobe* (1950), and a 'spiritual' biography, *Surprised by Joy* (1955).

Lewis, Jerry Lee (1935–) American rock singer and pianist noted for his flamboyant playing style and primitive rock 'n' roll lyrics.

Lewis, [Harry] Sinclair (1885–1951) American novelist. His work is particularly noted for its satirical view of small-town American life, e.g. *Babbitt* (1922). He was the first American to win the Nobel prize for literature, in 1930.

Lewis, [Percy] Wyndham (1884–1957) English painter, novelist and critic. His best-known fictional work is the novel *The Apes of God* (1930).

Lichtenstein, Roy (1923–97) American painter and sculptor who became the leading Pop Art painter of the 1960s with his highly coloured reproductions of sections of advertisements and cartoon strips.

Liddell, Eric Henry (1902–45) Scottish athlete, nicknamed the 'Flying Scot', who refused to compromise his sabbatarian principles by running on a Sunday during the 1924 Olympics. He became a missionary and died in a Japanese prisoner-of-war camp.

Liebknecht, Karl *see* LUXEMBOURG, ROSA.

Ligeti, György Sándor (1923–2006) Hungarian composer. He fled to Vienna in 1956, where he soon became established as one of Europe's leading avant-garde composers.

Lillo, George *see* AML domestic tragedy.

Limbourg or Limburg, Jean, Paul and Herman de (all *fl.* 1400–16) Dutch illuminators. Their masterpiece, the unfinished *Les Tres Riches Heures*, is one of the greatest illuminated manuscripts of all time.

Lincoln, Abraham (1809–65) American statesman. He became the 16th president of the United States in 1861 and led the Union to victory in 1865. Firmly opposed to slavery, he finally declared emancipation in 1863. He was assassinated while attending the theatre.

Lindbergh, Charles Augustus (1902–74) American aviator. He became the first man to fly the Atlantic solo and nonstop with his 1927 flight in the monoplane *Spirit of St Louis*. The kidnap and murder of his infant son in 1932 made world headlines.

Lippi, Fra Filippo (*c.*1406–69) Florentine painter. He took up painting while a monk and later forsook his vows to marry the mother of his son, **Filippino Lippi** (1457–1504), who also became a painter. An innovative painter, he was one of the first artists to explore and develop the *Madonna and Child* theme.

Liszt, Franz or Ferencz (1811–86) Hungarian pianist and composer. He made important contributions to musical form and was influential in his experimentation.

Liston, Sonny [Charles] (1932–71) American boxer who took up boxing after serving time in prison. He achieved 50 heavyweight victories in the course of his career.

Livingstone, David (1813–73) Scottish missionary and explorer. His discoveries during his African expeditions include Lake Ngami (1849) and the Victoria Falls (1855). He was also a vigorous campaigner against the slave trade. During his last expedition in search of the source of the Nile, he himself was 'discovered' by the Welsh-American adventurer **Henry Morton Stanley** (1841–1904).

Llosa, Mario Vargas *see* AML magic realism.

Lloyd, Clive Hubert (1944–) Guyanian-born West Indian cricketer. A fine batsman and fielder, he captained the West Indies team (1974–78, 1979–85).

Lloyd, Harold Clayton (1893–1971) American film comedian. He made hundreds of short silent films and is noted for his dangerous stunts.

Lloyd George, David, 1st Earl Lloyd George of Dwyfor (1863–1945) Welsh Liberal statesman. As chancellor of the exchequer (1908–15), he introduced far-reaching reforms in British society, notably the introduction of old-age pensions (1908) and the National Insurance Act (1911). Formerly a pacifist, he became minister of munitions (1915–16) and prime minister (1916–22) of coalition governments.

Lloyd Webber, Andrew [Baron Lloyd-Webber] (1948–) English composer. With the librettist **Tim Rice** (1944–), he composed several highly successful musicals, notably *Joseph and the Amazing Technicolor Dreamcoat*, *Jesus Christ Superstar*, and *Evita*. Other successes were *Cats*, adapted from T. S. ELIOT's *Old Possum's Book of Practical Cats*, *Phantom of the Opera* and *Sunset Boulevard*.

Lodge, David (1935–) English novelist and critic. His best-known novels are entertaining satires on academic life, e.g. *Small World* (1984).

Longfellow, Henry Wadsworth (1807–82) American poet. His narrative poems based on American legends and folk tales were among the most popular of the 19th century, e.g. *The Song of Hiawatha*.

Lonsdale, Dame Kathleen (1903–71) Irish physicist noted for her innovative work in X-ray crystallography. She was the first woman to be elected as a fellow of the Royal Society, in 1945.

Lorca, Federigo García (1899–1936) Spanish poet and dramatist. His dramatic masterpiece is his trilogy of tragedies on the plight of oppressed Spanish women: *Blood Wedding*, *Yarma*, and *The House of Bernarda Alba*. He was killed by Fascist forces at the beginning of the Spanish Civil War.

Lorenz, Konrad Zacharias (1903–89) Austrian ethologist and zoologist. He shared the 1973 Nobel prize for physiology or medicine with Nikolass TINBERGEN (1907-88) and Karl von FRISCH (1886-1982) for his work on animal behaviour.

Lorre, Peter [Laszlo Lowenstein] (1904–64) Hungarian stage and film actor. His first major film part, as the pathetic child murderer, in LANG's *M* (1931), established him as a star. Other films include *The Maltese Falcon* (1941) and *Casablanca* (1943).

Losey, Joseph (1909–84) American film director. Blacklisted during the McCarthy era, he came to work in England and had a great influence on the British film industry with films such as *The Servant* (1963), *Accident* (1967) and *The Go-Between* (1970).

Louis, Joe [Joseph Louis Barrow] (1914–81) US boxer, nicknamed the 'Brown Bomber'. He was world heavyweight champion for 12 years.

Lovelace, Richard *see* AML Cavalier Poets.

Lowei, Otto *see* Dale, Sir Henry Hallett.

Lowell, Amy *see* AML Imagism.

Lowry, L[aurence] S[tephen] (1887–1976) English painter. His paintings, which depict thin, dark 'matchstick' figures against a background of northern industrial life, became very popular in the mid-1960s.

Loyola, Saint Ignatius *see* Ignatius Loyola, Saint.

Lully, Jean Baptiste [Giovanni Battista Lulli] (1632–87) French composer of Italian origin. He worked in the French court, where he composed many operas and comedy ballets.

Lumière, Auguste Marie Louis Nicolas (1862–1954) **and Louis Jean Lumière** (1864–1948) French chemists and cinematographers. They invented the first operational cine camera and projector and a colour photography process.

Luther, Martin (1483–1546) German religious reformer. An Augustinian monk, he suffered a crisis of faith that led to his proclaiming a break with Rome following the nailing of his '95 theses' on the church door of Wittenberg. The Lutheran Reformation spread rapidly throughout Germany. Calvin, Zwingli, and others subsequently preached their variants of the new religion.

Luthuli or Lutuli, Chief Albert John (1898–1967) South African nationalist. He became president of the African National Congress (1952–60) and was awarded the 1961 Nobel peace prize for his advocacy of nonviolent resistance to apartheid.

Lutoslawski, Witold (1913–94) Polish composer and teacher. He wrote extensively,

including chamber, piano and vocal music, but is best known for his orchestral works, e.g. *Concerto for Orchestra*.

Luxemburg, Rosa (1871–1919) Polish-born German revolutionary and socialist theorist. With **Karl Liebknecht** (1871–1919), she founded the revolutionary Spartacus League in Berlin on the outbreak of World War I and later the German Communist Party. She and Liebknecht were killed after the failed revolt of 1919.

Ma, Yo-Yo (1955–) Chinese cellist of world renown who attracts large audiences for his classical performances and has won numerous awards.

MacArthur, Douglas (1880–1964) American general. He was commander of the US Far East forces in 1941. He was appointed supreme Allied commander in the southwest Pacific in 1942 and gradually rolled back the Japanese forces, accepting their surrender in 1945.

McCarthy, Joseph R[aymond] (1908–57) American politician. He became a Republican senator in 1946 and embarked upon a crusade against supposed communist sympathisers in public life (1950–54). His wide and increasingly bizarre accusations against innocent people came to an end shortly after he was accused, during a televised hearing, of having no shame.

McCartney, Sir Paul (1942–) English rock guitarist, singer and songwriter. He was a member of the Beatles (1961–70) with John Lennon, George Harrison and Ringo Starr. With Lennon, he formed one of the most successful songwriting partnerships of the 20th century. After the band's break-up, he formed the group Wings (1971–81) with his wife, **Linda** (1942–98).

McCullers, Carson [Smith] (1917–67) American novelist and short-story writer. Her works, many of them filmed, usually centre on loners and misfits and include *The Heart is a Lonely Hunter* (1940) and *The Ballad of the Sad Café* (1951).

MacDiarmid, Hugh [Christopher Murray Grieve] (1892–1978) Scottish poet and critic. Noted for his Communist and Nationalist sympathies, he influenced many writers, particularly with his masterpiece, *A Drunk Man Looks at the Thistle* (1926).

MacDonald, [James] Ramsay (1866–1937) Scottish statesman. He became the first British Labour prime minister (1924, 1929–31) and was prime minister of the (mostly Conservative) coalition government of 1931–35.

McEnroe, John Patrick Junior (1959–) American tennis player who achieved four US Open titles and three Wimbledon championships during the late 1970s and 1980s. McEnroe gained notoriety for his outbursts of temper becoming known for the catch phrase 'You cannot be serious'. He is now a highly respected and popular television commentator for tennis.

MacGonagall, William (*c*.1830–*c*.1902) Scottish poet, renowned for his memorably awful doggerel verse.

Machiavelli, Niccolò (1469–1527) Italian statesman and political theorist. His treatise on the art of ruling, *The Prince* (1513), takes a dim view of human nature, seeing humanity as essentially corrupt and therefore best ruled by whatever method ensures the stability of the state, even if the method entails merciless cruelty.

McIndoe, Sir Archibald [Hector] (1900–1960) New Zealand plastic surgeon who pioneered facial surgery on burns' victims.

Mackenzie, Sir [Edward Montague] Compton (1883–1972) English novelist, best known for his series of very popular comic novels set in the Scottish Western Isles, e.g. *Whisky Galore* (1947).

McKinley, William (1843–1901) American Republican politician and the 25th president, elected for two terms, from 1897–1901 and 1901. He was assassinated.

Maclean, Donald *see* Burgess, Guy.

McLuhan, [Herbert] Marshall (1911–80) Canadian critic and educator. His studies of mass culture and communication include the influential *The Medium is the Message* (1967). *See* AML Structuralism.

Macmillan, Sir [Maurice] Harold, 1st Earl of Stockton (1894–1986) English Conservative statesman and prime minister (1957–63) after Eden. Christened 'Supermac' by the cartoonist Vicky, he won the general election of 1959 on the slogan 'You've never had it so good'. His 'wind of change' speech in South Africa (1958) gained him much international respect.

Madison, James (1751–1836) Democratic-Republican politician and 4th president (1809–1813 and 1813–17).

Madonna [Madonna Louise Veronica Ciccone] (1958–) American singer and film actress. After studying performing arts and dance in Michigan and New York, Madonna began performing with New York rock bands before making her first recording as a singer in 1982. Her career in films has been less successful, although the film *Evita* (1996) finally brought acclaim for her acting ability.

Maeterlinck, [Count] Maurice (1862–1949) Belgian poet, writer and playwright. His masterpiece is *Pelléas et Mélisande* (1892), the basis for the opera by Debussy. He was awarded the Nobel prize for literature in 1911.

Magritte, René (1898–1967) Belgian painter. He became a major Surrealist painter in Paris in the 1930s, devising a style dubbed 'magic realism'.

Mahler, Gustav (1860–1911) Austrian composer and conductor. Of Jewish birth, he became a Roman Catholic but remained subject to anti-Semitic gibes while conductor of the Vienna State Opera (1897–1907). Regarded as both the last of the great Romantic composers of the 19th century and the first great composer of the modern era, his works include nine symphonies, song cycles and the great symphonic song cycle, *The Song of the Earth* (1908).

Major, John (1943–) English Conservative politician. He became an MP in 1979 and was appointed a junior minister by Margaret Thatcher in 1981. After her resignation, he was selected as Tory leader and was then prime minister (1990–97).

Makarios III [Mikhail Khristodoulou Mouskos] (1913–77) Cypriot statesman and Archbishop of the Orthodox Church in Cyprus, he became first president of Cyprus (1959–77) after independence.

Malan, Daniel F[rançois] (1874–1959) South African politician. A fervent believer in a racially divided society, he was prime minister (1948–54) and was responsible for the apartheid legislation.

Malcolm X [Malcolm Little] (1925–65) African-American nationalist leader. A convert to Islam, he became an advocate of violence in response to racism only if used in self-defence.

Malevich, Kasimir *see* AML Suprematism.

Malory, Sir Thomas (*fl.* 15th century) translator, largely from French sources, of a collection of Arthurian legends, *Le Morte D'Arthur.* The work includes several episodes recycled by generations of writers, e.g. the quest for the Holy Grail.

Mandela, Nelson Rolihlahla (1918–) South African lawyer and nationalist leader. Leader of the banned African National Congress, he was imprisoned in 1964 for life by the South African government. Upon his release in 1990, he helped to dismantle apartheid and was elected president in the first free elections in 1994. He retired as president in 1999.

Mandelstam, Osip (1891–1938) Russian poet. Denounced for reading a satirical poem about STALIN, he and his wife, **Nadezhda Mandelstam** (1899–1980), were sent into exile in Siberia, where he died. Nadezhda later wrote accounts of their life together.

Manet, Edouard (1832–83) French painter. His direct approach and fresh, painterly style was influenced by the Impressionists, although he never exhibited with them.

Manley, Michael Norman (1923–97) Jamaican statesman. He became leader of the socialist People's National Party in 1969 and prime minister (1972–80 and 1989–92). He was regarded as a spokesman for the Third World.

Mann, Thomas (1875–1955) German novelist and critic, primarily concerned with the role of the artist and the purpose of artistic creation in modern society. His works include *Death in Venice* (1912), *The Magic Mountain* (1930) and *The Confessions of the Confidence Trickster Felix Krull* (1954), a comedy. He was awarded the Nobel prize for literature in 1929 and fled Nazi Germany in 1933.

Mao Tse-tung or Mao Ze Dong (1893–1976) Chinese Communist statesman and Marxist philosopher. He was a founder of the Chinese Communist Party (1922). Following the Japanese occupation (1937–45), during which Nationalists and Communists collaborated against the Japanese, the Communists won the resumed civil war and Mao established his People's Republic (1949). His dictatorship became murderous as he sought to break traditional patterns of Chinese family life and launched his 'Cultural Revolution' (1966–69).

Maradona, Diego Armando (1960–) Argentinian footballer voted the best player of the 20th century. He played for his national side in four World Cup tournaments and was a member of the winning team in 1986.

Marat, Jean Paul (1743–93) French revolutionary and journalist. He repeatedly called for increased executions during the establishment of the Revolution and was stabbed to death in his bath by the Girondist aristocrat **Charlotte Corday** (1768–93).

Marc, Franz (1880–1916) German painter. With KANDINSKY, he founded the *Blaue Reiter* group of expressionist artists (*see* AML Blaue Reiter).

Marceau, Marcel (1923–2007) French mime artist. He was regarded as the world's leading mime artist.

Marciano, Rocky [Rocco Francis Marchegiano] (1923–69) American boxer. He was world heavyweight champion (1952–56) and never lost a professional fight.

Marconi, Guglielmo, Marchese (1874–1937) Italian physicist and electrical engineer. He shared the 1909 Nobel prize for physics for his development of wireless telegraphy and later developed short-wave radio transmissions.

Marcos, Ferdinand Edralin (1917–89) Filipino politician; president of the Philippines (1965–86). An autocratic ruler, he declared martial law in 1972, after which he ruled by oppressive and idiosyncratic decree. Deposed in 1986 after the popular unrest that brought AQUINO to power, he lived in exile in Hawaii with his wife, **Imelda** (1929–).

Marinetti, Filippo *see* AML Futurism.

Markiewicz, Constance Georgine, Countess (1868–1927) Irish nationalist. A member of Sinn Féin involved in the 1916 Easter Rising, she became the first woman to be elected to the British parliament in 1918 but refused to take her seat.

Markova, Dame Alicia [Lilian Alicia Marks] (1910–2004) English ballerina. She was a member of DIAGHILEV's Ballet Russe (1924–29) and then of the Vic-Wells Ballet, where she became prima ballerina (1933–35).

Marks, Simon, 1st Baron Marks of Broughton (1888–1964) English businessman. He inherited the Marks & Spencer chain of stores and helped to build it into a respected retail empire.

Marley, Bob [Robert Nesta Marley] (1945–81) Jamaican singer and songwriter. With his group, the Wailers, he became the world's leading reggae singer.

Marlowe, Christopher (1564–93) English dramatist and poet. The most famous of his works are *Tamburlaine the Great* (1590) and his masterpiece, *Doctor Faustus* (1604). He was probably a secret agent in the employ of the Elizabethan government and was killed in a tavern brawl.

Marquez, Gabriel Garcia *see* AML magic realism.

Marshall, Alfred (1842–1924) English economist. His works have been of great influence on modern economics. He devised concepts such as 'elasticity', 'consumer surplus', and 'time analysis'.

Marshall, George C[atlett] (1880–1959) American general and statesman. He was chief of staff of the US army during World War II and, as US secretary of state, oversaw the Marshall Aid Plan, for which he was awarded the 1953 Nobel peace prize.

Marshall, Malcolm Denzil (1958–99) West Indian cricketer renowned for his skill as a fast-bowler. He played for the West Indies and Hampshire on and off from 1978 to 1991. In the 1990s, he played provincial cricket for Natal (South Africa), and was briefly coach to Hampshire and the West Indian team before he died at the age of 41 from cancer.

Marx, Karl (1818–83) German philosopher. His theories on class struggle dominated 20th-century political thought from the Bolshevik Revolution to the collapse of the Communist regimes of eastern Europe in 1989–91. *Das Kapital*, his study of the economics of capitalism, appeared in 1867; subsequent volumes, edited by **Friedrich**

Engels (1820–95), appeared in 1885 and 1895. He also wrote *The Communist Manifesto* with Engels in 1848 and was one of the founders of the 'First International' in 1864.

Marx Brothers American comedy group of brothers consisting of **Arthur Marx (Harpo)** (1893–1964), **Milton Marx (Gummo)** (1894–1977), **Herbert Marx (Zeppo)** (1901–79), **Julius Marx (Groucho)** (1895–1977) and **Leonard Marx (Chico)** (1891–1961). The anarchic humour of the Marx Brothers' films was enormously popular with both critics and public. Their films include *A Night at the Opera* (1935).

Masaccio [Tommaso di Ser Giovanni di Mone] (1401–*c*.1428) Florentine painter. A key figure of the early Renaissance and in the development of perspective.

Mascagni, Pietro (1863–1945) Italian composer. His works include the perennial favourite, the one-act *Cavalleria Rusticana*.

Masefield, John [Edward] (1878–1967) English poet, whose best-known poem, from *Salt-Water Ballads* (1902), is 'I must go down to the sea again'. He was appointed poet laureate in 1930.

Mata Hari [Margarethe Geertruida Zelle] (1876–1917) Dutch spy. A dancer in Paris with many lovers, she became a German spy and was shot by the French for treason.

Matisse, Henri (1869–1954) French painter and sculptor. In the period before World War I he became a leading Fauvist (*see* AML Fauvists). A superb draftsman, he also designed ballet sets for DIAGHILEV.

Matthews, Sir Stanley (1915–2000) English football player. Regarded as one of the greatest wingers of all time (the 'Wizard of Dribble'), he won 54 international caps in a career that spanned 22 years.

Maugham, W[illiam] Somerset (1874–1965) English novelist and dramatist. His best-known novels are *Of Human Bondage* (1915) and *The Moon and Sixpence* (1919), the latter based on the life of the painter Paul GAUGUIN. He was a British secret agent during World War I, and his experiences then form the basis of his spy novel, *Ashenden* (1928).

Mauve, Anton *see* AML Hague School.

Maxwell, [Ian] Robert [Robert Hoch] (1923–91) Czechoslovakian-born British newspaper proprietor, publisher and politician. His mysterious death by drowning off the Canary Islands was followed by revelations of his mishandling of his companies' assets.

Mayakovsky, Vladimir *see* AML Futurism.

Mayer, Louis B[urt] [Eliezer Mayer] (1885–1957) Russian-born American film producer. He joined with GOLDWYN to form Metro-Goldwyn-Mayer in 1924 and became one of the most powerful of the Hollywood moguls.

Mbeki, Thabo (1942–) South African political leader. He was Nelson Mandela's choice as successor as leader of the African Natrional Congress and became South Africa's second post-apartheid president in a landslide victory in 1999.

Mead, Margaret (1901–78) American anthropologist. Her works, which include *Coming of Age in Samoa* (1928), argue that it is cultural conditioning that shapes personality, rather than heredity.

Medawar, Sir Peter Brian (1915–87) Brazilian-born British zoologist. He shared the 1960 Nobel prize for physiology or medicine with the Australian virologist **Sir Frank Macfarlane Burnet** (1899–1985) for his work on immunological tolerance.

Medici, Lorenzo de' (1449–92) Florentine aristocrat and statesman. Styled 'The Magnificent', he was a poet and a noted patron of the arts. His tomb in Florence was designed by MICHELANGELO.

Meinhoff, Ulrike (1934–76) German terrorist. With **Andreas Baader** (1943–77) and others, she founded the 'Red Army Faction' in 1970, an ultra-leftist terrorist organisation dedicated to using violence to bring about the collapse of West German 'capitalist tyranny'.

Meir, Golda (1898–1978) Russian-born Israeli stateswoman. Active in the fight for a Jewish state, she was minister of labour (1949–56) and of foreign affairs (1956–66) before becoming Israel's first female prime minister (1969–74).

Meitner, Lise (1878–1968) Austrian-born Swedish physicist. She and Otto HAHN discovered the radioactive element protactinium (1918). With her nephew, Otto FRISCH, and others, she discovered the process of nuclear fission in the late 1930s.

Melba, Dame Nellie [Helen Porter Mitchell] (1861–1931) Australian soprano. Renowned for her light, pure voice, she became one of the world's leading prima donnas in the late 1880s.

Melville, Herman (1819–91) American novelist, short-story writer and poet. His masterpiece is the novel *Moby Dick* (1851), a complex and symbolic narrative featuring the revengeful Captain Ahab. His short novel *Billy Budd, Foretopman*, published posthumously in 1924, was made into an opera by BRITTEN.

Mendel, Gregor Johann (1822–84) Austrian monk who was also a biologist and botanist. He discovered that traits such as colour or height had two factors (hereditary units) and that these factors do not blend but can be either dominant or recessive.

Mendelssohn, Felix [Jakob Ludwig Felix Mendelssohn-Bartholdy] (1809–47) German Romantic composer. His works include five symphonies, the opera *Elijah* (1846), songs, and the overtures *A Midsummer Night's Dream* (1826) and *Fingal's Cave* (1832).

Mengistu, Mariam Haile (1937–) Ethiopian dictator. He participated in the 1974 coup that toppled HAILE SELASSIE and established a brutal dictatorship after a further coup in 1977. He was toppled in turn by a rebellion in 1991 and went into exile.

Menotti, Gian Carlo (1911–2007) Italian-born American composer. His operas, for which he also wrote the librettos, employ a number of musical styles.

Menuhin, Sir Yehudi (1916–99) American-born British violinist. An infant prodigy, he became one of the world's leading virtuosos and founded a school (in 1962) for musically gifted children.

Messerschmitt, Willy [Wilhelm] (1898–1978) German aircraft designer and manufacturer. His planes include the first jet combat aircraft.

Messiaen, Olivier (1908–92) French composer and organist. His rhythmically complex works were often heavily influenced by religious mysticism.

Messmer, Otto (1894–1985) American cartoonist. His 'Felix the Cat' became the first cartoon superstar.

Meyerbeer, Giacomo (1791–1864) a German-born composer who visited Italy and wrote operas in the style of ROSSINI. His best-known work is *L'Africaine*.

Michelangelo Buonarotti (1475–1564) Florentine painter, sculptor, draftsman, architect and poet, an outstanding figure of the Renaissance. His masterpiece is the ceiling paintings for the Sistine Chapel (1508–12). He also worked on the tombs of Lorenzo and Giuliano de Medici, and on the rebuilding of St Peter's. He was an accomplished poet and wrote fine sonnets.

Middleton, Thomas (*c.*1570–1627) English dramatist. His two powerful tragedies, *The Changeling* (1622) and *Women Beware Women* (1627), are now highly regarded.

Milhaud, Darius (1892–1974) French composer. A member of 'Les Six', he was a highly prolific composer. His works, were mostly polytonal and often influenced by jazz.

Mill, John Stuart (1806–73) English philosopher and economist. A follower of BENTHAM, he elaborated the philosophy of the 'greater good' in his philosophy of utilitarianism. His most popular work is the defence of personal freedom *On Liberty* (1859).

Millais, Sir John Everett (1829–96) English painter. Along with Holman HUNT and ROSSETTI, he founded the Pre-Raphaelite Brotherhood and was known for his posed, studied tableaux in clashing colours.

Miller, Arthur (1915–2005) American dramatist. His tragedies include three classics of the American stage: *Death of a Salesman* (1949); *The Crucible* (1952), a comment on McCarthyism in the USA; and *A View from the Bridge* (1955), inspired by Greek drama (*see* AML tragedy). He was married to Marilyn MONROE (1955–61) for whom he wrote the screenplay for her last film, *The Misfits* (1961).

Miller, [Alton] Glenn (1904–44) American composer, band-leader and trombonist. His dance band became one of the most popular in the world.

Millet, Jean-François (1814–75) French painter. He earned his living as a portraitist and exhibited his first major genre painting, *The Winnower*, in 1848.

Millett, Kate (1934–) American feminist. Her works are a cornerstone of feminist fundamentalism.

Milligan, Spike [Terence Allan Milligan] (1918–2002) Anglo-Irish comedian and writer. With Peter SELLERS, the Welsh comedian and singer **Harry Secombe** (1921–2001) and the Anglo-Peruvian comedian **Michael Bentine** (1921–96), he wrote and performed in the radio comedy series *The Goon Show* (1951–59), which became a highly influential comedy series, with its manic wit and surreal invention.

Millikan, Robert Andrews (1868–1953) American physicist. He was awarded the 1923 Nobel prize for physics for his determination of the charge on the electron.

Milne, A[lan] A[lexander] (1882–1956) English writer and dramatist. His children's books featuring Winnie the Pooh are much loved classics of children's literature.

Milton, John (1608–74) English poet. One of the most formidably learned of all English poets, he had a European-wide reputation by his late twenties. His most famous prose work is the tract *Aeropagitica* (1644), a rousing defence of the liberty of free speech. His masterpiece is the great epic poem on the Fall of Man, *Paradise Lost* (1667–74).

Minghella, Anthony (1954–2008) British film-maker and screenwriter whose films included *The English Patient* (1997) for which he won an Academy Award for best director and *The Talented Mr Ripley* (1999). He received a CBE in 2001 and served as chairman of the British Film Institute.

Miró, Joan (1893–1983) Spanish painter. Influenced by PICASSO, his work became increasingly abstract over the years and was influential on the Abstract Expressionist painters.

Mitchell, R[eginald] J[oseph] (1895–1937) English aircraft designer. He designed the Supermarine Spitfire (1934–36).

Mitterrand, François [Maurice Marie] (1916–96) French statesman. He became leader of the Socialist Party in 1971 and the first socialist president of France (1981–95).

Mobutu, Sese Seko Nkuku Ngbendu Wa Za Banga [Joseph-Désiré Mobutu] (1930–1997) Zairean dictator. He assumed complete power over the Congo in 1965, changing the country's name to Zaire in 1971. In 1997 he was ousted from power by rebel forces. He fled the country and died in exile the same year.

Modigliani, Amedeo (1884–1920) Italian painter and sculptor. His best-known works are his African-influenced sculptures of elongated figures.

Mohammed or Muhammad (*c*.570–*c*.632) Arab prophet and founder of Islam. Born in Mecca, the son of a merchant, he began having revelations, sometime after 600, that he was the last prophet of Allah and His channel of communication with the world. He gathered together a band of followers and established himself at Medina in 622, from where, after several battles, his forces conquered Mecca in 629 and shortly afterwards all Arabia.

Molière [Jean-Baptiste Poquelin] (1622–73) French dramatist. His great comedies are as popular now as when they were first performed; only SHAKESPEARE's plays have been more widely performed. The plays include *Tartuffe* (1664), a satire on religious hypocrisy, *The Misanthrope* (1666), a study of a cynic in love, and *The Imaginary Invalid* (1673), a hilarious depiction of hypochondria and quack medicine.

Molotov, Vyacheslav Mikhailovich [Vyacheslav Mikhailovich Scriabin] (1890–1986) Russian statesman. He negotiated the non-aggression pact with Nazi Germany and became minister for foreign affairs (1953–56).

Mondrian, Piet [Pieter Cornelis Mondriaan] (1872–1944) Dutch painter. He developed a style of painting based on grids of lines against strong colours and co-founded the De Stijl group.

Monet, Claude Oscar (1840–1926) French Impressionist painter. His *Impression: Sunrise* (1872) gave its name to the movement. His works include the *Haystacks* (1891) and *Rouen Cathedral* (1894) series.

Monk, Thelonius [Sphere] (1920–82) American jazz pianist and composer. His

compositions include the classic 'Round Midnight'.

Monroe, James (1758–1835) Democratic-Republican politician and 5th president of the US (1817–25).

Monroe, Marilyn [Norma Jean Baker or Mortenson] (1926–62) American film actress. She became the epitome of the 'dumb blonde' sex symbol with such films as *Gentleman Prefer Blondes* (1953).Her last film, *The Misfits* (1961), was written by her third husband, Arthur MILLER. Her death was apparently the result of an overdose of sleeping pills.

Montessori, Maria (1870–1952) Italian educationalist. Her method of encouraging the child to learn at her or his own pace without restraint, was very influential on modern pedagogy.

Monteverdi, Claudio Giovanni Antonio (1567–1643) Italian composer. He introduced many new elements to the opera form and is regarded as the first major opera composer. His works include *Orfeo* and *The Coronation of Poppea*.

Montgomery of Alamein, Bernard Law, 1st Viscount (1887–1976) English soldier. In World War II he was given command of the 8th Army in Egypt in 1942 and won the Battle of Alamein, a victory recognised by CHURCHILL as a turning point in the war. He later commanded the Allied land forces on D Day.

Moore, Henry Spencer (1898–1986) English sculptor. His monumental sculptures, often semi-abstract in style but always based on organic form, resulted in him becoming the best known of modern sculptors.

More, Sir Thomas (1478–1535) English statesman and Roman Catholic saint. He was HENRY VIII's Lord Chancellor, and his refusal to recognise the annulment of Henry's marriage to Catherine of Aragon and declaration of supremacy over the Church in England led to his execution for treason. His greatest work is his fantasy of a supposedly ideally organised state, *Utopia* (1516). More was canonised in 1835 and has always been admired for his firm principles.

Moreira, Ronaldo de Assis [Ronaldhino Gaucho] (1980–) Brazilian footballer.

An impressive striker, he has twice won the FIFA World Player of the Year award (2004 and 2005). He was a member of the winning Brazilian World Cup team in 2002 and was again in his national side during the 2006 World Cup. He has played for Barcelona since 2003.

Morgan, Thomas Hunt (1866–1945) American geneticist and biologist. He was awarded the 1933 Nobel prize for physiology or medicine for his research into chromosomes and heredity.

Moro, Aldo (1916–78) Italian Christian democrat statesman. He was prime minister (1963–68 and 1974–76) and brought the Communist Party into close cooperation with his centre-left coalition shortly before his abduction and murder by the Red Brigade.

Morris, Desmond John (1928–) English zoologist. His studies of animal and human behaviour, e.g. *The Naked Ape* (1967) and *The Human Zoo* (1969), have been bestsellers.

Morris, William (1834–96) English poet, romance writer, artist and social reformer. He founded the Arts and Crafts Movement, drawing inspiration from the medieval guild system, and was a great influence on the development and character of British socialism.

Morrison, Jim (1943–71) American rock singer and songwriter. His band, The Doors, became a huge cult after his death (from alcohol and drug abuse).

Morton, Jelly Roll [Ferdinand Joseph Lemott] (1885–1941) American jazz pianist, composer and bandleader who is regarded as one of the founders of New Orleans jazz.

Moses, Edwin (1955–) American track-and-field athlete and star of the 400 metres hurdles, winning Olympic gold in 1976 and 1984 and setting a world record on four separate occasions.

Mosley, Sir Oswald Ernald (1896–1980) English Fascist leader. He founded the British Union of Fascists (1932–36). The thuggery and demagogy of his movement failed to attract much support, and he was interned during World War II.

Mossbauer, Rudolf Ludwig (1929–) German physicist. He shared the 1961 Nobel prize for physics with the American physicist **Robert Hofstadter** (1915–1990) for his discovery of the 'Mossbauer effect', involving gamma radiation in crystals.

Motion, Andrew *see* AML poet laureate.

Mountbatten, Louis Francis Victor Albert Nicholas, 1st Earl Mountbatten of Burma (1900–1979) British naval commander and statesman. Supreme Allied Commander in South-East Asia (1943–45) and viceroy of India (1947), he oversaw the transfer of power to the independent governments of India and Pakistan. He was assassinated by the IRA.

Moussorgsky, Modest *see* Mussorgsky, Modest.

Mozart, Wolfgang Amadeus (1756–91) Austrian musician and composer. A child prodigy and one of the most lyrical of all composers, his works include the operas *The Marriage of Figaro*, *Don Giovanni*, *Così fan tutte* and *The Magic Flute*, over 40 symphonies, concertos, string quartets, sonatas, 18 masses and the unfinished *Requiem*.

Mugabe, Robert Gabriel (1924–) Zimbabwean statesman. He became leader of the Zimbabwe African National Union in 1974, then, following the end of white minority rule, prime minister (1980–87) and finally president. He merged his ruling party with the Zimbabwe African People's Union in 1988 to form a one-party state.

Mulliken, Robert Sanderson (1896–1986) American chemist and physicist. He was awarded the 1986 Nobel prize for chemistry for his work on molecular structure and on chemical bonding.

Munch, Edvard (1863–1944) Norwegian painter. An Expressionist, his works, e.g. *The Scream*, are noted for their strong use of primary colours and emotions.

Munthe, Axel (1857–1949) Swedish physicist and psychiatrist. His autobiographical book, *The Story of San Michele* (1929), describing his experiences while practising medicine, became a world bestseller.

Murdoch, Dame Iris (1919–99) Irish-born English novelist whose novels, e.g. *A Severed Head* and *The Sea, The Sea*, are intellectual sex comedies with complex symbolism and a strong dash of the macabre. Her battle with Alzheimer's disease was chronicled by her husband, John Bayley.

Murdoch, [Keith] Rupert (1931–) Australian-born American newspaper tycoon. He inherited an Australian newspaper group from his father and expanded his media empire in Britain and America. His expansion into the US market necessitated his acquisition of US citizenship in 1985.

Musgrave, Thea (1928–) Scottish composer. Her early works were often on Scottish themes. Later compositions, often in serial form, include choral works and concertos.

Mussolini, Benito (Amilcare Andrea) (1883–1945) Italian dictator. Originally a socialist, he founded his fascist 'Blackshirt' Party in 1919 and was elected to parliament in 1921, establishing himself as dictator ('Il Duce') in 1922. He formed the Axis with HITLER in 1937 and declared war on the Allies in 1940. He was deposed in 1943 and later executed by partisans.

Mussorgsky or Moussorgsky, Modest Petrovich (1839–81) Russian composer. His best-known works include the opera *Boris Godunov* and the piano piece 'Pictures at an Exhibition'.

Muzorewa, Bishop Abel *see* SMITH, IAN.

Myrdal, [Karl] Gunnar (1898–1987) Swedish economist. He shared the 1974 Nobel prize for economics with HAYEK, largely for his work on the application of economic theory to the economies of the Third World.

Nabokov, Vladimir (1899–1977) Russian-born American novelist, who wrote in both Russian and English. His most famous novel is *Lolita* (1955).

Nagy, Imre (1896–1958) Hungarian statesman. He was appointed prime minister (1953–55) and forced to resign after attempting to liberalise communist policies. He became premier again in 1956, but was replaced after the Soviet invasion of that year.

Nansen, Fridtjof (1861–1930) Norwegian explorer, scientist and statesman. He traversed Greenland (1888–89) and almost reached the North Pole in 1895, achieving a record latitude. He was appointed commissioner for refugees (1920–22) by the League of Nations and awarded the 1922 Nobel peace prize.

Napoleon I [Napoleon Bonaparte] (1769–1821) emperor of France (1804–15). A brilliant and ruthless military leader, he established an empire throughout Europe, defeating coalitions of the other major powers. His invasion of Russia in 1812, and the murderous campaign in the Pyrenees against WELLINGTON's forces, led to the defeat of his armies at Leipzig in 1813 and Allied victory in 1814. Napoleon retired to Elba, from whence, in 1815, he came back to France, beginning the 'Hundred Days' campaign that resulted in his defeat at Waterloo and subsequent banishment to St Helena, where he died.

Nashe, Thomas (1567–1601) English writer of pamphlets and tracts on various subjects, which were usually satirical and often contained barbs directed against his many literary and religious enemies.

Nasser, Gamal Abdel (1918–70) Egyptian soldier and statesman. He took a leading part in the coup that deposed **King Farouk** (1920–65) in 1952 and became prime minister in 1954. He became president (1956–70) and precipitated the Suez Crisis by nationalising the Suez Canal (1956).

Navratilova, Martina (1956–) Czechoslovakian-born American tennis player. Regarded as one of the world's greatest tennis players, she defected to the USA in 1975.

Nehru, Jawaharlal (1889–1964) Indian nationalist leader and statesman. The son of the nationalist lawyer, **Motilal Nehru ('Pandit' Nehru)** (1861–1931), he joined the Indian National Congress in 1919 and was imprisoned many times in the 1930s and 40s for his nationalist views. He became the first prime minister of India (1947–64) following independence and the partition into India and Pakistan. His daughter Indira GANDHI was also prime minister.

Nelson, Horatio, Viscount Nelson (1758–1805) English naval commander. Renowned for his tactics, he became rear-admiral in 1797 after defeating the Spanish fleet at the battle of Cape St Vincent. The following year, he won a striking victory over the French at the Battle of the Nile and was killed by a sniper during his defeat of the French at Trafalgar in 1805.

Nero (37–68) Roman emperor. He succeeded CLAUDIUS in 54 and soon became infamous for his debauchery, vanity and paranoia. He had many people put to death or forced to kill themselves.

Nervi, Pier Luigi (1891–1979) Italian architect and engineer. An exponent of the virtues of reinforced concrete, his designs include the Pirelli skyscraper in Milan.

Netanyahu, Binyamin *see* RABIN, YITZHAK.

Newman, Cardinal John Henry (1801–90) English theologian. His spirited defence of his faith, *Apologia pro Vita Sua* (1864), was much admired by believers and non-believers alike.

Newman, Paul (1925–) American film actor. His films include *Hud* (1963), *Butch Cassidy and the Sundance Kid* (1969) and *The Color of Money* (1986), the last earning him an Oscar. A political activist of the moderate left, he has also raised considerable sums of money for charity through sales of his own-name food products.

Newton, Sir Isaac (1642–1727) English scientist, philosopher and mathematician. According to legend, observing the fall of an apple inspired him to discover the law of gravity. He also discovered (independently of LEIBNITZ) the differential calculus and the reflecting telescope, and devised the three laws of motion.

Nicholas II (1868–1918) Russian tsar (1895–1917). A weak ruler, alternating between bursts of liberalisation and repression, his authority was seriously weakened by Russia's defeat in the war with Japan (1904–05). He was deposed by the Bolsheviks in 1917, who later murdered him and his family.

Nicklaus, Jack William (1940–) American golfer. One of the greatest golfers of all time, he has won more major tournaments than any other player in history.

Niemöller, Martin (1892–1984) German Lutheran pastor. An outspoken opponent of HITLER and Nazi ideology, he was imprisoned in concentration camps (1937–45). He was president of the World Council of Churches (1961–68) and a prominent pacifist.

Nietzsche, Friedrich Wilhelm (1844–1900) German philosopher and poet whose works were highly critical of traditional morality and Christianity and proclaimed the advent of the superman. He was claimed by HITLER to be a spiritual forebear of Nazism, but Nietzsche, who despised anti-Semitism, would have rejected this.

Nijinsky, Vaslav (1890–1950) Russian ballet dancer and choreographer. He became a protégé of DIAGHILEV and is regarded as one of the greatest ballet dancers of all time.

Niven, David [James David Graham Nevins] (1909–83) Scottish film actor who established himself as the model urbane Englishman in many Hollywood productions.

Nixon, Richard Milhous (1913–94) American Republican politician. The 37th president (1969-74), he became the first president to resign from office, in August 1974, following the 'Watergate' scandal. He was pardoned in September 1974. While in office, he ended the Vietnam war and established rapprochement with China.

Nkrumah, Kwame (1909–72) Ghanaian statesman. He was the first president of Ghana (1957–66) after independence.

Nobel, Sir Alfred *see* AML Nobel prize.

Nolan, Sir Sidney [Robert] (1917–92) Australian painter. His paintings draw heavily upon Australian history and folklore.

Norman, Greg (1955–) Australian golf player. Nicknamed the 'White Shark', he has been successful in numerous tournaments including the British Open (1986 and 1993).

Nostradamus [Michel de Notredame] (1503–66) French astrologer and physician. He published two books of cryptic prophecies in rhymed quatrains which enjoyed a huge vogue.

Novello, Ivor [Ivor Novello Davies] (1893–1951) Welsh songwriter, composer and actor. His songs include 'Keep the Home Fires Burning', which was hugely popular with British soldiers during World War I, and 'We'll Gather Lilacs'.

Nuffield, William Richard Morris, 1st Viscount (1877–1963) English automobile manufacturer and philanthropist. He developed a Henry FORD-like system of mass production of cars, notably the Morris Oxford and the Morris Minor.

Nureyev, Rudolf (1939–93) Russian ballet dancer and choreographer. Regarded as the successor to Nijinsky, he formed a famous partnership with Fonteyn in 1962.

Nyerere, Julius Kambarage (*c.* 1922–1999) Tanzanian statesman. He became president (1962–85) and negotiated the union of Tanganyika and Zanzibar (1964), which formed Tanzania. He was widely regarded as Africa's leading statesman. His invasion of Uganda in 1978 brought Amin's dictatorship to an end.

Obote, [Apollo] Milton (1924–2005) Ugandan politician. He became Uganda's first prime minister (1962–66) after independence and became president (1966–71) after deposing King Mutesa II. He was in turn deposed by Amin and became president again (1980–85) after Amin's overthrow. He was deposed again in 1985.

O'Casey, Sean (1880–1964) Irish dramatist. His early plays, e.g. *Juno and Paycock* (1924), reflect the patriotism that followed the Easter Rising of 1916.

Oistrakh, David Fyodorovich (1908–74) Russian violinist. A widely admired virtuoso whose son, **Igor Davidovich Oistrakh** (1931–), also has an international reputation as a violinist.

Oldenburg, Claes *see* AML Pop Art.

Olivier, Laurence Kerr, Baron Olivier of Brighton (1907–89) English stage and film actor and director. Regarded as the leading British actor of the modern era, he played all the major Shakespeare roles and became an international film star. He was director of the National Theatre (1962–73). His second wife (of three) was Vivien Leigh.

O'Neill, Eugene Gladstone (1888–1953) American dramatist. His greatest play, *Long Day's Journey into Night* (1940–41), a study of family breakdown, was not performed until three years after his death. He was awarded the Nobel prize for literature in 1936 and won the Pulitzer prize on three occasions. *See also* AML tragedy.

Ono, Yoko *see* Lennon, John.

Oppenheimer, J[ulius] Robert (1904–67) American nuclear physicist. He resigned from the Los Alamos atom bomb project after the dropping of the bombs on Hiroshima and Nagasaki, and argued for cooperation with the USSR on the control of nuclear weapons.

Orff, Carl (1895–1982) German composer. His best-known work is the popular *Carmina Burana* (1937), a 'secular oratorio' based on medieval poems.

Ortega, Daniel (1945–) Nicaraguan politician. A leader of the Sandinista resistance movement that overthrew the dictatorship in 1979, he became president (1985–90). He was then an unsuccessful candidate for president in 1996 and 2001 before winning the 2006 presidential election.

Ortega y Gasset, José (1883–1955) Spanish philosopher who argued that democracy in the modern era could easily lead to tyrannies of either the left or right.

Orwell, George [Eric Arthur Blair] (1903–50) Indian-born English novelist and essayist. His two greatest novels have become classics: *Animal Farm* (1945), a grim allegory of the history of the Soviet Union, and *Nineteen Eighty-Four* (1949), an even grimmer picture of a totalitarian world.

Osborne, John James (1929–94) English dramatist. His first play, *Look Back in Anger* (1956), gave its name to the 'Angry Young Men', a group of playwrights who created realistic dramas of working-class life.

Oswald, Lee Harvey (1939–63) American alleged assassin of President Kennedy. He was arrested shortly after Kennedy's murder in Dallas in 1963 and was himself shot dead by **Jack Ruby** (1911–64) before he could come to trial.

Ovid [Publius Ovidius Naso] (43 bc–*c.* ad 17) Roman poet. His sensual, witty love poems have always been admired, but his long narrative poem *Metamorphoses*, which describes myths in which characters change their forms, is of greater significance. It was used as a source book by many Renaissance writers, e.g. Shakespeare.

Owens, Jesse [James Cleveland Owens] (1913–80) American athlete. One of the finest athletes of his generation, he won four gold medals in the 1936 Berlin Olympics. Adolf Hitler left the stadium to avoid congratulating the black, non-Aryan athlete.

Padarewski, Ignace Jan (1860–1941) Polish pianist, composer and statesman. Widely regarded as the greatest pianist of his day, he served as prime minister for ten months in 1919.

Pahlavi, Mohammed Reza (1919–80) Shah of Iran. He succeeded his father in 1941 and gradually established a dictatorship that was undermined by religious fundamentalists led by KHOMEINI and forced to flee his country in 1979.

Paine, Thomas (1737–1809) English-born American political theorist and pamphleteer. His highly influential pamphlet *Common Sense* (1776) was recognised by WASHINGTON as being a significant contribution to the Revolution. Paine moved to France where he was elected to the National Convention. He sided with the moderates, was imprisoned by ROBESPIERRE's faction and released after 11 months, having narrowly escaped execution.

Paisley, Revd Ian Richard Kyle (1926–) Northern Ireland Protestant clergyman, leader of the Democratic Unionist Party (1971–2008) and first minister of Northern Ireland (2007–2008). He is also a prolific author, lecturer and speaker.

Palestrina, Giovanni Pierluigi da (*c*.1525–1594) Italian composer. One of the greatest Renaissance composers, his compositions are practically all choral church works, including more than 90 masses, hymns, motets and madrigals.

Palmer, Arnold (1929–) American golfer with a fan club known as 'Arnie's army'. He was the first person to win the US Masters four times (1958, 1960, 1962 and 1964).

Palmer, Samuel (1805–81) English painter and engraver, noted for his pastoral landscapes. He was a follower of William BLAKE, who deeply influenced the visionary mysticism of his work.

Pankhurst, Emmeline (1857–1928) English suffragette and feminist. She and her daughter **Dame Christabel Harriette Pankhurst** (1880–1958) founded the Women's Social and Political Union in 1903, a campaigning organisation for women's suffrage. Her daughter **Estelle**

Sylvia Pankhurst (1882–1960) was also a suffragette as well as a pacifist.

Papandreou, Andreas George (1919–96) Greek socialist politician and Greece's first socialist prime minister (1981–89).

Parker, Charlie or Bird [Charles Christopher Parker] (1920–55) American jazz alto and tenor saxophonist. He became the leading exponent of 'bop' jazz in the 1940s and worked with Dizzy GILLESPIE *(see* AML bebop).

Parker, Dorothy Rothschild (1893–1967) American journalist, poet and short-story writer, noted for her dry wit and sharply ironic epigrams and satires.

Parnell, Charles Stewart (1846–91) Irish politician. An ardent Home Ruler, he became MP for Cork in 1880 but his career began to crumble in 1890 after he was cited in a divorce case.

Pascal, Blaise (1623–62) French theologian, mathematician and physicist. He made important discoveries in hydraulics and invented a calculating machine.

Pasternak, Boris Leonidovich (1890–1960) Russian poet and novelist. His great novel, *Dr Zhivago,* was first published in Italy in 1958. Awarded the 1958 Nobel prize for literature, he declined it, almost certainly out of fear of being stripped of his citizenship by the Soviet authorities were he to travel to Stockholm to accept it.

Pasteur, Louis (1822–95) French chemist who discovered that fermentation is caused by the presence of microorganisms and developed the process of pasteurisation to destroy them. He also developed immunisation processes against the diseases of rabies and anthrax.

Patrick, Saint (*fl.* 5th century) British missionary. He was sold into slavery in Ireland as a youth, escaped to France and became a monk. He returned to Ireland as a missionary and converted many to his faith. He became the patron saint of Ireland.

Patterson, Floyd (1935–2006) American boxer who won an Olympic medal in 1952 at the age of 17. At 21 he became the youngest boxer ever to have won the heavyweight title and he successfully defended it four times, only losing it 1959. He then regained the title in 1960, becoming the first boxer to do this.

Patton, George S[mith] (1885–1945) American general. In World War II he commanded the Allied invasion of North Africa (1942–43) and led the 3rd US army across France and Germany to the Czech border (1944–45).

Paul, Saint (d. *c*. AD 67) Christian apostle and missionary to the Gentiles. A pharisee, he was a notable persecutor of Christians before his 'Damascus Road' conversion. Many of the Epistles in the New Testament are his. According to tradition, he was executed during the reign of Nero.

Pauling, Linus Carl (1901–94) American chemist. He was awarded the 1954 Nobel prize for physics for his research into chemical bonding and molecular structure, and the 1962 Nobel peace prize for his criticisms of nuclear testing and his campaign for a multilateral test ban.

Pavarotti, Luciano (1935–2007) Italian operatic tenor who also crossed over into popular music and was regarded as one of the most powerful tenor singers of the 20th century. He was well known for his televised concerts and noted for his charity work.

Pavlov, Ivan Petrovich (1849–1936) Russian physiologist. He was awarded the 1904 Nobel prize for physiology or medicine for his work on the physiology of digestion and conducted experiments on the conditioning of reflexes.

Pavlova, Anna (1885–1931) Russian ballerina. FOKINE choreographed *The Dying Swan* for her. She also worked with DIAGHILEV and became world-famous.

Pears, Sir Peter (1910–86) English tenor. He was a close associate of Benjamin BRITTEN, several of whose tenor opera roles were written for him.

Peary, Robert Edwin (1856–1920) American naval commander and Arctic explorer. He is credited with being the first man to reach the North Pole (1909).

Peel, Sir Robert (1788–1850) British statesman. He became Home Secretary in 1828 and founded the Metropolitan police. He was prime minister twice (1834–35, 1841–6).

Peierls, Sir Rudolf Ernst (1907–95) German-born British physicist. With Otto FRISCH, he demonstrated the feasibility of an atom bomb during World War II.

Pelé [Edson Arantes do Nascimento] (1940–) Brazilian football player, universally recognised as one of the most skilful and entertaining players of all time.

Pepys, Samuel (1633–1703) English diarist and Admiralty official. His diary (written in code) was first published in 1825 and includes fascinating detail of life in 17th-century London.

Percy, Thomas *see* AML ballad.

Perón, Juan Domingo (1895–1974) Argentinian dictator. He was president (1946–55), but was deposed by the army and lived in exile until re-elected president (1973–74). His success was based to a large extent on his second wife, **[Maria] Eva [Duarte] Perón** (1919–52), an ex-actress nicknamed 'Evita'. His third wife, **Isabel Perón [Maria Estella]** (1931–) was president (1974–76) but was deposed.

Perry, Fred[erick John] (1909–95) English-born American tennis and table-tennis player. He was one of the most successful lawn tennis players of the 1930s, winning every major tournament.

Pétain, Henri Philippe Omer (1856–1951) French soldier and statesman. Appointed marshal of France in 1918 in recognition of his generalship during World War I, he headed the collaborationist Vichy government (1940–44) and was sentenced to death at the end of World War II (later commuted to life imprisonment).

Peter, Saint (d. *c*. AD 67) disciple of JESUS CHRIST and Christian apostle. A fisherman, he became one of Jesus's leading disciples and played a prominent role in establishing Christianity after the crucifixion and is regarded by Roman Catholics as the first pope. He is believed to have been martyred in Rome.

Peterson, Oscar Emmanuel (1925–2007) Canadian jazz pianist and composer. His Oscar Peterson Trio became one of the best-known small jazz groups of the 1950s.

Petrarch [Francesco Petrarca] (1304–74) Italian lyric poet and humanist. His work popularised the sonnet form, and he is recognised as the first major poet of the Renaissance.

Petronius [Gaius Petronius Arbiter] (d. *c*. AD 66) Roman courtier and satirist. His great satirical novel, the *Satyricon*, is an important landmark in Western literature.

Pevsner, Antoine *see* AML Constructivism.

Philby, Kim [Harold Adrian Russell Philby] (1911–88) English diplomat, journalist and secret-service double agent. He became a Soviet agent in 1933 and was recruited to the British Secret Service in 1940. He worked in the British embassy in Washington DC (1949–51) and as a foreign correspondent (1956–63) before fleeing to the USSR.

Piaf, Edith [Edith Giovanna Gassion] (1915–63) French singer and songwriter. Nicknamed 'Little Sparrow' for her small size and frail appearance, her songs include 'Non, Je Ne Regrette Rien'.

Piaget, Jean (1896–1980) Swiss psychologist. His studies of children's intelligence and perception have been highly influential on modern educationalists. *See also* AML Structuralism.

Picabia, Francis *see* AML Dada.

Picasso, Pablo (1881–1973) Spanish painter and sculptor. Regarded as the most influential artist of the modern era, with BRAQUE, he was the founder of Cubism. His 'blue period' (1901–04) works include *The Blue Room* (1901); Cubist works include *Les Demoiselles d'Avignon* (1906–07). He designed costumes and scenery for DIAGHILEV from 1917 and exhibited with the Surrealists in the mid-1920s. *Guernica* (1937), his strongest, perhaps best-known image, was a response to the fascist bombing of that Basque town during the Spanish Civil War.

Pickford, Mary [Gladys Mary Smith] (1893–1979) Canadian-born American film star. She appeared in silent films and was co-founder of the United Artists film studio (1919) with Charlie CHAPLIN and D. W. GRIFFITH.

Pierce, Franklin (1804–1869) American Democrat politician and 14th president (1853–1857).

Piero della Francesca (*c.*1416–92) Italian early Renaissance painter. From *c.*1460 he worked at the Urbino court, where he painted some of his finest works.

Piggott, Lester (1935–) British jockey. Considered to be one of the best flat racing jockeys of all time, he won the Derby nine times between 1954 and 1983. He retired for good in 1995.

Pindar (*c.*518–*c.*438 BC) Greek lyric poet, noted for his odes and carefully constructed, elaborate poems.

Pinochet [Ugarte], Augusto (1915–2006) Chilean general and dictator. He led the 1973 coup that deposed ALLENDE and became president (1974–90). He instituted monetarist economic policies that brought unprecedented economic stability to Chile. However, at the time of his death in December 2006, criminal charges were still pending against him for human rights abuses, tax evasion and embezzlement under his rule and afterwards.

Pinter, Harold (1930–) English dramatist, known for his halting, menacing dialogue and sinister pauses, e.g. in *The Caretaker* (1960).

Pirandello, Luigi (1867–1936) Italian dramatist and novelist. His two best-known plays are *Six Characters in Search of an Author* (1921) and *Henry IV* (1922), both of which question theatrical conventions. He was awarded the Nobel prize for literature in 1934.

Pisano, Giovanni (*c.*1245–*c.*1314) Pisan sculptor. A leading sculptor of his time, his works are expressive and elegant in the Gothic tradition.

Pissarro, Camille (1830–1903) West Indian-born French Impressionist painter. Influenced by both CONSTABLE and TURNER, he exhibited in all eight Impressionist exhibitions.

Pitt, William, 'the Elder', [1st Earl of Chatham] (1707–88) English statesman. He led Britain to victory in the Seven Years' War (1756–63) with France. His son, **William Pitt 'the Younger'** (1759–1806) became prime minister in 1783.

Planck, Max [Karl Ernst Ludwig] (1858–1947) German physicist. He formulated the quantum theory and was awarded the 1918 Nobel prize for physics.

Plath, Sylvia (1932–63) American poet and novelist. Her intense and highly expressive style has been very influential. She was married to TED HUGHES and committed suicide.

Plato (*c.*427–*c.*347 BC) Greek philosopher, regarded as the main founder of Western philosophy. Taught by SOCRATES, he was in turn ARISTOTLE's tutor. His many works, which take the form of dialogues, notably the *Symposium, Phaedo* and *The Republic*, have influenced almost every subsequent age and tradition.

Plotinus *see* AML Neoplatonism.

Pocock, Isaac *see* AML melodrama.

Poe, Edgar Allan (1809–49) American short-story writer, poet and critic. His macabre, highly Gothic horror stories are studies in pathological obsession, and his detective stories, e.g. 'The Murders in the Rue Morgue', have been highly influential.

Polk, James K. (1795–1849) American Democrat politician and the 11th president (1845–49).

Pollock, [Paul] Jackson (1912–56) American painter. He became the leading exponent of action painting in the late 1940s.

Pol Pot or Saloth Sar [Kompong Thom] (1929–97) Cambodian Communist politician. The establishment of his Maoist dictatorship cost the lives of three million people. The Khmer Rouge regime was overthrown by the Russian-backed Vietnamese invasion of 1979 but he remained a powerful figure.

Pompey *see* CAESAR, JULIUS.

Pompidou, Georges Jean Raymond (1911–74) French statesman. He was prime minister (1962–68) but was dismissed in 1968 by de Gaulle following the May student riots in Paris but elected president (1969–74).

Pope, Alexander (1688–1744) English poet. His mastery of the rhymed couplet, his deadly satire and gift for sustaining metaphor place him as one of the greatest English poets.

Porter, Cole Albert (1893–1964) American songwriter and composer. His highly popular songs, admired for their wit and lyricism, include 'Begin the Beguine' and 'Night and Day'.

Potter, [Helen] Beatrix (1866–1943) English writer and illustrator, known for her children's books featuring animal characters such as 'Peter Rabbit'.She was also noted for her work in conservation.

Poulenc, Francis (1899–1963) French composer. A member of 'Les Six' (*see* AML

Six, Les), he is particularly noted for his settings of verses from poetry.

Pound, Ezra Weston Loomis (1885–1972) American poet and critic. A generous supporter of younger writers, e.g. T. S. ELIOT and HEMINGWAY, he lived in Italy from 1925 and broadcast propaganda against the Allies during World War II. He was committed to a US asylum after the war until 1958, when he returned to Italy.

Poussin, Nicolas (1594–1665) French painter who is noted for his carefully composed pictures in a Classical style.

Presley, Elvis Aaron (1935–77) American rock singer. He became one of the most popular singers in the world in the mid-1950s and was an outstanding interpreter of ballads.

Priestley, J[ohn] B[oynton] (1894–1984) English novelist and dramatist. His huge output includes the play *An Inspector Calls* (1947).

Prokofiev, Sergei Sergeyevich (1891–1953) Russian composer and pianist. His works include seven symphonies, ballets, piano and violin concertos, and the well-known orchestral 'fairy tale', *Peter and the Wolf* (1936).

Proust, Marcel (1871–1922) French novelist, essayist and critic, known for his long semi-autobiographical novel, *A la recherche du temps perdu* (1913–27).

Puccini, Giacomo (1858–1924) Italian composer. His operas, e.g. *La Bohème, Tosca* and *Madame Butterfly*, are regarded as the last great lyrical and dramatic works in the Italian tradition.

Purcell, Henry (*c*.1659–95) English composer. His works include incidental music for the theatre, songs, church music and six operas, notably *Dido and Aeneas* and *The Fairy Queen*.

Pushkin, Aleksandr Sergeyevich (1799–1837) Russian poet, novelist and dramatist. Widely regarded as Russia's greatest poet, the best known of his works are the verse novel *Eugene Onegin* (1823–31) and the historical tragedy *Boris Gudonov* (1825). He died in a duel.

Putin, Vladimir Vladimirovich (1952–) Russian government official and politician. He served in the KGB for 15 years and became head of the Federal Security

Service (FSB), the KGB's successor, in 1998. Chosen as Yeltsin's prime minister in August 1999, he became acting president in December 1999 when Yeltsin resigned, then won the 2000 and 2004 presidential elections.

Pye, Henry James *see* AML poet laureate.

Qaddafi, Moammar al- *see* GADDAFI, MOAMMAR AL-.

Quant, Mary (1934–) English fashion designer. Her most famous design was the miniskirt, which became the symbol of 'swinging sixties' London.

Quisling, Vidkun (1887–1945) Norwegian Fascist leader. He was installed as prime minister (1942–45) by the Nazis and was executed for treason after the war.

Rabin, Yitzhak (1922–1995) Israeli politician and prime minister (1974–77, 1992–95). A veteran of the 1967 Arab-Israeli War, in his second term of office Rabin did much to convince Israelis that their security would not be compromised by making concessions to Palestinians in order to secure peace. In 1994 he was a signatory of the Israeli-Palestinian Peace Accord, along with Yasser ARAFAT. He was assassinated by a Jewish extremist while speaking at a peace rally in Tel Aviv.

Rachmaninov, Sergei (1873–1943) Russian composer and pianist. Influenced by TCHAIKOVSKY, his music was very much in the 19th-century Romantic tradition. His works include three symphonies, four piano concertos, the *Rhapsody on a Theme by Paganini* (1934), and many songs.

Radcliffe, Anne *see* AML Gothic novel.

Raleigh, Sir Walter (1552–1618) English courtier, poet and explorer. He became a favourite of ELIZABETH I after returning from a punitive expedition to punish Irish rebels in 1580. Imprisoned after Elizabeth's death, he was released to search for treasure on the Orinoco in 1616 and was executed on his return.

Rambert, Dame Marie [Cyvia Rambam] (1888–1982) Polish-born British ballet dancer, teacher and producer. After working with DIAGHILEV and NIJINSKY, she settled in Britain in 1917. She formed the Ballet Club in 1931, which, renamed Ballet Rambert in 1935, became the most influential ballet company in Britain.

Raphael [Raffaello Sanzio] (1483–1520) Italian painter. A leading figure of the High Renaissance, his portrayals of the Madonna and Holy Family combined Christian ideals with the grace and grandeur of Classical antiquity.

Rasputin, Grigori Efimovich (*c*.1871–1916) Russian monk. Claiming to have healing powers, he became a cult figure among the Russian aristocracy and influential on the royal household. He was assassinated.

Rauschenberg, Robert *see* AML Pop Art.

Ravel, Maurice (1875–1937) French composer. He was one of the leading impressionist composers of his time. His works include the small orchestral piece *Boléro*.

Ravi Shankar (1920–) Indian sitar player and composer. Regarded as one of India's greatest modern musicians, he became world-famous after teaching George HARRISON to play the sitar.

Ray, Man (1890–1976) American photographer and painter, he was a leading exponent of Surrealist photography.

Ray, Satyajit (1921–92) Indian film director. His films, popular in art houses the world over, include the *Apu* trilogy of life in rural India, i.e. *Pather Panchali* (1955), *Aparajito* (1956), *Apu Sansar* (1959), and *The Chess Players* (1977).

Reagan, Ronald Wilson (1911–2004) American film actor, Republican statesman and 40th president (1981–89). He appeared in around 50 films. As US president he pursued strong monetarist economic policies and a strong anti-communist foreign policy.

Redgrave, Sir Michael [Scudamore] (1908–85) English stage and film actor. He was married to the actress **Rachel Kempson** (1910–2003), and their children, **Vanessa Redgrave** (1937–), **Corin Redgrave** (1939–) and **Lynn Redgrave** (1943–) all became actors.

Reed, Sir Carol (1906–76) English film director. His films include *The Third Man* (1949), written by Graham GREENE and starring Orson WELLES, a bleak thriller set in postwar Vienna.

Reinhardt, Django [Jean Baptiste] (1910–53) Belgian guitarist, he formed the influential Quintette de Hot Club de Paris with GRAPPELLI.

Rembrandt [Rembrandt Harmensz van Rijn] (1606–69) Dutch painter, draftsman and etcher. His remarkable series of self-portraits reveal the depth and spiritual development of his work over 40 years.

Renoir, Pierre Auguste (1841–1919) French Impressionist painter. His form of Impressionism developed the use of perspective, solidity of form and preliminary sketches.

Resnais, Alain (1922–) French film director. One of the best known of the French 'New Wave' directors, his films include the romance *Hiroshima mon amour* (1959) and the experimental, 'Surrealist' *Last Year in Marienbad* (1961).

Reynolds, Albert (1933–) Irish politician. Elected in 1977 as a Fianna Fáil member, he held several posts under HAUGHEY but was sacked (1991). He eventually succeeded as the eighth *taoiseach* (prime minister) of the Republic of Ireland (1992–94).

Reynolds, Sir Joshua (1723–92) English painter and art theorist influenced by his studies of Renaissance and Baroque painting and Classical sculpture. A portraitist, he became first president of the Royal Academy.

Rice, Tim *see* LLOYD WEBBER, ANDREW.

Richard, Sir Cliff [Harry Rodger Webb] (1940–) Indian-born English singer and film actor, and an institution in British popular music.

Richard, Keith *see* JAGGER, MICK.

Richards, Viv [Sir Isaac Vivian Alexander] (1952–) Antiguan-born West Indian cricketer. One of the best batsmen and fielders in modern cricket, he captained the West Indies in fifty test matches (1980–91) and is the only West Indies captain never to lose a test series.

Richardson, Dorothy *see* AML interior monologue.

Richardson, Sir Ralph David (1902–83) English stage and film actor. Ranked with GIELGUD and OLIVIER as among the finest British actors of the 20th century, he was equally at home with the classics and modern roles.

Richardson, Samuel (1689–1761) English novelist. All his novels were written in epistolary form, and all were hugely popular. *See also* AML epistolary novel.

Richthofen, Manfred, Baron von (1882–1918) German fighter pilot, nicknamed the 'Red Baron'. He was credited with shooting down 80 Allied aircraft.

Rimbaud, Arthur (1854–91) French poet. An early Symbolist, he stopped writing poetry at the age of 19. Some of the pieces in his collection of hallucinatory, vivid prose poems, *Les Illuminations*, were set to music by BRITTEN. *See also* AML Surrealism.

Rimsky-Korsakov, Nikolay Andreyevich (1844–1908) Russian composer. His music is typically Russian, and he freely used local history, folk tunes, legends and myths as sources of inspiration. His works include 16 operas, three symphonies and numerous orchestral pieces.

Robbe-Grillet, Alain *see* AML novel.

Robeson, Paul Le Roy (1898–1976) American bass singer and actor. He qualified as a lawyer before becoming a highly popular stage actor in the 1920s. Notable performances include *Showboat* (1927) and *Othello* (1940). His warm, sensitive recordings of spirituals and folk songs were very popular. He was also a noted advocate of civil rights for African-Americans.

Robespierre, Maximilien Marie Isidore de (1758–94) French lawyer and revolutionary. He was elected to the National Assembly (1789) at the beginning of the French Revolution and became leader of the Jacobin group. He launched the infamous Reign of Terror, but was eventually guillotined himself.

Robinson, Mary (1944–) Irish barrister, politician and president of the Republic of Ireland (1990–97) and UN Commissioner for Human Rights (1997–2003). She was succeeded by **Mary McAleese** (1951–).

Robinson, Sugar Ray [Walker Smith Junior] (1929–89) American welterweight and middleweight boxer who began boxing in high school. He won the world middleweight title in 1951 and regained it in 1955 and 1958. His professional career lasted for 26 years.

Rodgers, Richard Charles (1902–79) American composer. With the librettist Lorenz HART, he created musicals such as *Pal Joey*. After Hart died, Rodgers collaborated with HAMMERSTEIN on several more successful musicals, e.g. *Oklahoma!*

Rodin, Auguste (1840–1917) French sculptor. He was responsible for reviving sculpture as an independent form rather than as an embellishment or decoration with works such as *The Thinker*.

Rogers, Ginger *see* ASTAIRE, FRED.

Rogers, Richard George [Baron Rogers of Riverside] (1933–) Italian-born English architect noted for his modernist and functional designs. He was responsible for the Pompidou Centre in Paris along with Italian architect, **Renzo Piano** (1937–). Other projects by Rogers include the Lloyds building and the Millenium Dome in London.

Rolls, Charles Stewart (1877–1910) English motor automobile manufacturer and aviator. He joined Henry ROYCE in automobile manufacture in 1906.

Rommel, Erwin (1891–1944) German soldier. During World War II, he commanded the Afrika Korps in North Africa, earning the nickname the 'Desert Fox' for his brilliant tactics. He committed suicide after the discovery of his complicity in an assassination attempt on HITLER.

Ronaldo, Luis Nazariode Lima (1976–) Brazilian footballer who has been a member of two winning national World Cup sides (1994 and 2002) and three-times winner of the FIFA World Player of the Year award. He currently plays for AC Milan.

Roosevelt, Franklin D[elano] (1882–1945) American Democratic statesman. He became 32nd president (1933–45) and in order to deal with the crisis of economic collapse instituted far-reaching 'New Deal' reforms. He was a popular and highly effective leader during World War II, dying shortly after the Yalta summit meeting with Churchill and Stalin.

Roosevelt, Theodore (1858–1919) American Republican statesman and 26th president (1901–09). He legislated against business monopolies, intervened forcefully during the Panama civil war to protect the construction of the Panama Canal, and won the 1906 Nobel peace prize for mediating the end of the Russo-Japanese war.

Rossetti, Christina Georgina (1830–94) English poet, noted for her reflective, occasionally melancholic religious poems. She also wrote for children. Her brother, **Dante Gabriel Rossetti** (1828–82), was both a poet and an artist, and a founder of the Pre-Raphaelite school of painting.

Rossini, Gioacchino Antonio (1792–1868) Italian composer, noted especially for his light operas, e.g. *The Barber of Seville*, *The Thieving Magpie*. His other works include a Stabat Mater.

Rostand, Edmond (1868–1918) French dramatist and poet. His best-known work is the verse drama *Cyrano de Bergerac* (1897).

Rostropovich, Mstislav (1927–2007) Russian cellist. One of the outstanding cellists of modern times, he has also given many recitals as a pianist, often accompanying his wife, the soprano **Galina Vishnevskaya** (1926–), in song recitals.

Rothko, Mark [Marcus Rothkovitch] (1903–70) Russian-born American painter. Having passed through Expressionism and Surrealism, he adopted Abstract Expressionism, creating large canvases with almost luminous rectangles of colour.

Rousseau, Henri Julien 'Le Douanier' (1844–1910) French painter. His naïve style remained unaffected by all trends, and he defied conventions of colour and perspective in his exotic imaginary landscapes and painted dreams.

Rousseau, Jean-Jacques (1712–78) Swiss-born French philosopher. His most notable fictional works are the novels *Julie, or the New Héloïse* (1761) and *Emile* (1762).These works and others, notably the political tract *The Social Contract* (1762), which begins with the famous statement 'Man is born free, and is everywhere in chains', were profoundly influential on the intellectual ferment that led to the French Revolution.

Rowe, Nicholas *see* AML poet laureate.

Rowling, J. K. [Joanne Murray née Rowling] (1965–) British authoress and creator of the world-famous Harry Potter series of children's fantasy books (1996–2007) which have sold more than 4 million copies. Rowling has contributed her support and a great deal of her wealth to many charitable causes.

Royce, Sir [Frederick] Henry (1863–1933) English engineer. In partnership with Charles ROLLS, he founded the automobile firm Rolls-Royce in 1906.

Rubens, Sir Peter Paul (1577–1640) Flemish painter and diplomat. His masterpiece is the triptych *Descent from the Cross*. In 1629 he was sent to England to negotiate peace with Charles I, who knighted him.

Rubinstein, Artur (1888–1982) Polish-born American pianist. An outstanding concert pianist, he was particularly noted for his CHOPIN recitals.

Ruby, Jack *see* OSWALD, LEE HARVEY.

Rushdie, [Ahmed] Salman (1947–) Indian-born British novelist. After the publication of *Satanic Verses* (1988), Ayatollah KHOMEINI pronounced a *fatwa*, or death sentence, for blasphemy on him. The Iranian government withdrew its support of the fatwa in 1998.

Ruskin, John (1819–1900) English writer, artist and influential art critic. His works dictated Victorian taste for over 50 years.

Russell, Bertrand Arthur William, 3rd Earl Russell (1872–1970) British philosopher. He made notable contributions to mathematical and philosophical theory and, with the help of his student, WITTGENSTEIN, logical positivism. He was awarded the 1950 Nobel prize for literature.

Russell, Ken (1927–) English film director especially noted for his film biographies of musicians, e.g. *Lisztomania* (1975).

Ruth, Babe [George Herman] (1895–1948] American baseball player widely considered to be the greatest star of the sport.

Rutherford, Ernest, 1st Baron Rutherford of Nelson (1871–1937) New Zealand physicist. He was awarded the 1908 Nobel prize for chemistry. In 1911 he deduced the existence of the atom's structure and was the first scientist to split the atom.

Sabin, Albert Bruce (1906–93) Polish-born American microbiologist. He developed the Sabin polio vaccine in the mid-1950s.

Sadat, [Mohammed] Anwar El (1918–81) Egyptian statesman. He succeeded NASSER as president in 1970. After the Arab-Israeli Yom Kippur War of 1973, he came under pressure to work towards peace in the Middle East. He signed a peace treaty with BEGIN, for which they were awarded

the 1978 Nobel peace prize. He was assassinated by Islamic fundamentalist soldiers during a military parade.

Sade, Donatien Alphonse François, Marquis de (1740–1814) French soldier and novelist. His highly licentious works include several novels, e.g. *Justine* (1791). The term 'sadism' derives from the dominant theme in his life and work.

Sakharov, Andrei Dimitrievich (1921–89) Russian physicist and dissident. He developed the Russian hydrogen bomb in the 1950s and subsequently campaigned for international control of nuclear weapons. He was awarded the 1975 Nobel peace prize.

Saladin [Salah al-Din al-Ayyubi] (1137–93) Sultan of Egypt and Syria. The leader of the Arab world during the Crusades.

Salam, Abdus *see* WEINBERG, STEVEN.

Salk, Jonas Edward (1914–95) American physician and microbiologist. He developed the Salk vaccine against polio.

Saloth Sar *see* POL POT.

Sappho (b. *c*.650 BC) Greek poet. The Greeks regarded her as one of the greatest of all lyric poets, but only short fragments of her work survive.

Sartre, Jean-Paul (1905–80) French philosopher, novelist and dramatist. His attempts at reconciling Existentialist philosophy (*see* AML Existentialism) with Marxism are now of historical interest, but his novels, e.g. *Nausea* (1938), are highly readable. He had a long-term relationship with Simone de Beauvoir.

Sax, Adolphe *see* AML saxhorn.

Schoenberg or Schönberg, Arnold Franz Walter (1874–1951) Austrian composer (US citizen from 1941). His early works, e.g. *Gurrelieder* (1900), are lush chromatic compositions in the late Romantic tradition. He then began composing atonal works and eventually developed his serial or '12-tone' method.

Schröder, Gerhard (1944–) German Social Democrat statesman. He succeeded Helmut KOHL as chancellor of Germany (1998–2005).

Schubert, Franz Peter (1797–1828) Austrian composer. His works include nine symphonies, the eighth (in B minor) being the 'Unfinished', string quartets and other chamber music. His songs, as in the song cycles *Die schöne Müllerin* and *Die Winterreise*, are regarded as some of the finest ever written, include settings of lyrics by HEINE and GOETHE, and others.

Schumacher, Ernst Friedrich (1911–77) German-born British economist. His book, *Small is Beautiful* (1973), became a founding text of the conservationist movement.

Schumacher, Michael (1969–) German Formula One racing driver who has won the World Championship seven times. He is also known for his charitable work. His younger brother **Ralf Schumacher** (1975–) was also a Formula One driver from 1997 to 2007.

Schumann, Robert Alexander (1810–56) German composer, who is noted for his espousal of Romantic values. His works include four symphonies, songs and much fine piano music. His wife, **Clara Schumann** (1819–96), was also a pianist and composer.

Scorsese, Martin (1942–) American film director. His films include *Taxi Driver* (1976), *Raging Bull* (1980) and *Goodfellas* (1990), all starring the actor most associated with his work, Robert DE NIRO.

Scott, Robert Falcon (1868–1912) English explorer. He led two Antarctic expeditions (1901–04, 1910–12). He died with four companions on his last expedition, returning from the South Pole after having reached it a month after AMUNDSEN. His son, **Sir Peter [Markham] Scott** (1909–89), was a naturalist and artist whose television documentaries and many books were notably influential in promoting conservation.

Scott, Sir Walter (1771–1832) Scottish novelist and poet. His early, highly Romantic narrative poems, set in the Scottish past, e.g. *The Lady of the Lake*, established his popularity with both the reading public and the literary world. His historical novels, particularly *Waverley* (1814), *The Heart of Midlothian* (1818) and *Ivanhoe* (1819), were influential and spawned a host of imitators.

Scriabin or Skryabin, Alexander Nikolaye-vich (1872–1915) Russian composer and pianist. His compositions often involved extra-musical effects, e.g. *Prometheus*, a piece for piano accompanied by coloured light projected on a screen.

Searle, Ronald William Fordham (1920–) English cartoonist and writer. Known primarily as the creator of the monstrous St Trinian's schoolgirls, he is regarded as one of the finest graphic artists of the 20th century. His haunting book *To the Kwai—and Back: War Drawings 1939–45* is a record of his experiences as a Japanese prisoner of war.

Secombe, Harry *see* MILLIGAN, SPIKE.

Segovia, Andrés, Marquis of Salobreña (1894–1987) Spanish guitarist. An internationally recognised virtuoso, he initiated a revival of interest in the classical guitar.

Sellers, Peter (1925–80) English actor and comedian. One of the founders of the Goon Show (*see* Spike MILLIGAN), he achieved further popularity as Inspector Clouseau in such films as *The Pink Panther* (1963).

Seneca [Lucius Annaeus Seneca] (*c.*4 BC–AD 65) Roman dramatist and Stoic philosopher. His verse tragedies were very influential on Elizabethan dramatists such as SHAKESPEARE.

Senna, Ayrton (1960–94) Brazilian Formula One racing driver who was tragically killed in action at the San Marino Grand Prix. He won 41 major races between 1985 and 1994.

Sennett, Mack [Michael Sinnott] (1880–1960) Canadian-born American film director and producer. He produced the manic 'Keystone Cop' comedies, which achieved international success. He also produced Charlie CHAPLIN's first films.

Seurat, Georges (1859–91) French painter, a leading Neoimpressionist. He developed the system of pointillism in which the painting is built up from tiny areas of pure colour.

Shackleton, Sir Ernest Henry (1874–1922) Anglo-Irish explorer. He served in Robert SCOTT's Antarctic expedition and commanded two further expeditions (1908–09, 1914–16).

Shadwell, Thomas *see* AML poet laureate.

Shakespeare, William (1564–1616) English dramatist and poet. His plays are divided into three groups. The first group (late

1580s–*c*.1594) consists of histories, e.g. the *Henry VI* trilogy, comedies such as *The Two Gentlemen of Verona*, and the tragedy of *Romeo and Juliet*. The second group (*c*.1595–*c*.1599) includes histories such as *King John, Henry IV Parts I* and *II*, the comedies *A Midsummer's Night's Dream* and *As You Like It*, and the tragedy *Julius Caesar*. The third group (*c*.1600–*c*.1612) includes the tragedies *Hamlet, Othello, King Lear, Macbeth, Antony and Cleopatra, Coriolanus* and *Timon of Athens*, the 'dark comedies', *Troilus and Cressida, All's Well That Ends Well* and *Measure for Measure*, and tragicomedies such as *The Winter's Tale* and *The Tempest*. Shakespeare's other major works are the narrative poems *Venus and Adonis* (1593) and *The Rape of Lucrece* (1594), and his *Sonnets. See also* AML tragedy.

Shankar, Ravi *see* RAVI SHANKAR.

Shankly, Bill [William] (1913–81) Scottish football player and manager. Regarded as one of the outstanding association football managers of the century, he transformed Liverpool FC into one of the most successful clubs of modern times.

Sharon, Ariel *see* RABIN, YITZHAK.

Shastri, Ravi (1962–) Indian cricketer and stalwart of the national side. He captained India's victorious team during the test match against the West Indies in 1988 but retired from the game at the early age of 30.

Shaw, George Bernard (1856–1950) Anglo-Irish dramatist and critic. He began his literary career as a drama, literary and music critic in the 1880s, and after a false start in novel-writing, began writing plays in the 1890s. His plays, e.g. *Pygmalion* (1913), have been very successful thanks to his mastery of witty dialogue. He was awarded the Nobel prize for literature in 1925.

Shelley, Mary Wollstonecraft (1797–1851) English novelist. She eloped with SHELLEY in 1814 and married him in 1816 after his wife died. Her masterpiece is *Frankenstein,* or *The Modern Prometheus* (1818), a Gothic fantasy that has been hailed as the first science fiction novel.

Shelley, Percy Bysshe (1792–1822) English poet. His talent for public scandal emerged at Oxford University, where he was expelled for co-writing a tract entitled *The Necessity of Atheism* (1811). Two years later he published his poem *Queen Mab,* which celebrates a future republican millennium of free love and vegetarianism. In 1814, he eloped with Mary Godwin (*see* Mary Wollstonecraft SHELLEY) and he drowned in a sailing accident in 1922. His greatest poems include *Prometheus Unbound* (1820); *Adonais* (1821), *Ode to the West Wind* and *To a Skylark* (both 1820).

Sheridan, Richard Brinsley (1751–1816) Irish dramatist and politician, noted for his superb comedies of manners, *The Rivals* (1775) and *School for Scandal* (1777), both firm repertory favourites. His other major play is *The Critic* (1779).

Shockley, William Bradford (1910–89) American physicist. He shared, with BARDEEN and the Chinese-born American physicist **Walter Brattain** (1902–87), the 1956 Nobel prize for physics for his development of the junction transistor.

Shostakovich, Dimitri Dimitriyevich (1906–75) Russian composer. Many of his works, e.g. the opera *Lady Macbeth of Mtensk,* were attacked for their disregard of socialist realism. His works include 15 symphonies, 15 string quartets and song cycles.

Sibelius, Jean (1865–1957) Finnish composer. His works reflect his strong Finnish nationalism and often draw on the Finnish traditional epic, *Kalevala*.

Sidney, Sir Philip (1554–86) English poet, soldier and courtier. His works include: *Arcadia* (1590), the first major English pastoral poem.

Sihanouk, King-Father Norodom (1922–) Cambodian statesman, formerly (elected) king of Cambodia (1941–55). He abdicated (in favour of his father) to become prime minister (1955–60) after independence from France in 1955, becoming head of state in 1960. He was deposed by a military coup in 1970 and fled to China, forming an alliance with POL POT's Khmer Rouge, who seized Cambodia in 1975. He again became head of state in 1975 and was deposed by Pol Pot the following year. After the Vietnamese invasion of 1979, Sihanouk formed a government in exile in an uneasy alliance with the Khmer Rouge. After the Vietnamese withdrawal in 1989, Sihanouk took part in peace negotiations and was reinstated as a constitutional monarch (1993–2004). One of his sons, **Norodom Sihamoni** (1953–) has been appointed king while he is now has the title of King-Father.

Sikorski, Wladyslaw (1881–1943) Polish general and statesman. He was premier of the Polish government in exile during World War II and commander in chief of the Free Polish armed forces. He was killed in an air crash.

Sikorsky, Igor Ivan (1889–1972) Russian-born American aeronautical engineer. He built the first four-engined aircraft in 1913 and the first successful helicopter in 1939.

Simpson, Wallis see WINDSOR, DUKE OF.

Sinatra, Frank [Francis Albert Sinatra] (1915–98) American singer and film actor. He was regarded as one of the finest modern popular singers, with a finely tuned jazz-like sense of phrasing. His films include *From Here to Eternity* (1953) and *Guys and Dolls* (1955).

Singer, Isaac Bashevis (1904–91) Polish-born American Yiddish writer. Much of his fiction deals with the now vanished world of Polish Judaism, e.g. *The Magician of Lublin* (1960). He was awarded the Nobel prize for literature in 1978.

Sisley, Alfred (1839–99) French painter of English extraction. Influenced by the Impressionists Renoir and Monet, he painted mainly carefully composed and sensitively coloured landscapes.

Skryabin see SCRIABIN.

Smith, Adam (1723–90) Scottish economist and philosopher. His book *Inquiry into the Nature and Causes of the Wealth of Nations* (1776), with its advocacy of free trade was of huge influence in the development of modern capitalist societies.

Smith, Bessie [Elizabeth Smith] (1895–1937) American blues singer, nicknamed the 'Empress of the Blues'. She became very popular with jazz audiences in the 1920s.

Smith, Ian Douglas (1919–2007) Zimbabwean politician. He was prime minister of Rhodesia (1964–79) and declared UDI (unilateral declaration of independence) from Britain in 1965 in order to maintain white minority rule. Majority rule came in 1979, with **Bishop Abel Muzorewa** (1925–) serving as caretaker premier (1979–80). MUGABE's Zanu Party won the 1980 election. Smith resigned his leadership of his party in 1987.

Smollett, Tobias George (1721–71) Scottish surgeon and novelist. His picaresque novels are cleverly plotted satirical works rich in characterisation.

Smuts, Jan Christian (1870–1950) South African statesman and philosopher. He commanded Boer forces during the Boer War and became prime minister (1919–24, 1939–48).

Sobers, Gary [Sir Garfield St Auburn] (1936–) West Indian cricketer. He is regarded as one of the finest all-rounders of all time.

Socrates (470–399 BC) Greek philosopher, the tutor of PLATO. The sources of his teachings are many and widely varied, but it is Plato's Socrates, with a gift for answering questions with another question, who has come down to posterity in Plato's 'Socratic' dialogues. The central theme in Socrates' thinking is a quest for truth through rigorous self-examination. He was forced to commit suicide by the Athenians for supposedly corrupting youths through teaching them 'impiety'.

Solti, Sir Georg (1912–97) Hungarian-born British conductor. His recording of WAGNER's Ring cycle was particularly renowned.

Solzhenitsyn, Aleksandr Isayevich (1918–) Russian novelist and historian. He exposed the corruption and cruelty of Russian society in works such as *One Day in the Life of Ivan Denisovich* (1962), based on his experiences in a Soviet labour camp and published in the USSR during a brief thaw in cultural restrictions, and *The First Circle* and *The Gulag Archipelago*, which both had to be published abroad (1968). He was awarded the Nobel prize for literature in 1970 and was deported from the USSR in 1974. He settled in the USA but returned to Russia in 1994.

Sondheim, Stephen Joshua (1930–) American songwriter and composer. He studied with HAMMERSTEIN and wrote the lyrics for BERNSTEIN's *West Side Story*, before writing the music and lyrics for several musicals, e.g. *A Funny Thing Happened on the Way to the Forum* and *Into the Woods*.

Sophocles (*c*.496–406 BC) Greek dramatist, seven of whose some 120 plays are extant. He was the most popular of the three great Athenian dramatists (the others being AESCHYLUS and EURIPIDES). The plays include *Oedipus Rex, Oedipus at Colonus* and *Antigone*. *See also* AML tragedy.

Sopwith, Sir Thomas Octave Murdoch (1888–1989) English aeronautical engineer. He designed and built the Sopwith Camel, one of the most successful fighter planes of World War I.

Sousa, John Philip *see* AML sousaphone.

Southey, Robert (1774–1843) English poet. Closely associated with WORDSWORTH and COLERIDGE, he was poet laureate from 1813.

Spassky, Boris Vasilyevich (1937–) Russian chess player. He was world champion (1969–72).

Spence, Sir Basil (1907–76) Indian-born Scottish architect. He is famous for a few important buildings, such as Coventry Cathedral, and notorious for some disastrous housing projects.

Spencer, Sir Stanley (1891–1959) English painter. An isolated figure in modern art best known for his series of religious paintings and, in his capacity as a war artist, for his *Shipbuilding on the Clyde* series of panels.

Spenser, Edmund (*c*.1552–99) English poet, noted particularly for his long allegorical poem *The Faerie Queene*.

Spielberg, Steven KBE (1947–) American film director, producer and screenwriter. His many films include some of the most successful ever made, e.g. *Jaws* (1975), *E.T.* (1982) and *Schindler's List* (1993) for which he received an Oscar.

Spitz, Mark (1950–) American swimmer who amassed a total of nine Olympic gold medals in 1968 and 1972. His record of achieving seven gold medals in the Munich Olympics in 1972 remains unequalled by any other athlete.

Spock, Dr Benjamin McLane (1903–98) American pediatrician. He advocated a 'permissive', non-authoritarian approach to the raising of infants that was popular in the 1960s.

Stalin, Joseph [Josef Vissarionovich Dzhugashvili] (1879–1953) Soviet dictator. After the Bolshevik Revolution, he manoeuvred his way into absolute power, shrewdly playing off his 'rightist' allies against TROTSKY and other 'leftists'. He forcibly collectivised Soviet agriculture in the 1930s and developed the Soviet Union's industrial base, using (and killing) many millions of prisoners as slave labour. His purges of the 1930s destroyed most of the surviving old Bolsheviks as well as the army leadership. He signed a non-aggression treaty with HITLER in 1939 and seized Poland's eastern territories after Hitler's September invasion. Later, forceful resistance from the Red Army, notably in the defence of Leningrad, the Battle of Stalingrad, and in massive infantry and tank battles, led directly to the defeat of Hitler's regime and the occupation of eastern Europe by Stalin's forces.

Stanislavsky, Konstantin (1863–1938) Russian director and actor, who was co-founder of the Moscow Art Theatre in 1897. The influence of his theory of acting (later dubbed 'method') has been immense. His theory is contained in such works as *An Actor Prepares* (1929) and *Building a Character* (1950).

Starr, Ringo [Richard Starkey] (1940–) English rock drummer and singer. He was the Beatles' drummer (1962–70).

Steel, Sir Richard (1672–1729) Anglo-Irish essayist and dramatist. With ADDISON, he contributed many notable essays to *The Tatler* and *The Spectator*.

Stein, Gertrude (1874–1946) American writer who sometimes applied the theory of abstract painting to her work, accounting for her reputation for obscurity and repetition. Her main works include *Tender Buttons* (1914), *The Making of Americans* (1925) and *The Autobiography of Alice B. Toklas* (1933).

Steiner, Rudolf (1861–1925) Austrian philosopher influenced by theosophy who formed his own movement of 'anthroposophy' in 1912 dedicated to developing the innate human capacity for spiritual perception through activities such as art and dance.

Steinway, Henry *see* AML Steinway.

Stevenson, Robert Louis Balfour (1850–94) Scottish novelist, poet and essayist. By the time his first important fictional work, *Treasure Island* (1883), had been published he had established himself as an author of note with essays, poems and two travel books, *Travels with a Donkey in the Cevennes* (1879) and *The Silverado Squatters* (1883). His masterpiece is *The Strange Case of Dr Jekyll and Mr Hyde* (1886), a disturbing story of dual personality. Other works include *Kidnapped* (1886), *The Master of Ballantrae* (1889) and the unfinished *Weir of Hermiston* (1896). Because of ill-health he settled in Samoa, where he died.

Stewart or Stuart, Prince James Francis Edward (1688–1766), also known as the 'Old Pretender', the son of James II and VII, who led two unsuccessful Jacobite revolts to regain the British throne (1708, 1715). His elder son, **Prince Charles Edward Louis Philip Stewart** or **Stuart** (1720–88), 'Bonnie Prince Charlie' or the 'Young Pretender', also led a Jacobite revolt against the Hanoverian King George III in 1745, fleeing Scotland when his Highland soldiers were defeated at Culloden in 1746. He died in Rome.

Stewart, Jackie [Sir John Young Stewart] (1939–) Scottish racing driver. He was world champion (1969, 1971, 1973) and retired in 1973. He is well-known in the United States as a commentator of racing television broadcasts,

Stockhausen, Karlheinz (1928–2007) German composer. Regarded as the leading exponent of 12-tone music, he also used electronic sounds.

Stokowski, Leopold (1882–1977) British-born American conductor. A populariser of classical music, he is best known for his collaboration with Walt DISNEY on the film *Fantasia* (1940).

Stopes, Marie Charlotte Carmichael (1880–1958) British scientist, a pioneer in the field of family planning and a campaigner for women's rights. She established a birth control clinic in Holloway in London (1920), which gave free contraceptive advice to the poor.

Stoppard, Sir Tom (1937–) Czech-born British Academy Award winning screenwriter and Tony Award winning playwright, his plays, e.g. *Rosencrantz and Guildenstern are Dead* (1966), are noted for their sharp, witty wordplay and fast, cleverly plotted action.

Stowe, Mrs Harriet Elizabeth Beecher (1811–96) American novelist. Her great anti-slavery novel *Uncle Tom's Cabin, or, Life Among the Lowly* (1852) has been described as a factor leading to the American Civil War.

Stradivari, Antonio *see* AML Stradivari.

Strasberg, Lee *see* AML method acting.

Strauss, Richard (1864–1949) German composer and conductor. His works include a series of richly orchestrated tone poems, e.g. *Also Sprach Zarathustra*, several operas, e.g. *Elektra* and *Der Rosenkavalier*, and *Four Last Songs*.

Strauss, Johann, 'the Younger' (1825–99) Austrian violinist, conductor and composer. One of a musical family, he wrote light music, especially Viennese waltzes, e.g. the 'Blue Danube' waltz, and 16 operettas, e.g. *Die Fledermaus*.

Stravinsky, Igor Fyodorovich (1882–1971) Russian composer. He composed ballet scores for DIAGHILEV, e.g. *Petrushka* (1911) and *The Rite of Spring* (1913), the first performance of the latter provoking a riot but now regarded as a milestone in modernist music. He later composed several austerely Neoclassical works, such as the opera-oratorio *Oedipus Rex* (1927), which also displayed the influence of SCHOENBERG's serial techniques.

Strindberg, Johan August (1849–1912) Swedish dramatist and novelist. His highly innovative works, e.g. the play *Miss Julie* (1888), influenced many 20th-century dramatists.

Stubbs, George (1724–1806) English painter and engraver, best known for his paintings of horses.

Suckling, Sir John *see* AML Cavalier Poets.

Sugar, Sir Alan Michael (1947–) British entrepreneur and businessman, founder of the Amstrad empire, who began his career with £100 savings selling aerials for cars from the back of a van and rose to be the head of an enterprise estimated to be worth in excess of £800 million.

Sun Yat-sen or Sun Zhong Shan (1866–1925) Chinese nationalist leader and statesman. He played a leading role in the overthrow of the Manchu dynasty and became the first president of the Republic of China in 1911–12.

Surrey, Earl of *see* AML blank verse.

Sutherland, Dame Joan (1926–) Australian soprano. One of the world's leading bel canto operatic sopranos, she was hailed as 'La Stupenda' after an *Alcina* performance in La Fenice, Venice, in 1960.

Sutherland, Graham Vivian (1903–80) English painter. He was an official war artist (1941–45) and subsequently became a portrait painter of note.

Swift, Jonathan (1667–1745) Anglo-Irish divine, poet and satirist. His masterpiece is *Gulliver's Travels* (1726), which culminates in Gulliver's voyage to the Houyhnhnms, intelligent horses whose nobility is contrasted with the brutality of humanity.

Swinburne, Algernon Charles (1837–1909) English poet and critic noted for his sensuous verse that frequently created scandal, not just for its sexuality but for the author's clear dislike of Christianity.

Synge, [Edmund] John Millington (1871–1909) Irish dramatist noted for his poetic rendering of Irish peasant speech. His masterpiece is *The Playboy of the Western World* (1907).

Taft, William H (1857–1930) American Republican politician and the 27th president (1909–13).

Tagore, Rabindranath (1861–1941) Indian poet and philosopher. Regarded by many Bengalis as their greatest writer, he was awarded the 1913 Nobel prize for literature.

Tailleferre, Germaine *see* AML Six, Les.

Tate, Nahum *see* AML poet laureate.

Tati, Jacques [Jacques Tatischeff] (1908–82) French actor and film director. An ex-rugby player, he became an international comedy star with his Monsieur Hulot creation, an engagingly incompetent character at odds with the modern world. Five Hulot films were made, including *Mr Hulot's Holiday* (1953) and *Mon Oncle* (1958).

Tatlin, Vladimir *see* AML Constructivism.

Tatum, Art[hur] (1910–56) American jazz pianist. He was an acclaimed virtuoso of jazz piano music in the 'swing' mode.

Tatum, Edward Lawrie (1909–75) American biochemist. With the American geneticist **George Wells Beadle** (1903–89), he demonstrated that biochemical reactions in cells are controlled by particular genes. With LEDERBERG, he discovered the phenomenon of genetic recombination in bacteria. All three shared the 1958 Nobel prize for physiology or medicine.

Tavener, Sir John Kenneth (1944–) English composer. He studied under **Lennox Berkeley** (1903–89) and became noted particularly for his religious compositions.

Tavener, John (*c*.1490–1545) English composer. He taught at Oxford University and is best known for his religious works.

Taylor, A[lan] J[ohn] P[ercivale] (1906–90) English historian. A renowned historian of the 20th century and often a controversial figure he became well known to the British public through his live lectures to television audiences.

Taylor, Dame Elizabeth Rosemond (1932–) English-born (of American parents) American film actress. Her films as a child include *National Velvet* (1945) and *Little Women* (1949). Regarded as one of the most beautiful film stars of her generation, her later films include *Cat on a Hot Tin Roof* (1958) and *Who's Afraid of Virginia Woolf?* (1966). The latter film co-starred her fifth husband, Richard BURTON, whom she married twice. She has devoted much time and energy to AIDS-related charities and fundraising.

Taylor, Zachary (1784–1850) American Whig politician and 12th president (1849–50).

Tchaikovsky, Peter Ilyich (1840–93) Russian composer. Notable for his strong melodic sense and rejection of an overtly nationalistic and 'folk' approach to composition, his works include tone poems, a violin concerto, operas, e.g. *Eugene Onegin*, the ballets *Swan Lake* and *The Sleeping Beauty* and the so-called 'Pathétique Sixth Symphony'.

Teilhard de Chardin, Pierre (1881–1955) French Jesuit theologian, philosopher and palaeontologist. He developed a theory of evolution, claiming that it was compatible with Roman Catholic teaching.

Te Kanawa, Dame Kiri (1944–) New Zealand soprano. She is regarded as one of the world's leading operatic sopranos.

Telemann, George Philipp (1681–1767) German composer. A highly prolific composer of the Baroque era, his works include over 40 operas and over 40 Passions.

Teller, Edward (1908–2003) Hungarian-born American physicist, known as the 'father of the hydrogen bomb' for his ground-breaking work in that field.

Temple, Shirley [Shirley Temple Black] (1928–) American film actress and Republican politician. She became the world's leading child film star. She is also notable for her diplomatic career as an adult.

Tendulkar, Sachin (1973–) Indian cricketer who was the first player to achieve fifty centuries in the international game. He has also achieved a century more than 35 times for his home team.

Teng Hsiao-p'ing *see* DENG XIAO PING.

Tennyson, Alfred, Lord, 1st Baron Tennyson (1809–92) English poet. He was appointed poet laureate in 1850, the year in which he published his elegy for his dead friend A. H. Hallam, *In Memoriam*.

Tenzing Norgay *see* HILLARY, EDMUND.

Terbrugghen, Hendrick *see* AML Utrecht School.

Thackeray, William Makepeace (1811–63) English novelist and essayist. His masterpiece is *Vanity Fair* (1847–48), a decidedly non-moralistic tale of the opportunistic 'anti-heroine' Becky Sharp, set during the Napoleonic wars. His other works include the novels *Pendennis* (1850) and *Henry Esmond* (1852).

Thatcher, Margaret Hilda, Baroness Thatcher (1925–) English Conservative stateswoman. She became MP for Finchley in 1959 and, as secretary of state for education and science (1970–74), ended the provision of free school milk. She defeated Edward HEATH in the Tory leadership campaign of 1975, becoming the first woman to lead a major British political party. As Britain's first woman prime minister (1979–1990), she launched an ideological crusade ('Thatcherism') against what she

perceived as the entrenchment of socialism in Britain, the principal elements of her attack being free-market policies and the privatisation of nationalised industries. Her policies were widely disliked by her political opponents and by moderate Tories. Increasing dissension within her cabinet over such issues as the highly controversial Community Charge (or Poll Tax) and the disarray of the Health Service led to her resignation in 1990 and the election of John MAJOR as prime minister.

Theresa of Calcutta, Mother [Agnes Gonxha Bojaxhiu] (1910–97) Yugoslavian-born Roman Catholic nun and missionary. She founded the Order of the Missionaries of Charity in 1950. Venerated by many people as a living saint, her work in Calcutta with orphans and the dying led to her being awarded the 1979 Nobel peace prize.

Theocritus *see* AML pastoral.

Theodorakis, Millis *see* AML bouzouki.

Thomas, Dylan Marlais (1914–53) Welsh poet. His best-known single work is *Under Milk Wood* (1954), a radio drama in poetic prose.

Thomas à Becket *see* BECKET, THOMAS À.

Thomas Aquinas, Saint (*c.*1225–74) Italian theologian and philosopher. His writings established the need for both reason and faith in Christianity, and have become a cornerstone in the teachings of the Roman Catholic Church.

Thompson, Emma (1959–) British actress. Her films include *Howards End* (1992) for which she won an Oscar (for best actress), *Sense and Sensibility* (1997), for which she wrote the screenplay and won an Oscar (for best adapted screenplay), *Primary Colours* (1998) and *Nanny McPhee* (2005) which she also wrote. She was married for a time to Kenneth BRANAGH, with whom she made several films, e.g. *Henry V* (1989) and *Peter's Friends* (1992). She is now married to Greg Wise (who starred with her in *Sense and Sensibility*).

Thomson, Sir George Paget (1892–1975) English physicist. He won the 1937 Nobel prize for physics with the American physicist **Clinton Davisson** (1881–1958) for their (independent) discovery of the diffraction of electrons by crystals.

Thomson, Sir Joseph John (1856–1940) English physicist. He was awarded the 1906 Nobel prize for physics for his discovery of the electron, one of the most significant discoveries in physics. Seven of his assistants went on to win Nobel prizes.

Thoreau, Henry David (1817–62) American philosopher whose advocacy of self-sufficiency and passive resistance to tyranny has been very influential, GANDHI being his most notable admirer.

Thurber, James Grover (1894–1961) American humorist, cartoonist and essayist, much of whose work first appeared in *New Yorker* magazine, including his most famous story, 'The Secret Life of Walter Mitty'.

Tiepolo, Giambattista (1696–1770) Italian artist, who was the greatest decorative fresco painter of the Rococo period.

Tinbergen, Jan (1903–1994) Dutch economist (brother of Niko TINBERGEN). He shared the 1969 Nobel prize for economics with the Norwegian economist **Ragnar Frisch** (1895–1973) for their work in the field of econometrics.

Tinbergen, Niko[laas] (1907–88) Dutch ethologist (brother of Jan TINBERGEN). He shared the 1973 Nobel prize for physiology or medicine (with LORENZ and Karl von FRISCH) for his ground-breaking studies of animal behaviour.

Tintoretto, Jacopo (1518–94) Venetian painter noted for his dynamic, highly imaginative use of lighting and highlighting.

Tippett, Sir Michael (1905–98) English composer. His works include several operas, e.g. *The Midsummer Marriage*, the oratorio *A Child of our Time*, symphonies, song cycles and chamber music.

Titian [Tiziano Vecelli] (*c.*1490–1576) Venetian painter, one of the great figures of world art. He studied with Giovanni BELLINI and worked with GIORGIONE, whom he succeeded as the master of Venetian painters for some 60 years.

Tito, Marshal [Josip Broz] (1892–1980) Yugoslav statesman. In 1941, after the German invasion of Yugoslavia, he organised a partisan force to fight the occupiers and succeeded in diverting British aid from other guerrilla forces to his own. After the war, he established a Communist government and broke with STALIN. He preserved a fragile Yugoslav unity, but 11 years after his death the break-up of the Yugoslav state began.

Tojo, Hideki (1885–1948) Japanese soldier. He became minister of war (1940–44) and prime minister (1941–44). He resigned in 1944 and was executed as a war criminal.

Tolkien, J[ohn] R[onald] R[euel] (1892–1973) South African-born British fantasy writer and scholar. He was a devout Roman Catholic and a close friend of C. S. LEWIS. Probably the most influential (and best-selling) fantasy writer, the works on which his fame rests are *The Hobbit* and *Lord of the Rings*.

Tolstoy, Count Leo Nikolayevich (1828–1910) Russian novelist, dramatist, short-story writer and philosopher. His spiritual self-questioning resulted in some of the world's greatest works of fiction, notably *War and Peace* (1863–69), a panoramic epic of the Napoleonic invasions of Russia, and *Anna Karenina* (1875–77), a tragic tale of adulterous love that raises profound questions about personal social morality.

Torvill, Jayne (1957–) **and Dean, Christopher** (1958–) English ice-dance skaters. They became world champions (1981–84), European champions (1981–82, 1984,1994) and Olympic champions (1984).

Toscanini, Arturo (1867–1957) Italian conductor. Regarded as one of the most authoritarian conductors of all time, he was renowned for his devotion to authenticity and for his remarkable musical memory.

Toulouse-Lautrec, Henri Marie Raymond de (1864–1901) French painter and lithographer. Influenced by VAN GOGH and DEGAS, his subjects were café clientele, prostitutes and cabaret performers in and around Montmartre.

Tracy, Spencer (1900–1967) American film actor. Noted for his straightforward, yet commanding, performances, he had a long personal and professional relationship with Katharine HEPBURN.

Trevelyan, George Macaulay (1876–1962) English historian. His highly readable works include *History of England* (1926).

Trevino, Lee (1939–) American golfer who has won the US Open title on two separate occasions (1968, 1971), along with the British Open(1971, 1972) and the PGA (1974, 1984).

Trollope, Anthony (1815–82) English novelist, whose more than 50 books are dominated by two main novel sequences: the 'Barsetshire' novels, which focus on the provincial lives of the gentry, clergy and middle classes; and the 'Palliser' novels of political life.

Trotsky, Leon [Lev Davidovich Bronstein] (1879–1940) Russian revolutionary. An advocate of 'permanent revolution', he believed that 'socialism could not be built in one country alone and supported the Mensheviks against Lenin's Bolsheviks. Forced into exile by STALIN in 1929, he was later assassinated by a Russian agent.

Truffaut, François (1932–84) French film director, critic and actor. His first film, the semi-autobiographical *The Four Hundred Blows* (1959), was widely praised. Other films include *Jules et Jim* (1961). He acted in several films, e.g. SPIELBERG's *Close Encounters of the Third Kind* (1977).

Truman, Harry S (1884–1972) American Democratic statesman. He became the 33rd president (1945–52) after F. D. ROOSEVELT's death, and he authorised the dropping of atom bombs on Hiroshima and Nagasaki. He approved the MARSHALL Plan of aid for Britain and Western Europe.

Trump, Donald John (1946–) American businessman, entrepreneur and television personality. He is the chief executive officer of his real estate empire and of Trump Entertainment and the net worth of his business enterprises is estimated to be in the order of $2.9 billion.

Turgenev, Ivan Sergeyevich (1818–83) Russian novelist, short-story writer and dramatist. His novels, e.g. *Fathers and Sons* (1862), explore such major issues of Russian life as serfdom and revolutionary change. The best known of his plays is *A Month in the Country* (1850).

Turing, Alan Mathison (1912–54) English mathematician. Regarded as one of the most important computer theoreticians. He played an important part in the code-breaking project at Bletchley Park in World War II, which deciphered the German 'Enigma' codes. He committed suicide.

Turner, Joseph Mallord William (1775–1851) English painter. Precociously talented, he exhibited his first work aged 15. After a trip to Italy in 1819 he became interested in gradations of shifting light and atmosphere. The works of the next two decades represent his finest period.

Twain, Mark [Samuel Langhorne Clemens] (1835–1910) American novelist, short-story writer and humorist. His two most famous novels, *The Adventures of Tom Sawyer* (1876) and *The Adventures of Huckleberry Finn* (1884), have become classics of children's literature.

Tyler, William (1790–1862) American Whig politician and 10th president (1841–45).

Tyndale, William *see* MORE, SIR THOMAS.

Tyson, Mike (1966–) American boxer and the youngest-ever winner of the World Heavyweight title in 1986. Talented but controversial, his later career was soured by his violent and anti-social behaviour, culminating in a prison term for rape.

Ustinov, Sir Peter Alexander (1921–2007) British actor, director, dramatist and raconteur (of Russian-French parentage). His plays include *The Love of Four Oranges* (1951) and *Romanoff and Juliet* (1956). Other works include an autobiography, *Dear Me* (1977). In the later part of his life (from 1969 until his death), his acting and writing tasks took second place to his work on behalf of UNICEF.

Tzara, Tristan *see* AML Dada.

Valentino, Rudolph [Rodolfo Guglielmi di Valentina d'Anton-guolla] (1895–1926) Italian-born American film actor. He became the leading screen personification of the romantic hero in many films, e.g. *The Son of the Sheik*. He died of peritonitis.

Van Allen, James Alfred (1914–2006) American physicist. He discovered, through detectors on the US satellite *Explorer I*, the Van Allen radiation belts outside the Earth's atmosphere.

Vanbrugh, Sir John (1664–1726) English dramatist and architect, noted for his witty comedies, e.g. *The Relapse* and *The Provok'd Wife*. He was also one of the finest architects of his day, the most famous of his buildings being Blenheim Palace.

Van Buren, Martin (1782–1862)American Democrat politician and 8th president (1837–41).

Van der Post, Sir Laurens Jan (1906–97) South African novelist, travel writer and mystic. His works are strongly influenced by JUNG and display a strong sympathy for the 'primitive' peoples of the world. His novels include *The Seed and the Sower* (1963), based on his experiences as a prisoner of war of the Japanese in World War II and filmed as *Merry Christmas, Mr Lawrence*. His travel books include two African classics, *Venture to the Interior* and *The Lost World of the Kalahari*.

Vanessa-Mae [Vanessa-Mae Vanakorn Nicholson] (1978–) British classical and pop violinist who enjoys world-wide acclaim for her virtuoso performances.

Van Eyck, Jan (*c*.1385–1441) Dutch painter. A master in the medium of oil painting, his paintings are both realistic and charged with a serene, spiritual atmosphere.

Van Gogh, Vincent *see* GOGH, VINCENT VAN.

Vasari, Giorgio (1511–74) Italian painter, writer and architect, noted particularly for his *Lives of the Most Eminent Painters, Sculptors and Architects*, an invaluable source book for the lives of Renaissance artists.

Vaughan Williams, Ralph (1872–1958) English composer. Like HOLST, he was heavily influenced by traditional English music, particularly folk song. His works include the choral *Sea Symphony, Fantasia on a Theme by Thomas Tallis*, operas, ballet music and song cycles.

Velàzquez or Velàsquez, Diego Roderiguez de Silva y (1599–1660) Spanish painter. His earliest paintings were *bodegones*, a type of Spanish genre painting consisting largely of domestic scenes, e.g. *An Old Woman Cooking Eggs* (1618). Influenced by TITIAN and TINTORETTO, he developed a lighter palette and finer brushwork. His works include the portrait of *Pope Innocent X* and *Surrender of Breda*.

Verdi, Giuseppe (1813–1901) Italian composer. His post-1850 operas, including *Il Trovatore, La Traviata, La Forza del Destino, Aida, Otello* and *Falstaff*, were hugely popular and remain constant favourites within the repertory of most opera companies. He was a deputy in the first Italian parliament of 1860.

Verlaine, Paul (1844–96) French poet, regarded with his friend and lover RIMBAUD as an early Symbolist.

Vermeer, Jan or Johannes (1632–75) Dutch painter. He is best remembered for his small-scale intimate interior scenes, carefully composed and lit, usually by daylight through a window.

Verne, Jules (1828–1905) French novelist whose innovative fantasy novels, e.g. *Voyage to the Centre of the Earth* (1864) and *20,000 Leagues Under the Sea* (1969), are regarded as the earliest great science fiction novels.

Verwoerd, Hendrik Frensch (1901–66) South African politician and prime minister (1958–66). He fostered apartheid, banned the African National Congress (1960) and took South Africa out of the Commonwealth in 1961.

Vettriano, Jack (1951–) Scottish painter. Born Jack Hogan he was self-taught and took up art in his twenties when his girlfriend bought him a set of paints. Looked down upon by some in the art world, he has become one of the most commercially successful living artists in Britain. His most popular work 'The Singing Butler' sold for £744,500 in 2004 but he is thought to make more money from the sale of reproductions of his paintings, mainly in the form of posters and postcards.

Vicky [Victor Weisz] (1913–66) German-born British cartoonist. He was one of the leading left-wing political cartoonists and caricaturists of his day.

Victoria [Alexandrina Victoria] (1819–1901) queen of Great Britain and Ireland (1837–1901), and from 1879 empress of India. She was married in 1840 to Prince Albert of Saxe-Coburg. They had four sons and five daughters: Victoria, Albert Edward (afterwards Edward VII), Alice, Alfred, Helena, Louise, Arthur, Leopold and Beatrice. She was a popular monarch, with a strong sense of vocation, family, principles and with political flair.

Vidal, [Eugene Luther] Gore (1925–) American novelist, dramatist and critic. His American historical fiction provides an unofficial and waspishly entertaining alternative history of the USA and its leaders, e.g. *Burr* (1973) and *1876* (1976).

Villa-Lobos, Heitor (1887–1959) Brazilian composer and conductor, His popular works combined elements of traditional Brazilian music with the European classical tradition.

Virgil [Publius Vergilius Maro] (70–19 BC) Roman poet. One of the most influential poets of all time, his masterpiece is the epic poem the *Aeneid,* which charts the progress of the Trojan hero Aeneas from the fall of Troy to the founding of the Roman state.

Visconti [di Modrone], Count Luchino (1906–76) Italian film director. He began his career as a stage designer, then worked as an assistant to film director Jean RENOIR. His films include *The Damned* (1969) and *Death in Venice* (1971), both starring BOGARDE.

Vishnevskaya, Galina *see* ROSTROPOVICH, MSTISLAV.

Voltaire [François Marie Arouet] (1694–1778) French philosopher, poet, historian, essayist, dramatist and essayist. Regarded as one of the most important of the French philosophers of the Enlightenment, his most influential single work is the *Philosophical Letters* (1734), a collection of witty, acerbic attacks on the tyranny of the *ancien régime*. His writings, with those of ROUSSEAU (with whom he disputed bitterly), are often described as the main intellectual roots of the French Revolution. His other works include the remarkable novel *Candide* (1759), which takes a markedly pessimistic view of human endeavour.

Von Braun, Wernher (1912–77) German-born American rocket engineer, he designed the V–1 and V–2 rocket bombs for Germany and later the Saturn moon rockets in the USA.

Wagner, [Wilhelm] Richard (1813–83) German composer. He achieved great success with his third opera, *Rienzi* (1842). The operas that followed, *The Flying Dutchman* (1843) and *Tannhäuser* (1845), were not so popular, and, in trouble with the authorities for his radical sympathies, he fled to Paris. He established his own theatre in Bayreuth in 1876, where he staged his *Ring of the Niebelung* cycle. His strongly Romantic works revolutionised opera, with their use of leitmotif and dramatic power.

Walcott, Derek Anton (1930–) St Lucian-born West Indian poet and dramatist who now divides his life between his home in the Caribbean and New York City. His poetry includes *Omeros*, a reworking in a Caribbean setting of themes from HOMER's *Odyssey* and *Iliad* and DANTE's *Divine Comedy*. His plays draw on Creole traditions and imagery. He was awarded the Nobel prize for literature in 1992.

Waldheim, Kurt (1918–) Austrian diplomat. After service as a Nazi intelligence officer in World War II, he entered the Austrian diplomatic service and became secretary-general of the United Nations (1972–82) and president of Austria (1986–92). Revelations about his role in the Nazi genocide machine in Yugoslavia during the war surfaced in the late 1980s.

Walesa, Lech (1943–) Polish trade union leader and statesman. He became the leader of the free trade union, Solidarity, in 1980, which forced substantial concessions from the Polish government. After the imposition of martial law in 1981, Solidarity was banned and he was imprisoned (1981–82). After his release, he was awarded the 1983 Nobel peace prize. A skilled negotiator, Walesa succeeded in getting Solidarity re-legalised, and, in 1989, in the first free elections in eastern Europe since the 1940s, a Solidarity government was formed with Walesa as president. He was defeated in the presidential elections of 1995.

Waller, Fats [Thomas Wright Waller] (1904–43) American jazz pianist and composer. He was an exponent of the 'stride' school of jazz piano and noted for his humorous lyrics.

Wallis, Sir Barnes Neville (1887–1979) English aeronautical engineer. He designed the 'bouncing bombs' used in the famous 1943 'Dambuster' bombing raids.

Walpole, Sir Robert, 1st Earl of Orford (1676–1745) English statesman. As Chancellor and First Lord of the Treasury he was, effectively, Britain's first prime minister from 1721–42, George I having little interest in the government of Britain. His son, **Horace Walpole, 4th Earl of Orford** (1717–97), was an author, noted for his vast correspondence and for his fascination with the 'Gothic', which expressed itself in his conversion of his house into a pseudo-medieval castle. He wrote the first Gothic novel, *The Castle of Otranto* (1764), which spawned a host of imitations.

Walton, Sir Earnest *see* COCKCROFT, SIR JOHN DOUGLAS.

Walton, Izaak (1593–1683) English author, best known for *The Compleat Angler* (1653), which is both a treatise on the art of angling and a celebration of the quiet life.

Walton, Sir William Turner] (1902–83) English composer. His works include a setting of Edith Sitwell's poem *Façade* for voice and instruments. His other works include the oratorio *Belshazaar's Feast* (1930–31), and several film scores, e.g. for OLIVIER's *Henry V* (1944).

Warhol, Andy [Andrew Warhola] (1930–87) American pop artist and film maker. He became the prime exponent of Pop Art in the early 1960s with his deliberately mundane works such as his reproductions of Campbell's soup cans and his repetitive portraits of contemporary icons, such as PRESLEY, MAO and Marilyn MONROE. His films include the three-hour *Sleep*.

Warne, Shane Keith (1969–) Australian cricketer regarded as one of the finest leg-spin bowlers in the history of cricket. He was the first player to take 708 wickets in test cricket. He retired in 2007.

Warton, Thomas *see* AML poet laureate.

Washington, George (1732–99) American general and first president of the United States (1789–97). He became commander of the American armed forces during the War of Independence in 1785 and led them to victory. After the Philadelphia Convention of 1787, he was president of the new country (1789–97).

Watson, James Dewey (1928–) American biologist. He and Francis CRICK discovered the 'double helix' structure of DNA, for which they shared (with Maurice WILKINS) the 1962 Nobel prize for physiology or medicine.

Watson-Watt, Sir Robert Alexander (1892–1973) Scottish physicist. He played a major role in the development of radar.

Watt, James (1736–1819) Scottish engineer. His improvements to the steam engine led directly to the rapid expansion of the Industrial Revolution.

Watteau, Jean-Antoine (1684–1721) French painter and an outstanding exponent of Rococo art. His work is noted for a delicacy of colour and sensitivity of composition not achieved by his imitators.

Watts, Charlie *see* JAGGER, MICK.

Waugh, Evelyn Arthur St John (1903–66) English novelist known for his brilliant satires. His novel, *Brideshead Revisited* (1945), although still a satire displays a growing spiritual concern. His masterpiece is his *Sword of Honour* trilogy, *Men at Arms* (1952), *Officers and Gentlemen* (1955), and *Unconditional Surrender* (1961), based on his own experiences with the Communist partisans in Yugoslavia in World War II. His son **[Alexander] Auberon Waugh** (1939–2001) was a successful writer and journalist, editor of the *Literary Review* and an exceptional wit.

Wayne, John [Marion Michael Morrison] (1907–79) American film actor. A screen actor of outstanding presence, he is best known as the star of many classic westerns, many of them directed by John FORD, e.g. *Stagecoach* (1939), *She Wore a Yellow Ribbon* (1949) and *The Searchers* (1956).

Webb, Beatrice Potter (1858–1943) *and* **Webb, Sidney James, Baron Passfield** (1859–1947) English social reformers and economists. Married in 1892, the Webbs were, with George Bernard SHAW and H. G. WELLS, the leading propagandists of Fabian socialism. They co-founded the London School of Economics (1895), founded the *New Statesman* (1913) and produced many pamphlets and articles.

Weber, Carl Maria Ernst von (1786–1826) German composer, conductor and pianist. He is considered to be the creator of German Romantic opera, using French opera as a framework and introducing German themes. He had a colossal influence on subsequent composers up to, and including, WAGNER. His works include the operas *Der Freischütz*, *Euryanthe* and *Oberon*, two symphonies, concertos, piano sonatas and many songs.

Weber, Max (1864–1920) German sociologist. Regarded as one of the founders of sociology, he devised the concept of 'ideal types' of real situations for comparative purposes.

Webern, Anton von (1883–1945) Austrian composer who was one of the leading exponents of the serial form of composition.

Webster, John (*c.*1578–*c.*1632) English dramatist, noted for two very powerful tragedies, *The White Devil* (*c.*1609–12) and *The Duchess of Malfi* (*c.*1613). His bleak and chilling dialogue has rarely been matched.

Weil, Simone (1909–43) French philosopher. From an intellectual Jewish family, she chose to live as a farm and industrial labourer during the 1930s, and worked for the Republican forces during the Spanish Civil War. She later developed a strong interest in Roman Catholic mysticism. She worked for the French Resistance in London, where she was diagnosed with tuberculosis and eventually died.

Weill, Kurt (1900–50) German composer, noted especially for his collaborations with BRECHT, e.g. *The Threepenny Opera* (1928). He fled from Germany in 1935, settling in the USA.

Weinberg, Steven (1933–) American physicist. He devised a theory of the unity of the forces operating on elementary particles that was independently arrived at by the Pakistani physicist and Nobel laureate **Abdus Salam** (1926–96) and later developed by the American physicist **Sheldon Glashow** (1932–). All three shared the 1979 Nobel prize for physics.

Weizmann, Chaim Azriel (1874–1952) Russian-born chemist and Israeli statesman. A distinguished scientist, he took part in the negotiations for a Jewish homeland and became the first president of Israel (1949-52).

Welles, [George] Orson (1915–85)American stage and film director and actor. He achieved notoriety with his radio production of WELLS's *War of the Worlds* in 1938, which sparked off mass panic in the USA. He co-wrote, produced and directed one of the greatest films of all time, *Citizen Kane* (1941), based on the life of HEARST. Other acting roles include, most notably, Harry Lime in Carol REED's masterpiece, *The Third Man* (1949).

Wellington, Arthur Wellesley, 1st Duke of (1769–1852) Anglo-Irish soldier and statesman, nicknamed the 'Iron Duke'. He distinguished himself in India and was appointed commander of the British forces in the Peninsular War (1808–14) and led the Allied forces to victory against NAPOLEON at Waterloo in 1815. He became Tory prime minister (1828–30) and opposed reform.

Wells, H[erbert] G[eorge] (1866–1946) English novelist and short-story writer. His science fiction works include several classics, e.g. *The Time Machine* (1895) and *The Shape of Things to Come* (1933). He was also propagandist with the WEBBS and others for Fabian socialism.

Wesley, John (1703–91) English evangelist. The 15th son of the poet and clergyman **Samuel Wesley** (1662–1735), he joined a small group of devout Anglicans, formed by his brother **Charles Wesley** (1707–88), who subsequently became known as 'Methodists', which name was used to describe the expanding movement and which remained within the Church of England in Wesley's lifetime.

West, Mae (1892–1980) American vaudeville artist, dramatist and film actress. Several of her plays were banned for obscenity, notably *Sex* (1926), for which she was briefly imprisoned. She became a star, renowned for her sardonic wit and sexuality, with such films as *She Done Him Wrong* (1933).

Whistler, James Abbott McNeill (1834–1903) US painter. He settled in London in 1859, where he was influenced by the Pre-Raphaelites and by Japanese art. He became famous as a portraitist, with works such as *Arrangement in Grey and Black*, a portrait of his mother.

Whitehead, William *see* AML poet laureate.

Whitman, Walt[er] (1819–92) American poet. His collection, *Leaves of Grass*, was first published in 1855 and is regarded as the most important single volume of poems in American literature.

Whittle, Sir Frank (1907–96) English aeronautical engineer. He designed the first operational jet engine for aircraft and the first successful flight was made in a Gloster in 1941.

Wilberforce, William (1759–1833) English philanthropist and politician. His long campaign to end the British slave trade led to its abolition in 1807.

Wilde, Oscar Fingal O'Flahertie Wills (1854–1900) Irish dramatist, poet, essayist, and wit. After the publication of *Poems* (1881), he made a highly successful tour of America, published his children's stories, *The Happy Prince and Other Tales*, in 1888, with his only novel, *The Picture of Dorian Gray*, following in 1890. The first of his great plays, *Lady Windermere's Fan*, appeared in 1892. The succeeding plays, *A Woman of No Importance* (1893), *An Ideal Husband* (1895) and *The Importance of Being Earnest* (1895) established him as the most important dramatist of the age, with their superbly witty dialogue and biting satire. He was jailed for homosexuality (1895–97) and during his imprisonment wrote *De Profundis*. After his release, he fled to France, where he wrote *The Ballad of Reading Gaol* (1898) and died in poverty.

Wilder, Billy [Samuel Wilder] (1906–2002) Austrian-born American film director and screenwriter. He emigrated to the US in the 1930s, winning Oscars for *The Lost Weekend*, *Sunset Boulevard* and *The Apartment*. Other films include *Double Indemnity*, *The Seven Year Itch* and *Some Like it Hot*.

Wilkins, Maurice Hugh Frederick (1916–2004) New Zealand physicist and biologist. His research into DNA structure resulted in CRICK and WATSON's discovery of the 'double helix' structure of DNA, for which Wilkins, Crick and Watson shared the 1962 Nobel prize for physics.

Williamson, Malcolm (1931–2003) Australian-born British composer. Master of the Queen's Music (1975–2003), his works include several operas and music for film and television.

Wilmot, John *see* ROCHESTER, 2ND EARL OF.

Wilson, Sir [James] Harold, **Baron of Rievaulx** (1916–95) English Labour statesman. He served in World War II as a civil servant and became an MP in 1945. He held various ministerial posts before succeeding GAITSKELL as Labour leader in 1963. He was prime minister (1964–70, 1974–76). He unexpectedly resigned in 1976, with CALLAGHAN succeeding him as prime minister.

Wilson, [Thomas] Woodrow (1856–1924) American Democratic statesman. He was 28th president (1913–21). In 1916 he declared war on Germany following the sinking of US vessels. His '14 points' speech of January 1918 set out US conditions for ending the war, including the disbandment of the German, Austro-Hungarian and Ottoman empires, and imposed the armistice with Germany on Britain and France.

Wittgenstein, Ludwig Josef Johann (1889–1951) Austrian-born British philosopher. He studied under Bertrand RUSSELL (1912–13), who observed that he was soon learning as much from his pupil as he had taught him.

Wodehouse, P[elham] G[renville] (1881–1975) English novelist and short-story writer who became a US citizen in 1955. His most famous literary creations are Bertie Wooster, a giddy young upper-middle-class man and his butler, Jeeves, a shrewd and competent man. Interned by the Nazis in World War II, he foolishly made some innocuous broadcasts from Germany, which led to his being branded a traitor.

Wollstonecraft, Mary (1759 –97) English feminist writer of *A Vindication of the Rights of Women* (1792). Wife of WILLIAM GODWIN and mother of MARY SHELLEY.

Wolsey, Cardinal Thomas (*c*.1475–1530) English cleric and statesman. He was made a privy councillor (1511) by HENRY VIII, who then appointed him archbishop of York (1514–30) and lord chancellor (1515–29). Instructed by the king in 1527 to negotiate with the pope the annulment of the king's marriage, his failure after two years of pressurising Rome led to his dismissal as lord chancellor (being succeeded by Sir Thomas MORE). He died on the journey from York to London to face charges of treason.

Wood, Sir Henry Joseph (1869–1940) English conductor. He founded the London Promenade Concerts (the 'Proms') in 1895, which he conducted until his death.

Woods, Tiger (1975–) American golfer who rose to dominate the sport in the late 1990s and is now one of the most successful golfers of all time. He has many notable wins to his name and is the youngest player to achieve a Grand Slam, and the youngest and fastest to win 50 tournaments on tour.

Woolf, [Adeline] Virginia (1882–1941) English novelist and critic. Her novels, including *To the Lighthouse* (1927) and *Orlando* (1928), are written in a fluid, poetic style using stream of consciousness narration. She suffered from bouts of manic depression throughout her life and finally committed suicide by drowning herself.

Wordsworth, William (1770–1850) English poet. The main figure of the English Romantic movement, his work successfully blended the personal with the natural and social worlds into a coherent whole. He enjoyed a close artistic relationship with Samuel Taylor COLERIDGE. He became poet laureate in 1843.

Wright, Orville (1871–1948) *and* **Wright, Wilbur** (1867–1912) American aviators and brothers. Cycle manufacturers, they designed and built the first heavier-than-air flying machine.

Wyman, Bill *see* JAGGER, MICK.

Yeats, W[illiam] B[utler] (1865–1939) Anglo-Irish poet and dramatist. Following Irish independence, he became a member of the Irish senate. He was awarded the Nobel prize for literature in 1923. His brother, **Jack B Yeats [John Butler Yeats]** (1870–1957) was an illustrator, particularly of children's books, before turning to painting and writing.

Yeltsin, Boris Nikolayevich (1931– 2007) Russian politician. A member of the Communist Party since 1960, he was brought into the Soviet Politburo by GORBACHEV in 1985. His subsequent assault on the ingrained inefficiency and corruption of that body resulted in his demotion from the post and from the Politburo. In the free elections of 1989, he was elected to the Congress of People's Deputies, and won an overwhelming majority of votes in the Russian presidential election of 1990. Re-elected in 1996 he resigned in 1999 and was succeeded by Vladimir PUTIN.

Zeffirelli, Franco (1923–) Italian stage and film director and designer. His films include *Romeo and Juliet* and the TV film *Jesus of Nazareth*.

Zhivkov, Todor (1911–98) Bulgarian Communist statesman. Prime minister (1962–71) and president (1971–89).

Zhou En Lai *see* CHOU EN-LAI.

Zidane, Zinedine Yazid (1972–) French footballer nicknamed 'Zizou'. Three times winner of the FIFA Football Player of the Year award, he was a member of the French national team that won the 1998 FIFA World Cup and Euro 2000. He retired in 2006 after being given a red card during the World Cup final.

Zola, Emile (1840–1902) French novelist. Regarded as the most prominent exponent of Naturalism in the novel, and a highly able propagandist for socialism and for social justice.

Zwingli, Huldreich or Ulrich (1484–1531) Swiss religious reformer. After LUTHER and CALVIN, he became the most influential of the Protestant reformers.

Countries of the World

Afghanistan a landlocked country in southern Asia. The greater part of the country is mountainous with a central mass of huge mountain ranges. Many of the peaks rise to enormous heights, the greatest being Nowshak at 24,557 feet (7,845 metres). The climate is generally arid with great extremes of temperature. There is considerable snowfall in winter, which may remain on the mountain summits all year round. The country experiences many earthquakes, and periods of severe drought. The main economic activity is agriculture. Successful cultivation takes place in the fertile plains and valleys although only 15 per cent of the land is suitable for farming. Its main exports have been fruit and nuts, carpets and wool, and the country is the world's leading producer of opium. Mineral resources are scattered and so far underdeveloped. Afghanistan has suffered from ongoing conflict during its modern history to the extent that its economy and infrastructure have been severely affected. After the Russian withdrawal from Afghanistan in 1989, the country was troubled by mainly ethnic conflict. In 1996, the Taleban, a fundamentalist Islamic group, took control. In 2001, they in turn were forced to withdraw from most of the country by a united US, Allied and Northern Alliance force. By 2005, Afghanistan was being governed by a democratically elected president and national assembly although fighting continues in areas of the country in the south and the east that are controlled by resurgent Taleban forces.

Area: 251,773 sq mi (652,225 sq km)
Population: 26,000,000
Capital: Kabul
Form of government: Republic
Religions: Sunni Islam, Shia Islam
Currency: Afghani

Albania a small mountainous country in the Balkan region of southeastern Europe. Its immediate neighbours are GREECE, SERBIA, MONTENEGRO and the former YugoslavRepublic of MACEDONIA and it is bounded to the west by the Adriatic Sea.

The climate is typically Mediterranean and although most rain falls in winter, severe thunderstorms frequently occur on the plains in summer. Winters are severe in the highland areas and heavy snowfalls are common. The main agricultural areas lie along the Adriatic coast and in the Korce Basin with about a fifth of the land being arable. Agriculture is held back because of a lack of modern equipment and unclear property rights. Industrial output is small. The principal industries are agricultural product processing, textiles, oil products, cement, iron, and steel. A shortage of energy resources and poor national road and rail networks are a barrier to better economic growth. The money sent home by Albanians working abroad, mainly in Greece and ITALY, remains an important source of revenue for the country. Albania has been afflicted by severe economic problems and in late 1996 public dissatisfaction with the government erupted into civil unrest, leading to a major revolt by citizen militias during which the government forces lost control. By March 1997 the country was on the brink of collapse and large numbers of refugees were leaving. The situation was reversed, however, when ethnic cleansing of Albanian inhabitants of the Kosovo region of Serbia in 1999 led to a flood of refugees into Albania, placing a huge burden on the country's economy. The country remains one of the poorest in Europe despite some economic progress.

Area: 11,009 sq mi (28,748 sq km)
Population: 3,581,000
Capital: Tirana (Tiranè)
Form of government: Republic
Religions: Sunni Islam, Christianity
Currency: Lek

Algeria a huge country in northern Africa that fringes the Mediterranean Sea in the north. Over four-fifths of Algeria is covered by the Sahara Desert to the south. Near the north coastal area the Atlas Mountains run east-west in parallel ranges. The Chelif, at 450 miles (724 kilometres) long, is the country's main river, rising in the Tell Atlas and flowing to the Mediterranean. The climate in the coastal areas is warm and temperate with most of the rain falling in winter. The summers are dry and hot with temperatures rising to over 89°F (32°C). Inland beyond the Atlas Mountains conditions become more arid and temperatures range from 120°F (49°C) during the day to 50°F (10°C) at night. Most of Algeria is unproductive agriculturally, but it does possess one of the largest reserves of natural gas and oil in the world. Algeria's main exports are oil-based products, fruit, vegetables, tobacco, phosphates and cork, while imports include textiles, foodstuffs, machinery, iron and steel. In more recent years, the country has been wracked by civil strife and terrorist attacks, and there is large-scale unemployment and a shortage of housing.

Area: 919,595 sq mi (2,381,741 sq km)
Population: 29,168,000
Capital: Algiers (Alger)
Form of government: Republic
Religion: Sunni Islam
Currency: Algerian dinar

American Samoa *see* Samoa, American.

Andorra a tiny principality, situated high in the eastern Pyrénées, between France and Spain. The state consists of deep valleys and high mountain peaks which reach heights of 9,843 feet (3,000 metres). Although only 12 miles (20 kilometres) wide and 19 miles (30 kilometres) long, the spectacular scenery and climate attract many tourists. About 10 million visitors arrive each year, during the cold weather when heavy snowfalls make for ideal skiing, or in summer when the weather is mild and sunny and the mountains are used for walking. Tourism and the duty-free trade are now Andorra's chief sources of income. Sheep and cattle are raised on the high pastures. Although Andorra has no airport or railroad, there is a good road system. In 1993, an Andorran government was elected and the country now has its own parliament after 715 years of being ruled by France's leader and the Spanish Bishop of Urgel.

Area: 175 sq mi (453 sq km)
Population: 65,900
Capital: Andorra la Vella
Form of government: Parliamentary Democracy

Religion: Christianity
Currency: Euro

Angola situated on the Atlantic coast of southern Africa, Angola lies about 10 degrees south of the equator and shares borders with Congo, Democratic Republic of Congo, Zambia and Namibia. Its climate is tropical with temperatures constantly between 68°F (20°C) and 77°F (25°C). The rainfall is heaviest in inland areas where there are vast equatorial forests. The country is also rich in minerals, however deposits of manganese, copper and phosphate are as yet unexploited. Diamonds are mined in the northeast and oil is produced near Luanda. Oil production is the most important aspect of the economy, making up about 90 per cent of exports which have traditionally included diamonds, fish, coffee and palm oil. Around 70 per cent of the workforce are engaged in agriculture. The Angolan economy was severely damaged by the 27-year civil war that ended in 2002 but oil exports have encouraged economic growth and reconstruction.

Area: 481,354 sq mi (1,246,700 sq km)
Population: 11,185,000
Capital: Luanda
Form of government: Republic
Religions: Christianity, traditional beliefs
Currency: Kwanza

Anguilla an island in the Leeward Islands group of the Caribbean Sea, now a self-governing British dependency. From 1967 until 1980 it was in federation with St Christopher (St Kitts) and Nevis. The country's main sources of revenue are tourism and offshore banking, and lobsters account for half of the island's exports.

Area: 37 sq mi (96 sq km)
Population: 12,400
Capital: The Valley
Form of government: British Overseas Territory
Religion: Christianity
Currency: East Caribbean dollar

Antigua and Barbuda located on the eastern side of the Leeward Islands, Antigua and Barbuda is a tiny state comprising three islands:Antigua, Barbuda and the uninhabited rocky islet of Redonda. Antigua's strategic position was recognised by the British in the 18th century when it was an important naval base and later by the USA who built the island's airport during World War II to defend the Caribbean and the Panama Canal. Although mainly low-lying, the country's highest point is Boggy Peak at 1,329 feet (405 metres). The climate is tropical. Tourism is the main industry and its numerous sandy beaches make it an ideal holiday destination. Barbuda is surrounded by coral reefs and the island is home to a wide range of wildlife. Cotton, sugar cane and fruits are cultivated and fishing is an important industry. More recently, offshore financial services also contribute to the success of the country's economy.

Area: 171 sq mi (442 sq km)
Population: 66,000
Capital: St John's
Form of government: Constitutional
  Monarchy
Religion: Christianity
Currency: East Caribbean dollar

Argentina the world's eighth largest country, which stretches from the Tropic of Capricorn to Cape Horn on the southern tip of the South American continent. To the west a massive mountain chain, the Andes, forms the border with CHILE. The climate ranges from warm temperate over the Pampas in the central region, to a more arid climate in the north and west, while in the extreme south conditions although also dry are much cooler. The vast fertile plains of the Pampas are the main agricultural area and produce cereals and wheat, while in other irrigated areas sugar cane, fruit and grapes for wine are grown. Meat processing, animal products and livestock production are major industries and also feature prominently in the export trade. A series of political and economic crises have resulted in an unstable economy which fails to provide reasonable living standards for the country's population.

Area: 1,073,518 sq mi (2,780,400 sq km)
Population: 39,920,000
Capital: Buenos Aires
Form of government: Federal Republic
Religion: Christianity
Currency: Peso

Armenia the smallest republic of the former USSR and part of the former kingdom of Armenia. It declared independence from the USSR in 1991. A landlocked Transcaucasian republic, its neighbours are TURKEY, IRAN, GEORGIA and AZERBAIJAN. The country is very mountainous, with many peaks over 9,900 feet (3,000 metres), the highest being Arragats Lerr at 13,435 feet (4,095 metres). Agriculture is mixed in the lowland areas. The main crops grown are grain, sugar beet and potatoes and livestock reared include cattle, pigs and sheep. Mining of copper, zinc and lead is important and to a lesser extent gold, aluminium and molybdenum, and industrial development is increasing. Territorial conflict with Azerbaijan over Nagorny Karabakh, under a ceasefire since 1994, has resulted in a trade blockade by Turkey and Azerbaijan and this has slowed economic development. Unemployment and poverty are still widespread and many young people have left the country in search of a better life.

Area: 11,506 sq mi (29,800 sq km)
Population: 2,796,000
Capital: Yerevan
Form of government: Republic
Religion: Christianity
Currency: Dram

Aruba a Caribbean island off the coast of Venezuela, until 1986 one of the NETHERLANDS ANTILLES. It is a prosperous self-governing dependency of the Netherlands. Tourism is its main source of economic revenue along with oil products.

Area: 75 sq mi (193 sq km)
Population: 87,000
Capital: Oranjestad
Form of government: Self-governing
  Dutch Territory
Religion: Christianity
Currency: Aruban florin

Australia the world's smallest continental landmass and a vast and sparsely populated island state in the southern hemisphere, comprising seven states. The most mountainous region is the Great Dividing Range, which runs down the entire east coast. Because of its great size, Australia's climates range from tropical monsoon to cool temperate and also large areas of desert. The majority of the country's natural inland lakes are salt water and are the remnants of a huge inland sea. The Great Barrier Reef is approximately 1,250 miles (2,000 kilometres) long and is the largest coral formation known in the world. Central and south Queensland are subtropical while north and central New South Wales are warm temperate. Much of Australia's wealth comes from agriculture, with huge sheep and cattle stations extending over large parts of the interior known as the Outback. Mining produces coal, natural gas, oil, gold, diamonds and iron ore. A strong services-based economy continues to grow. The focus of Australia's economy and foreign policy has slowly been shifting from Europe to its close neighbours in Asia.

Area: 2,988,902 sq mi (7,741,220 sq km)
Population: 20,264,800
Capital: Canberra
Form of government: Federal
  Parliamentary Democracy
Religion: Christianity
Currency: Australian dollar

Austria a landlocked country in central Europe surrounded by seven nations. The wall of mountains that runs across the centre of the country dominates the scenery. In the warm summers tourists come to walk in the forests and mountains and in the cold winters skiers come to the mountains that now boast over 50 ski resorts. The main river is the Danube and there are numerous lakes, principally Lake Constance (Bodensee) and Lake Neusiedler. Agriculture is based on small farms, many of which are run by single families. Dairy products, beef and lamb from the hill farms contribute to exports. More than 37 per cent of Austria is covered in forest, resulting in the paper-making industry near Graz. There are mineral resources of lignite, magnesium, petroleum, iron ore and natural gas and high-grade graphite is exported. Attachment to local customs is still strong and in rural areas men still wear lederhosen and women the traditional dirndl skirt on feast days and special occasions. Austria became part of the European Union in 1995.

Area: 32,378 sq mi (83,859 sq km)
Population: 8,192,000
Capital: Vienna (Wien)
Form of government: Federal Republic
Religion: Christianity
Currency: Euro

Azerbaijan a republic of the former USSR that declared itself independent in 1991. It is situated on the southwest coast of the Caspian Sea and shares borders with IRAN, ARMENIA, GEORGIA and RUSSIA. The Araks river separates Azerbaijan from the region known as Azerbaijan in northern Iran. The country is semi-arid and 70 per cent of the land is irrigated for the production of cotton, wheat, maize, potatoes, tobacco, tea and citrus fruits. It has rich mineral deposits of oil, natural gas, iron and aluminium. The most important mineral is oil, which is found in the Baku area from where it is piped through Georgia to the Turkish port of Ceyhan. Azerbaijan is only minimally developed industrially and its further development is hindered by its dispute with Armenia over the Nagorny-Karabakh region.

Area: 33,436 sq mi (86,600 sq km)
Population: 7,961,000
Capital: Baku
Form of government: Republic
Religions: Sunni Islam, Christianity,
  Shia Islam
Currency: Azerbaijani manat

Azores three groups of small islands in the North Atlantic, belonging to PORTUGAL but autonomous since 1976.

Area: 901 sq mi (2,335 sq km)
Population: 336,100
Capital: Ponta Delgada
Currency: Euro

Bahamas, the the Bahamas consist of an archipelago of 700 islands located in the Atlantic Ocean off the southeast coast of Florida. The largest island is Andros (1,600 square miles/4,144 square kilometres) and the two most populated are Grand Bahama and New Providence where the capital, Nassau, lies. Winters in the Bahamas are mild and summers warm. Most rain falls in May, June, September and October and the islands are also subject to hurricanes and tropical storms. The islands have few natural resources and for many years fishing and small-scale farming (citrus fruits and vegetables) were the only ways to make a living. Now, however, tourism is the most important industry and it employs almost half the workforce. Offshore banking is also a growing source of income.

Area: 5,358 sq mi (13,878 sq km)
Population: 305,000

Capital: Nassau
Form of government: Constitutional
  Monarchy
Religion: Christianity
Currency: Bahamian dollar

Bahrain a Gulf State comprising 33 low-lying islands situated between the QATAR peninsula and the mainland of SAUDI ARABIA. Bahrain Island is the largest and a causeway, called the King Fahd Causeway, linking it to Saudi Arabia was opened in 1986. The highest point in the state is only 402 feet (122 metres) above sea level. The climate is pleasantly warm between December and March, but very hot from June to November. Most of Bahrain is sandy and too saline to support crops but drainage schemes are now used to reduce salinity and fertile soil is imported from other islands. Oil was discovered in 1931 and revenues from oil now account for about 80 per cent of the country's total revenue. Bahrain is being developed as a major manufacturing state, the main enterprises being aluminium smelting and the manufacture of clothing, paper products and consumer goods. Traditional industries include pearl fishing, boat building, weaving and pottery. Agricultural products include vegetables, dates and fruits, with artesian wells providing irrigation mainly on the north coast.

Area: 268 sq mi (694 sq km)
Population: 698,585
Capital: Manama (Al Manamah)
Form of government: Monarchy (Emirate)
Religions: Shia Islam, Sunni Islam
Currency: Bahraini dinar

Bangladesh formerly the eastern province of PAKISTAN, Bangladesh is one of the world's most densely populated countries. It is bounded almost entirely by INDIA and to the south by the Bay of Bengal. The country is extremely flat and is virtually a huge delta formed by the Ganges, Brahmaputra and Meghna rivers. The country is subject to devastating floods and cyclones that sweep in from the Bay of Bengal. Most villages are built on mud platforms to keep them above water. The climate is tropical monsoon with heat, extreme humidity and heavy rainfall in the monsoon season (April to October) along with accompanying tornadoes. The short winter season is mild and dry. The

combination of rainfall, sun and silt from the rivers makes the land productive and it is often possible to grow three crops a year. Bangladesh produces about 70 per cent of the world's jute. There are few mineral resources although natural gas, coal and peat are found. Onshore and offshore gas reserves could provide some prosperity for the country in the future and industrial development is being encouraged but poverty remains widespread.

Area: 55,598 sq mi (143,998 sq km)
Population: 147,365,000
Capital: Dhaka
Form of government: Republic
Religions: Sunni Islam, Hinduism
Currency: Taka

Barbados the most easterly island of the West Indies, lying well outside the group of islands that make up the Lesser Antilles. Mainly surrounded by coral reefs, most of the island is low-lying and only in the north does it rise to 1,104 feet (336 metres) at Mount Hillaby. The climate is tropical, but the cooling effect of the northeast trade winds prevents the temperatures rising above 86°F (30°C). There are only two seasons, the dry and the wet, when rainfall is very heavy. At one time the economy depended almost exclusively on the production of sugar and its by-products, molasses and rum, and although the industry is now declining, sugar is still the principal export. Tourism has now taken over as the main industry, employing approximately 40 per cent of the island's labour force, although there are industries manufacturing furniture, clothing, electrical and electronic equipment. More recently, deposits of natural gas and petroleum have been discovered and a financial services industry also contributes to the country's economy.

Area: 166 sq mi (430 sq km)
Population: 279,000
Capital: Bridgetown
Form of government: Constitutional
  Monarchy
Religion: Christianity
Currency: Barbados dollar

Belarus (Belorussia, Byelorussia) a republic of the former USSR that declared itself independent in 1991. It borders POLAND to the west, UKRAINE to the south, LATVIA and LITHUANIA to the north and RUSSIA to the east. The country consists mainly of a low-lying plain and forests cover approximately one-third of the land. The climate is continental, with long severe winters and short warm summers. Although the economy is based overwhelmingly on industry, including oil refining, food processing, woodworking, and the production of chemicals, textiles, and machinery, output has gradually declined since 1991. Private business is almost non-existent. Agriculture accounts for approximately 20 per cent of employment, the main crops being flax, potatoes, and hemp. The main livestock raised are cattle and pigs. Extensive forest areas also contribute to the economy by supplying the raw materials for woodworking and papermaking. Belarus has retained close political and economic ties with Russia and remains dependent on Russia to meet its energy needs. A recent deal with Russia more than doubled the price it has to pay for gas.

Area: 80,155 sq mi (207,600 sq km)
Population: 9,700,000
Capital: Minsk
Form of government: Republic
Religions: Christianity, Islam
Currency: Belarussian rouble

Belau *see* PALAU.

Belgium a highly industrialised, relatively small country in northwest Europe with a short coastline on the North Sea. The Meuse river divides Belgium into two distinct geographical regions. To the north of the river the land slopes continuously for 93 miles (150 kilometres) until it reaches the North Sea where the coastlands are flat and grassy. To the south of the river is the forested plateau area of the Ardennes. Between these two regions lies the Meuse valley. Belgium is a densely populated country with few natural resources. Agriculture, which uses about 45 per cent of the land for cultivation or rearing of livestock, employs only 3 per cent of the workforce. About one-fifth of the country is covered with forests, with the wooded areas mainly used for recreation. The metal-working industry, originally based on the small mineral deposits in the Ardennes, is the most important industry and in the northern cities new textile industries are producing carpets and clothing.

Nearly all raw materials are now imported through the main port of Antwerp. There are three officially recognised languages in Belgium: Dutch, French and German.

Area: 11,783 sq mi (30,519 sq km)
Population: 10,379,000
Capital: Brussels
Form of government: Constitutional Monarchy
Religion: Christianity
Currency: Euro

Belize a small Central American country on the southeast of the Yucatan Peninsula in the Caribbean Sea. Its coastline on the Gulf of Honduras is approached through some 550 kilometres (342 miles) of coral reefs and keys (cayo). The coastal area and north of the country are low-lying and swampy with dense forests inland. In the south the Maya Mountains rise to 1100 metres (3609 feet). The subtropical climate is warm and humid and the trade winds bring cooling sea breezes. Rainfall is heavy, particularly in the south and hurricanes may occur in summer. The dense forests that cover most of the country provide valuable hardwoods such as mahogany. Most of the population make a living from forestry, fishing, or agriculture, although only 5 per cent of the land is cultivated. The main crops grown for export are sugar cane, citrus fruits (mainly grapefruit), bananas and coconuts. Industry is very under-developed, causing many people to emigrate to find work. Tourism is now the most important industry.

Area: 8,763 sq mi (22,696 sq km)
Population: 287,000
Capital: Belmopan
Form of government: Constitutional Monarchy
Religion: Christianity
Currency: Belizean dollar

Belorussia *see* BELARUS.

Benin an ice cream cone-shaped country with a very short coastline on the Bight of Benin on the southern coast of West Africa. The coastal area has white sandy beaches backed by lagoons and low-lying fertile lands known as barre country. In the northwest the Atakora Mountains are grassy plateaus that are deeply cut into steep forested valleys and on the grasslands sheep, cattle and goats are reared. The main rivers are the Donga, Couffo and Niger with its tributaries. The climate in the north is tropical and in the south equatorial. There are nine rainy months each year so crops rarely fail. Farming is predominantly subsistence and accounts for around 60 per cent of employment, with yams, cassava, maize, rice, groundnuts and vegetables forming most of the produce. The main exports are palm oil, palm kernels and cotton. The country is very poor, although since the late 1980s economic reforms have encouraged a market economy and Western financial aid has been sought. Tourism is now being developed but as yet facilities for this are few except in some coastal towns.

Area: 43,484 sq mi (112,622 sq km)
Population: 7,862,000
Capital: Porto-Novo
Form of government: Republic
Religions: Traditional beliefs,
   Christianity, Sunni Islam
Currency: CFA franc

Bermuda a country consisting of a group of 150 small islands in the western Atlantic Ocean. It lies about 572 miles (920 kilometres) east of Cape Hatteras on the coast of the United States. The hilly limestone islands are the caps of ancient volcanoes rising from the sea bed. The main island, Great Bermuda, is linked to the other islands by bridges and causeways. The climate is warm and humid, with rain spread evenly throughout the year but with the risk of hurricanes from June to November. Bermuda's chief agricultural products are fresh vegetables, bananas and citrus fruit, but 80 per cent of food requirements are imported. Many foreign banks and financial institutions operate from the island, taking advantage of the lenient tax laws. Other industries include ship repair and pharmaceuticals. Its proximity to the USA and the pleasant climate have led to a flourishing tourist industry.

Area: 20 sq mi (53 sq km)
Population: 64,000
Capital: Hamilton
Form of government: British Overseas
   Territory
Religion: Christianity
Currency: Bermudan dollar

Bhutan a country that is surrounded by INDIA to the south and CHINA to the north.

It reaches up from the foothills overlooking the Brahmaputra river to the southern slopes of the Himalayas. The Himalayas, which rise to over 24,600 feet (7,500 metres) in Bhutan, make up most of the country. The climate is hot and wet on the plains but temperatures drop progressively with altitude, resulting in glaciers and permanent snow cover in the north. The valleys in the centre of the country are wide and fertile and about 95 per cent of the workforce are farmers growing wheat, rice, potatoes and corn. Fruit such as plums, pears, apples and also cardamom are grown for export. There are many monasteries, with about 6,000 monks. Yaks reared on the high pasture land provide milk, cheese and meat. Vast areas of the country still remain forested as there is little demand for new farmland. Bhutan is one of the world's poorest and least developed countries. It has little contact with the rest of the world although restricted tourism has been encouraged in recent years. A hereditary monarchy has ruled since 1907 but the country is due to make a switch to a two-party state in 2008.

Area: 18,147 sq mi (47,000 sq km)
Population: 2,279,000
Capital: Thimphu
Form of government: Absolute Monarchy
Religions: Buddhism, Hinduism
Currency: Ngultrum

Bolivia a landlocked republic of central South America through which the great mountain range of the Andes runs. It is in the Andes that the highest navigable lake in the world, Lake Titicaca, is found. On the undulating depression south of the lake, the Altiplano, is the highest capital city in the world, La Paz. To the east and northeast of the mountains is a huge area of lowland containing tropical rainforests (the Llanos) and wooded savanna (the Chaco). The northeast has heavy rainfall while in the southwest it is negligible. Temperatures vary with altitude, from extremely cold on the summits to cool on the Altiplano, where at least half the population lives. Although rich in natural resources, such as lead, silver, copper, zinc, oil, and tin, Bolivia lacks the funds for their extraction, due to a lack of investment, and political instability. The country is self-sufficient in petroleum and exports natural gas. Agriculture produces soya beans, sugar cane, and cotton for export. Increased production of coca, from which cocaine is derived, has resulted in an illicit economy. The country remains one of the poorest in South America.

Area: 424,165 sq mi (1,098,581 sq km)
Population: 8,989,000
Capital: Sucre
Form of government: Republic
Religion: Christianity
Currency: Boliviano

Bosnia-Herzegovina a republic of former Yugoslavia that was formally recognised as an independent state in March 1992. It is a very mountainous country and includes part of the Dinaric Alps, which are densely forested and deeply cut by rivers flowing northwards to join the Sava river. Half the country is forested and lumber is an important product of the northern areas. One quarter of the land is cultivated and corn, wheat and flax are the principal products of the north. In the south, tobacco, cotton, fruits and grapes are the main products. Bosnia-Herzegovina has large deposits of lignite, iron ore, and bauxite, and its metallurgical plants create air pollution. Water is also polluted around these plants, with the Sava River being severely affected. Despite its natural resources the economy has been devastated by civil war, which began in 1991 following the secession of Croatia and Slovenia from the former Yugoslavia. Dispute over control of Bosnia-Herzegovina continued, leading to United Nations intervention in an attempt to devise a territorial plan acceptable to all factions. A peace agreement signed in late 1995 resulted in the division of the country into two self-governing provinces. Ethnic nationalism remains strong but a European Union peacekeeping force has helped maintain stability in the country, with the hope that integration will increase.

Area: 19,735 sq mi (51,129 sq km)
Population: 4,510,000
Capital: Sarajevo
Form of government: Republic
Religions: Christianity, Sunni Islam,
Currency: Marka

Botswana a landlocked republic in southern Africa, Botswana straddles the Tropic of Capricorn. Much of the west and southwest of the country forms part of the Kalahari Desert. In the north there is a huge area of marshland around the Okavango Delta, which is home for a wide variety of wildlife. With the exception of the desert area, most of the country has a subtropical climate but is subject to drought. In winter, days are warm and nights cold while summer is hot with sporadic rainfall. The people are mainly farmers and cattle rearing is the main activity. After independence in 1966, the exploitation of minerals started. In 1972 the first diamond mine was set up at Orapa and diamonds quickly became the country's most important export. Copper from the nickel/copper complex at Selebi-Pikwe was also exported. Exploitation of these mineral resources has facilitated a high rate of economic growth within the country. Coal is also mined but the majority is for domestic use. About 17 per cent of the land is set aside for wildlife preservation in national parks, game reserves, game sanctuaries and controlled hunting areas. Tourism is an important source of foreign revenue.

Area: 224,607 sq mi (581,730 sq km)
Population: 1,639,000
Capital: Gaborone
Form of government: Republic
Religions: Traditional beliefs, Christianity
Currency: Pula

Brazil a huge South American country bounded to the north, south and east by the Atlantic ocean. It is the fifth largest country in the world and covers nearly half of South America. The climate is mainly tropical, but altitude, distance from the sea and prevailing winds cause many variations. The Amazon river basin occupies over one-third of the country's area and much of this is covered by tropical rainforests. In the tropical areas winters are dry and summers wet and droughts may occur in the northeast where it is hot and arid. The main agricultural products exported are coffee, soya beans, orange juice and cocoa. Brazil is rich in minerals and is the only source of high grade quartz crystal in commercial quantities. It is also a major producer of chrome ore and it is now developing what is thought to be the richest iron ore deposits in the world.

Area: 3,300,171 sq mi (8,547,403 sq km)
Population: 188,078,000

Capital: Brasília
Form of government: Federal Republic
Religion: Christianity
Currency: Real

British Indian Ocean Territory a British colony consisting of the Chagos Archipelago, a group of five coral atolls in the middle of the Indian Ocean. (*Area*: 20 sq mi/52 sq km.)

Brunei a sultanate located on the northwest coast of the island of Borneo in southeast Asia, Brunei has one of the highest standards of living in the world. It is bounded on all sides by the Sarawak territory of MALAYSIA, which splits the sultanate into two separate parts. Broad tidal swamplands cover the coastal plains and inland Brunei is hilly and covered with tropical rainforests that occupy almost half the country's land area. The climate is tropical marine, hot and moist, with cool nights. Rainfall is heavy at the coast but even heavier inland. The main crops grown are rice, vegetables and fruit, but economically the country depends on its oil industry. Cloth weaving and metalwork are also small local industries. Oil production began in the 1920s and while oil and natural gas account for almost all exports at the moment, the country is trying to diversify its economy with eco-tourism and financial services.

Area: 2,226 sq mi (5,765 sq km)
Population: 379,000
Capital: Bandar Seri Begawan
Form of government: Sultanate
Religions: Sunni Islam, Christianity, Buddhism
Currency: Bruneian dollar

Bulgaria a southeast European republic located on the east Balkan peninsula and with a coast on the Black Sea. It is bounded to the north by ROMANIA, to the west by SERBIA and the Former Yugoslav Republic of MACEDONIA and to the south by GREECE and TURKEY. The centre of Bulgaria is crossed from west to east by the Balkan Mountains. The south of the country has a Mediterranean climate with hot dry summers and mild winters. Farther north the temperatures become more extreme and rainfall is higher in summer. The main river in Bulgaria is the Danube and about a third of the country is covered by forests. Traditionally Bulgaria is an agricultural country and a revolution in farming during the 1950s led to great increases in output. This was because of the collectivisation of farms and the use of more machinery, fertilisers and irrigation. Increased mechanisation led to more of the workforce being available to work in mines and industry. However, the country suffered very high rates of inflation and unemployment in the early 1990s after the break-up of the former Soviet Union and it has struggled to achieve a transition to democracy and a market economy. Living standards remain low. Despite some concerns about corruption and organised crime, Bulgaria became a member of the European Union in 2007.

Area: 42,823 sq mi (110,912 sq km)
Population: 7,385,000
Capital: Sofiya
Form of government: Republic
Religion: Christianity
Currency: Lev

Burkina Faso a landlocked state in West Africa, Burkina (formerly calledUpper Volta) lies on the fringe of the Sahara, to the north. It comprises a plateau region in the north which gives way southwards to an area of plains. The northern part of the country is arid and is more or less an extension of the Sahara Desert. The south is less dry and has savanna-type vegetation and scattered trees. Precipitation is generally low, the heaviest rain falling in the southwest, while the rest of the country is semi-desert. The dusty grey plains in the north and west have infertile soils that have been further impoverished by overgrazing and over-cultivation. About 85 per cent of the people live by subsistence farming and food crops include sorghum, millet, pulses, corn and rice. The main industries are textiles, metal products, the processing of agricultural products and the production of consumer items such as footwear and soap. Cotton is the main export, along with minerals such as gold and animal products. During the 1970s the country was severely affected by drought and this was followed by political instability in the 1980s. It has been linked to conflicts within the region and remains one of the world's poorest countries.

Area: 105,792 sq mi (274,000 sq km)
Population: 13,902,000

Capital: Ouagadougou
Form of government: Republic
Religions: Traditional beliefs, Sunni Islam
Currency: CFA franc

Burma *see* MYANMAR.

Burundi a small, densely populated country in central east Africa, bounded by RWANDA to the north, TANZANIA to the east and south and the Democratic Republic of CONGO to the west. One of the poorest nations in the world, Burundi consists mainly of an upland plateau at an elevation of 4,600–5,900 feet (1,400–1,800 metres). The climate is equatorial but modified by altitude. The savanna in the east is several degrees hotter than the plateau and there are two wet seasons. The soils are not rich but there is enough rain to grow crops in most areas for subsistence farming. The main food crops are bananas, sweet potatoes, peas, lentils and beans. Cassava is grown near the shores of Lake Tanganyika which is in the Great Rift Valley. The main cash crop is coffee, which accounts for 90 per cent of Burundi's export earnings. Cotton and tea are also cultivated for export. There is a little commercial fishing on Lake Tanganyika, otherwise industry is very basic. Since 1994 Burundi has been afflicted by ethnic conflict between the majority Hutu and minority Tutsi. Between 1994 and 1995 it is estimated that 150,000 people were killed as a result of ethnic violence. Some political and economic stability has come about after a final ceasefire in 2006.

Area: 10,747 sq mi (27,834 sq km)
Population: 8,090,000
Capital: Bujumbura
Form of government: Republic
Religions: Christianity, traditional beliefs
Currency: Burundi franc

Byelorussia *see* BELARUS.

Cambodia a southeast Asian state bounded by THAILAND, LAOS and VIETNAM, with its southern coast lying on the Gulf of Thailand. The country was devastated by its involvement in the Vietnam War (1960–75) followed by the brutal regime of the Khymer Rouge under Pol Pot (1975–79). The heart of the country is saucer-shaped and gently rolling alluvial plains are drained by the Mekong river. The Dangrek Mountains form the frontier with Thailand in the north-west. In general Cambodia has a tropical monsoon climate and about half the land is tropical forest. During the rainy season the Mekong swells and backs into the Tônlé Sap (Great Lake), increasing its size three-fold to about 4,015 square miles (10,400 kilometres). This seasonal flooding means the area is left with rich silt when the river recedes. Crop production depends entirely on the rainfall and floods but production was badly disrupted during the civil war when there was widespread famine, and yields still remain low. The cultivation of rice accounts for about 80 per cent of agricultural land and the other main crop is rubber, which grows in the eastern plateau. Despite the gradual rebuilding of the infrastructure in the early 1990s after years of oppression under the Khmer Rouge, Cambodia remains one of the world's poorest nations, relying heavily on foreign aid.

Area: 69,898 sq mi (181,035 sq km)
Population: 13,881,000
Capital: Phnom-Penh
Form of government: Constitutional Monarchy
Religion: Buddhism
Currency: Riel

Cameroon a triangular-shaped country of diverse landscapes in west central Africa. It stretches from Lake Chad at its apex to the northern borders of EQUATORIAL GUINEA, GABON and the CONGO in the south. The landscape ranges from low-lying lands, through the semi-desert Sahel to dramatic mountain peaks and then to the grassy savanna, rolling uplands, steaming tropical forests and hardwood plantations. Cameroon's jungles contain not only commercially valuable trees but also an immense diversity of other plants, many of which have been identified as useful for their medicinal properties. Farther south are the volcanoes, including the sporadically active Mount Cameroon, the highest peak at 13,250 feet (4,100 metres) and the palm beaches at Kribi and Limbe. The climate is equatorial with high temperatures and plentiful rain. The majority of the population are farmers who live in the south and in central Cameroon where they grow maize, millet, cassava and vegetables. In the drier north, where drought and hunger are well known, life is harder and this area is populated by semi-nomadic herders. Bananas, coffee and cocoa are the major exports although oil, gas and aluminium are becoming increasingly important. The country has suffered from many years of repressive rule and has faced internal and external conflict in recent years.

Area: 183,569 sq mi (475,442 sq km)
Population: 17,340,000
Capital: Yaoundé
Form of government: Republic
Religions: Traditional beliefs, Christianity, Sunni Islam
Currency: CFA franc

Canada the second largest country in the world and the largest in North America. Canada is a land of great climatic and geographical extremes. It lies to the north of the UNITED STATES and has Pacific, Atlantic and Arctic coasts. The country has the highest number of inland waters and lakes in the world, including the Great Lakes on the border with the USA. The Rocky Mountains and Coast Mountains run down the west side and the highest point, Mount Logan (19,524 feet/6,050 metres), is in the Yukon. Climates range from polar conditions in the north to cool temperate in the south, with considerable differences from west to east. More than 80 per cent of its farmland is in the prairies that stretch from Alberta to Manitoba. Wheat and grain crops cover three-quarters of the arable land. Canada is rich in forest reserves, which cover more than half the total land area. The most valuable mineral deposits (oil, gas, coal and iron ore) are found in Alberta. Most industry in Canada is associated with processing its natural resources and it is one of the world's main exporters of food products.

Area: 3,849,674 sq mi (9,970,610 sq km)
Population: 33,098,000
Capital: Ottawa
Form of government: Federal Parliamentary Democracy
Religion:Christianity
Currency: Canadian dollar

Canary Islands a group of islands that lie some 60 miles (95 kilometres) off the coast of WESTERN SAHARA and form an autonomous part of SPAIN. The main islands are Tenerife, Gran Canaria, Fuertaventura, Gomera, Lanzarote and La Palma.

Area: 2,808 sq mi (7,273 sq km)
Population: 1,493,000
Capital: Las Palmas, on Gran Canaria
Currency: Euro

Cape Verde one of the world's smallest nations, situated in the Atlantic Ocean about 400 miles (640 kilometres) northwest of SENEGAL. It consists of ten islands and five islets and there is an active volcano on Fogo, one of the islands. The islands are divided into the Windward group and the Leeward group. Over 50 per cent of the population live on São Tiago on which is Praia, the capital. The climate is arid with a cool dry season from December to June and warm dry conditions for the rest of the year. Rainfall is sparse and the islands suffer from periods of severe drought. Agriculture is mostly confined to irrigated inland valleys and the chief crops are coconuts, sugar cane, potatoes, cassava and dates. Bananas and some coffee are grown for export. Fishing for tuna and lobsters is an important industry but in general the economy is shaky and Cape Verde relies heavily on foreign aid. Because of its lack of natural resources and droughts, large numbers of its people have lived outside of the country for many years and the money they send home plays an important part in the country's economy. Tourism is being encouraged although the number of visitors is at present relatively low.

Area: 1,557 sq mi (4,033 sq km)
Population: 420,000
Capital: Praia
Form of government: Republic
Religion: Christianity
Currency: Cape Verdean escudo

Cayman Islands a group of three low-lying coral islands in the Caribbean Sea, 149 miles (240 kilometres) south of CUBA and northwest of JAMAICA. They are a British overseas territory. The group comprises Grand Cayman, by far the largest of the three, Cayman Brac and Little Cayman (the name is derived from the Carib Indian word for 'crocodile').The Cayman Islands are a popular destination for cruise liners, and a tax haven.

Area: 102 sq mi (264 sq km)
Population: 45,436
Capital: George Town, on Grand Cayman

Form of government: British Overseas
Territory
Religion: Christianity
Currency: Cayman Islands dollar

Central African Republic a landlocked
country in central Africa bordered by CHAD
in the north, CAMEROON in the west, SUDAN
in the east and the CONGO and Democratic
Republic of CONGO in the south. The terrain consists of 2,000–3,000 feet (610–915
metres) high undulating plateaus with
dense tropical forest in the south and a
semi-desert area in the east. The climate is
tropical with little variation in temperature
throughout the year. The wet months are
May, June, October and November. Floods
and tornadoes can occur at the beginning of
the rainy season. Most of the population live
in the west and in the hot, humid south and
southwest. Over 86 per cent of the working
population are subsistence farmers and
the main crops grown are cassava, groundnuts, bananas, plantains, millet and maize.
Livestock rearing is small-scale because
of the prevalence of the tsetse fly. Gems
and industrial diamonds are mined and
deposits of uranium, iron ore, lime, zinc and
gold have been discovered, although they
remain relatively undeveloped. The country's main exports are coffee, diamonds,
cotton, tobacco and lumber, although this
is hampered by the distance from a port.
Since the country's independence in 1960,
its political and economic fortunes have
been mixed, with widespread corruption and
violence. A Pan-African force has been in
the country since 2003 to help restore order
and stability.

Area: 240,535 sq mi (622,984 sq km)
Population: 4,303,000
Capital: Bangui
Form of government: Republic
Religions: Traditional beliefs, Islam,
Christianity
Currency: CFA franc

Chad a landlocked country in the centre of
northern Africa that extends from the edge
of the equatorial forests in the south to the
middle of the Sahara Desert in the north.
The climate is tropical, with adequate rainfall in the south, but the north experiences
semi-desert conditions. In the far north of
the country the Tibesti Mountains rise from

the desert sand more than 11,200 feet (3,415
metres). The southern part of Chad is the
most densely populated and its relatively
well-watered savanna has always been the
country's most arable region. Unless there
is drought, this area is farmed for cotton
(the main cash crop along with livestock
exports), millet, sorghum, groundnuts, rice
and vegetables. Fishing is carried out in
the rivers and in Lake Chad. As a result of
drought and civil war, Chad remains one of
the poorest countries in the world. In 2003
it became an oil-producing country but a
lack of infrastructure, ongoing unrest within
the country and conflict with neighbouring
Sudan mean that poverty is rife and the
economy continues to suffer.

Area: 495,755 sq mi (1,284,000 sq km)
Population: 9,944,000
Capital: N'Djamena
Form of government: Republic
Religions: Sunni Islam, traditional beliefs
Currency: CFA Franc

Channel Islands a group of islands in the
English Channel, close to the coast of France,
which are British crown dependencies.
The main islands are Jersey and Guernsey,
but the group also includes the smaller
inhabited islands of Alderney, Sark, Herm
and Brechou. (Area: 75 sq mi/194 sq km;
Population: 143,000)

Chile a country that lies like a backbone
down the Pacific coast of the South American continent with the Andes Mountains
extending its length. Its Pacific coastline
is 2,600 miles (4,184 kilometres) long and
the country is liable to volcanic explosions
and earthquakes. Because of its enormous
range in latitude it has almost every kind of
climate, from desert conditions to icy wastes.
The north, in which lies the Atacama Desert,
is extremely arid. The Atacama Desert is rich
in mineral deposits and has large quantities
of nitrates. The climate of the central region
is Mediterranean and that of the south cool
temperate. Sixty per cent of the population
live in the central valley where the climate
is similar to that of southern California. The
land here is fertile and the principal crops
grown are grapes, wheat, apples, sugar beet,
maize, tomatoes and potatoes. There is also
a significant wine-making industry. It is also
in the central valley that the vast copper

mine of El Teniente is located. This is one of the largest copper mines in the world and accounts for Chile's most important source of foreign exchange.

Area: 292,135 sq mi (756,626 sq km)
Population: 16,134,000
Capital: Santiago
Form of government: Republic
Religion: Christianity
Currency: Chilean peso

China the third largest country in the world, which covers a large area of East Asia and also includes over 3,400 islands. In western China most of the terrain is very inhospitable. In the northwest there are deserts that extend into MONGOLIA and RUSSIA and much of the southwest consists of the ice-capped peaks of TIBET. The southeast has a green and well-watered landscape comprising terraced hillsides and paddy fields and its main rivers are the Yangtze, Huang He and Xi Jiang. Most of China has a temperate climate but in such a large country wide ranges of latitude and altitudes produce local variations. China is an agricultural country and intensive cultivation and horticulture are necessary to feed its population of over one billion. After the death of Mao Tse-tung in 1976 and under the leadership of Deng Xiaoping, China experience d a huge modernisation of agriculture and industry as a result of the supply of expertise, capital and technology from Japan and the West. The country was opened up to tourists and, to a degree, adopted the philosophy of free enterprise, resulting in a dramatic improvement in living standards for a significant proportion of the population. China now has the world's fastest growing economy attracting huge amounts of foreign investment but there is a large economic gap between urban and rural China, and the ruling Communist Party still keeps a strict control over its citizens.

Area: 3,705,408 sq mi (9,596,961 sq km)
Population: 1,313,973,000
Capital: Beijing (Peking)
Form of government: Republic
Religions: Buddhism, Confucianism, Taoism
Currency: Yuan

Colombia a country situated in the north of South America, most of it lying between the equator and 10 degrees north. The Andes, which split into three ranges (the Cordilleras) in Colombia, run north along the west coast and gradually disappear towards the Caribbean Sea. Half of Colombia lies east of the Andes and much of this region is covered in tropical grassland. Towards the Amazon Basin the vegetation changes to tropical forest. The climates in Colombia include equatorial and tropical, according to altitude. Very little of the country is under cultivation although much of the soil is fertile. The range of climates results in an extraordinary variety of crops, of which coffee is the most important and includes cocoa beans, sugar cane, bananas, cotton and tobacco. Colombia is rich in minerals such as gold, silver, platinum and copper and produces about half of the world's emeralds. It is South America's leading producer of coal and petroleum is the country's most important foreign revenue earner. Despite its wealth of natural resources, Colombia has experienced decades of violent conflict, most of which involves the illegal trade in cocaine and outlawed armed groups.Inevitably the violence has deterred foreign investment.

Area: 439,737 sq mi (1,138,914 sq km)
Population: 43,593,000
Capital: Bogotá
Form of government: Republic
Religion: Christianity
Currency: Colombian peso

Comoros, the a country that consists of three volcanic islands in the Indian Ocean, situated between mainland Africa and MADAGASCAR. Physically, four islands make up the group but the island of Mayotte remained a French dependency when the three western islands became a federal Islamic republic in 1975. Since then the Comoros has experienced more than 20 coups and secession attempts which have left the country very dependent on foreign aid and its citizens among the poorest in Africa. The islands are mostly forested and the tropical climate is affected by Indian monsoon winds from the north. There is a wet season from November to April that is accompanied by cyclones. Only small areas of the islands are cultivated. Vanilla, copra, maize, cloves and essential oils are the most important products. The forests provide lumber for building and there is a small fishing industry. Money sent home by Comorans living abroad is an important part of the country's economy.

Area: 720 sq mi (1,865 sq km) excluding Mayotte
Population: 690,948
Capital: Moroni
Form of government: Republic
Religion: Sunni Islam
Currency: Comoran franc

Congo, Republic of formerly a French colony and now a republic, the Congo is situated in west central Africa where it straddles the equator. The climate is equatorial, with a moderate rainfall and a small range of temperature. The Bateke Plateau has a long dry season but the Congo Basin is more humid and rainfall approaches 9.8 inches (2,500 mm) each year. About 62 per cent of the total land area is covered with equatorial forest from which lumbers such as okoume and sapele are produced. Valuable hardwoods such as mahogany are exported. Cash crops such as coffee and cocoa are mainly grown on large plantations but food crops are grown on small farms usually worked by the women. A manufacturing industry is now growing and oil discovered offshore accounts for about 90 per cent of the Congo's revenues and exports. The remaining exports are wood, cocoa, sugar, coffee and diamonds. Ethnic and political fighting in the country became a full-scale civil war in 1997 and despite the peace accord of 2003 the country continues to be plagued by the activities of armed groups in the south.

Area: 132,047 sq mi (342,000 sq km)
Population: 3,702,000
Capital: Brazzaville
Form of government: Republic
Religions: Christianity, traditional beliefs
Currency: CFA franc

Congo, Democratic Republic of a vast country, formerly known as Zaire, situated in west central Africa. It has a short coastline of only 25 miles (40 kilometres) on the Atlantic Ocean. Rainforests, which cover about 55 per cent of the country, contain valuable hardwoods such as mahogany and ebony. The country is drained by the Congo (Zaire) river, which is largely navigable and its main tributaries. There is enormous

potential for hydroelectricity, but this is not yet exploited. Mountain ranges and plateaus surround the Congo basin and in the east the Ruwenzori Mountains overlook the lakes in the Great Rift Valley. In the central region the climate is hot and wet all year but elsewhere there are well-marked wet and dry seasons. Grazing land is limited by the infestation of the tsetse fly. Cassava is the main subsistence crop and coffee, tea, cocoa, rubber and palms are grown for export. The country has huge mineral resources, particularly in cobalt (around 65 per cent of the world's deposits), with copper, uranium, gold and diamonds being exported. Other natural resources include silver, iron ore and coal. These resources have fuelled civil war and ethnic conflict in the area. Five years of fighting were followed by elections and a national assembly was finally installed in 2006.

Area: 905,355 sq mi (2,344,858 sq km)
Population: 62,660,000
Capital: Kinshasa
Form of government: Republic
Religions: Christianity, Islam
Currency: Congolese franc

Cook Islands a group of 15 islands in the South Pacific, independent since 1965 but associated with NEW ZEALAND.

Area: 93 sq mi (240 sq km)
Population: 21,400
Capital: Avarua, on Rarotonga
Form of government: Self-governing in association with New Zealand
Religion: Christianity
Currency: New Zealand dollar

Costa Rica with the Pacific Ocean to the south and west and the Caribbean Sea to the east, Costa Rica is sandwiched between the Central American countries of NICARAGUA and PANAMA. Much of the country consists of volcanic mountain chains that run northwest to southeast. The climate is tropical with a small temperature range and abundant rain. The dry season is from December to April. The most populated area is the Valle Central in which the Spanish settled in the 16th century. The upland areas have rich volcanic soils that are good for coffee growing and the slopes provide lush pastures for cattle. Coffee and bananas are grown commercially and are the major agricultural exports. Costa

Rica's mountainous terrain provides hydro-electric power, which makes it almost self-sufficient in electricity. Its tropical forests and the sandy beaches of its Caribbean coast attract many visitors for its growing tourist industry. Tourism and technology are now the country's main industries.

Area: 19,730 sq mi (51,100 sq km)
Population: 4,075,000
Capital: San José
Form of government: Republic
Religion: Christianity
Currency: Costa Rican colon

Côte d'Ivoire (Ivory Coast) a former French colony in West Africa, Côte d'Ivoire is located on the Gulf of Guinea with GHANA to the east and LIBERIA and GUINEA to the west. The southwest coast has rocky cliffs but farther east there are coastal plains, which are the country's most prosperous region. The climate is tropical and affected by distance from the sea. The coastal area has two wet seasons, but in the north there is only the one. Côte d'Ivoire is basically an agricultural country with about 55 per cent of the workforce involved in producing cocoa, coffee, rubber, bananas and pineapples. It is the world's largest producer of cocoa and the fourth largest producer of coffee. These two crops bring in half the country's export revenue although lumber production is also of economic importance. After independence was achieved in 1960, industrialisation developed rapidly, particularly food processing, textiles and sawmills. Oil was discovered offshore in the late 1970s and there is mining for gold and diamonds. Civil war broke out in 2002 between the government-controlled south and the rebel -held north but a fragile peace has been maintained since 2003 with the help of a French and UN peacekeeping force patrolling a buffer zone separating the north from the south.

Area: 124,504 sq mi (322,463 sq km)
Population: 17,654,000
Capital: Yamoussoukro
Form of government: Republic
Religions: Traditional beliefs, Sunni Islam, Christianity
Currency: CFA franc

Croatia a republic of former Yugoslavia that made a unilateral declaration of independence on 25 June 1991. Located in southeast Europe, it is bounded to the west by the Adriatic Sea, to the north by SLOVENIA and ROMANIA and to the south by BOSNIA-HERZEGOVINA. Western Croatia lies in the Dinaric Alps. The eastern region, drained by the Rivers Sava and Drava, which both flow into the Danube, is low-lying and agricultural. The chief farming region is the Pannonian Plain. Over one-third of the country is forested, with beech and oak trees being predominant and lumber is a major export. Deposits of coal, bauxite, copper, petroleum, oil and iron ore are substantial and most of the republic's industry is based on their processing. In Istria in the north-west and on the Dalmatian coast tourism was a major industry until Croatia became embroiled in the Serbo-Croat war. Following the formal recognition of Croatia's independence by the international community, the country and its economy experienced several years of authoritarian nationalism. More recently, under a new government, Croatia is once again a popular tourist destination whose economy continues to grow and the country has made sufficient progress to apply for European Union membership (possibly in 2010).

Area: 21,824 sq mi (56,538 sq km)
Population: 4,501,000
Capital: Zagreb
Form of government: Republic
Religion: Christianity
Currency: Kuna

Cuba the largest and most westerly of the Greater Antilles group of islands in the West Indies. It is strategically positioned at the entrance to the Gulf of Mexico and lies about 87 miles (140 kilometres) south of the tip of Florida. Cuba is as big as all the other Caribbean islands put together and is home to a third of the whole West Indian population. The climate is warm and generally rainy and hurricanes are liable to occur between June and November. The island consists mainly of extensive plains and the soil is fertile. The most important agricultural product is sugar and its byproducts and the processing of these is the most important industry. Tobacco is also of commercial significance, with Havana cigars being known internationally. Most of Cuba's trade was with other communist countries, particularly the former USSR, and the country's economy has suffered without Soviet aid. More recently Cuba has seen investment from China and Latin America. Money sent home by Cubans working abroad remains crucial to the economy.

Area: 42,804 sq mi (110,861 sq km)
Population: 11,382,000
Capital: Havana (La Habana)
Form of government: Republic
Religion: Christianity
Currency: Cuban peso

Cyprus an island that lies in the eastern Mediterranean about 53 miles (85 kilometres) south of TURKEY. It is divided from west to east by two parallel ranges of mountains that are separated by a wide central plain open to the sea at either end. The highest point is Mount Olympus (6,401 feet/1,951 metres) in the southwest. The climate is Mediterranean, with very hot dry summers and warm damp winters. This contributes towards the great variety of crops grown, such as early potatoes, vegetables, cereals, tobacco, olives, bananas and grapes. The grapes are used for the strong wines and sherries for which Cyprus is famous. The main mineral found is copper while asbestos, gypsum and iron pyrites are also present. Fishing is a significant industry, but above all the island depends on visitors and it is the tourist industry that has led to a recovery in the economy since 1974, when it was invaded by Turkey, which still occupies the northern third of the island. The island has remained divided even after joining the European Union in 2004 (EU regulations apply only to the Greek Cypriot community), but talks continue in the hope of the island being reunited.

Area: 3,572 sq mi (9,251 sq km)
Population: 756,000
Capital: Nicosia
Form of government: Republic
Religions:Christianity, Sunni Islam
Currency: Cyprus pound/ Turkish lira in the north

Czech Republic a country that was newly constituted on 1 January 1993 with the dissolution of the 74-year-old federal republic of Czechoslovakia. It is landlocked, at the heart of central Europe, bounded by SLOVAKIA, GERMANY, POLAND and AUSTRIA.

Natural boundaries are formed by the Sudeten Mountains in the north, the Erzgebirge, or Ore Mountains, to the northwest and the Bohemian Forest in the southwest. The climate is humid continental, with warm summers and cold winters. Most rain falls in summer and thunderstorms are frequent. Agriculture, although accounting for only a small percentage of the national income, is highly developed and efficient. The main crops are sugar beet, wheat and potatoes. Over a third of the labour force is employed in industry, which has to import its raw materials and energy. The most important industries are iron and steel, coal, machinery, cement and paper. Recently investment has gone into electronics factories and research establishments. Tourism has increased post-Communism, with the country's many resorts, historic cities and winter sports facilities attracting visitors. The Czech Republic joined the European Union in 2004.

Area: 30,450 sq mi (78,864 sq km)
Population: 10,291,900
Capital: Prague (Praha)
Form of government: Republic
Religions: Christianity
Currency: Czech koruna

Denmark a small European state lying between the North Sea and the entrance to the Baltic. It consists of a western peninsula and an eastern archipelago of more than 500 islands, 100 of which are inhabited. The country is very low-lying and the proximity of the sea combined with the effect of the Gulf Stream result in warm sunny summers and cold cloudy winters. The scenery is flat and monotonous and the acidic soils need a great deal of fertilisation for a wide variety of crops to be grown. It is an agricultural country and three-quarters of the land is cultivated, mostly by the rotation of grass, barley, oats and sugar beet. Animal husbandry is, however, a particularly important activity, its produce including the famous Danish bacon and butter. Danish beer and lager are also famous throughout the world. It is estimated that 85 per cent of the population live in the towns and cities. Despite Denmark's limited range of raw materials, it produces a wide range of manufactured goods and is famous for its imaginative design in ceramics, furniture, silverware and porcelain. Denmark is a wealthy country with a high standard of living.

Area: 16,639 sq mi (43,094 sq km)
Population: 5,450,000 (excluding the FAEROE ISLANDS)
Capital: Copenhagen (København)
Form of government: Constitutional Monarchy
Religion: Christianity
Currency: Danish krone

Djibouti a country that is situated in north-east Africa and is bounded almost entirely by ETHIOPIA except in the southeast where it shares a border with SOMALIA and in the northwest with ERITREA. Its coastline is on the Gulf of Aden and it controls access to the Red Sea. Djibouti was formerly a French overseas territory but achieved independence in 1977. The land, which is mainly basalt plains, has some mountains rising to about 5,000 feet (1,500 metres). The climate is hot, among the world's hottest and extremely dry. Less than a tenth of the land can be farmed even for grazing so it has great difficulty supporting its modest population. Crops raised include fruits, vegetables and dates. Most foodstuffs for the urban population in Djibouti city are imported. Cattle, hides and skins are the main exports. There are small deposits of copper, iron ore and gypsum but these are not mined. The capital is linked to Addis Ababa by a railway and it handles Ethiopia's imports and exports. It is the country's location that is its most important economic asset ensuring foreign aid (from France and the US in particular), transit fees and harbour taxes.

Area: 8,958 sq mi (23,200 sq km)
Population: 486,530
Capital: Djibouti
Form of government: Republic
Religion: Sunni Islam
Currency: Djiboutian franc

Dominica discovered by Columbus, Dominica is the most northerly of the Windward Islands in the West Indies. It is situated between the islands of Martinique and Guadeloupe. The island is very rugged and with the exception of 87 square miles (225 square kilometres) of flat land, it consists of three inactive volcanoes, the highest of which is 4,747 feet (1,447 metres). There are many unnavigable rivers and Boiling Lake, situated in the south, often gives off sulphurous gases. The climate is tropical and even on the leeward coast it rains two days out of three. The wettest season is from June to October when hurricanes often occur. The steep slopes are difficult to farm but agriculture provides almost all Dominica's exports. Bananas are the main agricultural export, but copra, citrus fruits, cocoa, coconuts, bay leaves, cinnamon and vanilla are also revenue earners. Industry is mostly based on the processing of the agricultural products. There are the beginnings of a tourist industy.

Area: 290 sq mi (751 sq km)
Population: 69,000
Capital: Roseau
Form of government: Republic
Religion: Christianity
Currency: East Caribbean dollar

Dominican Republic a country that forms the eastern portion of the island of Hispaniola in the West Indies. It covers two-thirds of the island, the smaller portion consisting of HAITI. The climate is semi-tropical and occasionally hurricanes occur, causing great destruction. The west of the country is made up of four almost parallel mountain ranges and between the two most northerly is the fertile Cibao Valley. The southeast is made up of fertile plains. Although well endowed with fertile land, only about 30 per cent is cultivated. Sugar is the main crop and mainstay of the country's economy and is grown mainly on plantations on the southeast plains. Other crops grown are rice, coffee, bananas, cocoa and tobacco. Mining of gold, silver, platinum, nickel and aluminium is carried out, but the main industries are food processing and manufacture of consumer goods. The island has fine beaches and the tourism industry is now very important to the economy.

Area: 18,816 sq mi (48,734 sq km)
Population: 9,183,000
Capital: Santo Domingo
Form of government: Republic
Religion: Christianity
Currency: Dominican peso

East Timor a country at the the eastern end of the Lesser Sunda Islands in the Malay archipelago in southeast Asia, consisting of the eastern part of the island of Timor, a coastal enclave on the northwest and the islands of Ataúro and Jaco. Formerly a Portuguese overseas province, Portuguese Timor was illegally annexed by Indonesia in 1975, a claim that was never recognised by the UN. East Timor was the site of much civil unrest in its fight for independence, and its independence movement was violently suppressed by Indonesia. A referendum in 1999 officially ended Indonesia's occupation and after a transitional period under UN administration, it became an independent country in 2002. The UN also played a role in rebuilding the country winding up its support in 2005. Recent attacks, however, by rebel soldiers have prompted the UN to set up a new peacekeeping force with extra help from Australian trops. The economy is mainly supported by the export of maize and coffee but offshore oil and gas fields should ensure an improvement in the country's economy.

Area: 5,743 sq mi (14,874 sq km)
Population: 1,200,000
Capital: Dili
Form of government: Republic
Religions: Christianity, Islam
Currency: US dollar

Ecuador an Andean country situated in the northwest of the South American continent. It is bounded to the north by COLOMBIA and to the east and south by PERU. It also includes the Galapagos Islands, which are located about 600 miles (965 kilometres) west of the mainland. The country contains over 30 active volcanoes, with Mount Cotopaxi at 19,340 feet (5,895 metres) the highest active volcano on Earth. Running down the middle of Ecuador are two ranges of the Andes that are divided by a central plateau. The coastal area consists of plains and the eastern area is made up of tropical jungles. The climate varies from equatorial through warm temperate to mountain conditions according to altitude. It is in the coastal plains that plantations of bananas, cocoa, coffee and sugar cane are found. In contrast to this, the highland areas are adapted to grazing, dairying and cereal growing. The fishing industry is important on the Pacific Coast and processed fish such as tuna and shrimp are main exports. Ecuador is one of the world's leading producers of balsawood. Oil is produced in the eastern region and petroleum is Ecuador's most important export. Rapid economic growth in the 1960s has been replaced by recession in recent years and sweeping reforms have led to widespread unrest.

Area: 109,484 sq mi (283,561 s km)
Population: 13,547,000
Capital: Quito
Form of government: Republic
Religion: Christianity
Currency: US dollar

Egypt a country situated in northeast Africa, acting as the doorway between Africa and Asia. Its outstanding physical feature is the Tiver Nile, the valley and delta of which cover about 13,737 square miles (35,580 square kilometres). The climate is mainly dry but there are winter rains along the Mediterranean coast. The temperatures are comfortable in winter but summer temperatures are extremely high, particularly in the south. The rich soils deposited by floodwaters along the banks of the Nile can support a large population and the delta is one of the world's most fertile agricultural regions. Around 99 per cent of the population live in the delta and Nile valley where the main crops are rice, cotton, sugar cane, maize, tomatoes and wheat. This concentration makes it one of the most densely populated areas in the world. The main industries are food processing and textiles. The economy has been boosted by the discovery of oil which is enough to supply the country's needs and leave surplus for export. Natural gas production is increasing for domestic use and Egypt has a significant fishing industry, mainly in the shallow lakes and Red Sea. The Suez Canal, shipping and tourism connected with the ancient sites are also important revenue earners. The country has played an important role in Middle East politics in recent times.

Area: 386,662 sq mi (1,001,449 sq km)
Population: 78,603,000
Capital: Cairo (El Qâhira)
Form of government: Republic
Religions: Sunni Islam, Christianity
Currency: Egyptian pound

El Salvador the smallest and most densely populated state in Central America. It is bounded north and east by HONDURAS and has a Pacific coast to the south. Two volcanic ranges run from east to west across the country. The Lempa river cuts the southern ranges in the centre of the country and opens as a large sandy delta to the Pacific Ocean. Although fairly near the equator, the climate tends to be warm rather than hot and the highlands have a cooler temperate climate. The country is predominantly agricultural and 32 per cent of the land is used for crops such as coffee (the major crop and revenue earner), cotton, maize, beans, rice and sorghum and a slightly smaller area is used for grazing cattle, pigs, sheep and goats. Fishing is carried out, the most important being shrimp, although tuna, mackerel and swordfish are also caught. A few industries such as food processing, textiles and chemicals are found in the major towns. The country suffers from a high rate of inflation and unemployment and is one of the poorest countries in the West.

Area: 8,124 sq mi (21,041 sq km)
Population: 6,822,000
Capital: San Salvador
Form of government: Republic
Religion: Christianity
Currency: US dollar/Salvadoran colon

Equatorial Guinea a country that lies about 124 miles (200 kilometres) north of the equator on the hot humid coast of west Africa. The country consists of a square-shaped mainland area (Mbini), with its few small offshore islets and the islands of Bioko and Pagalu (Annobon). The climate is tropical. Bioko is a very fertile volcanic island and it is here that the capital, Malabo, is situated beside a volcanic crater flooded by the sea. It is also the centre of the country's cocoa production. Coffee and lumber are produced for export on the mainland. Large gas and oil deposits were discovered in the 1990s and the country is now one of sub-Saharan Africa's biggest oil producers with a fast-growing economy. However, the benefits of these oil revenues have not yet reached the vast majority of the country's people who continue to live in poverty.

Area: 10,830 sq mi (28,051 sq km)
Population: 540,000

Capital: Malabo
Form of government: Republic
Religion: Christianity
Currency: CFA franc

Eritrea formerly an autonomous province of ETHIOPIA the country gained independence in May 1993, shortly after a landslide vote in favour of sovereignty. Bounded by DJIBOUTI, SUDAN and ETHIOPIA, Eritrea has acquired Ethiopia's entire coastline along the Red Sea. Eritrea's climate is hot and dry along its desert coast but is colder and wetter in its central highland regions. Most of the population depend on subsistence farming. Eritrea's natural resources include gold, potash, zinc, copper, salt, fish and probably oil. Deforestation and the consequent erosion are partly responsible for the frequent droughts and resultant famines that have blighted this area in recent years. Future revenues may come from developing fishing, tourism and oil industries but the country's economy faces a huge challenge after more than thirty years of fighting. Famines and war with Ethiopia have left a great many of the people of Eritrea displaced and even now more than half of the population relies on food aid in order to survive.

Area: 45,406 sq mi (117,600 sq km)
Population: 4,786,000
Capital: Asmara
Form of government: Transitional government
Religions: Sunni Islam, Christianity
Currency: Nakfa

Estonia a country that has over 1,500 islands and lies to the northwest of RUSSIA, bounded to the north by the Gulf of Finland, to the west by the Baltic Sea and to the south by LATVIA. It is the smallest of the three previous Soviet Baltic Republics. Agriculture and dairy farming are the chief occupations. The main products are grain, potatoes, flax, vegetables, meat, milk and eggs. Livestock includes cattle, sheep, goats and pigs. Almost 22 per cent of Estonia is forested, mainly with aspen, pine, birch and fir and this provides material for sawmills, furniture, match and pulp industries. The country has rich, high quality shale deposits and phosphorous has been found near the capital, Tallinn. Peat deposits are substantial and supply some of the electric power stations. Estonia has about 72 per cent of its population living in urban areas, with almost a third living in the capital city. Tourism and investment from the West have greatly contributed to the country's economy and it became a member of the European Union in 2004.

Area: 17,413 sq mi (45,227 sq km)
Population: 1,324,800
Capital: Tallinn
Form of government: Republic
Religion: Christianity
Currency: Estonian kroon

Ethiopia a landlocked, East African country that has borders with Sudan, Kenya, Somalia, Djibouti and Eritrea. Most of the country consists of highlands that drop sharply toward Sudan in the west. Because of the wide range of latitudes, Ethiopia has many climatic variations between the high temperate plateau and the hot humid lowlands. There are mineral deposits of copper, iron, petroleum, platinum and gold, which have been exploited. The country is very vulnerable to drought. Around 80 per cent of the population are subsistence farmers. Coffee is the main source of rural income and the country's main export. Employment outside agriculture is confined to a small manufacturing sector in Addis Ababa. The country's population has endured periodic droughts and famines, a long civil war and a border war with Eritrea. Ethiopia's environmental, economic and political problems mean it is one of Africa's poorest nations.

Area: 426,373 sq mi (1,104,300 sq km)
Population: 74,777,000
Capital: Addis Ababa (Adis Abeba)
Form of government: Federal Republic
Religions: Christianity, Sunni Islam
Currency: Ethiopian birr

Faeroe (Faroe) Islands (Føroyar) a self-governing part of Denmark since 1948, consisting of a group of 18 basaltic islands situated in the North Atlantic, approximately halfway between the Shetland Islands and Iceland. The landscape is characterised by steep, stepped peaks rising out of the sea to nearly 3,000 feet (900 metres) and glaciated, trough-shaped valleys. Although the islands are inhabited, poor agricultural conditions compel the population to seek their living at sea. Fishing, including some whaling, is the main occupation and exports comprise fish and associated products. Danish aid is an important part of the country's economy but there is the potential for major offshore oil and gas and this has supported demands for full independence from Denmark.

Area: 540 sq mi (1,399 sq km)
Population: 47,000
Capital: Tørshavn
Form of government: Self-governing Region of Denmark
Religion: Christianity
Currency: Danish krone

Falkland Islands a British overseas territory situated in the South Atlantic, consisting of two large islands (West and East Falkland), separated by the 10-mile (16-kilometre) wide Falkland Sound and surrounded by some 200 smaller islands. Lying about 410 miles (650 kilometres) east of southern Argentina, these islands were invaded by Argentina in 1982 but recaptured by a British marine task force a few months later. The main economic activity is sheep farming. The highest point is Mount Usborne at 2,313 feet (705 metres). Over recent years, substantial income has been gained from the sales of licenses to permit foreign trawlers to fish in the Falklands exclusion zone. Considerable offshore oil reserves are also available.

Area: 4,700 sq mi (12,173 sq km)
Population: 2,967
Capital: Port Stanley
Form of government: British Overseas Territory
Religion: Christianity
Currency: Falkland pound

Fiji one of the largest nations in the western Pacific, consisting of some 800 islands and atolls of which only about 100 are inhabited. It is situated around the 180-degree International Date Line and lies about 17 degrees south of the equator. Fiji has high rainfall, high temperatures and plenty of sunshine all year round. The two main islands, Viti Levu and Vanua Levu, are extinct volcanoes and most of the islands in the group are fringed with coral reefs. The southeast of the islands have tropical rainforests but a lot of lumber has been felled and soil erosion is a growing problem. The main cash crop is sugar cane although copra, ginger and fish are also exported. Tourism is now a major industry and source of revenue but it has been adversely affected by ongoing political coups and ethnic unrest.

Area: 7,056 sq mi (18,274 sq km)
Population: 905,949
Capital: Suva
Form of government: Republic
Religions: Christianity, Hinduism
Currency: Fijian dollar

Finland a Scandinavian country that shares borders with SWEDEN, NORWAY and RUSSIA. Its coastline lies along the Gulf of Bothnia and the Gulf of Finland, both of which are arms of the Baltic Sea. Some 30,000 islands and islets line Finland's coast. Finnish Lapland in the north lies within the Arctic Circle. Most of mainland Finland is low-lying, becoming more hilly towards the north. Almost three-quarters of the country is forested, comprising mainly coniferous trees, such as spruce and pine, and there are many thousands of lakes. The climate has great extremes between summer and winter. Winter is very severe and lasts about six months but only for three months in the south. Summers are short but quite warm, with light rain throughout the country. Finland is largely self-sufficient in food and produces surpluses of dairy produce. Most crops are grown in the southwest. In the north reindeer are herded and forests yield great quantities of timber for export. Major industries are metals, machinery and electronics, paper and paper products, shipbuilding and chemicals. Finland has a modern, competitive economy. It became a member of the European Union in 1995.

Area: 130,559 sq mi (338,145 sq km)
Population: 5,231,000
Capital: Helsinki (Helsingfors)
Form of government: Republic
Religion: Christianity
Currency: Euro

France the largest country in western Europe, with a coastline on the English Channel, the Mediterranean Sea and on the Atlantic Ocean. The lowest parts of the country are the great basins of the north and southwest from which it rises to the Massif Central and the higher Alps, Jura and Pyrénées. The climate ranges from moderate maritime in the northwest to Mediterranean in the south. Farming is possible in

all parts of France, with forestry and fishing also providing some employment. The western shores are ideal for rearing livestock, while the Paris Basin is good arable land. In the southwest around Bordeaux, vineyards produce some of the world's best wines. The main industrial area of France is in the north and east and the main industries are iron and steel, engineering, chemicals, textiles and electrical goods. France has a long cultural history of art, literature, sculpture and music and is famous for its immense Gothic churches. France is an important player on the world stage and has long been one of the countries at the heart of European economic and political integration.

Area: 212,935 sq mi (551,500 sq km)
Population: 60,876,000
Capital: Paris
Form of government: Republic
Religion: Christianity
Currency: Euro

French Guiana *see* GUIANA.

French Polynesia a total of about 130 islands in the South Pacific Ocean administered as overseas territories by FRANCE. The islands include the Society Islands, the Tuamotu group, the Gambier group, the Tubual Islands and the Marquesas Islands.

Area: 1,544 sq mi (4,000 sq km)
Population: 274,578
Capital: Papeete
Form of government: Overseas Territory of France
Religion: Christianity
Currency: CFP franc

Gabon a small country in west central Africa that straddles the equator. It has a low narrow coastal plain and the rest of the country comprises a low plateau. Three-quarters of Gabon is covered by dense tropical forest. The climate is hot, humid and typically equatorial. Until the 1960s lumber was virtually Gabon's only resource and then oil was discovered. By the mid-1980s it was Africa's sixth largest oil producer and other minerals, such as manganese, uranium and iron ore, were being exploited. Deposits of lead and silver have also been discovered. Despite the earnings from these resources around two-thirds of the Gabonese people remain subsistence farmers, growing cassava, sugar cane, plantains and yams. The country has great tourism potential and as its oil reserves get smaller, eco-tourism could become more important to the economy.

Area: 103,347 sq mi (267,668 sq km)
Population: 1,424,000
Capital: Libreville
Form of government: Republic
Religions: Christianity, traditional beliefs
Currency: CFA franc

Gambia the smallest country in Africa, which pokes like a crooked finger into SEN-EGAL. The country is divided along its entire length by the River Gambia. On the coast there are pristine beaches and sand cliffs backed by mangrove swamps, with tropical jungle clothing much of the river banks away from the coast. In the dry season there is little rainfall, then the southwest monsoon sets in, with spectacular storms producing heavy rain for four months. Most Gambians live in villages with a few animals and grow enough millet and sorghum to feed themselves. Groundnuts are the main and only export crop of any significance. The river provides a thriving local fishing industry and the white sandy beaches on the coast are becoming increasingly popular with foreign tourists, although a military takeover in 1994 dealt tourism and trade a blow. The country has since returned to constitutional rule and remains relatively stable.

Area: 4,361 sq mi (11,295 sq km)
Population: 1,141,000
Capital: Banjul
Form of government: Republic
Religions: Sunni Islam, Christianity
Currency: Dalasi

Georgia a republic in the southwest of the former USSR, occupying the central and western parts of the Caucasus. It is bounded to the west by the Black Sea and shares borders with TURKEY, ARMENIA, AZERBAIJAN and RUSSIA. Georgia declared itself independent in 1991. Almost 40 per cent of the country is covered by forests. Agriculture, which is the main occupation of the population, includes tea cultivation and fruit growing, especially citrus fruits and viticulture. Georgia is rich in minerals, especially manganese, but imports the majority of its energy needs. Industries include coal, lumber, machinery, chemicals, silk, food processing and furniture. In the past, the Black Sea tourist trade exploited

the country's wealth of thermal and mineral springs very successfully and tourism should again become an economic mainstay. The country has long been dependent on Russia for its energy supply and in recent years prices have doubled causing Georgia to look to Azerbaijan for its gas supplies. The US has an increasing influence in the country. There have been periods of unrest and violence in the breakaway regions of Abkhazia and South Ossetia both of which have strong ties with Russia.

Area: 26,911 sq mi (69,700 sq km)
Population: 4,661,000
Capital: T'bilisi
Form of government: Republic
Religions: Christianity , Islam
Currency: Lari

Germany a large populous country in northern central Europe that comprises the former East and West German republics, unified in 1990. In the north is the North German Plain, which merges with the North Rhinelands in the west. Farther south, a plateau that stretches across the country from east to west is divided by the River Rhine. In the southwest the Black Forest separates the Rhine Valley from the fertile valleys and scarplands of Swabia. The Bohemian Uplands and Erz Mountains mark the border with the CZECH REPUBLIC. Generally the country has warm summers and cold winters. Agricultural products include wheat, rye, barley, oats, potatoes and sugar beet, but agriculture accounts for only a small percentage of employment and a third of the country's food has to be imported. The main industrial and most densely populated areas are in the Ruhr Valley. Products of the principal manufacturing industries include iron and steel, motor vehicles, mechanical and electrical equipment, aircraft, ships, computers, electronic and technical goods, chemicals and petrochemicals, pharmaceuticals, textiles, clothing and footwear, foods, beer, optical and high precision instruments. The German economy has struggled to cope with the demands of unification but Germany is now a key player within the European Union and the government continues to try and revive the economy.

Area: 137,735 sq mi (356,733 sq km)
Population: 82,422,000

Capital: Berlin
Form of government: Federal Republic
Religion:Christianity
Currency: Euro

Ghana a country located on the southern coast of West Africa between CÔTE D'IVOIRE and TOGO. In 1957, as the former British Gold Coast, it became the first African state in the region to achieve independence from European colonial rule. The climate on the coast is equatorial and towards the north there are steamy tropical evergreen forests which give way in the far north to tropical savanna. The landscape becomes harsh and barren near the border with BURKINA FASO. Cocoa, rubber, palm oil and coffee are grown in the south of the country. Ghana's most important crop is cocoa and cocoa exports are an essential part of the economy. There is also a successful tuna fishing industry. Ghana has important mineral resources, notably gold, diamonds, manganese ore and bauxite. Over the past three decades, the country has moved towards economic stability and democracy.

Area: 92,100 sq mi (238,537 sq km)
Population: 22,409,350
Capital: Accra
Form of government: Republic
Religions: Christianity, traditional beliefs
Currency: Cedi

Gibraltar a self-governing British overseas territory on the southwestern tip of SPAIN, where a limestone hill called the Rock of Gibraltar rises to 1,394 feet (425 metres). Its strategic importance, guarding as it does the western approaches to the Mediterranean and separated from MOROCCO by the narrow Straits of Gibraltar, has resulted in it being occupied at various periods of history by Phoenicians, Carthaginians, Romans, Visigoths, Moors, Spaniards and the British. In 1713, the Treaty of Utrecht awarded Gibraltar to Britain but Spain has never relinquished its claim to the Rock. The British armed forces, tourism, offshore finance and construction are the main sources of employment and most imports are from Britain. The Mediterranean climate and many sites of natural and historical interest attract numerous visitors each year.

Area: 2.5 sq mi (6.5 sq km)
Population: 29,000

Capital: Gibraltar
Form of government: British Overseas Territory
Religion: Christianity
Currency: Gibraltar pound

Greece the Greek peninsula is the most southeasterly extension of Europe and has over 1,400 islands lying off its coast and scattered throughout the Aegean Sea. Mainland Greece shares borders with ALBANIA in the northwest, MACEDONIA and BULGARIA in the north and TURKEY in the northeast. The northwestern and central regions of the country are rugged and mountainous, the main chain being the Pindus Mountains. About 70 per cent of the land is hilly, with harsh mountain climates and poor soils. There are few natural resources of economic value although there are deposits of petroleum and natural gas found under the Aegean Sea. The Greek islands and coastal regions have a typical Mediterranean climate with mild rainy winters and hot dry summers. Winter in the northern mountains is severe, with deep snow and heavy precipitation. About 21 per cent of the people are engaged in agriculture, mostly on small family farms. Forestry and fishing are carried out on a small scale. Greece has seen rapid economic and social change in recent years and it successfully organised the 2004 Olympic Games in Athens. Tourism is a major source of revenue for the country along with shipping but the government still has to cope with high unemployment and rising inflation.

Area: 50,949 sq mi (131,957 sq km)
Population: 10,688,000
Capital: Athens (Athínai)
Form of government: Republic
Religion: Christianity
Currency: Euro

Greenland (Kalaallit Nunaat) the largest island in the world (discounting continental land masses) and an autonomous Danish dependent territory. It lies mainly within the Arctic Circle, off the northeast coast of Canada. Its vast interior is mostly covered with a permanent ice cap that has a known thickness of up to 11,000 feet (3,300 metres). The ice-free coastal strips are characterised by largely barren mountains, rising to Gunnbjorn at 12,140 feet (3,700 metres) in the southeast. Glaciers flow into deeply indented fjords fringed by many islands, islets and icebergs. Of the small ice-free fringe, only about a third (58,000 square miles/150,000 square kilometres) can be classed as being inhabited, mainly in the southwest. The largely Inuit population is heavily dependent on fishing, and fish account for 95 per cent of exports. There is some sheep farming and mining of coal. Other mineral resources include iron ore, lead, zinc, uranium and molybdenum. Denmark is Greenland's main trading partner.

Area: 840,000 sq mi (2,175,600 sq km)
Population: 56,361
Capital: Gothåb (Nuuk)
Form of government: Self-governing territory of Denmark
Religion: Christianity
Currency: Danish krone

Grenada the most southerly of the Windward Islands chain in the Caribbean and its territory includes the southern Grenadine Islands to the north. The main island consists of the remains of extinct volcanoes with an attractive wooded landscape. The highest peak is Mount St Catherine at 2,750 feet (838 metres). In the dry season the typical climate consists of warm days and cool nights, but in the wet season it is hot day and night. Agriculture is the island's main industry and the chief crops grown for export are nutmeg, citrus fruits, cocoa, bananas and mace. Apart from the processing of its crops, Grenada has a small manufacturing industry and tourism is an important source of foreign revenue. It is a popular port of call for cruise ships.

Area: 133 sq mi (344 sq km)
Population: 89,703
Capital: St George's
Form of government: Independent state within the Commonwealth
Religion: Christianity
Currency: East Caribbean dollar

Guadeloupe a small group of islands in the Caribbean lying in the middle of the Lesser Antilles, with some islands in the Leeward Islands and some in the Windward Islands. Since 1946 Guadeloupe has been a French Overseas Territory. Ninety per cent of the population live on the two main islands of Basse Terre and Grande Terre. Basse Terre

is mountainous, covered with rainforest and dominated by the Soufrière volcano at 4,318 feet (1,467 metres). Grande Terre is flat and dry with white sandy beaches. The other islands include Marie Galante, La Désirade, Iles des Saints, St Barthélémy and St Martin. The islands have a warm and humid climate with rainfall heaviest between May and November. Main exports include bananas, sugar and rum. Tourism is important to the economy which is supported by French foreign aid.

Area: 658 sq mi (1,705 sq km)
Population: 431,000
Capital: Basse Terre
Other main town: Pointe-à-Pitre
Form of government: French Overseas Territory
Religion: Christianity
Currency: Euro

Guam the most southerly and the largest of the Mariana Islands in the northwest Pacific. It consists mainly of a high, coraline limestone plateau with some low volcanic mountains in the south of the island. Guam's climate is tropical with a rainy season from July to December. An unincorporated territory of the USA, its economy depends to a large extent on US government activities and its military installations. Exports include copra, palm oil and processed fish. The country has also become a financial centre, particularly for mainland and Asian banks and tourism has come to play an important role in its economy.

Area: 212 sq mi (549 sq km)
Population: 171,019
Capital: Agana
Form of government: Unincorporated Territory of the USA
Religion: Christianity
Currency: US dollar

Guatemala a country situated between the Pacific Ocean and the Caribbean Sea where North America meets Central America. It is mountainous, with a ridge of volcanoes running parallel to the Pacific coast. It has a tropical climate. The Pacific slopes of the mountains are exceptionally well watered and fertile and it is here that most of the population is settled. Coffee-growing on the lower slopes dominates the economy, although bananas, sugar, cardamom, petroleum and shellfish are exported. The forested area of the country (about 36 per cent) plays an important part in the country's economy and produces balsam, cabinet woods, chicle and oils. There are also deposits of petroleum and zinc, while lead and silver are mined. Industry is mainly restricted to the processing of agricultural products. Most trade is with the USA. Guatemala is politically a very unstable country and its ongoing civil conflict has practically destroyed tourism.

Area: 42,042 sq mi (108,889 sq km)
Population: 12,293,000
Capital: Guatemala City
Form of government: Republic
Religions: Christianity, traditional beliefs
Currency: Quetzal

Guiana (French) situated on the northeast coast of South America and still an overseas department of FRANCE, Guiana is bounded to the south and east by BRAZIL and to the west by SURINAM. The climate is tropical with heavy rainfall. Guiana's economy relies almost completely on subsidies from France. The small area of land that is cultivated produces rice, manioc and sugar cane. Recently the French have tried to develop the tourist industry and exploit the extensive reserves of hardwood in the jungle interior. This has led to a growing sawmill industry and the export of logs. Natural resources, in addition to lumber, include bauxite, cinnabar (mercury ore) and gold (although this is in scattered deposits). The Ariane rocket launch site of the European Space Agency is located at Kourou on the north coast.

Area: 34,749 sq mi (90,000 sq km)
Population: 199,509
Capital: Cayenne
Form of government: French Overseas Department
Religion: Christianity
Currency: Euro

Guinea located on the coast at the 'bulge' in Africa, Guinea is a lush green beautiful country about the same size as the UNITED KINGDOM. It has a tropical climate with constant heat and a high rainfall near the coast. Its principal rivers are the Gambia and the Bafing while the Niger rises in the forests of the Guinea Highlands. Guinea has great agricultural potential and many of its coastal swamps and forested plains have been cleared for the cultivation of rice, cassava, yams, maize and vegetables. Around 80 per cent of the population are subsistence farmers. Further inland on the plateau of Fouta Djallon, dwarf cattle are raised and in the valleys bananas and pineapples are grown. Coffee and kola nuts are important cash crops grown in the Guinea Highlands to the southwest. Minerals such as bauxite, iron ore, diamonds, gold and uranium are mined. However economic development and stability are being hampered by the presence of refugees from the fighting in Sierra Leone and Liberia, and ongoing economic mismanagement.

Area: 94,926 sq mi (245,857 sq km)
Population: 9,690,000
Capital: Conakry
Form of government: Republic
Religion: Sunni Islam
Currency: Guinean franc

Guinea-Bissau formerly a Portuguese territory but granted independence in 1974, Guinea-Bissau is located south of SENEGAL on the Atlantic coast of West Africa. The republic's territory includes over 60 coastal islands, including the archipelago of Bijagós. The country rises from a deeply indented and island-fringed coastline to a low inland plateau and hills on the border with neighbouring GUINEA. The climate is tropical, with abundant rain from June to November but hot dry conditions for the rest of the year. The main crops grown by the country's subsistence farmers are rice, groundnuts, cassava, sugar cane, plantains, maize and coconuts. Fishing is an important export industry although cashew nuts are the principal export. Years of Portuguese rule and civil war have left Guinea-Bissau impoverished. With massive foreign debt, it is one of the poorest West African states and political instability continues to adversely affect its economy.

Area: 13,948 sq mi (36,125 sq km)
Population: 1,442,000
Capital: Bissau
Form of government: Republic
Religions: Traditional beliefs, Sunni Islam
Currency: CFA franc

Guyana the only English-speaking country in South America, situated on the northeast coast of the continent on the Atlantic Ocean. Guyana was formerly called British Guiana but achieved independence in 1966. The country is intersected by many rivers and the coastal area comprises tidal marshes and mangrove swamps. Rice is grown on this narrow coastal area and vast plantations produce sugar. Ninety per cent of the population live in the coastal area where the climate is moderated by sea breezes. Sugar and its by-products and rice are the mainstay of the country's economy, while tropical fruits and vegetables are grown mainly for home consumption. Guyana's principal mineral is bauxite, but gold, manganese and diamonds are also exploited. It remains among the region's poorest countries due to political instability, ethnic unrest and poor economic management.

Area: 83,000 sq mi (214,969 sq km)
Population: 767,245
Capital: Georgetown
Form of government: Republic
Religions: Christianity, Hinduism, Islam
Currency: Guyanese dollar

Guyane *see* GUIANA (FRENCH).

Haiti occupying the western third of the large island of Hispaniola in the Caribbean, Haiti is a mountainous country consisting of five different ranges separated by deep valleys and plains. The highest point reaches 8,793 feet (2,680 metres) at Pic La Selle. The climate is tropical but semi-arid conditions can occur in the lee of the central mountains. Hurricanes and severe thunderstorms are a common occurrence. Agriculture is the chief occupation, with around 80 per cent of the population concentrated in rural areas. Many farmers grow only enough to feed their families and the export crops of coffee, sugar and sisal are grown on large estates. Severe soil erosion caused by extensive forest clearance has resulted in a decline in crop yields and environmental damage. The country has only a limited amount of natural resources, including bauxite, salt, copper and gold. Haiti is the poorest country in the Americas and has experienced many uprisings and attempted coups.

Area: 10,714 sq mi (27,750 sq km)
Population: 8,308,000
Capital: Port-au-Prince
Form of government: Republic

Religions: Christianity, Voodooism
Currency: Gourde

Honduras a fan-shaped country in Central America that spreads out towards the Caribbean Sea at the Gulf of Honduras. Four-fifths of the country is covered by mountains that are indented with river valleys running towards the very short Pacific coast. There is little change in temperatures throughout the year and rainfall is heavy, especially on the Caribbean coast where temperatures are also higher than inland. The highlands are covered with forests, mainly of oak and pine, while palms and mangroves grow in the coastal areas. The country is sparsely populated and only about 25 per cent of the land is cultivated. Bananas, coffee and sugar are important crops and these are grown mainly on the coastal plains of the Pacific and Caribbean. Forestry is one of the principal industries. However, Honduras remains one of the least developed countries in the region due to military rule, crime and natural disasters such as Hurricane Mitch in 1998.

Area: 43,277 sq mi (112,088 sq km)
Population: 7,326,000
Capital: Tegucigalpa
Form of government: Republic
Religion: Christianity
Currency: Lempira

Hong Kong formerly a British dependent territory, Hong Kong became a special administrative region of China in 1997. Located in the South China Sea, it consists of Hong Kong Island (once a barren rock), the peninsula of Kowloon and about 386 square miles (1,000 square kilometres) of adjacent land known as the New Territories. Hong Kong is situated at the mouth of the Pearl River about 81 miles (130 kilometres) southeast of Guangzhou (Canton). The climate is warm subtropical with cool dry winters and hot humid summers. Hong Kong has no natural resources and even its water comes from reservoirs across the Chinese border. Its main assets are its magnificent natural harbour and its position close to the main trading routes of the Pacific. Hong Kong's economy is based on free enterprise and trade, an industrious work force and an efficient and aggressive commercial system. Hong Kong's main industries are textiles, clothing, tourism and electronics but its economy is now mainly services-based.

Area: 415 sq mi (1,075 sq km)
Population: 6,940,000
Form of government: Special Administrative Region of China
Religions: Buddhism, Taoism, Christianity
Currency: Hong Kong dollar

Hungary landlocked in the heartland of Europe, Hungary is dominated by the great plain to the east of the River Danube, which runs from north to south across the country. In the west lies the largest lake in Central Europe, Lake Balaton. Winters are severe, but the summers are warm and although wet in the west, summer droughts often occur in the east. Agricultural produce includes wheat, maize, sunflower seeds, potatoes, pigs, cattle, poultry and dairy products. Even prior to the collapse of communism in the country, the government was moving towards a free market economy. Industries include mining, metallurgy and the production of construction materials, processed foods, pharmaceuticals and motor vehicles. Tourism is also an important industry. Foreign investment is high and in 2004 the country became a member of the European Union.

Area: 35,920 sq mi (93,032 sq km)
Population: 9,981,000
Capital: Budapest
Form of government: Republic
Religion: Christianity
Currency: Forint

Iceland a large island situated in a tectonically unstable part of the North Atlantic Ocean, just south of the Arctic Circle. The island has over 100 volcanoes, at least one of which erupts every five years. One-ninth of the country is covered by ice and snow fields and there are about 700 hot springs, which are an important source of central heating, particularly in the volcanic areas. In the capital city, the majority of homes and industries are heated by this method. The climate is cool temperate, but because of the effect of the North Atlantic Drift it is mild for its latitude. Permanent daylight occurs for three months in summer and the beautiful Aurora Borealis (Northern Lights) can be seen from the end of August. The southwest corner is the most densely populated area as the coast here is generally free from ice. Very little of the land can be cultivated and the main crops are root vegetables such as turnip and potatoes. Fishing and fish processing are a mainstay of the Icelandic economy, with much of the catch of Atlantic cod being exported. Aluminium and ferrosilicon, nitrates for fertilisers, cement and chemicals are produced for export. Other manufactured goods include paints, textiles, clothing, footwear and knitted products. Tourism is also of growing importance to the island.

Area: 39,769 sq mi (103,000 sq km)
Population: 275,000
Capital: Reykjavík
Form of government: Republic
Religion: Christianity
Currency: Icelandic krona

India a vast country in South Asia that is dominated in the extreme north by the world's youngest and highest mountains, the Himalayas, which extend about 1,500 miles (about 2,400 kilometres) along India's northern and eastern borders. The range contains Mount Everest and K2. At the foot of the Himalayas, a huge plain, drained by the Indus and Ganges rivers, is one of the most fertile areas in the world and the most densely populated part of India. Farther south the ancient Deccan plateau extends to the southern tip of the country. India generally has four seasons, the cool, the hot, the rainy and the dry. About 70 per cent of the population depend on agriculture for their living and the lower slopes of the Himalayas represent one of the world's best tea-growing areas. Rice, sugar cane and wheat are grown in the Ganges plain and there is a comprehensive system of irrigation to aid agriculture. India is self-sufficient in all its major food crops and main exports include agricultural products, precious stones, jewellery, engineering products, clothes and chemicals, software services and technology. Now a major power in its own right and a nuclear weapons state, India has encouraged foreign investment and its economy is benefitting in particular from its skills in the field of information technology. Nonetheless it still has problems with rural poverty, social unrest and violence within the country, and external disputes with Pakistan.

Area: 1,269,346 sq mi (3,287,590 sq km)
Population: 1,095,351,000
Capital: New Delhi
Form of government: Federal Republic
Religions: Hinduism, Islam, Sikhism, Christianity, Jainism, Buddhism
Currency: Indian rupee

Indonesia a country made up of 13,667 islands that are scattered across the Indian and Pacific Oceans in a huge crescent. It is the world's fourth most highly populated country and has the world's largest Muslim population. Its largest landmass is the province of Kalimantan, which is part of the island of Borneo. Sumatra is the largest individual island. Java, however, is the dominant and most densely populated island. The climate is generally tropical monsoon and temperatures are high all year round. The country has 130 active volcanoes and earthquakes are frequent in the southern islands. Overpopulation is a big problem, especially in Java where its fertile rust-coloured soil is in danger of becoming exhausted. Rice, maize and cassava are the main crops grown. Indonesia has the largest reserves of tin in the world and is one of the world's leading rubber producers. Other mineral resources found are bauxite, natural gas, nickel and copper. Oil production is also important. Indonesia's resources are not as yet fully developed but the development of the country's economy has been hampered by the devastation caused by the 2004 tsunami as well as ongoing political instability, corruption, human rights violations, and armed separatist movements in Aceh and Papua.

Area: 735,358 sq mi (1,904,569 sq km)
Population: 245,452,000
Capital: Jakarta
Form of government: Republic
Religions: Sunni Islam, Christianity, Hinduism
Currency: Indonesian rupiah

Iran lying across The Gulf from the Arabian Peninsula and stretching from the Caspian Sea to the Arabian Sea, Iran is a land dominated by mountains in the north and west, with a huge expanse of desert in its centre. The climate is hot and dry, although more temperate conditions are found on the shores of the Caspian Sea.

In winter, terrible dust storms sweep the deserts and almost no life can survive. Most of the population live in the north and west, where Tehran is situated. The only good agricultural land is on the Caspian coastal plains, where wheat, barley, potatoes and rice are grown. Fresh and dried fruit are the country's main food exports. About 5 per cent of the population are nomadic herdsmen who wander in the mountains. Most of Iran's oil is in the southwest and other valuable minerals include coal, iron ore, copper and lead. Precious stones are found in the northeast. Main exports are petrochemicals, carpets and rugs, textiles, raw cotton and leather goods. A rapid expansion in the economy from petroleum industry revenue slowed dramatically after the Islamic revolution in the late 1970s and an eight-year war with IRAQ. Despite its huge oil and gas reserves, the country is faced with finding jobs for its young population, most of whom are unemployed. Recently, it has defied international pressure over its nuclear programme.

Area: 634,293 sq mi (1,648,195 sq km)
Population: 68,688,000
Capital: Tehran
Form of government: Republic
Religion: Shia Islam
Currency: Iranian rial

Iraq located in southwest Asia, wedged between the Gulf and SYRIA, Iraq is almost landlocked except for its outlet to the Gulf at Shatt al Arab. Its two great rivers, the Tigris and the Euphrates, flow from the northwest into the Gulf at this point. The climate is arid, with very hot summers and cold winters. The high mountains on the border with TURKEY are snow-covered for six months of the year while desert in the southwest covers nearly half the country. Traditionally an agricultural country, the only fertile land in Iraq is in the basins of the Tigris and Euphrates, where wheat, barley, rice, tobacco, cotton and a variety of fruit including dates are grown. Oil has traditionally been the country's main export providing ninety-five per cent of the its foreign earnings. Iraq profited from the great oil boom of the 1970s, but during the war with Iran, oil terminals in the Gulf were destroyed and the Trans-Syrian Pipeline closed. Iraq invaded Kuwait in 1990, leading to the Gulf War in 1991 in which Iraq was defeated by UN forces. The country was already in a state of economic crisis by the time US-led coalition forces deposed Sadam Hussein in 2003. Since then it has been a battleground between insurgents and the Iraqi security and coalition forces and many fear that the increasing tension and violence between Shia and Sunni Muslims may descend into civil war.

Area: 169,235 sq mi (438,317 sq km)
Population: 26,783,000
Capital: Baghdad
Form of government: Republic
Religions: Shia Islam, Sunni Islam
Currency: Iraqi dinar

Ireland, Republic of one of Europe's most westerly countries, situated in the Atlantic Ocean and separated from Great Britain by the Irish Sea. It has an equable climate, with mild southwest winds, which makes temperatures uniform over most of the country. The Republic extends over four-fifths of the island of Ireland and the west and southwest are mountainous, with the highest peak reaching 3,416 feet (1,041 metres) at Carrauntoohil. The central plain is largely limestone covered by boulder clay, which provides good farmland and pasture with about 80 per cent of the land being under agriculture. The main rivers are the Erne and the Shannon. Livestock production, including cattle, sheep, pigs and horses, is the most important agricultural activity. The rural population have tended to migrate to the cities, mainly Dublin, which is the main industrial centre and the focus of radio, television, publishing and communications. Lack of energy resources and remoteness from major markets did slow industrial development but, by taking full advantage of membership of the European Union, the economy has improved markedly in recent years from largely agricultural to modern and technologically advanced, with tourism also making an important contribution.

Area: 27,137 sq mi (70,284 sq km)
Population: 4,062,000
Capital: Dublin (Baile Atha Cliath)
Form of government: Republic
Religion: Christianity
Currency: Euro

Israel occupying a long narrow stretch of land in the southeast of the Mediterranean, Israel's eastern boundary is formed by the Great Rift Valley through which the River Jordan flows to the Dead Sea. The south of the country is made up of a triangular wedge of the Negev desert, which ends at the Gulf of Aqaba. The Negev desert has mineral resources, such as copper, phosphates and manganese, plus commercial amounts of natural gas and petroleum. Other assets are the vast amounts of potash, bromine and other minerals found in the Dead Sea. The climate in summer is hot and dry; in winter it is mild with some rain. The south of the country is arid and barren. Most of the population live on the coastal plain bordering the Mediterranean where Tel Aviv (Tel Aviv-Yafo) is the country's main commercial centre. Jerusalem in the Judean Mountains is the seat of government (and under Israeli law the country's capital). Israel's agriculture is based on collective settlements known as kibbutz. The country is virtually self-sufficient in foodstuffs and a major exporter of its produce. A wide range of products is processed or finished in the country and main exports include finished diamonds, textiles, fruit, vegetables, chemicals, machinery and fertilisers. Tourism also makes an important contribution to the economy. Israel's uneasy relationship with its Arab neighbours and Palestinian nationals in the Palestinian territories has often flared up into open conflict in the region.

Area: 8,130 sq mi (21,056 sq km)
Population: 6,352,000
Seat of government: Jerusalem (but most foreign embassies are in Tel Aviv)
Form of government: Parliamentary democracy
Religions: Judaism, Sunni Islam, Christianity
Currency: New Israeli shekel

Italy a republic in southern Europe that comprises a large peninsula and two main islands of Sicily and Sardinia. The Alps form a natural boundary with its northern and western European neighbours and the Adriatic Sea to the east separates it from the countries of former YUGOSLAVIA. The Apennine Mountains form the backbone of Italy and extend the full length of the peninsula. Between the Alps and the Apennines lies the Po Valley, a great fertile lowland. Sicily and Sardinia are largely mountainous. Much of Italy is geologically unstable and it has four active volcanoes, including Etna, Vesuvius and Stromboli. Italy enjoys warm dry summers and mild winters. In the south farms are small and traditional. Industries in the north include motor vehicles, textiles, clothing, leather goods, glass and ceramics. Although there is a lack of natural resources, almost 60 per cent of the land is under crops and pasture and there is an abundance of building stone, particularly marble. The coastal waters are rich in marine life, with anchovy, sardine and tuna being of commercial importance. Tourism is an important source of foreign currency. One of the countries at the heart of the European Union, Italy's economy has recently faced problems and growth has been slow.

Area: 116,320 sq mi (301,268 sq km)
Population: 58,133,000
Capital: Rome (Roma)
Form of government: Republic
Religion: Christianity
Currency: Euro

Jamaica an island state in the Caribbean Sea about 93 miles (150 kilometres) south of CUBA. The centre of the island comprises a limestone plateau and this is surrounded by narrow coastal flatlands and palm-fringed beaches. The highest mountains, the Blue Mountains, are in the east of the island. The climate is tropical, with high temperatures at the coast and slightly cooler and less humid conditions in the highlands. Jamaica suffers from severe earthquakes and the island lies right in the middle of the hurricane zone. The crops grown include sugar cane, bananas, peppers, ginger, cocoa and coffee. The mining of bauxite and alumina plays a very important part in Jamaica's economy. Tourism is a particularly important industry, with over one million visitors annually but its future is threatened by widespread crime and lawlessness.

Area: 4,243 sq mi (10,990 sq km)
Population: 2,758,000
Capital: Kingston
Form of government: Parliamentary Democracy
Religion: Christianity
Currency: Jamaican dollar

Japan located on the eastern margin of Asia and consisting of four major islands, Honshu, Hokkaido, Kyushu and Shikoku and many small islands, Japan is separated from the mainland of Asia by the Sea of Japan. The country is made up of six chains of steep serrated mountains, which contain about 60 active volcanoes. Earthquakes are frequent and widespread and often accompanied by giant waves (tsunami). A devastating earthquake occurred in 1995 when more than 5,000 people died and over 300,000 were left homeless. Summers are warm and humid and winters mild, except on Hokkaido, which is covered in snow in winter. Japan's agriculture is highly advanced, with extensive use made of fertilisers and miniature machinery for the small fields. Fishing is very important, both for domestic consumption and export. Heavy industries, such as iron and steel, shipbuilding, chemical and petrochemical, used to account for almost three-quarters of Japan's export revenue, but now it has to rely on the success of its manufacturing industry which produces automobiles, televisions, videos, electronic equipment, cameras, watches, clocks, robots and textiles. Japan's financial crisis of 1997 and bouts of recession prompted economic reforms which have helped it to retain one of the world's largest economies.

Area: 145,870 sq mi (377,801 sq km)
Population: 127,463,000
Capital: Tokyo
Form of government: Constitutional Monarchy
Religions: Shintoism, Buddhism, Christianity
Currency: Yen

Jordan almost landlocked except for a short coastline on the Gulf of Aqaba, Jordan is bounded by SAUDI ARABIA, SYRIA, IRAQ and ISRAEL. Almost 80 per cent of the country is desert and the rest comprises the East Bank Uplands and Jordan Valley, part of the Great Rift Valley. In general, summers are hot and dry and winters cool and wet, with variations related to altitude. The east has a desert climate. Since under 5 per cent of the land is arable and only part of this is irrigated, production of grain is insufficient for the country's needs although some fruits and vegetables are grown for export. The capital, Amman, is the main industrial centre of the country and the industries produce phosphates, fertilisers, petroleum products, cement and iron. With no oil reserves of its own, Jordan is heavily dependent on aid. It is one of the few Arab nations to have signed a peace agreeement with Israel and is an ally of the US.

Area: 37,738 sq mi (97,740 sq km)
Population: 5,906,000
Capital: Amman
Form of government: Constitutional
  Monarchy
Religion: Sunni Islam
Currency: Jordanian dinar

Kazakhstan the second largest republic of the former USSR, which extends from the coast of the Caspian Sea to the northwest corner of MONGOLIA. The west of the country is low-lying, the east hilly and in the southeast mountainous areas include parts of the Tian Shan and Altai ranges. Parts of the country, particularly the mountainous regions, are subject to earthquakes. The climate is continental and very dry, with great extremes of temperature. Much of the country is desert and semi-desert, with wastelands of stone, sand and salt. Crops can be grown only in the wetter northwest regions or on land irrigated by the Syrdar'ya river. Extensive pastoral farming is carried out and cattle, sheep and goats are the main livestock reared. The country is rich in mineral resources, particularly oil and gas, copper, lead, zinc, coal, tungsten, and iron ore. Kazakhstan declared itself independent in 1991, since when economic prospects have remained positive. Although environmental problems have been left as a legacy of past Soviet exploitation (e.g. the overdraining of the Aral Sea) and poverty is still widespread, oil development has brought rapid economic growth in recent years and political stability has encouraged foreign investment.

Area: 1,049,156 sq mi (2,717,300 sq km)
Population: 15,671,000
Capital: Astana
Form of government: Republic
Religions: Sunni Islam, Christianity
Currency: Kazakh tenge

Kenya located in East Africa, Kenya straddles the equator and extends from Lake Victoria in the southwest to the Indian Ocean in the southeast. Highlands run north to south through central Kenya and are divided by the steep-sided Great Rift Valley. The coastal lowlands have a hot humid climate but in the highlands it is cooler and rainfall heavier. In the east it is very arid. The southwestern region is usually well watered, with huge areas of fertile soil. A wide variety of crops are grown for domestic consumption, such as wheat, maize and cassava. Tea, coffee, horticultural products, sisal, sugar cane and cotton are grown for export. Oil refining at Mombasa is the country's largest single industry and other industry includes food processing and textiles. Mining is carried out on a small scale for soda ash, gold and limestone, but large quantities of silver and lead exist near Mombasa. Tourism is an important source of foreign revenue, the many wildlife and game reserves being a major attraction. Politically more stable than many other African countries, Kenya nevertheless suffers from high unemployment, poverty and crime, and recent waves of political and ethnic unrest after controversial elections caused the deaths of some 1,500 people.

Area: 224,081 sq mi (580,367 sq km)
Population: 34,707,000
Capital: Nairobi
Form of government: Republic
Religions: Christianity, Islam, traditional
  beliefs
Currency: Kenyan shilling

Kiribati formerly known as the Gilbert and Ellice Islands, Kiribati comprises three groups of coral atolls and one isolated volcanic island spread over a large expanse of the central Pacific Ocean. The group includes the former Gilbert Islands, the Phoenix Islands (now Rawaki) and the southern Line Islands. The largest island is Kiritimati, formerly known as Christmas island. Rising sea levels threaten many of the low-lying islands.The climate is maritime equatorial, with a rainy season from October to March. Most islanders are involved in subsistence agriculture. Tuna fishing is an important industry, with coconuts and palm products being the main cash crops. Ocean Island (Banaba) was a rich source of phosphate deposits (guano) but these are now exhausted causing many of the population to leave the country. Fishing licences, overseas aid and money sent home by workers abroad help the economy.

Area: 280 sq mi (726 sq km)
Population: 96,000
Capital: Tarawa
Government: Republic
Religion: Christianity
Currency: Australian dollar

Korea, Democratic People's Republic of (North) a country occupying the northern half of the Korean peninsula in east Asia and formerly known as North Korea. It is one of the few countries still under communist rule. The Yala and Tumen rivers form its northern border with CHINA and RUSSIA. Its southern border with the Republic of KOREA is just north of the 38th parallel. It is a mountainous country, three-quarters of which is forested highland or scrubland, with Paektu-San the highest peak at 9,003 feet (2,737 metres). The climate is warm temperate, although winters can be cold in the north. Most rain falls during the summer. Nearly 90 per cent of its arable land is farmed by cooperatives and rice is the main crop grown. Minerals found include magnesite, zinc, copper, lead, tungsten, gold, and silver. Coal deposits and hydroelectric power generate electricity, and substantial deposits of iron ore are found near Pyongyang and Musan. Sixty per cent of the labour force is employed in industry, the most important of which are metallurgical, building, cement, and chemicals. Tuna, anchovy, and seaweeds are the main produce of the fishing industry. In recent years natural disasters and poor economic management have led to the country relying on foreign aid to feed many of its people. Grave concern was felt among other countries in the region and the rest of world when North Korea declared itself a nuclear state. However in 2007 an agreement was reached whereby the country agreed to shut down its main nuclear reactor in return for fuel oil and food aid.

Area: 46,540 sq mi (120,538 sq km)
Population: 23,113,000
Capital: Pyongyang
Form of government: Socialist Republic
Religion: Traditional beliefs

Currency: North Korean won

Korea, Republic of (South) formerly South Korea, the country occupies the southern half of the Korean peninsula in eastern Asia. It is bordered in the north by a demilitarised zone which acts as a buffer between the former South and North Koreas. Most of the country is hilly or mountainous, with the highest ranges running north to south along the east coast. The west is lowland and extremely densely populated. The extreme south has a humid warm temperate climate while farther north it is more continental. Most rain falls in summer. Cultivated land represents only 23 per cent of the country's total area and the main crops are rice, onions, potatoes, barley and maize. An increasing amount of fruit, such as melons, apples and peaches, is now produced. The country has few natural resources but does produce coal, graphite and iron ore. It has a flourishing manufacturing industry and is one of the world's leading supplier of cars, machinery and electronic equipment, toys and footwear. Other important industries are steel and petrochemicals. Its people enjoy a much higher standard of living than their northern neighbours as a result of the country's transformation into one of the world's major economies but South Korea has continued to followed a 'sunshine' policy of engagement with North Korea.

Area: 38,368 sq mi (99,373 sq km)
Population: 48,846,000
Capital: Seoul (Soul)
Form of government: Republic
Religions: Buddhism, Christianity
Currency: South Korean won

Kuwait a tiny Arab state on the Gulf, comprising the city of Kuwait at the southern entrance of Kuwait Bay, a small undulating desert wedged between IRAQ and SAUDI ARABIA AND nine small offshore islands. It has a dry desert climate, cool in winter but very hot and humid in summer. There is little agriculture because of lack of water. The major crops produced are melons, tomatoes, onions and dates. The country's water comes from the desalination of seawater. Shrimp fishing is becoming an important industry. Large reserves of petroleum and natural gas are the mainstay of the economy. Apart from oil, industry includes boat-building, plastics, petrochemicals, gases, cement and building materials. In recent years, Kuwait has provided an important transit route for forces and civilians moving in and out of war-torn Iraq.

Area: 6,880 sq mi (17,818 sq km)
Population: 2,418,100
Capital: Kuwait City (Al Kuwayt)
Government: Constitutional Emirate
Religions: Sunni Islam, Shia Islam
Currency: Kuwaiti dinar

Kyrgyzstan a central Asian republic of the former USSR, independent since 1991. It is located on the border with northwest CHINA. Much of the country is occupied by the Tian Shan Mountains, which rise to spectacular peaks. The highest is Pik Pobedy at 24,406 feet (7,439 metres), lying on the border with China. In the northeast of the country is Issyk Kul, a large lake heated by volcanic action, so it never freezes in winter. Most of the country is semi-arid or desert, but climate is greatly influenced by altitude. Soils are badly leached except in the valleys, where some grains are grown. Grazing of sheep, horses and cattle is extensive. Industries include non-ferrous metallurgy, machine building, coal mining, tobacco, food processing, textiles, gold mining and hydroelectricity. The country has large mineral deposits of gold, coal and uranium, while its natural gas and oil reserves have not, as yet, been developed. There is high unemployment and poverty, and corruption is an ongoing problem in an unstable political environment.

Area: 76,641 sq mi (198,500 sq km)
Population: 5,213,000
Capital: Bishkek
Form of government: Republic
Religions: Sunni Islam, Christianity
Currency: Som

Laos a landlocked communist country in southeast Asia that is ruggedly mountainous, apart from the Mekong river plains along its border with THAILAND. The Annam Mountains, which reach 8,203 feet (2,500 metres), form a natural border with VIETNAM. It has a tropical monsoon climate, with high temperatures throughout the year and heavy rains in summer. Laos is one of the poorest countries in southeast Asia and its development has been retarded by

war, drought and floods. It is primarily an agricultural country, with rice being the principal crop grown on small peasant plots. The mighty Mekong river provides the main means of transport as well as irrigation for the rice paddies. There is some export of timber products, coffee and clothes but most manufactured goods must be imported. Thailand is the largest foreign investor in Laos. The country remains one of the world's poorest nations.

Area: 91,429 sq mi (236,800 sq km)
Population: 6,368,000
Capital: Vientiane
Form of government: Republic
Religion: Buddhism
Currency: New kip

Latvia a Baltic state that regained its independence in 1991 with the break-up of the former Soviet Union. It is located in northeast Europe on the Baltic Sea and is sandwiched between ESTONIA and LITHUANIA. It has cool, wet summers and long, cold winters. Latvians traditionally lived by agriculture, forestry, fishing and seafaring. The chief agricultural occupations are cattle and dairy farming and the main crops grown are oats, barley, rye, potatoes and flax. Latvia's population is now over 70 per cent urban and agriculture is no longer the mainstay of the economy. It has a well-developed industrial base and produces electronic and electrical equipment, paper, cement, chemicals, textiles, woollen goods, furniture and foodstuffs. There are abundant deposits of peat and gypsum but no fossil fuels and minerals, which has made the country heavily dependent on imports of oil, gas and electricity. Economic development was difficult in the years following independence but Latvia now enjoys a free market economy and in 2004 it became a member of European Union.

Area: 24,942 sq mi (64,600 sq km)
Population: 2,274,000
Capital: Riga
Form of government: Republic
Religion: Christianity
Currency: Latvian lat

Lebanon a mountainous country in the eastern Mediterranean. A narrow coastal plain runs parallel to its 149-mile (240-kilometre) Mediterranean coast and gradually rises to the spectacular Lebanon Mountains, which are snow-covered in winter. The Anti-Lebanon Mountains form the border with SYRIA AND between the two ranges lies the Beqaa Valley. The climate is Mediterranean, with short warm winters and long hot and rainless summers. Rainfall can be torrential in winter and snow falls on high ground. Lebanon is an agricultural country, the main regions of production being the Beqaa Valley and the coastal plain, although erosion is a common problem in the uplands. Main products include olives, grapes, bananas, citrus fruits, apples, cotton, tobacco and sugar beet. Industry is small scale and manufactures include cement, fertilisers and jewellery. There are oil refineries at Tripoli and Sidon. Lebanon's economy is based on commercial services such as banking, but civil war, invasions by Israel and factional fighting have created severe problems for the economy. After Israel's military campaign in 2006 against Hezbollah—a major military and political force within Lebanon—the country is concentrating once more on rebuilding its economy.

Area: 4,015 sq mi (10,400 sq km)
Population: 3,874,900
Capital: Beirut (Beyrouth)
Form of government: Republic
Religions: Shia Islam, Sunni Islam, Christianity
Currency: Lebanese pound

Lesotho a small, landlocked kingdom entirely surrounded by the Republic of SOUTH AFRICA. Snow-capped mountains and treeless uplands, cut by spectacular gorges, cover two-thirds of the country. The climate is pleasant with variable rainfall. Winters are generally dry with heavy frosts in lowland areas and frequent snow in the highlands. Because of the mountainous terrain, only one-eighth of the land can be cultivated and the main crop is maize. Yields are low because of soil erosion on the steep slopes and overgrazing by herds of sheep and cattle. A major new water project to supply South Africa with water will help the economy but most foreign exchange comes from money sent home by Lesotho workers in South Africa.

Area: 11,720 sq mi (30,355 sq km)
Population: 2,022,000

Capital: Maseru
Form of government: Constitutional Monarchy
Religions: Christianity, traditional beliefs
Currency: Loti

Liberia located in West Africa, Liberia has a 348-mile (560-kilometres) coast stretching from SIERRA LEONE to CÔTE D'IVOIRE. It is the only African country never to be ruled by a foreign power. It has a treacherous coast, with rocky cliffs and lagoons enclosed by sand bars. Inland the land rises to a densely forested plateau dissected by deep, narrow valleys. Farther inland still, there are beautiful waterfalls and the Nimba Mountains rise to a maximum height of 5,748 feet (1,752 metres). Subsistence agriculture produces cassava and rice while rubber, coffee and cocoa are produced for export. The Nimba Mountains are rich in iron ore, which accounted for a large percentage of the country's export earnings. In the 1990s, the economy suffered greatly because civil war and the country's role in a rebellion in neighbouring Sierra Leone led to food shortages and the drying up of foreign investment. Presidential elections were held in late 2005 but UN peacekeepers are still in place and the country continues to suffer from unemployment, corruption and poverty.

Area: 43,000 sq mi (111,369 sq km)
Population: 3,195,000
Capital: Monrovia
Form of government: Republic
Religions: Traditional beliefs, Sunni Islam, Christianity
Currency: Liberian dollar

Libya a large North African country that stretches from the south coast of the Mediterranean to and in some parts beyond, the Tropic of Cancer. The Sahara covers much of the country, extending right to the Mediterranean coast at the Gulf of Sirte. The only green areas are the scrublands found in the northwest and the forested hills near Benghazi. The coastal area has mild wet winters and hot dry summers, but the interior has had some of the highest recorded temperatures of anywhere in the world. Around 18 per cent of the people work on the land, the main agricultural region being in the northwest, near Tripoli. The main crops produced are wheat, barley, peanuts, vegetables and fruits. Sheep, goats and cattle are reared. One of the world's largest producers of oil and natural gas, Libya has to import most of its food, machinery, transport equipment and consumer products. Other industries include food processing, the production of petrochemicals, iron, steel and aluminium, cement and textiles. Libya was shunned for many years by the West after the bombing of a PanAm plane above Lockerbie in Scotland but since taking responsibility for the incident and renouncing weapons of mass destruction, Libya's relations with the West are much improved

Area: 679,362 sq mi (1,759,540 sq km)
Population: 5,900,739
Capital: Tripoli (Tarabulus)
Form of government: Jamahiriya (a state of the masses)
Religion: Sunni Islam
Currency: Libyan dinar

Liechtenstein the principality of Liechtenstein is a tiny central European state situated on the east bank of the River Rhine, bounded by AUSTRIA to the east and SWITZERLAND to the west. To the east and south lie the foothills of the Austrian Alps. The highest peak, on the border with Switzerland, is Grauspitz at 8,527 feet (2,599 metres). The climate is mild alpine. Approximately one-third of the country is covered by forests. Once an agricultural country, Liechtenstein has rapidly moved into industry in the last 30 years, with a variety of light industries such as textiles, high quality metal goods, precision instruments, ceramics and pharmaceuticals. It is a popular location for the headquarters of foreign companies in order that they can benefit from the country's favourable tax laws. Other income is derived from tourism, international banking and financial services and the sale of postage stamps.

Area: 62 sq mi (160 sq km)
Population: 33,987
Capital: Vaduz
Form of government: Constitutional Monarchy
Religion: Christianity
Currency: Swiss franc

Lithuania a country that lies to the northwest of RUSSIA and BELARUS and is bounded to the north by LATVIA and west by POLAND. It is the largest of the three former Soviet Baltic republics. Before 1940 Lithuania was a mainly agricultural country but it has since been considerably industrialised, with the main exports being industrial machinery, textiles, clothing and fertilisers. Most of the land is lowland, covered by forest and swamp, and the main agricultural products are rye, barley, sugar beet, flax, meat, milk and potatoes. About 20 per cent of the population is engaged in agriculture, principally dairy farming and livestock production. Amber is found along the Baltic coast and used by Lithuanian craftsmen for making jewellery. The economy was troubled during the 1990s by financial scandals involving government members and banking institutions but Lithuania has reformed its economy and seen dramatic economic growth since it joined the European Union in 2004.

Area: 25,174 sq mi (65,200 sq km)
Population: 3,585,100
Capital: Vilnius
Form of government: Republic
Religion: Christianity
Currency: Litas

Luxembourg, Grand Duchy of a small independent landlocked country bounded by BELGIUM on the west, FRANCE on the south and GERMANY on the east. In the north of the duchy a wooded plateau, the Oesling, rises to 1,804 feet (550 metres) and in the south a lowland area of valleys and ridges is known as the Gutland. Northern winters are cold and raw, with snow covering the ground for almost a month, but in the south winters are mild and summers cool. In the south the land is fertile and crops grown include maize, roots, tubers and potatoes, with livestock also being raised. It is in the south, also, that (declining) beds of iron ore are found and these form the basis of the country's iron and steel industry. The country is very industrialised but the financial sector and tourism play increasingly important parts in the economy. In the east, Luxembourg is bordered by the Moselle river in whose valley grapes are produced for wine. The capital, Luxembourg City, is the seat of the European Court of Justice.

Area: 998 sq mi (2,586 sq km)

Population: 474,400
Capital: Luxembourg City
Form of government: Constitutional
 Monarchy
Religion: Christianity
Currency: Euro

Macau (Macao) formerly a Portuguese colony, Macau reverted to China in 1999, becoming a special administrative region under Chinese sovereignty. One of the most densely populated places in the world, Macau consists of a rocky, hilly peninsula, connected by a sandy isthmus to China's Zhongshan (Tangjiahuan) island and the two small islands of Taipa and Coloâne. A free port, it is a leading trade, fishing and tourist centre with gambling casinos and textile, clothing, toy, plastics, fireworks and food processing industries.

Area: 7 sq mi (18 sq km)
Population: 453,000
Capital: Macao
Form of government: Special Administrative Region of China
Religions: Buddhism, Christianity
Currency: Pataca

Macedonia, the Former Yugoslav Republic of (FYROM) a country that, under the name of Macedonia, declared its independence from the former Yugoslavia in November 1991. However GREECE, angered at the use of 'Macedonia'—also the name of the neighbouring Greek province –imposed a trade embargo and convinced the United Nations not to recognise the nation's independence. In 1993, Macedonia was admitted to the UN after changing its official name to the Former Yugoslav Republic of Macedonia. In 1995 an agreement was reached with Greece whereby both countries would respect the territory, sovereignty and independence of the other, with Macedonia agreeing to adopt a new flag. A landlocked country, Macedonia shares its borders with ALBANIA, BULGARIA, Greece and SERBIA. Its terrain is mountainous, covered by deep valleys, with several large lakes. The River Vardar is the country's longest river and divides the country, flowing into Greece and eventually emptying into the Aegean Sea. The climate consists of hot, dry summers and cold winters with considerable snow. The poorest of the six former Yugoslav republics, it sustains itself through agriculture and its coal industries. Some of its natural resources include chromium, lead, zinc, nickel, iron ore and lumber. In 2005 Macedonia became a candidate for European Union membership after greater recognition was given to its ethnic Albanian minority in 2004.

Area: 9,928 sq mi (25,713 sq km)
Population: 2,050,000
Capital: Skopje
Form of government: Republic
Religions: Christianity, Islam
Currency: Macedonian denar

Madagascar an island state situated off the southeast coast of Africa, separated from the mainland by the Mozambique Channel. Madagascar is the fourth largest island in the world and the centre of it is made up of high savanna-covered plateaus. In the east, forested mountains fall steeply to the coast and in the southwest the land falls gradually through dry grassland and scrub. The staple food crop is rice and although only 5 per cent of the land is cultivated, 80 per cent of the population grow enough to feed themselves. Cassava, potatoes, maize, beans and bananas are also grown, but some 58 per cent of the land is pasture and there are more cattle than people. There is mining for chromite, graphite, mica and salt and an oil refinery at Toamasina on the east coast. The main export earners are coffee, vanilla, cloves, chromium and petroleum products. Due to Madagascar's isolation from mainland Africa, there are several species of plants and animals that are quite different from mainland species. As a result, many tourists come to Madagascar to explore this aspect of the country's fauna and flora.

Area: 226,658 sq mi (587,041 sq km)
Population: 18,595,000
Capital: Antananarivo
Form of government: Republic
Religions: Traditional beliefs,
 Christianity, Islam
Currency: Madagascar ariary

Malawi a country that lies along the southern and western shores of the third largest lake in Africa, Lake Malawi. To the south of the lake the Shire river flows through a valley overlooked by wooded, towering mountains. The tropical climate has a dry season from May to October and a wet season for the remaining months. Agriculture is the predominant occupation and many Malawians live off their own crops but the land is under threat from rapid population growth. Exports include tea grown on the terraced hillsides in the south and tobacco on the central plateau, and sugar is also an important crop. Malawi has uranium, bauxite and coal deposits but mining is limited. National parks and game reserves draw tourists but the country remains one of the poorest in the world.

Area: 45,747 sq mi (118,484 sq km)
Population: 13,013,000
Capital: Lilongwe
Form of government: Republic
Religions: Traditional beliefs, Islam, Christianity,
Currency: Malawian kwacha

Malaysia, the Federation of Malaysia lies in the South China Sea in southeast Asia and comprises peninsular Malaysia on the Malay Peninsula and the states of Sabah and Sarawak on the island of Borneo. Malaysia is affected by the monsoon climate. The northeast monsoon brings rain to the east coast of peninsular Malaysia in winter and the southwest monsoon brings rain to the west coast in summer. Throughout the country the climate is generally tropical and temperatures are uniformly hot throughout the year. Peninsular Malaysia has always had thriving rubber-growing and tin-dredging industries and now palm oil production is also important on the east coast. Sabah and Sarawak have grown rich by exploiting their natural resources, the forests. There is also some offshore oil and new industries such as electronics are expanding around the capital, Kuala Lumpur. In recent years tourism has also become an important industry. Malaysia's economy remains healthy and the country is politically stable.

Area: 127,320 sq mi (329,758 sq km)
Population: 24,385,000
Capital: Kuala Lumpur
Form of government: Constitutional Monarchy
Religions: Islam, Buddhism, Hinduism, Christianity
Currency: Ringgit

Maldives, Republic of the a country that lies 398 miles (640 kilometres) southwest of SRI LANKA in the Indian Ocean and comprises 1,200 low-lying coral islands grouped into 12 atolls. Roughly 202 of the islands are inhabited and the highest point is only 5 feet (1.5 metres) above sea level which leaves them vulnerable to rising sea levels. Independence was gained in 1965, with a republic being formed three years later. The climate is hot and humid and affected by monsoons from May to August. The islands are covered by coconut palms and some millet, cassava, yams and tropical fruit are grown. However, rice, the staple diet of its islanders, is imported. The most important natural resource is marine life and fishing is an important occupation. The chief export is now canned or frozen tuna. Tourism is now developing fast and has taken over from fishing as the major foreign currency earner.

Area: 115 sq mi (298 sq km)
Population: 359,000
Capital: Malé
Form of government: Republic
Religion: Sunni Islam
Currency: Rufiyaa

Mali a landlocked state in West Africa of vast and monotonous plains and plateaus. It rises to 3,790 feet (1,155 metres) in the Adrar des Iforas range in the northeast. The Sahara in the north of the country is encroaching southwards. In the south there is some rain and plains are covered by grassy savanna and a few scattered trees. The River Niger runs through the south of the country. Fish are plentiful in the river and its water is used to irrigate the land. Only a fifth of the land can be cultivated. Rice, cassava and millet are grown for domestic consumption and cotton for export. The country's main exports include cotton, gold, foodstuffs and livestock. Iron ore and bauxite have been discovered but have yet to be exploited. Mali is one of the poorest countries in the world. It has suffered from droughts, rebellions and many years of military rule but is now relatively peaceful. Its economy is still very dependent on foreign aid and money sent home from its workers abroad.

Area: 478,841 sq mi (1,240,192 sq km)
Population: 11,716,000

Capital: Bamako
Form of government: Republic
Religions: Sunni Islam, traditional beliefs
Currency: CFA franc

Malta a small republic in the middle of the Mediterranean Sea, lying just south of the island of Sicily. It comprises three islands, Malta, Gozo and Comino, which are made up of low limestone plateaus with little surface water. The climate is Mediterranean, with hot, dry sunny summers and little rain. Lack of water has led to the production of desalination plants that produce up to 70 per cent of the country's needs. Winters are cooler and wetter. Malta is virtually self-sufficient in agricultural products and exports potatoes, vegetables, wine and cut flowers. It is an important centre for container and freight shipping. Tourism has also boomed and is the country's main source of revenue. Malta joined the European Union in 2004 and since then has had an increasing problem with immigration from North Africa.

Area: 122 sq mi (316 sq km)
Population: 400,214
Capital: Valletta
Form of government: Republic
Religion: Christianity
Currency: Maltese lira

Marshall Islands a self-governing republic under a compact of free association with the US. It comprises a scattering of over 1,000 coral atolls and islets, arranged in two parallel chains, Ratak and Ralik, located in eastern Micronesia in the western Pacific Ocean and lying to the northwest of Kiribati. The climate is tropical maritime, with little variation in temperature and rainfall that is heaviest from July to October. Some of the atolls were used for nuclear testing between 1947 and 1962. Bikini atoll is still uninhabitable. The US has paid compensation but the Marshall Islands have petitioned for additional payment. The main occupations are fishing and subsistence agriculture, with the chief exports being copra, fish and coconut oil. Fishing rights are sold to other countries. The US still has a missile test site in the islands on Kwajalein atoll and gives a large amount of foreign aid to the country. Attempts are being made to diversify the economy to lessen the country's dependence on US. aid

Area: 70 sq mi (181 sq km)
Population: 60,422
Capital: Dalag-Uliga-Darrit (on Majuro atoll)
Form of government: Republic in Free Association with the US
Religion: Christianity
Currency: US dollar

Martinique one of the larger of the islands in the Windward Islands group in the southern Caribbean, lying between Dominica and St Lucia. It is administered as an overseas department of France. The centre of the island is mountainous, while the quality of its beaches has played a role in its development as a tourist resort. It has a volcano, Mont Pelée (4,750 feet /1,448 metres), that erupted in 1902, wiping out the town of St Pierre and killing all but one of its inhabitants. Martinique is periodically subjected to hurricanes that can cause considerable damage. Sugar, bananas, pineapples, citrus fruits, nutmeg and spices are grown in some parts of the island. The economy relies mainly on tourism.

Area: 425 sq mi (1,102 sq km)
Population: 436,000
Capital: Fort-de-France
Form of government: Overseas Department of France
Religion: Christianity
Currency: Euro

Mauritania a country nearly twice the size of France located on the west coast of Africa. About 47 per cent of the country is desert, the Sahara covering much of the north. The only settlements found in this area are around oases, where a little millet, dates and vegetables can be grown. The main agricultural regions are in the Senegal river valley in the south. The rest of the country is made up of the drought-stricken Sahel grasslands. The majority of the people are traditionally nomadic herdsmen, but severe droughts since the late 1960s and early 1970s killed about 70 per cent of the nation's animals and the population has settled along the Senegal river. Production of iron ore and other deposits provide the country's main exports and development of these and the fishing industry on the coast are important to the country's economy which is very reliant on foreign aid. Offshore oil and natural reserves are expected to bring about prosperity in the future. Mauritania has experienced some internal political unrest and been involved in disputes with its neighbours. A military coup in 2005 was followed by presidential elections in 2007 and a return to democracy is promised.

Area: 395,956 sq mi (1,025,520 sq km)
Population: 3,177,000
Capital: Nouakchott
Form of government: Republic
Religion: Sunni Islam
Currency: Ouguiya

Mauritius a beautiful island with tropical beaches, lying about 20 degrees south in the Indian Ocean and 497 miles (800 kilometres) east of MADAGASCAR. It became independent in 1968. The islands of Rodrigues and Agalega are also part of Mauritius. Mauritius is a volcanic island with many craters surrounded by lava flows. The central plateau rises to over 2,625 feet (800 metres), then drops sharply to the south and west coasts. The climate is hot and humid, southwesterly winds bringing heavy rain in the uplands and there is the possibility of cyclones during December to April. The island has well-watered fertile soil, ideal for the sugar plantations that cover 45 per cent of the island. Although the export of molasses and sugar still dominate the economy, diversification is being encouraged. Other crops such as tea, tobacco, peanuts and vegetables are grown. The clothing and electronic equipment industries have become increasingly important and tourism is now the third largest source of foreign revenue.

Area: 788 sq mi (2,040 sq km)
Population: 1,240,000
Capital: Port Louis
Form of government: Republic
Religions: Hinduism, Christianity, Sunni Islam
Currency: Mauritian rupee

Mexico the most southerly country in North America. It has its longest border with the UNITED STATES to the north, a long coast on the Pacific Ocean and a smaller coast in the west of the Gulf of Mexico. It is a land of volcanic mountain ranges and high plateaus. The highest peak is Citlaltepetl, 18,697 feet (5,699 metres), which is permanently snow-capped. Coastal lowlands are found in the west and east. Its wide range of latitude and relief produce a variety of climates. In the north there are arid and semi-arid conditions while in the south there is a humid tropical climate. Thirty per cent of the labour force is involved in agriculture, growing maize, wheat, kidney beans and rice for subsistence and coffee, cotton, fruit and vegetables for export, although some irrigation is needed. Forests cover around a quarter of the country with trees such as ebony, mahogany and walnut. Mexico has substantial and varied mineral deposits, such as silver, coal, phosphates, gold and uranium, as well as large reserves of oil and natural gas. Developing industries are petrochemicals, textiles, machinery and transport equipment, and food processing. Tourism also makes an important contribution to the country's economy. Although Mexico is a major oil producer and exporter, its rural areas do not benefit from these oil revenues and rely on money sent home by Mexicans working in the US.

Area: 756,066 sq mi (1,958,201 sq km)
Population: 107,449,000
Capital: México City
Form of government: Federal Republic
Religion: Christianity
Currency: Mexican peso

Micronesia, Federated States of this self-governing republic became independent in 1986 under a compact of free association with the US which has recently been renegotiated and renewed. It comprises an archipelago of over 600 islands, including Pohnpei (Ponape), Truk (Churk) Islands, Yap Islands and Kosrae. Mostly uninhabited, they are located in the western Pacific Ocean, about 2,500 miles (4,025 kilometres) southwest of Hawaii. The climate is tropical maritime, with high temperatures and rainfall all year round but a pronounced precipitation peak between July and October. The country's main exports are fishing and copra. There are significant phosphate deposits but the island's isolation restricts development. Tourism is a growing trade and the country receives financial aid from the US but the economy of the region remains fragile with relatively high unemployment.

Area: 271 sq mi (702 sq km)

Population: 108,000
Capital: Palikir
Form of government: Constitutional
  Government in Free Association
  with the US
Religion: Christianity
Currency: US dollar

Moldova (Moldavia) a Soviet socialist republic from 1940 until 1991 when it became independent of the former USSR. It is bounded to the west by ROMANIA and to the north, east and south by UKRAINE. Two thirds of Moldovans are of Romanian descent. The republic consists of a hilly plain with an average height of around 500 feet (150 metres). Its main rivers are the Prut in the west and the Dnister in the north and east. Moldova's soils are fertile and crops grown include wheat, corn, barley, tobacco, sugar beet, soybeans and sunflowers. There are also extensive fruit orchards, vineyards and walnut groves. Food processing is the main industry, particularly sugar refining and wine making. Other industries include metalworking, engineering and the manufacture of electrical equipment. After independence, the economy declined, inflation soared and the country is now one of the poorest in Europe. There has been ongoing unrest and conflict in the country notably in the breakaway region of Trans-Dniester, which seeks independence and a closer relationship with RUSSIA, and in the Turkish-speaking region of Gagauz which also wants independence from Moldova.

Area: 13,012 sq mi (33,700 sq km)
Population: 4,466,000
Capital: Chisinau
Form of government: Republic
Religion: Christianity
Currency: Moldovan leu

Monaco a tiny but very wealthy principality on the Mediterranean Sea, surrounded landwards by the Alpes Maritimes department of FRANCE. It comprises a rocky peninsula and a narrow stretch of coast. It has mild moist winters and hot dry summers. The ancient fortified town of Monaco-ville is situated on a rocky promontory and houses the royal palace and the cathedral. The Monte Carlo district has its world-famous casino and La Condamine has thriving businesses, stores, banks and attractive residential areas.

Fontvieille is an area reclaimed from the sea where marinas and light industry are now located. Light industry includes chemicals, plastics, electronics, engineering and paper, but it is tourism that is the main revenue earner. The sale of stamps, tobacco, insurance and banking industries also contribute to the economy. Well-known annual events such as the Monte Carlo Rally and Monaco Grand Prix are held in the principality.

Area: 0.4 sq mile (1 sq kilometre)
Population: 32,000
Capital: Monaco
Form of government: Constitutional
  Monarchy
Religion: Christianity
Currency: Euro

Mongolia a landlocked country in northeast Asia that is bounded to the north by RUSSIA and by CHINA to the south, west and east. Most of Mongolia is mountainous. In the northwest are the Hangayn Mountains and the Altai, rising to 14,312 feet (4,362 metres). In the south there are grass-covered steppes and the desert wastes of the Gobi. The climate is very extreme and dry, with long, very cold winters and short, mild summers. Agriculture, particularly the rearing of livestock, is the main economic activity and source of employment in Mongolia. Under Communism, all cultivation and livestock rearing was state-controlled but Mongolia has now started to move towards a free market economy. Crops grown include cereals (wheat, barley and oats), potatoes and some other vegetables but cultivation is heavily dependent on irrigation. Mongolia has valuable reserves of iron ore, coal, copper, molybdenum, fluorspar, tungsten, uranium, gold and silver. Manufacturing industries are generally on a small scale and include the processing of wool, hides, leather, furs, meat and dairy produce, textiles, wooden goods, agricultural equipment and building products. The collapse of trade with the former Soviet Union has created severe economic problems for Mongolia and it is increasingly looking to the US, Japan and the European Union for trade and economic assistance although its main trading partners are Russia and China.

Area: 604,829 sq mi (1,566,500 sq km)
Population: 2,832,000

Capital: Ulaanbaatar
Form of government: Republic
Religion: Buddhism
Currency: Tugrik

Montenegro a country that lies in southeastern Europe between the Adriatic Sea and SERBIA. It declared its independence after a referendum in 2006 when 55% of the population voted for separation from the Union of Serbia and Montenegro—a remnant of the former Yugoslavia whose six constituent republics were Serbia, CROATIA, SLOVENIA, BOSNIA-HERZEGOVINA, MACEDONIA and Montenegro. Montenegro borders Croatia, Bosnia-Herzegovina, Serbia, Kosovo and Albania. Its climate is mediterranean with hot dry summers and autumns and relatively cold winters with heavy snow inland. The terrain consists of a highly indented coastline and a narrow coastal plain backed by high rugged limestone mountains and plateaus. Montenegro suffers from destructive earthquakes. The country's agricultural products include grains, tobacco, potatoes, olives, grapes and citrus fruits. Its natural resources consist of bauxite and hydroelectricity, and the production of aluminium is its dominant industry. Other economic activities include food processing, steelmaking, and the production of consumer goods. There is still widespread unemployment but the country has begun to attract foreign revenue through its tourism industry. Also an agreement signed with the European Union in 2007 is the first step towards ultimate EU membership.

Area: 5,333 sq mi (13,812 sq km)
Population: 630,500
Capital: Podgorica
Form of government: Republic
Religions: Christianity, Islam
Currency: Euro

Morocco a country in northwest Africa strategically placed at the western entrance to the Mediterranean Sea. It is a land of great contrasts, with high rugged mountains, the arid Sahara and green Atlantic and Mediterranean coasts. The country is split from southwest to northeast by the Atlas Mountains. The north has a pleasant Mediterranean climate with hot dry summers and mild moist winters. Farther south winters are warmer and summers even hotter. Snow often falls in winter on the Atlas Mountains. Morocco is mainly a farming country, with wheat, barley and maize being the main food crops and it is one of the world's chief exporters of citrus fruit. The economy is very mixed.Its main wealth comes from phosphates, reserves of which are the largest in the world, while coal, lead, iron and manganese ores are also produced. It is self-sufficient in textiles, has automobile assembly plants, soap and cement factories and a large sea fishing industry. Tourism is a major source of revenue, as are remittances sent home by Moroccans who work abroad. Recent economic policies have brought some stability to the country's economy but unemployment is high in urban areas and living standards for many are still very low.

Area: 172,414 sq mi (446,550 sq km)
Population: 33,241,000
Capital: Rabat
Form of government: Constitutional Monarchy
Religion: Sunni Islam
Currency: Moroccan dirham

Mozambique a republic located in southeast Africa and one of the world's poorest countries. A coastal plain covers most of the southern and central territory, giving way to the western highlands and north to a plateau including the Nyasa Highlands. The Zambezi river separates the high plateaus in the north from the lowlands in the south. The country has a humid tropical climate with highest temperatures and rainfall in the north. Normally conditions are reasonably good for agriculture but drought and severe flooding have over the years ruined the countryside. A lot of industry was abandoned because of lack of expertise when the Portuguese left the country. The civil war between 1977 and 1992, the severe drought and floods that the country has experienced since independence—all have had an adverse economic effect and the country continues to rely heavily on foreign aid.

Area: 309,496 sq mi (799,380 sq km)
Population: 19,686,000
Capital: Maputo
Form of government: Republic

Religions: Traditional beliefs,
Christianity, Sunni Islam
Currency: Metical

Myanmar, Union of (Burma) a rural, densely forested country, Myanmar is the second
largest country in southeast Asia. It is ruled
by a military junta which wields absolute
power. The heartland of the country is the
valley of the Irrawaddy. The north and west
of the country are mountainous and in the
east the Shan Plateau runs along the border
with THAILAND. The climate is equatorial at
the coast, changing to tropical monsoon over
most of the interior. The Irrawaddy river
flows into the Andaman Sea, forming a huge
delta area that is ideal land for rice cultivation. Rice is the country's staple food and accounts for half the country's export earnings.
Tropical fruits such as bananas, mangoes,
citrus and guavas grow well in the fertile
coastal regions. Myanmar is rich in lumber
and mineral resources such as natural gas,
petroleum, jade, and natural rubies, but
poor communications, lack of development,
and civil unrest mean that these resources
have not been fully exploited, which has at
least contributed to the preservation of the
country's natural environment.

Area: 261,228 sq mi (676,578 sq km)
Population: 47,382,000
Capital: Rangoon (Yangon)
Form of government: Republic
Religions: Buddhism, Christianity, Islam
Currency: Kyat

Namibia a country situated on the Atlantic
coast of southwest Africa. There are three
main regions in the country: running down
the entire Atlantic coastline is the Namib
Desert; east of the Namib is the Central
Plateau of mountains, rugged outcrops,
sandy valleys and poor grasslands; east
again and north is the Kalahari Desert.
Namibia is hot and dry and the little rain
it does get falls mainly over Windhoek,
the capital, and even here it only amounts
to 8–10 inches (200–250 millimetres) per
year. It is essentially a stock-rearing country
(sheep, cattle and goats) with subsistence
agriculture mainly in the north. Diamonds
are mined as are other minerals such as
gold, silver, lead, zinc, uranium and copper.
Namibia's output of diamonds amounts
to almost a third of the world's total. One

of Africa's richest fishing grounds lies off
the coast of Namibia. The country's main
trading partner is SOUTH AFRICA.

Area: 318,261 sq mi (824,292 sq km)
Population: 2,044,000
Capital: Windhoek
Form of government: Republic
Religions: Christianity, traditional beliefs
Currency: Namibian dollar

Nauru the world's smallest republic. It is an
island situated just 25 miles (40 kilometres)
south of the equator and halfway between
AUSTRALIA and HAWAII. It is an oval-shaped
coral island only 12 miles (20 kilometres) in
diameter and is surrounded by a reef. The
centre of the island comprises a plateau that
rises to 197 feet (60 metres) above sea level.
Most of the population live along a narrow
coastal belt of fertile land. The climate is
tropical with a high and irregular rainfall.
The country was very rich, due entirely
to the deposits of high quality phosphate
rock in the central plateau, which was sold
for fertiliser to Australia, NEW ZEALAND,
JAPAN and KOREA. But phosphate deposits
are almost exhausted and the government
is attempting to diversify, with help from
Australia, to ensure the economic future of
the country. New economic activities include
tourism and offshore finance.

Area: 8 sq mi (21 sq km)
Population: 13,287
Capital: Nauru
Form of government: Republic
Religion: Christianity
Currency: Australian dollar

Nepal a long narrow rectangular country,
landlocked between CHINA and INDIA on the
flanks of the eastern Himalayas. Its northern
border runs along the mountain tops. In this
border area is Mount Everest, at 29,028
feet (8,848 metres) the highest mountain in
the world and Nepal also has the six other
highest mountains within its borders. The
climate is subtropical in the south and all
regions are affected by the monsoon. Nepal
is one of the world's poorest and least developed countries, with most of the population
trying to survive as subsistence farmers.
Some mineral deposits, such as copper,
iron ore, mica and ochre, exist but, because
of the country's inaccessible terrain, have
not been completely charted. Nepal's main

exports are carpets, foodstuffs, clothing and leather goods, with the principal sources of foreign revenue being tourism and Gurkha soldiers' foreign earnings. Foreign aid is vital to the country's economy. The country experienced ongoing civil strife during a decade of fighting by Maoist rebels but in 2007 the Maoists joined an interim government, bringing their rebellion to an end.

Area: 56,827 sq mi (147,181 sq km)
Population: 28,287,000
Capital: Kathmandu
Form of government: Constitutional
   Monarchy
Religions: Hinduism, Buddhism
Currency: Nepalese rupee

Netherlands, the situated in northwest Europe, the Netherlands (also known as Holland) is bounded to the north and west by the North Sea. It is one of the world's most densely populated countries. Around half of the Netherlands is below sea level and the Dutch have tackled some huge reclamation schemes to add some land area to the country. The Netherlands has mild winters and cool summers. Natural vegetation is now confined mainly to grasses and heathers, with small areas of beech, ash, pine and oak forests being carefully maintained. Agriculture and horticulture are highly mechanised and the most notable feature is the sea of glass under which salad vegetables, fruit and flowers are grown. Manufacturing industries include chemicals, machinery, petroleum, refining, metallurgy and electrical engineering. The main port of the Netherlands, Rotterdam, is the largest in Europe.

Area: 15,770 sq mi (40,844 sq km)
Population: 16,491,000
Capital: Amsterdam
Seat of government: The Hague
Form of government: Constitutional
   Monarchy
Religion:Christianity
Currency: Euro

Netherlands Antilles an autonomous country within the NETHERLANDS, spread over the southern Caribbean Sea and consisting of two sets of islands, the Southern Netherlands Antilles (Bonaire and Curaçao) and the Northern Netherlands Antilles (Saba, St Maarten and St Eustatius). The five islands are set to become individual

territories in 2008, thus dissolving the federation: Curaçao and St Maarten will become autonomous territories of the Netherlands while Bonaire, St Eustatius and Saba will be given city status within the Netherlands. Saba is the highest island in the group rising to 2,854 feet (870 metres) at Mount Scenery. ARUBA was part of the group until 1986. The islands have a tropical climate. Oil refining and tourism are the most important economic activities

Area: 309 sq mi (800 sq km)
Population: 221,736
Capital: Willemstad
Form of government: Autonomous Country
   within the Netherlands
Religion: Christianity
Currency: Netherlands Antillean guilder

New Caledonia (Nouvelle Calédonie) the most southerly of the Melanesian countries in the Pacific Ocean. The main island, Nouvelle Calédonie, is 248 miles (400 kilometres) long and rises to a height of 5,377 feet (1,639 metres) at Mount Panie. The island is divided into two natural regions by the mountain range that runs down its centre: a dry west coast covered with gum tree savanna and a tropical east coast. It has a Mediterranean-type climate with rainfall at its heaviest between December and March. The country is rich in mineral resources, particularly nickel, which accounts for 90 per cent of its exports. The main tourist resorts are on the east coast of Nouvelle Calédonie. It is a French overseas territory and there has been much unrest in the country between the indigenous Melanesians and the French settlers over the question of independence. While this issue has not yet been resolved, in 1998 greater autonomy was given to the country by France in the Noumea Accord and a vote on independence is due to be held sometime between 2014 and 2019.

Area: 7,172 sq mi (18,575 sq km)
Population: 219,246
Capital: Noumea
Form of government: French Overseas
   Territory
Religions: Christianity, traditional beliefs
Currency: CFP franc

New Zealand a country that lies southeast of AUSTRALIA in the South Pacific. It comprises two large islands (North Island and South Island), Stewart Island and the Chatham Islands and many smaller islands. The vast majority of the population live on North Island. New Zealand enjoys very mild winters with regular rainfall and no extremes of heat or cold. North Island is hilly, with isolated mountains, earthquakes, active volcanoes, hot mineral springs and geysers. On South Island, the Southern Alps run north to south and the highest point is Mount Cook at 12,313 feet (3,753 metres). The Canterbury Plains lie to the east of the mountains. Two-thirds of New Zealand is suitable for agriculture and grazing. Meat, wool and dairy goods are the main agricultural products but tourism has overtaken agriculture as the main source of foreign revenue. Forestry supports the pulp and paper industry and a considerable source of hydroelectric power produces cheap electricity for the manufacturing industry, which now accounts for 30 per cent of New Zealand's exports. Mining is also an important industry, with petroleum, natural gas, limestone, gold and iron ore being exploited. New Zealand plays an active role in Pacific affairs and most of its immigrants now come from Asia and Pacific island countries.

Area: 104,454 sq mi (270,534 sq km)
Population: 4,076,000
Capital: Wellington
Form of government: Constitutional Monarchy
Religion: Christianity
Currency: New Zealand dollar

Nicaragua a country that lies between the Pacific Ocean and the Caribbean Sea, on the isthmus of Central America and is sandwiched between HONDURAS to the north and COSTA RICA to the south. The east coast contains forested lowland and is the wettest part of the country. Behind this is a range of volcanic mountains and the west coast is a belt of savanna lowland running parallel to the Pacific coast. The western region, which contains the two huge lakes, Nicaragua and Managua, is where most of the population live. The whole country is subject to devastating earthquakes. Nicaragua is primarily an agricultural country and 65 per cent of the labour force work on the land. There are mineral deposits of gold, copper and

silver, with gold being of prime importance. The main exports are coffee, tobacco, sugar, meat and gold. The country remains one of the poorest in the Americas after many years of civil unrest and natural calamities such as Hurricane Mitch in 1998.

Area: 50,193 sq mi (130,668 sq km)
Population: 5,570,000
Capital: Managua
Form of government: Republic
Religion: Christianity
Currency: Gold cordoba

Niger a landlocked republic in West Africa, just south of the Tropic of Cancer which is rated by the UN as the world's poorest country. Over half the country is covered by the encroaching Sahara in the north and the south lies in the drought-stricken Sahel. In the extreme southwest corner, the River Niger flows through the country and in the extreme southeast lies Lake Chad, but the rest of the country is very short of water. The people in the southwest fish and farm their own food, growing rice and vegetables on land flooded by the river. Farther from the river, crops have failed as a result of successive droughts since the 1960s. Niger is an agricultural country, mainly of subsistence farmers, with the raising of livestock being the major activity. It is looking to oil exploration and gold mining to boost its economy although uranium mined in the Aïr Mountains continues to be the country's largest foreign revenue earner.

Area: 489,191 sq mi (1,267,000 sq km)
Population: 12,525,000
Capital: Niamey
Form of government: Republic
Religions: Sunni Islam, traditional beliefs
Currency: CFA franc

Nigeria a large and populous country in West Africa. From the Gulf of Guinea it extends north to the border with NIGER. It has a variable landscape, from the swampy coastal areas and tropical forest belts of the interior, to the mountains and savanna of the north. The two main rivers are the Niger and the Benue and just north of their confluence lies the Jos Plateau. The climate is hot and humid and rainfall, heavy at the coast, gradually decreases inland. The dry far north is affected by the Harmattan, a hot dry wind blowing from the Sahara.

About three-quarters of the land is suitable for agriculture and a wide variety of crops is raised by subsistence farmers. The main agricultural products are cocoa, rubber, groundnuts and cotton, with only cocoa being of any export significance. The country depends on revenue from its crude petroleum exports, which have a low sulphur content and therefore produce less air pollution, making it attractive to American and European countries. Full independence was achieved by Nigeria in 1960 but due to several factors, including the complex ethnic make-up of the country, the country's progress has frequently been interrupted by strife and internal dissent.

Area: 356,669 sq mi (923,768 sq km)
Population: 131,859,000
Capital: Abuja
Form of government: Federal Republic
Religions: Sunni Islam, Christianity, traditional beliefs
Currency: Nigerian naira

Northern Mariana Islands situated in the northwest Pacific Ocean, the country consists of mainly volcanic islands with coral limestone and lava shores. In 1986, the islanders voted for commonwealth status in union with the USA and they were granted US citizenship. The island receives millions of dollars in aid from the US. Tourism and the manufacture of clothing are the main industries.

Area: 179 sq mi (464 sq km)
Population: 82,459
Capital: Saipan
Form of government: Commonwealth in Political Union with the USA
Religions: Christianity, traditional beliefs
Currency: US dollar

Norway a country that occupies the western half of the Scandinavian peninsula in northern Europe and is surrounded to the north, west and south by water. It shares most of its eastern border with SWEDEN and almost one-third of the country is north of the Arctic Circle. It is a country of spectacular scenery, with fjords, cliffs, rugged uplands and forested valleys. It has some of the deepest fjords in the world and has a huge number of glacial lakes. The climate is temperate as a result of the warming effect of the Gulf Stream. Summers are mild and although the winters are long and cold, the waters off the west coast remain ice-free. Agriculture is chiefly concerned with dairying and fodder crops. Fishing is an important industry and the large reserves of forest, which cover just over a quarter of the country, provide lumber for export. Industry is now dominated by petrochemicals based on the reserves of Norwegian oil in the North Sea. The country enjoys a very high standard of living thanks to its annual oil revenues and it has chosen not to join the European Union.

Area: 125,050 sq mi (323,877 sq km)
Population: 4,610,500
Capital: Oslo
Form of government: Constitutional Monarchy
Religion: Christianity
Currency: Norwegian krone

Oman situated in the southeast of the Arabian Peninsula, Oman is a small country in two parts: a small mountainous area overlooking the Strait of Hormuz, which controls the entrance to The Gulf; and the main part of the country, which consists of barren hills rising sharply behind a narrow coastal plain. Inland the hills extend into the unexplored Rub al Khali (The Empty Quarter) in Saudi Arabia. Oman has a desert climate with exceptionally hot and humid conditions from April to October and as a result of the extremely arid environment, less than one per cent of the country is cultivated, the main produce being dates and limes, which are exported. The economy is almost entirely dependent on oil, providing 90 per cent of the country's exports, although there are also deposits of asbestos, copper and marble. Tourism is another source of revenue.

Area: 119,498 sq mi (309,500 sq km)
Population: 3,102,000
Capital: Mascat (Musqat)
Form of government: Sultanate
Religions: Ibadi Islam, Sunni Islam, Shia Islam
Currency: Omani rial

Pakistan a country that lies just north of the Tropic of Cancer and has as its southern border the Arabian Sea. The valley of the Indus river splits the country into a highland region in the west and a lowland region in the east. A weak form of tropical monsoon climate occurs over most of the country and conditions in the north and west are arid. Temperatures are high everywhere in summer but winters are cold in the mountains. Most agriculture is subsistence, with wheat and rice as the main crops. Cotton and rice are the main cash crops, but the cultivated area is restricted because of waterlogging and saline soils. Pakistan's wide range of mineral resources has not been extensively developed and industry concentrates on food processing, textiles, consumer goods and handicrafts, including carpets and pottery. Alternating periods of civilian and military rule together with regional conflicts have adversely affected the stability and economy of the country. The dispute with INDIA over Kashmir has fuelled fears of a regional arms race but an ongoing peace process has reduced the tension between the two countries.Pakistan has been involved in fierce fighting on the Pakistani-Afghan border in its fight against terrorism in the region.

Area: 307,374 sq mi (796,095 sq km)
Population: 165,803,000
Capital: Islamabad
Form of government: Federal Republic
Religions: Sunni Islam, Shia Islam, Hinduism, Christianity
Currency: Pakistan rupee

Palau a republic consisting of a group of approximately 350 islands, lying in the western Pacific, 7 degrees north of the equator and about 625 miles (900 kilometres) equidistant from NEW GUINEA to the south and the PHILIPPINES to the west. A barrier reef to the west forms a large lagoon dotted with islands. Coral formations and marine life here are amongst the richest in the world and the country is keen to promote sustainable tourism. Formerly known as Belau, the republic became independent in 1994 and it has an agreement of free association with the United States on whom it still relies for financial aid. Taiwan also provides aid and the Taiwanese are the country's main visitors. Tourism, subsistence fishing and agriculture, and a clothing industry are the mainstays of the economy. Natural resources include minerals (particularly gold and sea-bed deposits) and forests.

Area: 177 sq mi (459 sq km)
Population: 20, 579
Capital: Koror
Form of government: Republic in Free Association with the USA
Religions: Christianity, traditional beliefs
Currency: US dollar

Palestinian Autonomous Regions Palestine was an ancient historical region on the eastern shore of the Mediterranean Sea, also known as 'The Holy Land' because of its symbolic importance for Christians, Jews, and Muslims. It was part of the Ottoman Empire from the early part of the 16th century until 1917, when it was captured by the British. The Balfour Declaration of 1917 increased Jewish hopes that they might be enabled to establish a Jewish state in Palestine. This was realized in 1948 with the United Nations' creation of the State of Israel, which partitioned Palestine between Jordan and Israel. This act created hostility among Israel's Arab neighbours and Palestinians indigenous to the area, many of whom left, particularly for neighbouring Jordan. Since that time, the territory has been disputed, leading to a series of wars between the Arabs and Israelis and to conflict between Israeli forces and the Palestine Liberation Organization. The disputed areas between the latter include the West Bank, the Gaza Strip, and parts of Jerusalem. In 2005 Israel withdrew its settlers from the Gaza Strip and parts of the West Bank in the hope of reviving an international peace plan for the region but in the 2006 Palestinian polls the militant Islamic movement Abbas were victors over the Fatah faction and with ongoing tension between the two factions any sort of peace agreement with Israel still seems distant.

Panama a country of immense strategic importance located at the narrowest point in Central America. Only 36 miles (58 kilometres) separates the Caribbean Sea from the Pacific Ocean at Panama, and the Panama Canal, which divides the country, is the main route from the Caribbean and the Atlantic to the Pacific. The climate is tropical, with high temperatures throughout the year and only a short dry season from January to April. The country is heavily forested and very little is cultivated. Rice is the staple food. The economy is heavily dependent on the Canal, which it plans to widen, and income from it is a major foreign currency earner. Off shore finance, petroleum products, bananas, coffee, shrimps, and a growing tourism industry all contribute to the country's economy.

Area: 29,157 sq mi (75,517 sq km)
Population: 3,191,000
Capital: Panama City
Form of government: Republic
Religion: Christianity
Currency: Balboa

Papua New Guinea a country in the southwest Pacific, comprising the eastern half of the island of New Guinea together with hundreds of islands including New Britain, the Bismarck Archipelago and New Ireland. There are active volcanoes on some of the islands and mainland and almost 100,000 people were evacuated in 1994 when two erupted on New Britain. The country has a mountainous interior surrounded by broad swampy plains. The climate is tropical, with high temperatures and heavy rainfall. Subsistence farming is the main economic activity although some coffee, cocoa and copra are grown for cash. Lumber is produced for export and the fishing and fish processing industries are developing. Mineral resources such as copper, gold and silver are are slowly being exploited and the country has oil and natural gas reserves. Papua New Guinea still receives valuable aid from Australia, which governed the territory until its independence in 1975.

Area: 178,704 sq mi (462,840 sq km)
Population: 4,400,000
Capital: Port Moresby
Form of government: Republic
Religion: Christianity
Currency: Kina

Paraguay a small landlocked country in central South America, bordered by Bolivia, Brazil and Argentina. The climate is tropical, with abundant rain and a short dry season. The River Paraguay splits the country into the Chaco (a flat semi-arid plain on the west) and a partly forested undulating plateau on the east. Almost 95 per cent of the population live east of the river, where crops grown on the fertile plains include cassava, sugar cane, maize, cotton and soya

beans. Immediately west of the river, on the low Chaco, are huge cattle ranches that provide meat for export. Deposits of minerals, including iron, petroleum and manganese, are not exploited commercially. The lumber industry is important, however, with tannin and petitgrain oil also being produced. With three important rivers, the Paraguay, Parana and Pilcomayo, the country has many impressive waterfalls, such as the Guaira Falls. In cooperation with its neighbours, it has developed its potential for hydroelectric power to the full and is able to meet all its energy needs. Years of political instability have, however, contributed to a lack of economic progress and some 60 per cent of the population live in poverty.

Area: 157,048 sq mi (406,752 sq km)
Population: 6,506,000
Capital: Asunción
Form of government: Republic
Religion: Christianity
Currency: Guaraní

Peru a country located just south of the equator, on the Pacific coast of South America. It has three distinct regions from west to east: the coast, the high sierra of the Andes and the tropical jungle. The climate on the narrow coastal belt is mainly desert, while the Andes are wet and east of the mountains is equatorial with tropical forests. Most large-scale agriculture is in the oases and fertile, irrigated river valleys that cut across the coastal desert. Sugar and cotton are the main exports. Sheep, llamas, vicunas and alpacas are kept for wool. The fishing industry was once the largest in the world but recently the shoals have become depleted. Anchovies form the bulk of the catch and are used to make fish meal. Iron ore, silver, copper and lead, as well as natural gas and petroleum, are extracted in large quantities and are an important part of the economy. The economy in the late 1980s was damaged by the declining value of exports, inflation, drought and guerrilla warfare, and violence linked to the drugs trade (cocaine) is still a problem. The economy has seen some growth but most of the population continue to live in poverty.

Area: 496,225 sq mi (1,285,216 sq km)
Population: 25,015,000
Capital: Lima

Form of government: Republic
Religion: Christianity
Currency: Nuevo sol

Philippines a country comprising a group of 7,107 islands and islets in the western Pacific that are scattered over a great area. There are four main groups: Luzon and Mindoro to the north, the Visayan Islands in the centre, Mindanao and the Sulu Archipelago in the south and Palawan in the southwest. Manila, the capital, is on Luzon. Most of the islands are mountainous and earthquakes are common. The climate is humid, with high temperatures and high rainfall. Typhoons can strike during the rainy season from July to October. Rice, cassava, sweet potatoes and maize are the main subsistence crops and coconuts, sugar cane, pineapples and bananas are grown for export. Agriculture employs around 42 per cent of the workforce. Mining is an important industry and its main products include gold, silver, nickel, copper and salt. Fishing is of major importance too and there are sponge fisheries on some of the islands. Other prime industries include textiles, food processing, chemicals and electrical engineering. The economy continues to rely on money sent home by Filipinos working overseas.

Area: 115,813 sq mi (300,000 sq km)
Population: 90,123,000
Capital: Manila
Form of government: Republic
Religions: Christianity, Sunni Islam
Currency: Philippine peso

Pitcairn Islands an island group and a British overseas territory situated in the southeast Pacific Ocean. The islands are volcanic with high lava cliffs and rugged hills. The islanders are direct descendants of the HMS *Bounty* mutineers and their Tahitian wives. Subsistence agriculture produces a wide variety of tropical and subtropical crops but the sale of postage stamps is the country's main revenue earner.

Area: 2 sq mi (5 sq km)
Population: 50
Form of government: British Overseas Territory
Religion: Christianity
Currency: New Zealand dollar

Poland a country situated on the North European Plain. It borders GERMANY to the west, the CZECH REPUBLIC and SLOVAKIA to the south and BELARUS and UKRAINE to the east. Poland consists mainly of lowlands and the climate is continental, marked by long severe winters and short warm summers. Over one-quarter of the labour force is involved in predominantly small-scale agriculture. The main crops are potatoes, wheat, barley, sugar beet and fodder crops. The industrial sector of the economy is large scale. Poland has large deposits of coal and reserves of natural gas, copper and silver and is a main producer of sulphur. Vast forests stretching inland from the coast supply the paper and furniture industries. Other industries include food processing, engineering, shipbuilding, textiles and chemicals. Poland became a member of the Europoean Union in 2004, fifteen years after the end of Communist rule. It has successfully created a market economy but incomes are still low and unemployment has led to many workers looking for work in western Europe. Tourism is on the increase, and the country's main tourist attractions include its Baltic resorts, mountains, as well as its cultural and historical sites.

Area: 124,808 sq mi (323,250 sq km)
Population: 38,518,000
Capital: Warsaw (Warszawa)
Form of government: Republic
Religion: Christianity
Currency: Zloty

Portugal a country in the southwest corner of Europe that makes up about 15 per cent of the Iberian Peninsula and is the least developed country in western Europe. The most mountainous areas of Portugal lie to the north of the River Tagus. In the northeast are the steep-sided mountains of Trasos-Montes and to south of this the Douro valley running from the Spanish border to Oporto on the Atlantic coast. South of the Tagus is the Alentajo, with its wheat fields and cork plantations. The Alentejo continues to the hinterland of the Algarve where there are groves of almond, fig and olive trees. Agriculture employs one-quarter of the labour force and crops include wheat, maize, grapes and tomatoes. Portugal's most important natural resources are minerals, including coal, iron ore, tin and copper. The country's port and Madeira wine are renowned and the country is a main exporter of olive oil. The manufacturing industry includes textiles, clothing, footwear, food processing and cork products. The economy has increasingly become a service-based economy, and tourism, particularly in the south, is the main foreign currency earner.

Area: 35,514 sq mi (91,982 sq km)
Population: 10,620,000
Capital: Lisbon (Lisboa)
Form of government: Republic
Religion: Christianity
Currency: Euro

Puerto Rico the most easterly of the Greater Antilles islands, lying in the Caribbean between the DOMINICAN REPUBLIC and the VIRGIN ISLANDS of the United States. It is a self-governing commonwealth in association with the USA and includes the main island, Puerto Rico, the two small islands of Vieques and Culebra, and a fringe of smaller uninhabited islands. The climate is tropical, modified slightly by cooling sea breezes. The main mountains on Puerto Rico are the Cordillera Central, which reach 4,390 feet (1,338 metres) at the peak of Cerro de Punta. Dairy farming is the most important agricultural activity but the whole agricultural sector has been overtaken by industry in recent years. Tax relief and cheap labour encourage American businesses to be based in Puerto Rico. Products include textiles, clothing, electrical and electronic goods, plastics, pharmaceuticals and petrochemicals. Tourism is another developing industry and there is potential for oil exploration both on and offshore.

Area: 3,427 sq mi (8,875 sq km)
Population: 3,736,000
Capital: San Juan
Form of government: Self-governing Commonwealth (in association with the USA)
Religion: Christianity
Currency: US dollar

Qatar a little emirate that lies halfway along the coast of The Gulf. It consists of a low barren peninsula and a few small islands. The climate is hot and uncomfortably humid in summer and the winters are mild with rain in the north. Most fresh water comes from natural springs and wells or from desalination plants. Some vegetables and fruit are

grown but the herding of sheep, goats and some cattle is the main agricultural activity. The country is famous for its high quality camels. The discovery and exploitation of oil has resulted in a high standard of living for the people of Qatar, with some of the revenue being used to build hospitals and a road system and to provide free education and medical care. The Dukhan oil field has an expected life of 40 years and the reserves of natural gas are enormous. In order to diversify the economy, new industries such as iron and steel, cement, fertilisers and petrochemical plants have been developed.

Area: 4,247 sq mi (11,000 sq km)
Population: 885,350
Capital: Doha (Ad Dawhah)
Form of government: Emirate
Religion: Sunni Islam
Currency: Qatar riyal

Réunion a French overseas department in the Indian Ocean, south of Mauritius. The island is mountainous and has one active and several extinct volcanoes. Most people live on the coastal lowlands and the economy is dependent upon tourism and the production of rum, sugar, maize, potatoes, tobacco and vanilla. French aid is given to the country in return for its use as a French military base.

Area: 969 sq mi (2,510 sq km)
Population: 664,000
Capital: Saint-Denis
Form of government: French Overseas Department
Religion: Christianity
Currency: Euro

Romania apart from a small extension towards the Black Sea, Romania is almost a circular country. It is located in southeast Europe, bordered by UKRAINE, HUNGARY, SERBIA and BULGARIA. The Carpathian Mountains run through the north, east and centre of Romania and these are enclosed by a ring of rich agricultural plains that are flat in the south and west but hilly in the east. The core of Romania is Transylvania within the Carpathian arc. Romania's main river is the Danube, which forms a delta in its lower course. The country has cold snowy winters and hot summers. Agriculture in Romania has been neglected in favour of industry, but major crops include maize, sugar beet, wheat, potatoes and grapes for wine. Industry includes mining, metallurgy, mechanical engineering and chemicals. Forests support lumber and furniture-making industries in the Carpathians. There have been periods of severe food shortage, with high unemployment and a low standard of living. After the overthrow of the Communist regime in 1989, a new constitution was approved by referendum. The post-communist government has worked to bring about changes and improve the economy and Romania joined the European Union in 2007.

Area: 92,043 sq mi (238,391 sq km)
Population 22,303,000
Capital: Bucharest (Bucuresti)
Form of government: Republic
Religion: Christianity
Currency: Leu

Russia (the Russian Federation) the largest country in the world (with over one-ninth of the world's land area) that extends from eastern Europe through the Ural Mountains east to the Pacific Ocean. The Caucasus Range forms its boundary with GEORGIA and AZERBAIJAN and it is here that the highest peak in Europe, Mt Elbrus (18,510 feet/5,642 metres), is located. In the east, Siberiais drained toward the Arctic Ocean by the great Rivers Ob, Yenisey and Lena and their tributaries. Just to the south of the Central Siberian Plateau lies Lake Baikal, the world's deepest freshwater lake (5,370 feet/1,637 metres). The Ural Mountains form the boundary between Asia and Europe and are where a variety of mineral resources are found. The environment ranges from vast frozen wastes in the north to subtropical deserts in the south. Agriculture is organised into either state or collective farms that mainly produce sugar beet, cotton, potatoes and vegetables. The country has extensive reserves of coal, oil, gas, iron ore and manganese. Major industries include iron and steel, cement, transport equipment, engineering, armaments, electronic equipment and chemicals. The Russian economy has benefited from its oil wealth but the country is still beset by many problems including the ongoing conflict in Chechnya.

Area: 6,592,850 sq mi (17,075,400 sq km)
Population: 146,100,000

Capital: Moscow (Moskva)
Form of government: Republic
Religions: Christianity, Sunni Islam, Shia Islam
Currency: Russian rouble

Rwanda a small republic in the heart of central Africa that lies just 2 degrees south of the equator. It is a mountainous country with a central spine of highlands from which streams flow west to the Congo river and east to the Nile. Active volcanoes are found in the north where the land rises to about 14,765 feet (4,500 metres). The climate is highland tropical, with temperatures decreasing with altitude. The soils are not fertile and subsistence agriculture dominates the economy. Staple food crops are sweet potatoes, cassava, dry beans, sorghum and potatoes. Soil erosion, overgrazing and droughts lead to famine, making the country very dependent on foreign aid. The main cash crops are Arabic coffee, tea and pyrethrum. There are major reserves of natural gas under Lake Kivu in the west, but these are largely unexploited. The country has faced massive upheaval and the disruption of its economic life following the tragic tribal genocide wars in 1994, and there is ongoing ethnic division and rivalry between the Hutus and Tutsis both within and without the country including conflict within neighbouring Democratic Republic of the Congo.

Area: 10,169 sq mi (26,338 sq km)
Population: 5,397,000
Capital: Kigali
Form of government: Republic
Religions: Christianity, traditional beliefs
Currency: Rwandan franc

St Christopher (St Kitts) and Nevis the islands of St Christopher (popularly known as St Kitts) and Nevis lie in the Leeward group in the eastern Caribbean and in 1983 became a sovereign democratic federal state with the British monarch as head of state. St Kitts consists of three extinct volcanoes linked by a sandy isthmus to other volcanic remains in the south. The highest point on St Kitts is Mount Liamuiga, 4,314 feet (1,315 metres) and the islands have a tropical climate. Sugar cane is grown on the fertile soil covering the gentle slopes and sugar is the chief export crop but market gardening and livestock farming are being expanded on the steeper slopes above the cane fields. Some vegetables, coconuts, fruits and cereals are grown. Industry includes sugar processing, brewing, distilling and bottling. St Kitts has a major tourist development at Frigate Bay. Nevis, 2 miles (3 kilometres) south, is an extinct volcano. Farming is declining and tourism is now the main source of income.

Area: 101 sq mi (261 sq km)
Population: 41,000
Capital: Basseterre
Form of government: Constitutional
  Monarchy
Religion: Christianity
Currency: East Caribbean dollar

St Helena a volcanic island in the south Atlantic Ocean which is a British overseas territory and an administrative centre for the islands of Tristan da Cunha to the south and Ascension Island to the north. Napoleon Bonaparte was exiled here by the British from 1815 until his death in 1821. The main exports are fish, lumber and handicrafts.

Area: 47 sq mi (122 sq km)
Population: 5,200
Capital: Jamestown
Form of government: British Overseas
  Territory
Currency: St Helena pound

St Lucia one of the Windward Islands in the eastern Caribbean. It lies to the south of MARTINIQUE and to the north of ST VINCENT. It was controlled alternately by the French and the British for some 200 years before becoming fully independent in 1979. St Lucia is an island of extinct volcanoes and the highest peak is 3,117 feet (950 metres). In the west are Les Pitons, two green peaks that rise directly from the sea to over 2,460 feet (750 metres). The climate is tropical, with a rainy season from May to August. The economy depends on the production of bananas and, to a lesser extent, coconuts and mangoes. Production, however, is often affected by hurricanes, drought and disease. There are some manufacturing industries, which produce clothing, cardboard boxes, plastics, electrical parts and drinks. Tourism is increasing in importance and Castries, the capital, is a popular calling point for cruise liners.

Area: 240 sq mi (622 sq km)
Population: 168,458
Capital: Castries
Form of government: Constitutional
  Monarchy
Religion: Christianity
Currency: East Caribbean Dollar

St Pierre and Miquelon two islands to the south of Newfoundland, Canada, which are an overseas territory administered by FRANCE. They are the last French possessions in North America and have a substantial fishing industry.

Area: 93 sq mi (240 sq km)
Population: 6,300
Capital: Saint Pierre
Form of government: French Overseas
  Territory
Religion: Christianity
Currency: Euro

St Vincent and the Grenadines an island of the Lesser Antilles, situated in the eastern Caribbean between ST LUCIA and GRENADA. It is separated from Grenada by a chain of some 600 small islands known as the Grenadines, the northern islands of which form the other part of the country. The largest of these islands are Bequia, Mustique, Canouan, Mayreau and Union. The climate is tropical, with very heavy rain in the mountains. St Vincent Island is mountainous and a chain of volcanoes runs up the middle of the island. The volcano Soufrière (4,049 feet/1,234 metres) is active and last erupted in 1979. Farming is the main occupation on the island. Bananas are the main export and it is the world's leading producer of arrowroot starch. There is little manufacturing and the government is trying to promote tourism. Unemployment is high, however and tropical storms are always a threat to crops.

Area: 150 sq mi (388 sq km)
Population: 117,848
Capital: Kingstown
Form of government: Constitutional
  monarchy
Religion: Christianity
Currency: East Caribbean dollar

Samoa called Western Samoa until 1997, a state that lies in the Polynesian sector of the Pacific Ocean, about 447 miles (720 kilometres) northeast of FIJI. It consists of seven small islands and two larger volcanic islands, Savai'i and Upolu. Savai'i is largely covered by volcanic peaks and lava plateaus while Upolu is home to two-thirds of the country's population and the capital, Apia. The climate is tropical, with high temperatures and very heavy rainfall. The islands have been fought over by the Dutch, British, Germans and Americans, but they now enjoy a traditional Polynesian lifestyle. Subsistence agriculture is the main activity and copra, cocoa and coconuts are the main exports. Many tourists visit the grave of the Scottish writer Robert Louis Stevenson, who died here and whose home is now the official home of the king. The economy is still dependent on money sent home by its workers abroad.

Area: 1,093 sq mi (2,831 sq km)
Population: 166,000
Capital: Apia
Form of government: Constitutional Monarchy
Religion: Christianity
Currency: Tala

Samoa, American an unincorporated territory of the USA, lying close to Samoa in the Pacific Ocean and comprising five main volcanic islands and two coral atolls. The bulk of the population live on the islands of Tutaila and Ta'u. The five main islands are hilly and for the most part covered in thick forest or bush and the climate is tropical with lots of rain. The chief exports are canned tuna, pet foods, watches and handicrafts.

Area: 77 sq mi (199 sq km)
Population: 64,000
Capital: Pago Pago
Form of government: Unincorporated Territory of the USA
Religion: Christianity
Currency: US dollar

San Marino a tiny landlocked state in central ITALY, lying in the eastern foothills of the Apennines and one of the smallest republics in the world. Tradition has it that in AD 301, a Christian sought refuge from persecution on Mount Titano. The resulting community prospered and was recognised in 1291 by Pope Nicholas IV as being independent. San Marino has wooded mountains and pasture land clustered around Mount Titano's limestone peaks, which rise to 2,425 feet (739 metres). San Marino has a mild Mediterranean climate. Most of the population work on the land or in forestry. Wheat, barley, maize, olives and vines are grown and the main exports are wood machinery, chemicals, wine, textiles, tiles, varnishes and ceramics, while dairy produce is the main agricultural product. Some 3.5 million tourists visit the country each year and much of the country's revenue comes from the sale of stamps, postcards, souvenirs and duty-free liquor. Italian currency is in general use but San Marino issues its own coins. In 1992 San Marino became a member of the United Nations and it is a full member of the Council of Europe.

Area: 24 sq mi (61 sq km)
Population: 25,000
Capital: San Marino
Form of government: Republic
Religion: Christianity
Currency: Euro

São Tomé and Príncipe a state comprising two volcanic islands that lie off the west coast of Africa. São Tomé is covered in extinct volcanic cones, reaching 6,641 feet (2,024 metres) at the highest peak. The coastal areas are hot and humid. Príncipe is a craggy island lying to the northeast of São Tomé. The climate is tropical, with heavy rainfall from October to May. Seventy per cent of the workforce work on the land, mainly in state-owned cocoa plantations that were nationalised in 1975, after independence. The other main agricultural products are coconuts, melons, copra, bananas and melons. Since crops grown are primarily for export, about 90 per cent of food has to be imported. Small manufacturing industries include food processing and lumber products. The country has suffered from political instability for some time but the economy should benefit from the recent discovery of oil in the Gulf of Guinea.

Area: 372 sq mi (964 sq km)
Population: 135,000
Capital: São Tomé
Form of government: Republic
Religion: Christianity
Currency: Dobra

Saudi Arabia a state that occupies over 70 per cent of the Arabian Peninsula. Over 95 per cent of the country is desert and the largest expanse of sand in the world, Rub al Khali (The Empty Quarter), is found in the southeast of the country. In the west, a narrow, humid coastal plain along the Red Sea is backed by steep mountains. The climate is hot, with very little rain and some areas have no precipitation for years. The government has spent a considerable amount on reclamation of the desert for agriculture and the main products are dates, tomatoes, watermelons and wheat, which are grown in the fertile land around the oases. Saudi Arabia exports wheat and shrimps and is self-sufficient in some dairy products. The country's prosperity, however, is based almost entirely on the exploitation of its vast reserves of oil and natural gas. Industries include petroleum refining and the production of petrochemicals and fertilisers. Saudi Arabia is one of the most important countries in the Arab and Muslim world because it is the birthplace of Islam and because it is one of the world's biggest oil producers.

Area: 830,000 sq mi (2,149,690 sq km)
Population: 27,019,000
Capital: Riyadh (Ar Riyād)
Form of government: Monarchy
Religions: Sunni Islam, Shia Islam
Currency: Riyal

Senegal a former French colony in West Africa that extends from the most western point in Africa, Cape Verde, to the border with MALI. Senegal is mostly low-lying and covered by savanna. The Fouta Djallon Mountains in the south rise to 4,971 feet (1,515 metres). The climate is tropical, with a dry season from October to June. The most densely populated region is in the southwest. Almost 80 per cent of the labour force work in agriculture, growing peanuts and cotton for export and millet, sugar cane, maize, rice and sorghum as subsistence crops. Increased production of crops such as rice and tomatoes is encouraged in order to achieve self-sufficiency in food. The country's economy is largely dependent on peanuts but there is a growing manufacturing sector, including food processing, cement, chemicals and tinned tuna, while tourism is also expanding Although Senegal's economy is stable, there is still widespread poverty and

unemployment and the country remains dependent on foreign aid.

Area: 75,955 sq mi (196,722 sq km)
Population:11,987,000
Capital: Dakar
Form of government: Republic
Religions: Sunni Islam, Christianity
Currency: CFA franc

Serbia a landlocked country that borders on eight countries: HUNGARY, ROMANIA, BULGARIA, FYR MACEDONIA, ALBANIA, MONTENEGRO, BOSNIA-HERZEGOVINA and CROATIA. It came into being in 2006 as the successor state to the former Union of Serbia and Montenegro. Serbia contained two autonomous provinces – Kosovo in the south and Vojvodina in the north. (Kosovo, declared itself independent in February 2008 but Serbia refuses to recognise this declaration and NATO-led peacekeepers continue to keep the peace within Kosovo between the ethnic Albanian majority and the Serb minority). In the north there are fertile Danube plains, with limestone ranges to the east and and rugged mountains and hills in the southeast. The main rivers are the Danube and its tributaries, the Sava, Tisza and Morava. The north has cold winters and hot humid summers while other parts have cold winters with heavy snowfall and hot dry summers. Serbia contains important mineral reserves including copper, antimony, lead, bauxite, coal, petroleum, natural gas, zinc, chromium and gold. It produces and exports food, machinery, and transport equipment. Unemployment is a problem and the country still has a lot of progress to make in terms of a transition to a market economy.

Area: 34,116 sq miles/88,361 sq km
Population: 9,900,000 (includes Kosovo population of approximately 2 million)
Capital: Belgrade
Form of government: Republic
Religion: Christianity
Currency: Serbian Dinar

Seychelles a group of volcanic islands that lie in the western Indian Ocean, about 746 miles (1,200 kilometres) from the coast of East Africa. About 40 of the islands are mountainous and consist of granite while just over 50 are coral islands. The climate is tropical maritime with heavy rain. About 90 per cent of the people live on the island of

Mahé, which is the site of the capital, Victoria. The staple foods are coconut, imported rice and fish, while some fruits are grown for home consumption Tourism accounts for about 90 per cent of the country's foreign exchange earnings and employs one-third of the labour force. Export trade is based on petroleum (after importation), copra, cinnamon bark and fish. The only mineral resource is guano. The Seychelles was a one-party socialist state until 1991, when a new constitution was introduced. The first free elections were held in 1993 and the country is now stable and prosperous.

Area: 175 sq mi (455 sq km)
Population: 81,500
Capital: Victoria
Form of government: Republic
Religion: Christianity
Currency: Seychelles rupee

Sierra Leone a country on the Atlantic coast of West Africa, bounded by Guinea to the north and east and by Liberia to the southeast. The country possesses a fine natural harbour where the capital and major port of Freetown is situated. A range of mountains, the Sierra Lyoa, rise above the capital on the Freetown Peninsula. Elsewhere the coastal plain is up to 70 miles (110 km) wide, rising to a plateau and then to mountains which are part of the Guinea Highlands Massif. The climate is tropical, with heavy rain during a rainy season lasting from May to November. The country's staple food is rice that is grown in the swamplands at the coast by the subsistence farmers. Other crops grown include sorghum, cassava, millet, sugar, and groundnuts. Civil War (1991–2002) and ongoing ethnic conflict resulted in the displacement of more than 2 million people. A UN peacekeeping force supported the country through national elections in 2002 but the gradual withdrawal of the force during 2004 and 2005 has challenged the country's long-term stability. Reconstruction is being aided by the export of diamonds and the exploitation of the country's mineral reserves. The first elections since the withdrawal of the UN peacekeepers were held peacefully in 2007 but the country's new leader is faced with the difficult task of addressing the corruption and mismanagement of the past.

Area: 27,699 sq mi (71,740 sq km)
Population: 5,497,000
Capital: Freetown
Form of government: Republic
Religions: Sunni Islam, Christianity, traditional beliefs
Currency: Leone

Singapore one of the world's smallest yet most successful countries. It comprises one main island and 58 islets that are located at the foot of the Malay Peninsula in southeast Asia. The main island of Singapore is very low-lying and the climate is hot and wet throughout the year. Only 1.6 per cent of the land area is used for agriculture, most food being imported. The country has a flourishing electronics industry. The financial services industry is also an important contributor to the country's economy and tourism is an important source of foreign revenue. The people of Singapore enjoy one of the highest standards of living in the world but the country is also known for the conservatism of its leaders.

Area: 239 sq mi (618 sq km)
Population: 4,492,000
Capital: Singapore
Form of government: Parliamentary Democracy
Religions: Buddhism, Sunni Islam, Christianity, Hinduism
Currency: Singapore dollar

Slovakia (Slovak Republic) a country that was constituted on 1 January 1993 as a new independent nation, following the dissolution of the 74-year-old federal republic of Czechoslovakia. Landlocked in central Europe, its neighbours are the Czech Republic to the west, Poland to the north, Austria and Hungary to the south and a short border with Ukraine in the east. The northern half of the republic is occupied by the Tatra Mountains, which form the northern arm of the Carpathian Mountains. This region has vast forests and pastures used for intensive sheep grazing and is rich in high-grade minerals such as copper, iron, zinc and lead. The southern part of Slovakia is a plain drained by the Danube and its tributaries. Farms, vineyards, orchards and pastures for stock form the basis of southern Slovakia's economy. Tourism is now increasing at the country's ski resorts and historic cities. In the early 1990s unemployment increased and inflation was high, resulting in a lowering in the standard of living but more recent economic reforms have seen an increase in foreign investment. Slovakia became a member of the European Union in 2004.

Area: 18,928 sq mi (49,035 sq km)
Population: 5,374,000
Capital: Bratislava
Form of government: Republic
Religion: Christianity
Currency: Slovak koruna

Slovenia this former Yugoslav republic is bounded to the north by Austria, to the west by Italy, to the east by Hungary and to the south by Croatia. Most of Slovenia is situated in the Karst Plateau and in the Julian Alps, which has Mount Triglav as its highest point at 9,393 feet (2,863 metres). The Julian Alps are renowned for their scenery and the Karst Plateau contains spectacular cave systems. The northeast of the republic is famous for its wine production and tourism is also an important industry. Although farming and raising livestock are the chief occupations, Slovenia is very industrialised and urbanised. Iron, steel and aluminium are produced and mineral resources include oil, coal, lead, uranium and mercury, natural gas and petroleum. Slovenia has also been successful in establishing many new light industries and this has given the country a well-balanced economic base for the future, with unemployment lessening and industrial output increasing. Slovenia became a member of the European Union in 2004.

Area: 7,821 sq mi (20,256 sq km)
Population: 1,991,000
Capital: Ljubljana
Form of government: Republic
Religions: Christianity, Islam
Currency: Tolar

Solomon Islands a state that lies in an area between 5 and 12 degrees south of the equator, to the east of Papua New Guinea, in the Pacific Ocean. The country consists of six large islands and innumerable smaller ones. The larger islands are mountainous and covered by forests, with rivers prone to flooding. Guadalcanal is the main island and the site of the capital, Honiara. The climate is hot and wet and typhoons are frequent.

The main food crops grown are coconut, cassava, sweet potatoes, plantains, yams, rice, taros and bananas. Mineral resources such as phosphate rock and bauxite are found in large amounts and some alluvial gold is produced. There are high rates of unemployment and illiteracy among the people and civil conflict has brought the country close to anarchy. An Australian peacekeeping force arrived in the country in 2003 and their efforts to restore law and order and economic stability have led to modest growth in the economy.

Area: 11,157 sq mi (28,896 sq km)
Population: 391,000
Capital: Honiara
Form of government: Parliamentary Democracy
Religion: Christianity
Currency: Solomon Islands dollar

Somalia a country that lies on the horn of Africa's east coast. It is bounded on the north by the Gulf of Aden and on the south and east by the Indian Ocean and its neighbours include Djibouti, Ethiopia and Kenya. The country is arid and most of it is low plateau with scrub vegetation. Its two main rivers, the Juba and Shebelle, are used to irrigate crops. Most of the population live in the mountains and river valleys and there are a few towns on the coast. The country has little in the way of natural resources but there are deposits of copper, petroleum, iron, manganese and marble. Years of ongoing fighting between rival warlords and a lack of central government have left Somalia to deal with lawlessness, famine and disease. A transitional government emerged in 2004 and this is backed by the UN but the task of reconciling a country divided into warring clans is a daunting one.

Area: 246,201 sq mi (637,657 sq km)
Population: 9,1180,000
Capital: Mogadishu (Muqdisho)
Form of government: Parliamentary Democracy
Religion: Sunni Islam
Currency: Somali shilling

South Africa lies at the southern tip of the African continent with a huge coastline on both the Atlantic and Indian Oceans. The country occupies a huge saucer-shaped plateau, surrounding a belt of land that drops in steps to the sea. The rim of the saucer rises in the east to 11,424 feet (3,482 metres) in the Drakensberg mountain range. In general the climate is healthy, with plenty of sunshine and relatively low rainfall. This varies with latitude, distance from the sea and altitude. Of the total land area, 58 per cent is used as natural pasture although soil erosion is a problem. The main crops grown are maize, sorghum, wheat, groundnuts and sugar cane. A drought-resistant variety of cotton is also now grown. South Africa has extraordinary mineral wealth. This includes gold, coal, copper, iron ore, manganese, diamonds and chrome ore. A system of apartheid existed in South Africa from 1948 until the early 1990s, denying black South Africans civil rights and promoting racial segregation. During this time the country was subjected to international economic and political sanctions. In 1990 F. W. de Klerk, then president, lifted the ban on the outlawed African National Congress and released its leader, Nelson Mandela, who had been imprisoned since 1962. This heralded the dismantling of the apartheid regime and in the first multiracial elections, held in 1994, the ANC triumphed, with Mandela voted in as the country's president. Since that time South Africa has once again become an active and recognised member of the international community but although its economy is one of Africa's largest with strong financial and manufacturing industries, unemployment remains high and incomes low for most of the country's population.

Area: 471,445 sq mi (1,221,037 sq km)
Population: 44,187,000
Capital: Pretoria (administrative), Cape Town (legislative)
Form of government: Republic
Religions: Christianity, Hinduism, Islam, traditional beliefs
Currency: Rand

Spain a country in southwest Europe occupying the greater part of the Iberian Peninsula, which it shares with PORTUGAL. It is a mountainous country, sealed off from the rest of Europe by the Pyrénées, which rise to over 11,155 feet (3,400 metres). Much of the country is a vast plateau, the Meseta Central, cut across by valleys and gorges. Its longest shoreline is the one that borders the Mediterranean Sea. Most of the country has a form of Mediterranean climate, with mild moist winters and hot dry summers. Spain's major rivers, such as the Douro, Tagus and Guadiana, flow to the Atlantic Ocean while the Guadalquivir is the deepest. Spain's principal agricultural products are cereals, vegetables and potatoes and large areas are under vines for the wine industry. Livestock farming is important, particularly sheep and goats. Industry represents 72 per cent of the country's export value and production includes textiles, paper, cement, steel and chemicals. Tourism is a major revenue earner, especially from the resorts on the east coast.

Area: 195,365 sq mi (505,992 sq km)
Population: 40,397,000
Capital: Madrid
Form of government: Constitutional Monarchy
Religion: Christianity
Currency: Euro

Sri Lanka a teardrop-shaped island in the Indian Ocean, lying south of the Indian Peninsula, from which it is separated by the Palk Strait. The climate is equatorial, with a low annual temperature range, but it is affected by both the northeast and southwest monsoons. Rainfall is heaviest in the southwest while the north and east are relatively dry. Agriculture engages 47 per cent of the work force and the main crops are rice, tea, rubber and coconuts, although sugar, rice and wheat have to be imported. Amongst the chief minerals mined and exported are precious and semiprecious stones. Graphite is also important. The main industries produce food, beverages, tobacco, textiles, clothing, leather goods, chemicals and plastics. Politically, Sri Lanka has been afflicted by ethnic divisions between the Sinhalese and Tamils. Attempts by the Tamil extremists to establish an independent homeland have at times brought the northeast of the country to the brink of civil war, and the situation remains volatile. The revenue from tourism is slowly increasing but the country was badly hit by the Asian tsunami of 2004 when much of its shoreline was damaged.

Area: 25,332 sq mi (65,610 sq km)
Population: 20,220,000
Capital: Colombo

Form of government: Republic
Religions: Buddhism, Hinduism, Christianity, Sunni Islam
Currency: Sri Lankan rupee

Sudan the largest country in Africa, lying just south of the Tropic of Cancer in northeast Africa. The country covers much of the upper Nile basin and in the north the river winds through the Nubian and Libyan deserts, forming a palm-fringed strip of habitable land. In 1994, the country was divided into 26 states, compared to the original nine. The climate is tropical and temperatures are high throughout the year. In winter, nights are very cold. Rainfall increases in amount from north to south, the northern areas being virtually desert. Sudan is an agricultural country, subsistence farming accounting for 80 per cent of production and livestock are also raised. Cotton is farmed commercially and accounts for about two-thirds of Sudan's exports. Sudan is the world's greatest source of gum arabic, used in medicines, perfumes, processed foods and inks. Other forest products are tannin, beeswax, senna and lumber. Because of a combination of years of civil war—between the mainly Muslim north and the Christian and traditional beliefs south—and drought, Sudan's infrastructure is badly damaged and the country is in need of reconstruction. Fighting in the Darfur region has led to a humanitarian crisis.

Area: 967,500 sq mi (2,505,813 sq km)
Population: 41,236,000
Capital: Khartoum (El Khartum)
Form of government: Republic
Religions: Sunni Islam, traditional beliefs, Christianity
Currency: Sudanese dinar

Suriname a republic in northeast South America that was formerly known as Dutch Guiana. It is bordered to the west by GUYANA, to the east by (French) GUIANA and to the south by BRAZIL. Suriname comprises a swampy coastal plain, a forested central plateau and southern mountains. The climate is tropical, with heavy rainfall concentrated mainly from December to April. Agriculture remains fairly underdeveloped. Crops cultivated include rice, bananas, citrus fruits, sugar cane, coffee and cocoa. Molasses and rum are produced along with some manufactured goods and there is an important coastal shrimp fishery. Suriname's economy is based on the mining of bauxite, which accounts for 80 per cent of its exports. The country has important mineral reserves of iron ore, nickel, copper, platinum and gold. Suriname's natural resources also include oil and lumber. The country has a reasonably high standard of living but lacks the infrastructure to further develop its economy.

Area: 63,037 sq mi (163,265 sq km)
Population: 423,000
Capital: Paramaribo
Form of government: Republic
Religions: Hinduism, Christianity, Sunni Islam
Currency: Suriname guilder

Swaziland a landlocked hilly enclave almost entirely within the borders of the Republic of SOUTH AFRICA. The mountains in the west of the country rise to about 6,500 feet (almost 2,000 metres), then descend in steps of savanna towards hilly country in the east. The climate is subtropical, moderated by altitude. The land between 1,300–2,800 feet (approximately 400–850 metres) is planted with orange groves and pineapple fields, while on the lower land sugar cane flourishes in irrigated areas. Forestry production centres mainly on pine since it matures extremely quickly because of Swaziland's climate. Coal is mined and manufacturing includes fertilisers, textiles, leather and tableware. Many Swazis live in poverty and the country's workforce has been adversely affected by AIDS.

Area: 6,704 sq mi (17,364 sq km)
Population: 1,133,000
Capital: Mbabane
Form of government: Monarchy
Religions: Christianity, traditional beliefs
Currency: Lilangeni

Sweden a large country in northern Europe that makes up half the Scandinavian peninsula. It stretches from the Baltic Sea north to well within the Arctic Circle. The south is generally flat with many lakes, the north mountainous and along the coast there are over 20,000 islands and islets. Summers are warm but short while winters are long and cold. In the north snow may lie for four to seven months. Dairy farming is the predominant agricultural activity and also the production of livestock, including cattle, pigs and sheep. Only 7 per cent of Sweden is cultivated, with the emphasis on fodder crops, potatoes, rape seed, grain and sugar beet. About 57 per cent of the country is covered by forest and the sawmill, wood pulp and paper industries are all of great importance. Sweden is one of the world's leading producers of iron ore, most of which is extracted from within the Arctic Circle. Other main industries are engineering and the production of electrical goods, motor vehicles and furniture making, as well as fine crafts such as glassware, ceramics, silverware and items made from stainless steel. Sweden has an advanced social welfare system and its citizens enjoy a high standard of living. The country is known for its neutrality and although a member of the European Union it is not a member of Nato.

Area: 173,732 sq mi (449,964 sq km)
Population: 8,843,000
Capital: Stockholm
Form of government: Constitutional
   Monarchy
Religion: Christianity
Currency: Krona

Switzerland a landlocked country in central Europe, sharing its borders with FRANCE, ITALY, AUSTRIA, LIECHTENSTEIN and GERMANY. The Alps occupy over 70 per cent of the country's area, forming two main east-west chains divided by the Rivers Rhine and Rhône. The climate is either continental or mountain type. Summers are generally warm and winters cold and both are affected by altitude. Northern Switzerland is the industrial part of the country and where its most important cities are located. Basle is famous for its pharmaceuticals and Zürich for electrical engineering and machinery. Although the country has to import much of its raw materials, these often become high-value exports such as clocks, watches and other precision engineering products. Hydroelectricity accounts for approximately 60 per cent of the country's power supplies, with most of the remainder coming from nuclear power plants. Switzerland has huge earnings from international finance and tourism. It is active in many UN and international organisations but retains a strong commitment to neutrality.

Area: 15,940 sq mi (41,284 sq km)
Population: 7,544,000
Capital: Bern
Form of government: Federal Republic
Religion: Christianity
Currency: Swiss franc

Syria or the Syrian Arab Republic a country in southwest Asia that borders on the Mediterranean Sea in the west. Much of the country is mountainous behind a narrow fertile coastal plain. The eastern region is desert or semi-desert, a stony inhospitable land. The coast has a Mediterranean climate, with hot dry summers and mild wet winters. About 50 per cent of the workforce get their living from agriculture: sheep, goats and cattle are raised; while cotton, barley, wheat, tobacco, grapes, olives and vegetables are grown. Some land is unused because of lack of irrigation. Reserves of oil are small compared to neighbouring IRAQ, but it has enough to make the country self-sufficient and provide three-quarters of the nation's export earnings. Industries producing textiles, leather, chemicals and cement have developed rapidly in the last 20 years, with the country's craftsmen producing fine rugs and silk brocades. Foreign revenue is gained from tourism and also from countries who pipe oil through Syria. In the 1967 Arab–Israeli War, Syria lost the Golan Heights to Israel. Despite peace talks between the two countries, the Golan Heights remain under Israeli control. Syria has experienced periods of political unrest due in part to the many diverse ethnic and religious groups in its country.

Area: 71,498 sq mi (185,180 sq km)
Population: 18,881,000
Capital: Damascus (Dimashq)
Form of government: Republic
Religion: Sunni Islam
Currency: Syrian pound

Taiwan an island that straddles the Tropic of Cancer in East Asia. It lies about 100 miles (161 kilometres) off the southeast coast of mainland CHINA. It is predominantly mountainous in the interior, with more than 60 peaks attaining heights of 10,000 feet (3,040 metres). The highest of all is the Jade Mountain (Yu Shan) which stands at 12,960 feet (3,940 metres). Taiwan's independence, resulting from the island's seizure by nationalists in 1949, is not fully accepted internationally and China lays claim to the territory. The climate is warm and humid for most of the year and winters are mild with rainy summers. The soils are fertile and a wide range of crops, including tea, rice, sugar cane and bananas, is grown. Natural resources include gas, marble, limestone and small coal deposits. Taiwan is a major international trading nation with some of the most successful export-processing zones in the world, accommodating domestic and overseas companies. Exports include machinery, electronics, textiles, footwear, toys and sporting goods.

Area: 13,800 sq mi (35,742 sq km)
Population: 23,036,000
Capital: T'ai-pei
Form of government: Republic
Religions: Taoism, Buddhism, Christianity
Currency: New Taiwan dollar

Tajikistan a republic of southern central former USSR that declared itself independent in 1991. It is situated near the Afghani and Chinese borders. The south is occupied by the Pamir mountain range, whose snow-capped peaks dominate the country. More than half the country lies over 9,840 feet (3,000 metres). Most of the country is desert or semi-desert and pastoral farming of cattle, sheep, horses and goats is important. Some yaks are kept in the higher regions. The lowland areas in the Fergana and Amudarya valleys are irrigated so that cotton, mulberry trees, fruit, wheat and vegetables can be grown. The Amudarya river is also used to produce hydroelectricity. The republic is rich in deposits of coal, lead, zinc, oil and uranium. Tajikistan is Central Asia's most impoverished nation. In the civil war (1992–97) which followed its independence tens of thousands of people were killed or made homeless. Since then the economy has grown but unemployment remains high and much of the population lives in poverty.

Area: 55,250 sq mi (143,100 sq km)
Population: 7,320,000
Capital: Dushanbe
Form of government: Republic
Religions: Sunni Islam, Shia Islam
Currency: Somoni

Tanzania a country that lies on the east coast of central Africa and comprises a large mainland area and the islands of Pemba and Zanzibar. The mainland consists mostly of plateaus broken by mountainous areas and the East African section of the Great Rift Valley. The climate is very varied and is controlled largely by altitude and distance from the sea. The coast is hot and humid, the central plateau drier and the mountains semi-temperate. Eighty per cent of Tanzanians make a living from the land, producing corn, cassava, millet, rice, plantains and sorghum for home consumption. Cash crops include cotton, tobacco, tea, sisal, cashews and coffee. The two islands produce the bulk of the world's needs of cloves. Diamond mining is an important industry and there are also sizeable deposits of iron ore, coal and tin. Fishing is also important with the bulk of the catch caught in inland waters. Although Tanzania is one of the poorest countries in the world, it has a wealth of natural wonders, such as the Serengeti Plain and its wildlife, the Ngorongoro Crater, Mount Kilimanjaro and the Olduvai Gorge, all of which attract large numbers of tourists, making a significant contribution to the country's economy.

Area: 362,162 sq mi (938,000 sq km)
Population: 37,445,100
Capital: Dodoma
Form of government: Republic
Religions: Sunni Islam, Christianity, Hinduism
Currency: Tanzanian shilling

Thailand a country about the same size as FRANCE, located in southeast Asia. It is a tropical country of mountains and jungles, rainforests and green plains. Central Thailand is a densely populated, fertile plain and the mountainous Isthmus of Kra joins southern Thailand to MALAYSIA. Thailand has a subtropical climate, with heavy monsoon rains from June to October, a cool season from October to March and a hot season from March to June. It is rich in many natural resources, such as mineral deposits of gold, coal, lead and precious stones, with rich soils, extensive areas of tropical forests and natural gas offshore. The central plain of Thailand contains vast expanses of paddy fields that grow enough rice to rank Thailand as one of the world's leading producers. The narrow southern peninsula is very wet and it is here that rubber is produced. Other crops grown are cassava, maize, pineapples and sugar cane. Fishing is an increasingly important industry, with prawns being sold for export. Tourism also contributes to the country's economy. The industrial and service industries began to expand thanks to the rapidly growing economy of the 1980s and although badly affected by the 1997 southeast Asian financial crisis, the economy is now fully recovered with strong export growth. The country faces unrest in its southern provinces where a minority Muslim population has renewed its separatist struggle.

Area: 198,115 sq mi (513,115 sq km)
Population: 64,631,000
Capital: Bangkok (Krung Thep)
Form of government: Constitutional monarchy
Religions: Buddhism, Sunni Islam
Currency: Baht

Togo a tiny country with a narrow coastal plain on the Gulf of Guinea in West Africa and grassy plains in the north and south that are separated by the Togo Highlands (2,300–3,235 feet/700–986 metres), which run from southwest to northeast. High plateaus, mainly in the more southerly ranges, are heavily forested with teak, mahogany and bamboo. Togo has a tropical climate with a major rainy season from March to July and a minor one from October to November. The north is affected by the dry harmattan wind from the Sahara during December and January. Over 80 per cent of the population is involved in subsistence agriculture, with yams, cassava, sorghum and millet as the principal crops. Minerals, particularly phosphates, are now the main export earners, along with raw cotton, coffee, cocoa, cement and palm kernels. Political unrest has been ongoing for many years and many people fled the country during election violence in 2005. Relatively free and fair parliamentary elections were held 2007 and after years of political unrest Togo is finally being re-welcomed into the international community

Area: 21,925 sq mi (56,785 sq km)
Population: 5,701,000

Capital: Lomé
Form of government: Republic
Religions: Traditional beliefs, Christianity, Sunni Islam
Currency: CFA franc

Tonga a country situated about 20 degrees south of the equator and just west of the International Date Line in the Pacific Ocean. It comprises over 170 islands, only about 40 of which are inhabited with a low limestone chain of islands in the east and a higher volcanic chain in the west. The climate is warm with heavy rainfall and destructive cyclones are likely to occur every few years. Yams, cassava and taro are grown as subsistence crops and fish from the sea supplement the diet while foods such as pumpkins, bananas, vanilla and coconuts are exported. The main industry is coconut processing. About 70 per cent of the workforce is occupied in either fishing or agriculture while many Tongans are employed overseas. Tourism, foreign aid from countries such as the United Kingdom, Australia and New Zealand and the income sent home from overseas workers all contribute to the country's economy.

Area: 288 sq mi (747 sq km)
Population: 114,000
Capital: Nuku'alofa
Form of government: Constitutional Monarchy
Religion: Christianity
Currency: Pa'anga

Trinidad and Tobago the islands constitute the third largest British Commonwealth country in the West Indies and are situated off the Orinoco Delta in northeastern VENEZUELA. They are the most southerly of the Lesser Antilles Islands. Trinidad consists of the mountainous Northern Range in the north and undulating plains in the south. It has a huge, asphalt-producing lake, Pitch Lake, which is approximately 104 acres (42 hectares) in size. Tobago is actually a mountain that is about 1,800 feet (550 metres) above sea level at its peak. The climate is tropical with little variation in temperatures throughout the year and a rainy season from June to December. Trinidad is one of the oldest oil-producing countries in the world. Output is small but provides 90 per cent of Trinidad's exports. Sugar cane, cocoa, citrus fruits, vegetables and rubber trees are grown for export, but imports of food now account for 10 per cent of total imports. Tobago depends mainly on tourism for revenue. A slump in the economy in the 1980s and early 1990s saw widespread unemployment but economic growth has improved in recent times and the country remains one of the most prosperous in the region.

Area: 1,981 sq mi (5,130 sq km)
Population: 1,297,000
Capital: Port of Spain
Form of government: Republic
Religions: Christianity, Hinduism, Sunni Islam
Currency: Trinidad and Tobago dollar

Tunisia a North African country that lies on the south coast of the Mediterranean Sea. It is bounded by ALGERIA to the west and LIBYA to the south. Northern Tunisia consists of hills, plains and valleys. Inland mountains separate the coastal zone from the central plains before the land drops down to an area of salt pans and the Sahara. The climate ranges from warm temperate in the north, where there are vineyards and forests of pine, cork oak and junipers, to desert in the south. Agriculture produces wheat, barley, olives, grapes, tomatoes, dates, vegetables and citrus fruits and the fishing industry is of growing importance, producing mainly pilchards, sardines and tuna. Twenty-six per cent of the workforce is engaged in these two occupations, but overall there is a general lack of employment. The mainstays of Tunisia's modern economy are oil from the Sahara, phosphates, natural gas and tourism on the Mediterranean coast.

Area: 62,592 sq mi (162,155 sq km)
Population: 10,175,000
Capital: Tunis
Form of government: Republic
Religion: Sunni Islam
Currency: Dinar

Turkey with land on the continents of Europe and Asia, Turkey forms a bridge between the two. It guards the sea passage between the Mediterranean and the Black Sea. Turkey occupies an area in which seismic activity is a frequent occurrence and the country regularly experiences devastating earthquakes. Only 5 per cent of its area (Thrace) is in Europe and a much larger area (Anatolia) is in Asia. European Turkey is fertile agricultural land with a Mediterranean climate. Asiatic Turkey is bordered to the north by the Pontine Mountains and to the south by the Taurus Mountains. The climate here ranges from Mediterranean to hot summers and bitterly cold winters in the central plains. Agriculture employs almost half the workforce, with the major crops being wheat, sugar beet, barley, fruits, maize and oil seeds. The country's main exports are iron and steel, textiles, dried fruits, tobacco, leather clothes and petroleum products. The manufacturing industry includes iron and steel, textiles, motor vehicles and Turkey's famous carpets. The main mineral resources are iron ore, coal, chromium, magnetite, zinc and lead. Tourism is a fast-developing industry and plays an increasingly important role in the economy. The economy has been growing in strength but foreign debt is still a burden. Turkey became a European Union candidate country in 1999 and membership talks began in 2005. Accession negotiations are expected to take about 10 years.

Area: 299,158 sq mi (774,815 sq km)
Population: 70,413,000
Capital: Ankara
Form of government: Republic
Religion: Sunni Islam
Currency: Turkish lira

Turkmenistan a central Asian republic of the former USSR that declared itself a republic in 1991. It lies to the east of the Caspian Sea and borders IRAN and AFGHANISTAN to the south. Much of the west and central areas of Turkmenistan are covered by the sandy Karakum Desert. The east is a plateau that is bordered by the Amudarya river. The Amudarya has been diverted to form the important Kara Kum Canal which is one of the longest canals in the world and provides irrigation and drinking water for the southeastern parts of the country. The climate is extremely dry and most of the population live in oasis settlements near the rivers and by the extensive network of canals. Agriculture is intensive around the settlements and consists of growing cotton, cereals, silk, fruit and rearing Karakul sheep. This occupies around 45 per cent of the workforce. There are rich mineral deposits, particularly natural gas, petroleum, sulphur, coal, salt and copper and manufacturing industries include textile manufacturing, food processing and carpet weaving. The economy remains, however, largely under-developed and the country largely closed to the outside world.

Area: 188,456 sq mi (488,100 sq km)
Population: 5,042,000
Capital: Ashkhabad (Ashgabat)
Form of government: Republic
Religions: Sunni Islam, Christianity
Currency: Manat

Turks and Caicos Islands two island groups that form the southeastern archipelago of the Bahamas in the Atlantic Ocean. Only six of the islands are inhabited. A British crown colony, the country's economy relies mainly on tourism and offshore finance. The climate is subtropical cooled by southeast trade winds which blow all the year round. The country also enjoys strong links with Canada.

Area: 166 sq mi (430 sq km)
Population: 23,000
Capital: Grand Turk
Form of government: British Crown
   Colony
Religion: Christianity
Currency: US dollar

Tuvalu a country located just north of Fiji, in the South Pacific, consisting of nine coral atolls. The group was formerly known as the Ellice Islands and the main island and capital is Funafuti. The climate is tropical, with an annual average rainfall of 120 inches (3,050 millimetres). Coconut palms are the main crop and fruit and vegetables are grown for local consumption. Sea fishing is extremely good and largely unexploited, although licenses have been granted to Japan, Taiwan and the Republic of Korea to fish the local waters. Revenue comes from copra (the only export product), foreign aid, the sale of elaborate postage stamps to philatelists and income sent home from Tuvaluans who work abroad.

Area: 10 sq mi (24 sq km)
Population: 11,810
Capital: Funafuti
Form of government: Constitutional
   Monarchy
Religion: Christianity
Currency: Tuvalu dollar/Australian dollar

Uganda a landlocked country in east central Africa. The equator runs through the south of the country and for the most part it is a richly fertile land, well watered, with a kindly climate. In the west are the Ruwenzori Mountains, which reach heights of 16,762 feet (5,109 metres) and are snow-capped. The lowlands around Lake Victoria, once forested, have now mostly been cleared for cultivation. Agriculture employs over 80 per cent of the labour force and the main crops grown for subsistence are plantains, cassava and sweet potatoes. Coffee is the main cash crop and accounts for over 90 per cent of the country's exports. Cotton and tea are important to the country's economy as is mahogany from the country's forests. Virtually all the country's power is produced by hydroelectricity, the plant on the Victoria Nile being of major importance. Since the 1980s and following years of civil turmoil and unrest, Uganda has slowly been rebuilding its shattered economy and, in spite of some resurgence of earlier violence, attempts are being made to expand the tea plantations in the west, to develop a copper mine, and to introduce new industries to Kampala, the capital

Area: 93,065 sq mi (241,038 sq km)
Population: 28,195,000
Capital: Kampala
Form of government: Republic
Religions: Christianity, traditional beliefs,
   Sunni Islam
Currency: Uganda shilling

Ukraine a former Soviet socialist republic that declared itself independent of the former USSR in 1991. Its neighbours to the west are Poland, Slovakia, Hungary and Romania and it is bounded to the south by the Black Sea. To the east lies Russia and to the north the republic of Belarus. Drained by the Dnepr, Dnestr, Southern Bug and Donets rivers, Ukraine consists largely of fertile steppes. The climate is continental, although this is greatly modified by the proximity of the Black Sea. The Ukrainian steppe is one of the chief wheat-producing regions of Europe. Other major crops include corn, sugar beet, flax, tobacco, soya, hops and potatoes, with agriculture accounting for about a quarter of all employment. There are rich reserves of coal and raw materials for industry. The central and eastern regions form one of the world's densest industrial concentrations. Manufacturing industries include ferrous metallurgy, heavy machinery, chemicals, food processing, gas and oil refining. The European Union is now the country's biggest trading partner but Russia remains its largest individual trading partner. Ukraine depends on Russia for its gas supplies and forms an important part of the pipeline transit route for Russian gas exports to Europe. Since 2006 there have been ongoing disputes between Russia and Ukraine over rises in the price of gas. Ukraine hopes to become a member of the European Union with 2015 as a possible entry date.

Area: 233,090 sq mi (603,700 sq km)
Population: 46,299,000
Capital: Kiev (Kiyev)
Form of government: Republic
Religion: Christianity
Currency: Rouble

United Arab Emirates (UAE) a federation of seven oil-rich sheikdoms located in The Gulf, namely Abu Dhabi, Dubai, Sharjah, Ajman, Umm al Qaiwain, Ras el Khaimah, and Fujairah. As well as its main coast on the Gulf, the country has a short coast on the Gulf of Oman. The land is mainly flat sandy desert except to the north on the peninsula where the Hajar Mountains rise to 6,828 feet (2,081 metres). The summers are hot and humid with temperatures reaching 120°F (49°C), but from October to May the weather is warm and sunny with pleasant, cool evenings. The only fertile areas are the emirate of Ras al Khaimah, the coastal plain of Fujairah and the oases. Abu Dhabi and Dubai are the main industrial centres and, using their wealth from the oil industry, they are now diversifying industry by building aluminium smelters, cement factories and steel-rolling mills. Prior to development of the oil industry, traditional occupations were pearl diving, growing dates, fishing and camel breeding. Dubai is the richest state in the world.

Area: 32,278 sq mi (83,600 sq km)
Population: 4,440,000
Capital: Abu Zabi (Abu Dhabi)
Form of government: Federal

Religions: Sunni Islam, Shia Islam
Currency: Dirham

United Kingdom of Great Britain and Northern Ireland (UK) a country situated in northwest Europe, comprising the island of Great Britain and the six counties of Northern Ireland, plus many smaller islands, especially off the west coast of Scotland. The south and east of Britain is low-lying and the Pennines form a backbone running through northern England. Scotland has the largest area of upland and Wales is a highland block. Northern Ireland has a few hilly areas. The climate is cool temperate with mild conditions and an even annual rainfall. The UK is primarily a highly urbanised industrial and commercial country. Only two per cent of the workforce are employed in agriculture and, although production is high thanks to modern machinery and scientific methods, the UK still has to import one third of its food. Major crops include barley, potatoes, sugar beet and wheat, while livestock raised includes sheep, cattle, pigs and poultry. Fishing is also an important industry. The UK has to import most of the materials it needs for its industries as it lacks natural resources apart from coal, iron ore, oil and natural gas. Service industries play an increasingly large part in the UK's economy, as does tourism. The UK has devolved powers to Scotland, Wales and Northern Ireland – the Scottish Parliament and the National Assembly of Wales opened in 1999 and the Northern Ireland Assembly eventually in 2007. The UK plays an important role in the EU but it has not adopted the euro as currency. There has been an influx of workers from new EU member countries and this together with concerns about terrorism after recent suicide bomb attacks has led the country to take a fresh look at the issues around multiculturalism and national identity.

Area: 94,248 sq mi (244,101 sq km)
Population: 60,609,000
Capital: London
Form of government: Constitutional Monarchy
Religion: Christianity
Currency: Pound sterling

United States of America (USA) a country that stretches across central north America, from the Atlantic Ocean in the east to the

Pacific Ocean in the west and from CANADA in the north to MEXICO and the Gulf of Mexico in the south. It is the fourth largest country in the world and consists of fifty states, including outlying Alaska, northwest of Canada, and Hawaii in the Pacific Ocean. The climate varies a great deal in such a large country: in Alaska, there are polar conditions and in the Gulf coast and in Florida conditions may be subtropical. The highest point is Mount McKinley at 20,322 feet (6,194 metres). Natural resources include vast mineral reserves, including oil and gas, coal, copper, lead, uranium gold, tungsten and lumber. Although agricultural production is high, it employs only 1.5 per cent of the population because primarily of its advanced technology. The USA is a world leader in oil production. The main industries are iron and steel, chemicals, motor vehicles, aircraft, telecommunications equipment, computers, electronics and textiles. The terrorist attacks of September 2001 caused the country to look again at its role as the world's most powerful nation, with military campaigns in Afghanistan and Iraq as part of its 'war on terror'.

Area: 3,536,278 sq mi (9,158,960 sq km)
Population: 298,444,000
Capital: Washington DC
Form of government: Federal republic
Religion: Christianity,
Currency: US dollar

Uruguay one of the smallest countries in South America. It lies on the east coast of the continent, to the south of BRAZIL and is bordered to the west by the Uruguay river, Rio de la Plata to the south and the Atlantic Ocean to the east. The country consists of low plains and plateaus. The Negro river, which rises in Brazil, crosses the country from northeast to southwest, dividing Uruguay almost into two halves. The climate is temperate and rainfall plentiful and the natural vegetation is prairie grassland. Some of the river valleys are wooded but Uruguay lacks the dense forests of other parts of South America. About 90 per cent of the land is suitable for agriculture but only about 8 per cent is cultivated, the remainder being used to graze the vast herds of cattle and sheep that provide over 35 per cent of Uruguay's exports in the form of wool, hides

and meat. The cultivated land is made up of vineyards, rice fields and groves of olives and citrus fruits. The main crops grown are sugar beet and cane, rice, wheat, potatoes, corn and sorghum. The country has scarce mineral resources and hydroelectric power supplies most of its energy needs. Important industries include textile manufacture, food processing, oil refining, steel, aluminium, electrical goods and rubber. The country is recovering from economic problems in the region in 2002.

Area: 68,500 sq mi (177,414 sq km)
Population: 3,431,000
Capital: Montevideo
Form of government: Republic
Religion: Christianity
Currency: Uruguayan peso

Uzbekistan a central Asian republic of the former USSR that declared itself independent in 1991. It lies between KAZAKHSTAN and TURKMENISTAN and encompasses the southern half of the Aral Sea. The republic has many contrasting regions. The Tian Shan region is mountainous, the Fergana region is irrigated and fertile, the Kyzlkum Desert (one of the world's largest) is rich in oil and gas, the lower Amudarya river region is irrigated and has oasis settlements and the Usturt Plateau is a stony desert. Uzbekistan is one of the world's leading cotton producers and Karakul lambs are reared for wool and meat. Its main industrial products are agricultural machinery, textiles and chemicals. It also has significant reserves of natural gas.

Economic growth has been checked by concerns about political instability and much of the economy remains based on the centralised state-owned model. There are serious pollution problems where the Aral Sea lies. This has greatly decreased in size from its use for irrigation and is contaminated with toxins, salts and sands that poison the water supply of the surrounding population. Hydroelectric schemes supply much of the republic's electricity needs.

Area: 172,742 sq mi (447,400 sq km)
Population: 24,000,000
Capital: Tashkent
Form of government: Republic
Religion: Sunni Islam
Currency: Soum

Vanuatu a country, formerly known as the New Hebrides (so named by Captain Cook in 1774), located in the southwest Pacific Ocean, southeast of the Solomon Islands and about 1,087 miles (1,750 kilometres) east of Australia. It consists of some 12 islands and 60 islets. Most of the islands are volcanic and densely forested, with raised coral beaches and fringed by coral reefs. The largest islands are Espírtu Santo, Malekula and Efate, on which the capital, Vila, is sited. Vanuatu has a tropical climate that is moderated by the southeast trade winds from May to October. Cultivated land is generally restricted to the coastal plains and the main cash crops are copra, cocoa beans and coffee. Meat and fish are also exported and light industries include food processing and handicrafts for an increasing tourist industry. The majority of the labour force is engaged in subsistence farming, raising taro, yams and bananas. Eco-tourism is an increasingly important industry. Vanuatu receives most of its foreign aid from Australia which has been encouraging economic reform in the country.

Area: 4,706 sq mi (12,189 sq km)
Population: 208,869
Capital: Vila
Form of government: Republic
Religions: Christianity, traditional beliefs
Currency: Vatu

Vatican City State a state, established in 1929, that lies in the heart of Rome on a low hill on the west bank of the River Tiber. It is the world's smallest independent state and headquarters of the Roman Catholic Church. It is a walled city with six gates and is made up of the Vatican Palace, the Papal Gardens, St Peter's Square and St Peter's Basilica. The state has its own police, newspaper, telephone and telegraph services, coinage, stamps, radio station and train station and recently it launched a low cost charter flight service to holy sites around the world. The radio station, Radio Vaticana, broadcasts a service in 34 languages from transmitters within the Vatican City. The pope exercises sovereignty and has absolute legislative, executive and judicial powers.

Area: 0.2 sq mile (0.44 sq kilometre)
Population: 1,000
Capital: Vatican City

Form of government: Papal commission
Religion: Christianity
Currency: Euro

Venezuela a country that forms the northernmost crest of South America. Its northern coast lies along the Caribbean Sea and it is bounded to the west by Columbia and to the southeast and south by Guyana and Brazil. In the northwest a spur of the Andes runs southwest to northeast. The River Orinoco cuts the country in two and north of the river run the undulating plains known as the Llanos. South of the river are the Guiana Highlands. The climate ranges from warm temperate to tropical. In the Llanos area, cattle are herded across the plains. There are also rich fishing grounds around the coast and off Venezuela's 72 islands. Sugar cane and coffee are grown for export, but petroleum and gas account for around 80 per cent of export earnings. Venezuela's economy is built on its oilfields located in the Maracaibo region but it also has other important mineral reserves including bauxite, iron ore, coal and precious metals and stones, such as gold, silver, platinum and diamonds. Despite this wealth of natural resources, most of the population live in poverty and unemployment is high. The economy has been adversely affected by political unrest.

Area: 352,145 sq mi (912,050 sq km)
Population: 25,730,000
Capital: Caracas
Form of government: Federal republic
Religion: Christianity
Currency: Bolivar

Vietnam a long narrow country in southeast Asia that runs down the coast of the South China Sea. It has a narrow central area that links broader plains centred on the Red (Hong) and Mekong rivers. This narrow zone, now known as Mien Trung, is hilly and makes communications between north and south difficult. The climate is humid, with tropical conditions in the south and subtropical in the north. The far north can be very cold when polar air blows over Asia. Agriculture, fishing and forestry employ around 74 per cent of the labour force. The main crop is rice but cassava, maize and sweet potatoes are also grown for domestic consumption. Soya beans, tea, coffee and rubber are grown for export. Major industries are food processing, textiles, cement, cotton and silk manufacture. Fishing is also an important export trade. Vietnam, still recovering from the ravages of many wars this century, is now one of southeast Asia's fastest growing economies. Foreign investment has grown and a stock exchange was opened in 2000.

Area: 128,066 sq mi (331,689 sq km)
Population: 75,181,000
Capital: Hanoi
Form of government: Socialist Republic
Religions: Buddhism, Taoism, Christianity
Currency: New dong

Virgin Islands, British a British overseas territory lying at the northwestern end of the Lesser Antilles in the Caribbean Sea. It comprises four large islands and 36 islets and cays. Only 16 of the islands are inhabited. Most of the islands are hilly and wooded and the climate is subtropical moderated by trade winds. Agriculture produces livestock, coconuts, sugar cane, fruit and vegetables, but only a small percentage of the land available to agriculture is under cultivation. The main industries are tourism and offshore finance and these dominate the economy.

Area: 58 sq mi (151 sq km)
Population: 23,098
Capital: Road Town
Form of government: British Overseas Territory
Religion: Christianity
Currency: US dollar

Virgin Islands, US 50 islands that are part of the Virgin Islands group in the northwest of the Lesser Antilles in the Caribbean Sea. A self-governing US territory, this group of 50 volcanic islands are rugged and mountainous with a subtropical climate. The main islands are St John (around two-thirds of which is a National Park), St Croix and St Thomas. Agriculture is not well developed and most of the country's food has to be imported. There is a small manufacturing industry but tourism is the mainstay of the economy with many cruise ships calling at the island of St Thomas in particular.

Area: 134 sq mi (347 sq km)

Population: 108,605
Capital: Charlotte Amalie
Form of government: Self-governing US Territory
Religion: Christianity
Currency: US dollar

Wallis and Futuna Islands the two island groups are 142 miles (230 kilometres) apart in the southern central Pacific Ocean and are the smallest and poorest of France's overseas territories. The climate is warm and humid with a cyclone season between October and March. Subsistence farming and fishing are the main activities with copra the only important export.

Area: 77 sq mi (200 sq km)
Population: 16,000
Capital: Mata-Uru
Form of government: French Overseas Territory
Religion: Christianity
Currency: CFP franc

Western Sahara a disputed territory of western Africa, with a coastline on the Atlantic Ocean. Consisting mainly of desert, it is rich in phosphates. It was a Spanish overseas province until 1976, when it was partitioned between MOROCCO and MAURITANIA. Since 1979, the entire territory has been claimed and administered by Morocco, against the wishes of an active separatist movement, the Frente Polisario. Moroccan sovereignty is not universally recognised and the United Nations has attempted to oversee a referendum to decide the struggle but without success so far. It is a poor country with many following a nomadic existence.

Area: 102,703 sq mi (266,000 sq km)
Population: 273,000
Capital: Laâyoune (El Aaiún)
Form of government: Republic (*de facto* controlled by Morocco)
Religion: Sunni Islam
Currency: Moroccan dirham

Western Samoa *see* SAMOA.

Yemen a country bounded by SAUDI ARABIA in the north, OMAN in the east, the Gulf of Aden in the south and the Red Sea in the west. The country was formed after the unification of the previous Yemen Arab Republic and the People's Democratic Republic of Yemen (South Yemen) in 1989.

At that point, however, there was no active integration of the two countries and politically the country remained divided between north and south. In 1994 a civil war that lasted three months broke out between the former North and South Yemen, which resulted in a high rate of inflation, damage to the infrastructure and devaluation of the currency. Most of the country comprises rugged mountains and trackless desert lands. The country is almost entirely dependent on agriculture. The main crops are coffee, cotton, wheat, vegetables, millet, sorghum and fruit. Fishing is an important industry. Manufacturing industries produce textiles, paints, matches, plastic, rubber and aluminium goods. Attempts to modernize the country's industry are hampered by a lack of funds and economic problems have caused unrest.

Area: 203,850 sq mi (527,978 sq km)
Population: 21,456,000
Capital: San'a
Form of government: Republic
Religions: Shia Islam, Sunni Islam
Currency: Riyal

Zaire *see* Congo, Democratic Republic of the.

Zambia a country, situated in central Africa, that is made up of high plateaus. Bordering it to the south is the Zambezi river and to the southwest the Kalahari Desert. It has some other large rivers and lakes, the largest of which is Lake Bangweulu. The climate is tropical, modified somewhat by altitude. Agriculture is underdeveloped and vulnerable to weather variations, leading to some food shortages, as a consequence of which large quantities of food have to be imported. The principal subsistence crops grown are corn, sugar cane and cassava, and cattle are raised. The majority of the country's power is provided by the Kariba Dam on the Zambezi river. Zambia's economy relies heavily on the mining of copper, lead, zinc and cobalt. The World Bank has encouraged Zambia to develop her vast agricultural

potential and tourism as the country has a wide range of wildlife and large game parks. However, copper still accounts for most of the country's foreign earnings.

Area: 290,587 sq mi (752,618 sq km)
Population: 11,502,000
Capital: Lusaka
Form of government: Republic
Religions: Traditional beliefs, Christianity
Currency: Kwacha

Zimbabwe a landlocked country in southern Africa. It is a country with spectacular physical features and teeming with wildlife. It is bordered in the north by the Zambezi river, which flows over the mile-wide Victoria Falls before entering Lake Kariba. In the south, the River Limpopo marks its border with South Africa. A great plateau between 4,000–5,000 feet (about 1,200–1,500 metres) in height occupies the central area. Only one third of the population lives in towns and cities, the largest of which is the capital, Harare. The climate is tropical in the lowlands and subtropical in the higher land. Tobacco, sugar cane, cotton, wheat, and maize are grown and form the basis of processing industries. Zimbabwe is rich in mineral resources such as coal, chromium, nickel, gold, platinum, and precious metals, and mining accounts for around 30 per cent of foreign revenue. Tourism has the potential to be a major growth industry thanks to the country's many tourist attractions, including several wildlife parks, the Victoria Falls, and Great Zimbabwe. However, during the years of President Mugabe's rule, the agriculture-based economy has collapsed after the forced seizure of white-owned commercial farms, and the country has had to put up with a very high inflation rate, high unemployment and political unrest.

Area: 150,872 sq mi (390,757 sq km)
Population: 12,236,000
Capital: Harare
Form of government: Republic
Religions: Traditional beliefs, Christianity
Currency: Zimbabwe dollar